CURRENT TOPICS
IN PLANT SCIENCE

Current Topics in
PLANT SCIENCE

Edited by James E. Gunckel

BOTANY DEPARTMENT
RUTGERS UNIVERSITY
NEW BRUNSWICK, NEW JERSEY

1969

 Academic Press   New York and London

ACADEMIC PRESS, INC.
111 Fifth Avenue, New York, New York 10003

United Kingdom Edition published by
ACADEMIC PRESS, INC. (LONDON) LTD.
Berkeley Square House, London W1X6BA

LIBRARY OF CONGRESS CATALOG CARD NUMBER: 73-84227

PRINTED IN THE UNITED STATES OF AMERICA

LIST OF CONTRIBUTORS

Numbers in parentheses indicate the pages on which the authors' contributions begin.

ALVA A. APP (12), Boyce Thompson Institute for Plant Research, Inc., Yonkers, New York

GEORGE S. AVERY (262), Brooklyn Botanic Garden, Brooklyn, New York

WARREN BALGOOYEN (262), Brooklyn Botanic Garden, Brooklyn, New York

DOMINICK V. BASILE (120), Department of Biological Sciences, Columbia University, New York, New York

NESTOR BOHONOS (289), The Children's Cancer Research Foundation Inc., and Department of Pathology, Harvard Medical School at Children's Hospital, Boston, Massachusetts

R. F. BOZARTH (31), Boyce Thompson Institute for Plant Research Inc., Yonkers, New York

ARMIN C. BRAUN (67), The Rockefeller University, New York, New York

EDWARD H. BUCKLEY (17), Boyce Thompson Institute for Plant Research Inc., Yonkers, New York

MARIA M. BULIS (12), Boyce Thompson Institute for Plant Research Inc., Yonkers, New York

ELI V. CRISAN (32), Boyce Thompson Institute for Plant Research Inc., Yonkers, New York

ROBERT H. DAINES (436), Department of Plant Biology, College of Agriculture and Environmental Science, Rutgers University, New Brunswick, New Jersey

A. A. DE HERTOGH (16), Boyce Thompson Institute for Plant Research Inc., Yonkers, New York

FRANK E. EGLER (420), Aton Forest, Norfolk, Connecticut

JOSEPH EWAN (155), Department of Biology, Tulane University, New Orleans, Louisiana

NORMAN R. FARNSWORTH (367), Department of Pharmacognosy, School of Pharmacy, University of Pittsburgh, Pittsburgh, Pennsylvania

FLORENCE FLEMION (15), Boyce Thompson Institute for Plant Research Inc., Yonkers, New York

HERMAN GERSHON (54), Boyce Thompson Institute for Plant Research Inc., Yonkers, New York

A. E. HITCHCOCK (60), Boyce Thompson Institute for Plant Research Inc., Yonkers, New York

GEORGE M. HOCKING (273), School of Pharmacy, Auburn University, Auburn, Alabama

R. CECIL M. JACK (33, 45), Boyce Thompson Institute for Plant Research Inc., Yonkers, New York

J. S. JACOBSON (60), Boyce Thompson Institute for Plant Research Inc., Yonkers, New York

TETSUO KOYAMA (201), c/o Dr. H. Merxmüller, Direktor Botanische Staatssmmilung, Munich, Germany

HENRY J. LAURENCOT, JR. (24), Boyce Thompson Institute for Plant Research Inc., Yonkers, New York

D. C. MCCUNE (16, 60), Boyce Thompson Institute for Plant Research Inc., Yonkers, New York

D. C. MACLEAN (16, 60), Boyce Thompson Institute for Plant Research Inc., Yonkers, New York

GEORGE L. MCNEW (3), Boyce Thompson Institute for Plant Research Inc., Yonkers, New York

ALBERTO L. MANCINELLI (144), Department of Biological Science, Columbia University, New York, New York

R. H. MANDL (60), Boyce Thompson Institute for Plant Research Inc., Yonkers, New York

KARL MARAMOROSCH (46), Boyce Thompson Institute for Plant Research Inc., Yonkers, New York

EDWIN B. MATZKE (117), Department of Biological Sciences, Columbia University, New York, New York

LAWRENCE P. MILLER (35), Boyce Thompson Institute for Plant Research Inc., Yonkers, New York

ULRICH NÄF (97), Plant Morphogenesis Laboratory, Manhattan College, Bronx, New York

WILLIAM A. NIERING (403), Botany Department, Connecticut College, New London, Connecticut

RAULO PARMEGIANI (54), Boyce Thompson Institute for Plant Research Inc., Yonkers, New York

LIVIJA RAUDZÉNS (117), Department of Biological Sciences, Columbia University, New York, New York

JAMES L. REVEAL (229), Department of Botany, Brigham Young University, Provo, Utah

WILLIAM J. ROBBINS (71), The Rockefeller University, New York, New York

D. W. ROBERTS (48), Boyce Thompson Institute for Plant Research Inc., Yonkers, New York

RICHARD EVANS SCHULTES (336), Botanical Museum of Harvard University, Cambridge, Massachusetts

ALFRED E. SCHUYLER (167), Department of Botany, Academy of Natural Sciences, Philadelphia, Pennsylvania

S. GALEN SMITH (177), Wisconsin State University, Whitewater, Wisconsin

RICHARD C. STAPLES (37), Boyce Thompson Institute for Plant Research Inc., Yonkers, New York

WILLIAM C. STEERE (134, 253), The New York Botanical Garden, Bronx, New York

TOM STONIER (431), Plant Morphogenesis Laboratory, Manhattan College, Bronx, New York

GORDON H. SVOBODA (303), Eli Lilly Research Laboratories, Indianapolis, Indiana

ROY L. TAYLOR (161), The Botanical Gardens, University of British Columbia, Vancouver, Canada

D. C. TORGESON (58), Boyce Thompson Institute for Plant Research Inc., Yonkers, New York

WALTER TULECKE (26), Boyce Thompson Institute for Plant Research Inc., Yonkers, New York

N. JOE TURNER (50), Boyce Thompson Institute for Plant Research Inc., Yonkers, New York

BRUCE R. VOELLER (77), The Rockefeller University, New York, New York

DALTON WANG (15, 27), Boyce Thompson Institute for Plant Research Inc., Yonkers, New York

ANDREW T. WEIL (355), Harvard Medical School at Children's Hospital, Boston, Massachusetts

ERIC S. WEINBERG (77), The Rockefeller University, New York, New York

LEONARD H. WEINSTEIN (24, 60), Boyce Thompson Institute for Plant Research Inc., Yonkers, New York

HENRY N. WOOD (74), The Rockefeller University, New York, New York

WILLARD K. WYNN (30), Boyce Thompson Institute for Plant Research Inc., Yonkers, New York

PREFACE

Science is not adequately reported to people, considering its impact on their lives. There is a general information lag. The scientific community is troubled in trying to recover information as a basis for sound scientific judgment. This book, then, is intended to appeal to plant scientists and to the general public by summarizing current thinking and research on a number of basic biological problems.

For plant scientists this book presents an overview of the research programs of a number of institutions and individuals in the New York area associated with the Torrey Botanical Club. Topics included are the control of growth and morphogenesis, processes of disease induction in plants and insects, and the activities of fungi, all treated as problems of molecular or cell physiology; normal and abnormal plant growth; and various aspects of morphogenesis. A section on taxonomy treats some subjects of interest to John Torrey: the family Cyperaceae, the genus *Eriogonum,* and a North American Flora, but these are modern treatments of work begun over 100 years ago.

The general public will be especially interested in the role of botanical gardens in plant research and education; in the use of plants and plant products for flavors, aromatics, antibiotics, and drugs, especially hallucinogens, in modern medicine; and problems of man and his environment—especially pesticides, air pollution, and conservation of natural areas.

Each chapter represents material presented at a scheduled symposium; hence the papers are related and afford a broad coverage of the topic. Each paper includes an introduction and statement of the problem, a materials and methods section, results and discussion, and a pertinent bibliography. This volume differs from the usual "current topics" or "annual review" in having broad coverage of the field of plant science rather than detailed current treatment of just one area.

The Torrey Botanical Club was founded in New York City in 1867. To plan a suitable centennial program, President W. J. Crotty appointed the following Centennial Committee: Dr. Gily Bard (Hunter College), Dr. Detlev W. Bronk (The Rockefeller University), Dr. Ralph Cheney

(Long Island University), Dr. Lawrence J. Crockett (City College of New York), Dr. William J. Crotty (New York University), Dr. James E. Gunckel (Chairman, Rutgers University), Dr. Edwin B. Matzke (Columbia University), Dr. John McLaughlin (Fordham University), Dr. George McNew (Boyce Thompson Institute for Plant Research), Dr. Norman Morengo (C. W. Post College), Dr. Peter Nelson (Brooklyn Botanic Garden), Dr. William C. Steere (New York Botanical Garden), Dr. Tom Stonier (Manhattan College), and Dr. Annette Hervey and Miss Mathilde Weingartner (ex officio). The symposia planned by this committee to run throughout 1967 were presented under the general heading, "The Evolution of Botanical Science in a Metropolitan Environment over the Past Hundred Years." The numerous references will enable the reader to pursue any of the topics discussed to whatever depth and breadth is desirable.

New Brunswick, New Jersey   JAMES E. GUNCKEL
June, 1969

CONTENTS

B.   Processes of Disease Induction in Plants and Insects

C.   Environmental Health — The Activities of Fungi

Contents

D. Environmental Health — Air Pollution

Section II.   Normal and Abnormal Plant Growth

Section III.   Aspects of Morphogenesis

Section IV. Aspects of Taxonomy

Section V. The Role of Botanical Gardens in Plant Research and Education

Section VI. Phytopharmacology in Modern Medicine

Contents

Section VII.   An Attack on Some Unresolved Problems of Plant Life in the Environment of a Major City

I
Cell Physiology

Cell Physiology as an Approach to Solving the Problems of Plant Life

George L. McNew

A hundred years is a long time in modern science but only a day in the evolution of man's social and economic structure. It is well, therefore, for us to pause and look back upon those eventful years following the Civil War to find perspective for ourselves as professional botanists, operating in the New York area and celebrating the centennial of the founding of the Torrey Botanical Club.

The founders of the Torrey Club could not have conceived what would prevail today in our community, the nation, or the science they loved. At the end of the War between the States, the nation was an agrarian society with ten people laboring on farms to support one person in industry and commerce, whereas today the produce of each farmer supports over 22 urbanites and provides substantial quantities of food for less fortunate countries. Gone are the wide-open spaces with free land for the taking — a West to be conquered, the great granary of the Midwest to be perfected, and the plantation system of the South to be remodeled. The City of New York, where the Torrey Club was being founded, had not broken its insular boundaries to overflow into Westchester County and Connecticut to the north, Long Island to the east, and New Jersey to the south and west. The botany at the city's doorsteps was to be drowned in a sea of humanity that was to swell out as a part of the great megalopolis of the eastern United States.

Furthermore, the foundations were being laid for a revolution in classical botany even as the club was being organized in the tradition of the liberal arts universities. The U.S. Department of Agriculture had been established only four years before (May 15, 1862), and the great land-grant college movement was launched with the signing of the Morrill Act by President Lincoln on July 2, 1862 (Eddy, 1957; Knoblauch *et al.*, 1962). Federal support of agricultural research in the several states was not to be formalized by the Hatch Act until March 2, 1887, but the nation was on its way to creating a sound scientific background to guide the development of agriculture (Knoblauch *et al.*, 1962). The leadership of botanical research would inevitably gravitate to these new centers of study with emphasis on the application of ideas to revolutionizing agricultural practices. The Torrey Club and much of its membership was to follow a parallel course on a different track with great freedom in pursuit of botanical knowledge of a more fundamental sort but with less financial support behind the effort.

The research objectives of 100 years ago were designed to serve the needs of an essentially virgin science. The first step in every science is the collection and classification of subject matter into a workable body of knowledge. Taxonomy ruled supreme and was challenged only by the interest in comparative morphology and morphogenesis of plants. The search for an understanding of the function of plants was coming along in the background as witnessed by the publication of a textbook, "Plant Chemistry," by John W. Draper (1844), a professor at New York University and a lifelong resident of Hastings-on-Hudson.

Ahead of these founding fathers were the exhilarating experiences of revolutionary discoveries such as: the laws of heredity, the concept and nature of enzymes, proof of parasitism of plants by fungi and bacteria, the discovery of viruses and their characterization, development of the cyto-genetic concepts of reproduction, discovery of photoperiodism and vernalization, explanation of photosynthetic processes, proof of antibiotic interaction between living things, the concept of competitive forces in the evolution of plant societies, and the host of other things we now accept as part of the gospel of botany. An exciting era of adjustment in science, social structure, and agricultural operations was being inaugurated as the club came into existence.

The question today is, How well have we adjusted to the changing times and the demands upon our skills? In the symposia to be given monthly during the ensuing year, our colleagues in the several centers of botanical endeavor of the metropolitan area will discuss the special niches they have made for themselves in this particular environment. The avenues of service available to us are tremendously diverse; therefore it is fitting that the symposia be presented under the general heading, "The

Evolution of Botanical Science in a Metropolitan Environment over the Past Hundred Years."

Today we hope to demonstrate how The Boyce Thompson Institute is readjusting its research objectives and *modus operandi* to a new set of circumstances. The idea of a botanical research institute began to be formulated in the mind of Wm. B. Thompson in the waning days of World War I (Crocker, 1948). At the time of the Institute's dedication on September 24, 1924, plant physiology and plant pathology were coming to the forefront in botanical science. The great problems of plant growth in health and in disease were ripe for exploration. Chemistry had gained a dynamic foothold in the United States after World War I when our country was denied the products of German chemical industry. Organic chemistry had just begun to evolve. Somewhere in the great wilderness that lay between the concept of the nature of plant reactions and the kinetics of organic molecules lay the field that we now know as plant biochemistry.

It was natural that these early students of physiology at Boyce Thompson Institute should turn to the new concepts of chemistry in seeking answers to their questions. The basic philosophy of the Institute since its founding has been that it should strive to discover basic principles of living matter which would serve in solving practical problems. Because the Institute has always been dedicated to the solution of problems, the basic research is purposefully oriented rather than directed toward the gratification of personal curiosity of its scientists. We firmly believe that the scientist armed with sound understanding of the principles of living matter can solve problems of all sorts more efficiently by reasoning from natural laws than by hit-or-miss exploratory tests.

In defining the areas of research to be attacked by the Institute, fundamentally broad questions were posed to the scientist to give him great freedom to exercise his imagination, skills, and creativeness. Some of the questions attacked in those early days may be recalled as a part of our history. What is the nature of plant growth and differentiation, and how is it regulated? What are the forces behind dormancy in seeds, buds, and tubers, and how can they be manipulated to man's wishes? How does a plant—a cultivated crop or a microorganism—synthesize a cellulose fiber by polymerization reactions? What is a virus, and how does it operate? What mechanisms of fungitoxicity are operative in protecting plants from disease?

There is not sufficient time to discuss what was achieved as a result of this approach to research but, as a late comer upon the scene, I suggest that never before in the history of our science did such a small body of dedicated men exert so much influence on the thinking of their colleagues in botany. All too frequently the search for new principles ends in solving practical problems of plants such as breaking the dormancy of seeds, prolonging the effective storage of seeds, preventing the sprouting of tubers, controlling weeds by selective hormonal types of chemicals, designing new types of fungitoxicants, and so on. The story of those first eventful 25 years (1922–1947) has been summarized very well by the first Managing Director, William Crocker (Crocker, 1948).

When a new management was installed in 1949, reappraisal and reorientation of program were inevitable. The economic status of the Institute had deteriorated from its early affluence to a subsistence level, because the purchasing power of its dollars from investment had been eroded by the inflation during and after World War II. Furthermore, the cost of research operations had spiraled as equipment and procedures became more expensive. No longer could the needs of a highly creative scientist be met by providing him with microscope, petri dish, and scalpel.

Glorious new opportunities for research were presenting themselves in every botanical discipline as new techniques employing physicochemical principles were perfected for tracing the activity of molecules by isolating, analyzing, manipulating, and converting them into other metabolites. However, these techniques employing radioactive tracers, electron microscopes, complicated respirometers, infrared and ultraviolet spectrophotometry, paper, column, and gas chromatography, mass spectrometry, and nuclear magnetic resonance were expensive to implement, and they required new skills.

To take advantage of the situation, the Institute either had to obtain new sources of support, economize by reducing the scope of its activities, or seek greater efficiency through internal reogranization of program. To a certain extent each of these managerial possibilities has been exploited, so it is well to appraise the directional effects and difficulties embodied in each.

The strong trend toward seeking contracts for applied research from industry and government, already apparent in the Institute in 1949, could be accentuated. It was a tempting path for solving the financial dilemma, since the Institute's fine reputation for innovation with agricultural chemicals gave it an advantage over the so-called "independent" industrial research laboratories that were springing up to fill the demand. It also was obvious that the sensational new development with biologically active molecules would create demands for intensive research for years to come, and the Institute was equipped with many of the skills and facilities for executing such research. However, much of the research would have to be pedestrian, dead-end endeavor with respect to creating new principles or opening new vistas of research. It was decided that such research would be encouraged only to the extent that it could provide a testing ground for new hypotheses, would solicit the skills of organic chemists in industry to synthesize a variety of organic molecules of interest to the Institute, and would make it possible to use the bioassay research facilities of the Institute to maximum efficiency.

The idea of reducing the scope of purely basic research activities to one or two neglected areas of basic research and plumb them in depth was dropped after careful study. Certainly there was great need for research in a score of areas such as physiology of parasitism, biochemical genetics, chemical control of heredity, the physiological impact of environment pollution, the biochemical mechanisms of toxicants, or the forces of antibiosis in the rhizosphere of plants. However, an institution with limited perspective and restricted research effort can become economically unsound and self-defeating. The kind of research needed would require all the complex skills and equipment, much of which would be used infrequently and, therefore, inefficiently. The inevitable result would be high overhead per unit operation and excessive diversion of funds from direct research effort to maintenance and managerial functions.

It was obvious that the desirable reorganization of research effort to give depth to basic research in this fashion also called for reasonable breadth of programs so the research facility would be used fully. How could the Institute build on the broad program and skills already established? Obviously, it would not be easy but, if each line of endeavor provided a measure of support to the others, if each scientist could talk the language of the others and respond to their ideas, if each program could use similar equipment and benefit from new techniques and skills of its sister programs, a dynamic mutually self-supporting Institute could be created.

But where do an entomologist, a virologist, a biochemist, a microbiologist, a plant pathologist, a geneticist, and a plant physiologist — to name a few disciplines — find a common meeting ground where their ideas and concepts contribute to each other's intellectual growth and progressiveness? The answer is obvious: at the level of the living cell. Any new knowledge on the metabolic activities of one type of cell contributes to the understanding of cells in other organisms. The great universality of biochemical processes follows such general laws that it can be trusted as a general principle. There is, however, just enough diversity to give spice to such research and keep every researcher on his toes. Therefore this institution decided to concentrate its research on cell physiology as the most practical solution to its needs.

As you listen this afternoon to the speakers explaining what they are doing and why, and as you go from laboratory to laboratory, you may get an awful feeling that you are seeing in operation a thing called molecular biology. Our only excuse is that the name either had not been coined or had not been advertised vigorously by its evangelists when we launched our conversion. We still maintain that our interests are in cell physiology, even though we draw freely upon molecular biology for the basic concepts and reasoning with which we attack problems.

We realized at the outset that our conversion to a philosophy of cell physiology would not be achieved easily. It meant that the physiology laboratories had to be reequipped, the old morphology laboratories had to be redesigned, and new analytical laboratories had to be created, but fortunately neither Rome nor the house of science was built in a day and the conversion did not have to be done overnight. The shift could be gradual as emphasis in research was reoriented and as the staff gained new skills and were brought into contact with new concepts.

The managerial philosophy behind this decision was based on three facts that make it compatible with established institutional policies and aspirations. We believe fully that the fate of an organism is determined by the activities of its cells. The man who understands what goes on inside the cell has the knowledge to regulate the organism to suit his desires. If we know what a toxicant does to biochemical processes, someone should be able to design a better organic molecule to destroy weeds, insects, parasitic fungi, and so on, so we can protect crops or conversely escape damage from environmental pollutants. If we know how selective permeability of membranes operates, we should be able to design safer molecules for release in the environment or for use in crop protection. Once we understand how a virus intercepts, diverts, or destroys the hereditary message of the cell, we should conceive ways to prevent virus diseases. Knowledge of the nucleic acid metabolism and regeneration of proteins should be indispensable to finding new methods of regulating dormancy and growth. As a matter of fact, once we know the genetic code embodied in the nucleotide sequence of DNA, we should be able to create synthetic RNA to divert hereditary mechanims of plants to the desires of mankind: for example, plants with higher protein content, disease resistance, less palatability for insects. This difficult basic research should be the most practical thing in the world. As a matter of fact, it is about our only hope for creating new methods of protecting and manipulating plant life to meet the growing demands of our civilization.

The second point is that this approach offers something to every scientist. It provides a challenge to creativeness and ingenuity of perception that should spark the best effort from any man. Yet it can be made to operate at almost any level of sophistication. Finally, we conceived of this program as being of sufficient breadth and potential creativeness to attract research funds in a steady flow. Thus the several programs could be made to grow and expand to fulfill the ambitions of the scientists, who would be restricted only by the scope of their intellectual resources and aspirations.

What you will hear and see today, therefore, is the product of 15 years of hard work by the staff in remodeling, building, creating, and improving the financial base of the Institute. Many of the faces will be new to you as the younger breed with all its enthusiasm takes over and propels us along the pathway into the hidden secrets of the cell. Some of the techniques may be foreign to your experience, but they should be neither incomprehensible nor so complex that most of you could not use them if given a few days of instruction.

The general facts behind what you see and hear today may be of interest to you. We are an endowed, nonprofit corporation with a net worth in the order of 25 million dollars. The current budget calls for expenditures of about 2 million dollars, of which almost $1,100,000 will be derived from grants, contracts, gifts, and other external sources and well over $900,000 will be generated from internal sources, primarily income from investments. Nourishment for our modernization and expansion program is provided in the 1967 budget by allocations of over $105,000 for major new equipment, over $30,000 for remodeling and construction of new facilities, and $93,000 is earmarked for a reserve to prevent obsolescence of present facilities and equipment from causing stagnation in the future.

The Board of Directors has authorized this investment of almost a quarter of a million dollars for our future because it has confidence in the capabilities and dedication of the staff. There are 35 senior scientists of Ph.D. grade or its equivalent who are charged with execution of over 50 separate projects and, even more important, with generating new ideas to help solve old problems. There is roughly an equal number of research assistants and associates (holders of B.S. and M.S. degrees) who help to carry out the research ideas and execute the research plans of the scientists. About 30 laboratory aides without professional degrees also assist in the laboratories. Behind these research teams are about 60 of us who serve in administration, clerical services, technical services, such as library and illustration, physical plant maintenance and engineering, or plant culture in greenhouses, farms, and forests.

Unfortunately, today you will see only the Yonkers plant, which provides approximately 107,000 square feet of floor space and over half an

acre of greenhouses on 174 silver-plated acres of land. The building, with
its fine library, intricate installations, and specialized equipment, could
not be replaced for 4 million dollars, and the land has a current sale value
of almost twice as much. The outlying areas include the 20-acre experimental farm for small field plots lying nearby in the Nepera Park area
of Yonkers and a 450-acre farm 90 miles to the north in Dutchess County
which provides for long-range experiments, evaluation of tree-breeding
progeny, and recreational facilities for the staff such as a private lake and
hiking trails.

Complete and well-equipped laboratories for forest entomology research have been established in a 700-acre ponderosa pine forest near
Grass Valley, California, and in a 240-acre southern pine forest near
Beaumont, Texas. Entomologists and supporting staff are operative the
year around, and the group in California also manages a field station in a
western white pine forest owned by Potlatch Forest Industries at Headquarters, Idaho. The interesting point is that we have gone to locations
where there is a problem of interest to us. We have given depth to our
studies by picking three problem situations which were analogous but
operated with a different set of actors. The victim of bark beetle attack
at each site is a species of *Pinus (P. ponderosae, P. monticolae,* or *P.
taeda).* It is being attacked by a primary species of *Dendroctonus (D.
brevicomis, D. ponderosae,* and *D. frontalis,* respectively) with secondary
effects from associated species of *Ips.* Much of the supporting chemical
services are being provided in Yonkers where the necessary complement
of equipment is available. Frozen biological materials can be delivered
here in three to eight hours after collection. Even this program has come
down to an intriguing molecular basis as we seek to identify and study the
biological properties of the pheromones being produced in the hindguts
of the several beetles.

Only the skeleton of the modern Boyce Thompson Institute is revealed
by these policies and managerial manipulations. Let us now turn our attention to the people who breathe life into it by generating ideas and
clothe it with the flesh of good solid data. We want to expose you to three
symposiettes in this symposium: the control of growth and morphogenesis,
the processes of disease induction in plants and insects, and a look into
environmental health—the activities of fungi and air pollution.

REFERENCES

Crocker, William. (1948). "Growth of plants—Twenty years' research at Boyce Thompson
    Institute." Reinhold, New York.

Draper, John W. (1844). "Chemistry of Plants." London.

Eddy, E. D. (1957). "Colleges for Our Land and Our Time; the Land Grant Idea in American Education." Harper and Row, New York.

Knoblauch, H. C., Law, E. M., and Meyer, W. P. (1962). State Agricultural Experiment Stations. *U. S. Dept. Agr. Misc. Publ.* **904.**

A. THE CONTROL OF GROWTH AND MORPHOGENESIS

Seed Physiology at Boyce Thompson Institute*

Alva A. App and Maria M. Bulis

Research concerning the preservation of seeds during storage and the effects of various environmental conditions on seed germination has been conducted continuously since the founding of the Institute. The importance of storage to the seed industry is based on the necessity of holding seeds from the time of harvest until planting and the need to store excess harvest for one or more seasons. In addition, safe, prolonged storage also provides a constant source of valuable seed stock for genetic experiments.

The keeping quality of various types of seeds under controlled storage conditions at Boyce Thompson has been investigated for many years. Vegetable seeds stored under different humidities and temperatures in May 1932 and tested at intervals thereafter have demonstrated the superiority of below-freezing temperatures to those above freezing for the maintenance of viability (Barton, 1935a, 1939, 1940). Short-lived onion seeds, which are much reduced in germination after 1 year at room temperature, live for at least 30 years at a temperature of −4°C. Extended safe storage, especially at below-freezing temperatures, has been demonstrated for seeds of carrot, eggplant, lettuce, onion, pepper, and tomato. In addition to the vegetable seeds mentioned, below-freezing storage has been shown to be of value in keeping seeds of conifers, *Tilia*, nuts, elm, and ash (Barton, 1935b, 1953, 1954b).

---

*Primarily a review of the work by Lela V. Barton, deceased July 31, 1967.

The safe storage of conifer seeds is of special importance because a good seed crop is not produced each year and a constant supply of large quantities of seeds is required for reforestation programs throughout the world. In storage tests of Douglas fir, western red cedar, western hemlock, and Sitka spruce it has been shown that not only is below-freezing temperature beneficial in keeping the seeds viable but also, the lower the temperature (to $-18°C$), the longer is the life span. A temperature of $-18°C$ has preserved the original vigor of these seeds for 7 years; $-10°C$ and $-5°C$ were much less effective.

Much work has been done with respect to seed dormancy. The term dormancy is defined as the failure of viable seeds to germinate when placed under conditions of moisture and temperature which would ordinarily bring about sprouting; it does not refer to the dormancy of the dry, resting seed. Moist, low-temperature pretreatment for breaking the dormancy of embryos has been demonstrated to be effective for more than 100 species. This common requirement of perennial plants assures that the seeds remain ungerminated until the following growing season. The exact time and temperature for the pretreatment of many species have been determined (Barton, 1930, 1933, 1936, 1951, 1954a; Crocker and Barton, 1931).

Some seeds have dormant embryos which do not after-ripen in a moist medium at low temperature because their seed coats are impermeable to water. The term after-ripening refers to the preparation of the seed for resumption of growth. It is essential to make the coat permeable before the low-temperature treatment is given. This is done by a variety of treatments including mechanical scarification, soaking in concentrated sulfuric acid, alcohol, or hot water, and by temperature treatments. Differential responses to mechanical seed treatment by two subfamily groups of Leguminosae suggest two types of seed-coat impermeability. Evidence obtained indicates that morphological differences in the structures surrounding the embryos account for the observed differences (Barton, 1947). Another type of dormancy, described for the first time at the Institute, is that in which the seed germinates without any pretreatment to form a root, but low temperature must be given to break the dormancy of the shoot. This is termed epicotyl dormancy (Barton, 1933, 1936).

It is becoming increasingly clear that the process of breaking dormancy is not the result of the alteration in status of one key component in the cell, but rather involves the reorientation of the general metabolic pattern of the cell. For example, during breaking of epicotyl dormancy in tree peony there are appreciable changes in amino acid content, amides, organic acids, organic phosphates, carbohydrates and proteins (Barton,

1961; Barton and Bray, 1962; Fine and Barton, 1958). The initiation of the process is very probably controlled by one or more specific hormones.

Current research is concerned with the initiation of protein synthesis and nucleic acid metabolism during seed germination. Investigation of the control of these processes and the mechanism of protein synthesis is of particular interest (App and Gerosa, 1966). Knowledge of the mechanism of plant protein synthesis may afford the opportunity to alter selectively the composition of seed storage proteins and thereby enhance their nutritional value to both animal and man.

REFERENCES

App, A. A., and Gerosa, M. M. (1966). A soluble fraction requirement in the transfer reaction of protein synthesis by rice embryo ribosomes. *Plant Physiol.* **41**, 1420–1424.

Barton, L. V. (1930). Hastening the germination of some coniferous seeds. *Am. J. Botan.* **17**, 88–115.

Barton, L. V. (1933). Seedling production of tree peony. *Contrib. Boyce Thompson Inst.* **5**, 451–460.

Barton, L. V. (1935a). Storage of vegetable seeds. *Contrib. Boyce Thompson Inst.* **7**, 323–332.

Barton, L. V. (1935b). Storage of some coniferous seeds. *Contrib. Boyce Thompson Inst.* **7**, 379–404.

Barton, L. V. (1936). Germination and seedling production in *Lilium* sp. *Contrib. Boyce Thompson Inst.* **8**, 297–309.

Barton, L. V. (1939). A further report on the storage of vegetable seeds. *Contrib. Boyce Thompson Inst.* **10**, 205–220.

Barton, L. V. (1940). Some effects of treatment of seeds with growth substances on dormancy. *Contrib. Boyce Thompson Inst.* **11**, 229–240.

Barton, L. V. (1947). Special studies on seed coat impermeability. *Contrib. Boyce Thompson Inst.* **14**, 355–362.

Barton, L. V. (1951). Germination of seeds of *Juniperus virginiana* L. *Contrib. Boyce Thompson Inst.* **16**, 387–393.

Barton, L. V. (1953). Seed storage and viability. *Contrib. Boyce Thompson Inst.* **17**, 87–103.

Barton, L. V. (1954a). Effect of presoaking on dormancy in seeds. *Contrib. Boyce Thompson Inst.* **17**, 435–438.

Barton, L. V. (1954b). Effect of subfreezing temperatures on viability of conifer seeds in storage. *Contrib. Boyce Thompson Inst.* **18**, 21–24.

Barton, L. V. (1961). Biochemical studies of dormancy and after-ripening of seeds. II. Changes in oligobasic organic acids and carbohydrates. *Contrib. Boyce Thompson Inst.* **21**, 147–161.

Barton, L. V., and Bray, J. L. (1962). Biochemical studies of dormancy and after-ripening of seeds. III. Nitrogen metabolism. *Contrib. Boyce Thompson Inst.* **21**, 465–472.

Crocker, W., and Barton, L. V. (1931). After-ripening, germination and storage of certain rosaceous seeds. *Contrib. Boyce Thompson Inst.* **3**, 385–404.

Fine, J. M., and Barton, L. V. (1958). Biochemical studies of dormancy and after-ripening in seeds. I. Changes in free amino acid content. *Contrib. Boyce Thompson Inst.* **19**, 483–500.

Characteristics of Fine Structure and Nucleic Acid Metabolism in Apical Meristems of Physiological Dwarfs of Rosaceous Plants

Florence Flemion and Dalton Wang

Chilled seeds of various rosaceous species, such as peach and *Rhodotypos,* produce normal plants, whereas seedlings from nonchilled seeds are physiologically dwarfed; that is, the shoot apices are abnormal and telescoped, and they frequently exhibit chlorotic leaves. Since the site of this dwarfing factor remains in the undifferentiated tissues in the upper 2 or 3 mm of the shoot tip, an ultrastructural study of this apical meristem region was undertaken.

Plastids in shoot apices of physiologically dwarfed seedlings differ from normal ones in the more frequent occurrence of membrane-bound inclusions in the surface cells, in their progressive accumulation of starch basipetally into the pith rib meristem, and in the greater abundance of tubular lamellae primarily in the leaf primordia. Chlorotic portions of malformed leaves and the colorless streaked areas of the shoot apices in the dwarf contain plastids whose normal development appears to have been blocked at various stages. There is no evidence that plastids may have achieved more advanced development and then undergone degeneration.

Comparative studies of the biosynthesis of pyrimidine nucleotides from ^{14}C-labeled orotic acid were made on seedlings of *Rhodotypos* following after-ripening at 5°C for periods of 3, 6, and 11 weeks. These treatments produced physiological dwarf, semidwarf, and normal plants, respectively. Within 4 and 8 hr, seedlings after-ripened for 3 weeks yielded uracil nucleotides containing 12.5 and 20.5% of the total radioactivity in the soluble fractions, and those after-ripened for 6 weeks gave 10.5 and 22.1%. The percentages of radioactivity in these nucleotides obtained from seedlings after-ripened for 11 weeks were 20.9% and 38% with respective feeding periods. These results showed a close correlation between the degree of after-ripening of the seedlings and the rate of the biosynthesis of pyrimidine nucleotides from orotic acid and stimulation of the nucleotide biosynthesis by low-temperature treatment.

15

GENERAL REFERENCES

Flemion, Florence (1933). Physiological and chemical studies of after-ripening of *Rhodo-typos kerrioides* seeds. *Contrib. Boyce Thompson Inst.* **5**, 143–159.
Flemion, Florence, and Beardow, Jane. (1965). Production of peach seedlings from non-chilled seeds. II. Effect of subsequent cold periods on growth. *Contrib. Boyce Thompson Inst.* **23**, 101–107.
Flemion, Florence, Dengler, R. E., Dengler, N. G., and Stewart, K. D. (1967). Ultrastructure of the shoot apices and leaves of normal and physiologically dwarfed peach seedlings. I. Plastid development. *Contrib. Boyce Thompson Inst.* **23**, 331–344.

Relationship between RNA Metabolism and the Effect of Growth Regulants in Pea Seedlings

D. C. McCune, A. A. De Hertogh, and D. C. MacLean

Both natural and synthetic growth regulants can profoundly affect the growth and development of the plant by altering the cellular processes of elongation and differentiation. Extensive investigations of the changes in cell metabolites, enzyme activities, and cell wall development have still not explained the mechanism by which growth regulants induce cell elongation. Consequently, recent research has been directed toward the effects of growth regulants on the mechanisms of gene action and control.

Different approaches have been used to attack this problem. Some investigations have determined the effect of inhibitors of DNA synthesis, DNA-directed RNA synthesis, or RNA-directed protein synthesis on growth regulant activity. Other studies have been made of the effects of growth regulants on the RNA complement of the cell and the synthesis or turnover of RNA. Both approaches have been used at Boyce Thompson Institute to study the effects of growth substances on cell elongation.

Sections from the internodes of Alaska pea seedlings grown in the light show an elongation of 1 mm/hr if they are incubated in optimal concentrations of indole acetic acid (IAA) or 2,4-dichlorophenoxyacetic acid (2,4-D). However, actinomycin D, which inhibits the synthesis of RNA from a DNA template, also inhibits IAA- or 2,4-D-induced elongation (De Hertogh *et al.*, 1965). IAA and 2,4-D also increase the rate of incorporation of ^{14}C-orotate into RNA, and actinomycin D inhibits this effect of IAA and 2,4-D in a manner that is similar to its effect on elongation. The analysis of mononucleotides from hydrolyzed RNA samples shows that IAA and 2,4-D do not increase the specific activities of UMP and CMP, and therefore the increased labeling of total RNA may result from a change in the rate of synthesis or turnover of one fraction.

These studies indicate that the cell elongation promoted by IAA and 2,4-D requires a continued synthesis of RNA in order to express this action. Whether growth substances act through, or are dependent on, RNA metabolism requires further study and more specific information about the nature of the changes induced in the RNA complement of the cell.

REFERENCE

De Hertogh, A. A., McCune, D. C., Brown, J., and Antoine, D. (1965). The effect of antagonists of RNA and protein biosynthesis on IAA and 2,4-D induced growth of green pea stem sections. *Contrib. Boyce Thompson Inst.* **23,** 23–31.

Regulation of Male Gametogenesis.
A Search for New Bioregulants*

Edward H. Buckley

Male gametogenesis in higher plants is the process of differentiation and development which leads to the formation of pollen. Male gametogenesis was selected for study because of its agronomic importance, particularly in hybrid seed production, which for most crop plants is either very limited or nonexistent owing to a lack of female breeding plants (i.e., male-sterile breeding lines). The more general objectives of the program are to determine the means by which differentiation of form and function occurs.

---

*This work was initiated under the sponsorship of the International Minerals and Chemical Corp., Skokie, Illinois.

Biologists now accept that, generally, each living cell of a multicellular organism contains identical DNA coded chromosomes. For example, Steward *et al.* (1964) were able to culture phloem cells of carrot until some developed into plants which grew to produce flowers and set seed, thereby demonstrating clearly that the genetic information in cells remains complete. Yet, with the same genetic information, the cells of various plant parts differ in both form and function. The theoretical explanation for this is that development occurs when different parts of the genetic information are used in programed sequence during the life cycle. So far, all tests of the theory, limited as they are, do support the concept. The factors that determine which parts of the genetic information should be used in each cell at any one stage of the life cycle, however, are still completely unknown.

The major challenge to biologists in the 1960's and 1970's is to discover the regulation mechanisms of development. Of course, some natural plant regulants (plant hormones) have been found. The three main groups are the auxins [first exploited at the Boyce Thompson Institute by Zimmerman and Hitchcock (Crocker *et al.*, 1935; Hitchcock and Zimmerman, 1947; Zimmerman and co-workers, 1935, 1943, 1948)], the gibberellins, and the kinins. However, these hormones do not fit the criteria necessary for development regulation at the gene level. The responses they elicit are too gross, the concentration requirement for effectiveness is too high, and there appears to be more than just technical difficulty in finding meaningful chemical associations between these plant regulants and DNA. Consequently, other types of development regulants must be operative and must be found by analyzing the processes of development.

If male gametogenesis can be thought of as only one of the gene-programed phases of the life cycle, composed of numerous coordinated and sequential events, then two aspects become apparent. First, the majority of the event systems may be "turned off" most of the time and they must be "turned off" so specifically that other event systems are not affected. Second, at any one time a particular event system may be "turned on" in cells that are located in several different tissues in various parts of the plant. It is probable that the specific process of gametogenesis is due predominantly to a specific combination and sequence of common events and only slightly to the few unique chemical and physical events that occur. However, all are presumably essential for normal development.

The sequences of chemical events that are regulated are undoubtedly catalyzed by enzymes. Hence the pronounced impact on biological thought when Jacob and Monod (1961) set forth their theory for the regulation of protein (enzyme) synthesis. Briefly, the theory states that the chromosomal control system for a single enzyme (or enzyme system) comprises three genes, a structural gene, an operator gene, and a regulator gene. The structural gene, through the process of transcription, functions as a DNA template on which messenger RNA (mRNA) is produced and then is released into the nucleus and cytoplasm. In turn, through the coded process of translation, the mRNA acts as a coding template for protein synthesis when appropriately attached to ribosomes (an aggregate of several ribosomes attached along a single strand of mRNA is referred to as a polysome). The regulator gene on the chromosome is thought to produce, by transcription, an RNA molecule which functions directly as a repressor or, more likely, functions as an mRNA which, by translation directs the synthesis of repressor protein [only two repressors have been isolated, the λ repressor (Ptashne, 1967) and the lac repressor (Gilbert and Müller-Hill, 1967), both in *E. coli,* and both appear to be protein]. The repressor molecule represses mRNA synthesis on the structural gene only when it is attached to the operator gene adjacent to the structural gene. In some cases a specific repressor molecule must be associated with a specific co-repressor (a low molecular weight molecule) before it has the proper stereochemistry to fit onto a particular operator gene. Such a system appears ideally suited to the regulation of an enzyme required in metabolism. Here the metabolic product can function as the co-repressor for the appropriate repressor molecule to "shut off" synthesis of enzyme when sufficient product is on hand. In the remaining cases the repressor molecule, in its native form, binds to the operator gene but falls away from the operator gene when a specific low molecular weight antirepressor (or enzyme inducer) interacts with the repressor. The latter system seems preferentially suited to the regulation of developmental processes which are "turned off" during the majority of the life cycle.

Therefore a search for specific antirepressors as development regulants is warranted. What may be required as a specific gametocide is a modified antirepressor. One type of modified antirepressor would be a compound which interacts with a particular repressor without removing it from its operator gene. Simultaneously it would have to block the site of interaction for the correct antirepressor so that the antirepressor could not function on arrival. Consequently mRNA synthesis on the adjacent structural gene would remain inhibited. Another modified antirepressor would be one that removed the repressor from the gene for a prolonged period of time, allowing uncontrolled transcription of mRNA from a particular structural gene. The later types of antirepressors are called gratuitous inducers; they have been studied in *E. coli* (Burnstein *et al.,* 1965). It should be clarified that the Jacob-Monod scheme pertains to bacteria, and modified and different systems must occur in higher plants. For example, repressors (along with their co-repressors and antirepressors) could interact with almost any RNA species and serve to block any of the initiation processes required to make a protein.

The detection of a natural antirepressor from sporogenous cells was set as the first major goal in the program. Consequently the first question was, how? For example, could an antirepressor be found by using the sporogenous cells of anthers as a bioassay? This question cannot be answered affirmatively yet, but there are some encouraging prospects that can be reported.

Most of these investigations have been done with anthers of *Lilium longiflorum* var. Croft in which there is a useful correlation between flower bud size and the stage of development of the sporogenous cells in the anthers (Taylor, 1959). The anthers are relatively large and are free of microbial contamination while the bud remains closed. Furthermore, the closed bud can be surface-sterilized with Clorox and with ethanol. But two problems were encountered when excised anthers were used. One problem was that the content of extractable polysomes (the sites of protein synthesis) decreased rapidly while the monomers (ribosomes not likely attached to mRNA and therefore not synthesizing protein) increased, indicating that the tissues were not normal and that protein synthesis was affected adversely. The other problem, which was most acute during meiosis and shortly thereafter, was that materials fed into the wound of the detached filament moved almost exclusively to the tapetal cells which form a lining around the sporogenous cells and nourish them. Only after several hours did the applied materials and their metabolic products begin to move into the sporogenous tissues. This thwarted the use of meaningful short-term experiments or pulse label experiments with radioactive compounds. However, these problems could be overcome when the bud and anthers were left attached to the plant.

To maintain aseptic conditions the whole lily plant was wrapped in sterilized paper and brought into the transfer hood where the bud was surface-sterilized and where the sepals and petals were partially dissected to expose the anthers. Desiccation of the bud was prevented with a cover of Saran wrap. Radiochemicals were applied to a small wound at the uppermost end of an anther. Under these conditions the polysome populations remained stable for at least 6 hr (the longest period examined), and the distribution of radiochemicals into the sporogenous cells was much improved. Also, this method seems to coincide more with the natural developmental scheme because there is a gradient in the stages of development within the sporogenous cells of each anther during meiosis. The uppermost cells lead in maturation while the basal sporogenous cells may lag behind by some 20 hr. This gradient of maturation during meiosis suggests that regulants are synthesized in the upper portion of each anther and that they move down through the interconnected sporogenous cells (Heslop-Harrison, 1966) to program development. Therefore it appears that technically the lily anther can be used as a bioassay tool. However, mandatory for its use in bioassay was finding morphological and chemical markers within the sporogenous cells which are recognizable processes related to development.

Excellent morphological markers are available during meiosis (a 9- to 10-day period) merely by observing the chromosomal configurations. Later in the development of the pollen there is another period of 2 to 3 days when mitotic divisions occur and again chromosomes can be used as markers.

Chemical markers that would indicate gene-programed stages of development were also required. Technological limitations make it impossible to analyze for gene repression at particular chromosomal loci in higher plants. Nor is it possible to recognize directly the synthesis or presence of specific types of mRNA. However, appreciable advances have been made in the separation of proteins by discontinuous electrophoresis in polyacrylamide gel (Davis, 1964); this tool was used to reveal changes in protein in sporogenous cells throughout pollen development.

By far the most rapid changes were observed during meiosis. Densitometer tracings of the electrophoretic protein separations are shown in Figs. 1 and 2 for the various stages of meiosis. Linskens (1966), with the same techniques, demonstrated protein changes in the sporogenous cells of *Lilium henryi*. Although his densitometer tracings are appreciably different, they also reveal characteristic patterns for each stage of meiosis. However, the pertinence of these data as chemical markers has become dubious. For instance, qualitative changes in the proteins cannot be distinguished from quantitative changes among proteins already present. Also, changes in isoenzymes that might be detected at various stages of development are as likely to be artifacts of extractions as of genetic origin, as vigorously discussed recently (Vesell, 1968).

Furthermore, during meiosis the population of extractable polyribosomes in the sporogenous cells essentially disappeared just when they might be expected to be most prolific if numerous new proteins

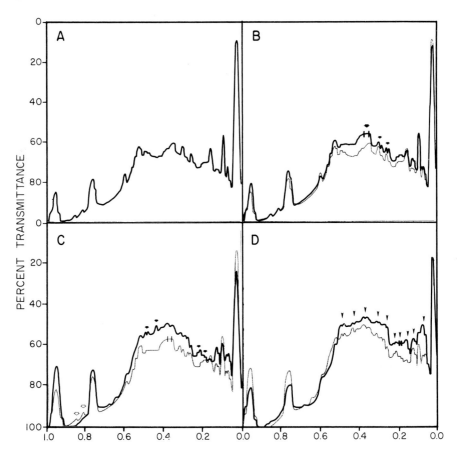

FIG. 1. Protein changes in sporogenous cells of anthers *(Lilium longiflorum)* during the first 6 days of meiosis as revealed by densitometer tracings of protein bands stained with Amido Schwartz reagent after disc electrophoresis in polyacrylamide gels. Solid lines are typical tracings for extractable proteins (at neutral pH) 1 to 2 days before meiosis begins (A), during leptotene (B), zygotene (C), and during early pachytene (D). A dotted line represents the superimposed tracing of the previous stage to facilitate comparison. Solid arrows designate new or particularly characteristic protein bands for each stage. Open arrows indicate regions of lost bands.

were being synthesized. One interpretation for this apparent loss in both polyribosomes and single ribosomes is that the ribosomal population becomes membrane-bound during meiosis. Membrane-bound ribosomes would not be detected easily because they sediment rapidly as an aggregate during centrifugation. Such a component has been observed which sediments to the bottom of the cell in the analytical centrifuge before

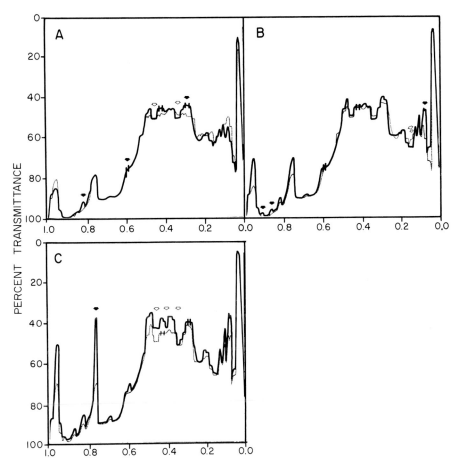

FIG. 2. Continuation of Fig. 1 showing protein changes in sporogenous cells of anthers (*Lilium longiflorum*) during the last 3 to 4 days of meiosis. Solid lines are typical tracings for late pachytene (A), diplotene and diakinesis combined (B), and meiotic divisions I and II combined (C).

the rotor accelerates to 15,000 rpm or even less. Future studies may clarify these details.

Prime interest lies in the fact that lily anthers promise to provide a useful bioassay system for the detection of regulators of development. But further work is necessary to find a good chemical marker to complement the anatomical markers.

REFERENCES

Burnstein, C., Cohn, M., Kepes, A., and Monod, J. (1965). Rôle du lactose et de ses produits métaboliques dans l'induction de l'opéron lactose chez *Escherichia coli*. *Biochim. Biophys. Acta* **95**,634–639.

Crocker, W., Hitchcock, A. E., and Zimmerman, P. W. (1935). Similarities in the effects of ethylene and the plant auxins. *Contrib. Boyce Thompson Inst.* **7**,231–248.

Davis, B. J. (1964). Disc electrophoresis. II. Method and application to human serum proteins. *Ann. N.Y. Acad. Sci.* **121**,404–427.

Gilbert, W., and Müller-Hill, B. (1967). The lac operator is DNA. *Proc. Natl. Acad. Sci. U.S.* **58**,2415–2421.

Heslop-Harrison, J. (1966). Cytoplasmic continuities during spore formation in flowering plants. *Endeavor* **25**,65–72.

Hitchcock, A. E., and Zimmerman, P. W. (1947). Response and recovery of dandelion and plantain after treatment with 2,4-D. *Contrib. Boyce Thompson Inst.* **14**,471–492.

Jacob, F., and Monod, J. (1961). Genetic regulatory mechanisms in the synthesis of proteins. *J. Mol. Biol.* **3**,318–356.

Linskens, H. F. (1966). Die Änderung des Protein- und Enzym-musters während der Pollenmeiose und Pollenentwicklung. Physiologische Untersuchungen zur Reifeteilung. *Planta* **69**,79–91.

Ptashne, M. (1967). Specific binding of the λ phage repressor to λ DNA. *Nature* **214**, 232–234.

Steward, F. C., Mapes, M. O., Kent, A. E., and Holsten, R. D. (1964). Growth and development of cultured plant cells. *Science* **143**,20–27.

Taylor, J. H. (1959). Autoradiographic studies of nucleic acids and proteins during meiosis in *Lilium longiflorum*. *Am. J. Botany* **46**,477–484.

Vesell, E. S. (ed.). (1968). Second Conference on "Multiple Molecular Forms of Enzymes," Dec. 1966. *Ann. N.Y. Acad. Sci.* **151**,1–689.

Zimmerman, P. W. (1943). The formative influences and comparative effectiveness of various plant hormone-like compounds. *Torreya* **43**,98–115.

Zimmerman, P. W., and Hitchcock, A. E. (1948). Plant hormones. *Ann. Rev. Biochem.* **17**,601–626.

Zimmerman, P. W., and Wilcoxon, F. (1935). Several chemical growth substances which cause initiation of roots and other responses in plants. *Contrib. Boyce Thompson Inst.* **7**,209–229.

Aromatic Biosynthesis in Plants*

Leonard H. Weinstein and Henry J. Laurencot, Jr.

Studies on the chemical changes associated with aging in cut roses re-

*This work was sponsored in part by NSF Grant No. GB-286 and the Atomic Energy Commission.

vealed that the dominant nonvolatile organic acid of petal and leaf tissues was quinic acid and that it constituted as much as 10% of the dry weight of young leaves (Weinstein *et al.,* 1958). This massive accumulation, which was greater than that reported for any other plant, naturally led to speculations about its metabolic role in this species. The level of quinic acid was found to increase in the developing rose until the bloom was at about half-maturity, after which it decreased (Weinstein *et al.,* 1959a). This result suggested that quinic acid was metabolized in the rose. Similar results were also obtained in rose stem tissue cultures at various ages (Weinstein *et al.,* 1962).

Randomly ^{14}C-labeled quinic acid, and the related shikimic acid, were biosynthesized by supplying young rose plants in the light with ^{14}CO$_2$. Purified ^{14}C-labeled quinic acid was supplied to cut roses for varying periods of time. The major labeled compounds isolated and identified were shikimic acid and free and bound tyrosine and phenylalanine (Weinstein *et al.,* 1959a,b). These results clearly demonstrated that quinic acid was a precursor to the formation of the aromatic nucleus in roses. It was clear that quinic acid was first converted into shiki-mic acid and that the aromatic ring was biosynthesized via the shi-kimic acid pathway. Continued studies with ten other higher plants showed that in all cases labeled tyrosine and phenylalanine were formed and that in all but one case labeled shikimic acid was also present (Wein-stein, 1961). Further investigation also showed that quinic acid was a precursor to the formation of tryptophan. Although quinic acid is con-verted into shikimic acid, tyrosine, and phenylalanine in a CO$_2$-free atmosphere, this does not apply for conversion into tryptophan, which requires CO$_2$.

REFERENCES

Weinstein, L. H., Porter, C. A., and Laurencot, H. J., Jr. (1959a). Quinic acid as a pre-cursor in aromatic biosynthesis in the rose. *Contrib. Boyce Thompson Inst.* **20,** 121–134.
Weinstein, L. H., Porter, C. A., and Laurencot, H. J., Jr. (1959b). Evidence for the con-version of quinic acid to shikimic acid in roses. *Nature* **183,** 326.
Weinstein, L. H., Porter, C. A., and Laurencot, H. J., Jr. (1961). Role of quinic acid in aromatic biosynthesis in higher plants. *Contrib. Boyce Thompson Inst.* **21,** 201–214.
Weinstein, L. H., Smith, W. R., and Laurencot, H. J., Jr. (1958). Senescence of roses. III. Isolation and identification of *l*-quinic acid from Better Times roses. *Contrib. Boyce Thompson Inst.* **19,** 341–348.
Weinstein, L. H., Tulecke, W., Nickell, L. G., and Laurencot, H. J., Jr. (1962). Biochem-ical and physiological studies of tissue cultures and the plant parts from which they are derived. III. Paul's Scarlet rose. *Contrib. Boyce Thompson Inst.* **21,** 371–386.

Plastid Function in Plant Tissue Cultures*

Walter Tulecke

Tissue cultures of higher plants usually fail to develop a vigorous complement of chloroplasts. This failure is sometimes correlated with an acceleration in growth rate and lack of differentiation in the tissues. The reasons for these developments are not well understood.

Haploid tissue cultures derived from the male and female gametophytes of *Ginkgo biloba* L. are being used to study plastid function and cell differentiation *in vitro*. The tissue derived from the female gametophyte shows the maternal inheritance of plastid function and also differentiates specialized cells. The tissue is composed of green parenchyma cells which contain chloroplasts; other cells specialize to form tracheids, or cells which store tannins or crystalline materials similar to those found in normal leaf cells. The expression of maternal inheritance in this tissue thus relates plastid function to specialized cell types. In contrast, the male tissue (derived from the pollen) is white, friable, and composed of undifferentiated cells which contain amyloplasts; this tissue never forms chloroplasts of specialized cells.

One interesting development in these studies was the derivation of an albino tissue from the female green tissue culture. This was done by serial transfer in the dark. The albino tissue lost its capacity to differentiate specialized cells as it lost its capacity to form chloroplasts. The female albino tissue culture resembled the male albino in all characters thus far tested. Essentially, then, the expression of the maternal inheritance (chloroplast development in the female tissue) was prevented by the prolonged exclusion of light. The paternal characteristic of amyloplast development was present in the two albino tissues, neither of which would turn green in the light.

Experiments were designed to feed a precursor of porphyrins (δ-aminolevulinic acid, ALA) to the albino and other achlorophyllous tissues. The intent was to overcome a possible lesion in the biosynthetic capacity of the chlorophyll-deficient tissues and perhaps locate different inter-

*This project was supported in part by funds from Grant No. GB-3618 from the National Science Foundation.

26

mediates in chlorophyll synthesis. The haploid tissues of *Ginkgo* (as well as tissues of *Rosa, Taxus,* and *Agave*) formed protoporphyrin from ALA. The protoporphyrin was extracted and identified by paper chromatography and absorption spectroscopy. That no magnesium protoporphyrin was formed indicated the existence of a block at this point in the synthesis of chlorophyll. Localization of protoporphyrin synthesis in the plastids was demonstrated by ultraviolet and electron microscopy. Various nutritional and environmental factors were tested for their effect on the albino and achlorophyllous tissue cultures in an attempt to induce or improve chloroplast development in cells cultured *in vitro.* These studies are continuing.

Other lines of research on the growth of higher plant cells in continuous liquid culture and on organisms (such as bacteria and fruit tree leaf rollers) which grow in the presence of higher plant cells are indicated in the General References.

GENERAL REFERENCES

Tulecke, W. (1965). Haploidy vs. diploidy in the reproduction of cell type. *Symp. Soc. Develop. Growth* **24,** 217–241.

Tulecke, W. (1966). Continuous cultures of higher plant cells in liquid media: the advantages and potential use of a phytostat. *Ann. N.Y. Acad. Sci.* **139,** 162–175.

Tulecke, W. (1967). Plastid function in plant tissue cultures. I. Porphyrin synthesis by dark-grown haploid albino and diploid albino cultures. *Am. J. Botany* **54,** 797–804.

Tulecke, W., and Colavito, Luke (1966). Fruit-tree leaf rollers on plant tissue cultures and on leaves of *Ginkgo biloba. J. Econ. Entomol.* **59,** 1277–1278.

Tulecke, W., Orenski, S. W., Taggart, R., and Colavito, L. (1965). Isolation of an organism resembling *Achromobacter liquefaciens. J. Bacteriol.* **89,** 905–906.

Carbon Metabolism of Amino Acids in Plants*

Dalton Wang

In previous investigations of the transformation of glycine to sugars in

*These investigations were sponsored in part by National Science Foundation Grant No. GB-3985.

wheat leaves a pathway of glyoxylate-serine metabolism was proposed. This pathway also apparently operates in leaves of peas and in isolated chloroplasts of tobacco plants. The rate of transformation was reduced markedly in the dark. However, the amount of ^{14}C incorporated into the acidic fraction remained at nearly the same level in experiments performed in the light or in the dark.

An enhancement of the movement of the isotope from glycine to sugars by either glycolate or glyoxylate was found when experiments were performed in the light. In contrast, the effect of glycolate or glyoxylate in leaves held in the dark was chiefly on the transfer of the label to the organic acid fraction rather than to sugars. Furthermore, glycolate exerts its effect in the dark mainly on the synthesis of an unknown acidic compound referred to as glycine derivative from glycine-2-^{14}C. This glycine derivative could be synthesized from either glycine-1-^{14}C, glycine-2-^{14}C, serine-3-^{14}C, or glycerate-3-^{14}C.

A ^{14}C-enriched glycine derivative was isolated, and its metabolism in leaves was investigated. This derivative was found to be rapidly metabolized in the leaves which were held either in the light or in the dark. In the light a considerable portion of the glycine derivative was utilized in the synthesis of sugars, but the major portion of the isotope from this derivative was metabolized to amino acids. In contrast, little, if any, sugar was formed from this derivative when experiments were performed in the dark because the isotope was transferred almost exclusively into amino acids. Evidently the glycine derivative was quickly converted into alanine either in the light or in the dark. The amount of radioactivity was found in glutamate, aspartate, and serine in a descending order. On the basis of the available evidence, the possible position occupied by the glycine derivative in the pathway of glyoxylate-serine metabolism is:

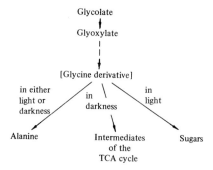

Of special interest in these studies has been the discovery of a relatively large number of phosphorylated compounds, the majority of which, the phosphorylated polypeptides, are not heretofore described. Intensive studies are under way to determine their origin and functional role in cell metabolism. Because such compounds could very well serve in several roles, for example, as intermediates in the synthesis of protein or phosphoprotein, or as intermediates in energy metabolism, a careful investigation is warranted.

GENERAL REFERENCES

Wang, D. (1966). Carbon metabolism of ^{14}C-labeled amino acids in wheat leaves. IV. Effect of glyoxylate, acetate, or pyruvate on alanine metabolism. *Contrib. Boyce Thompson Inst.* **23,** 269–274.

Wang, D., and Burris, R. H. (1965). Carbon metabolism of ^{14}C-labeled amino acids in wheat leaves. III. Further studies on the role of serine and glycine metabolism. *Plant Physiol.* **40,** 415–418.

Wang, D., and Mancini, D. (1966). Studies on ribonucleic acid-polyphosphate in plants. *Biochim. Biophys. Acta* **129,** 231–239.

Wang, D., and Pichitakul, N. (1969). Carbon metabolism of ^{14}C-labeled amino acids in wheat leaves. V. Effect of glycolate on glycine metabolism. (Submitted for publication.)

B. PROCESSES OF DISEASE INDUCTION IN PLANTS AND INSECTS

Changes in Metabolism of Rust-Infected Tissues of Bean*

Willard K. Wynn

Since most of the rust fungi cannot be grown on artificial media, they must be studied while associated with their host plants. Metabolic investigations of rust infection are difficult to interpret because one can never be sure whether the observed changes are due to the host, the parasite, or a complex interaction of the two.

A means of overcoming this problem is to study the metabolism which occurs in the rust fungus but not in the plant. The metabolism of mannitol has been chosen, since this compound is present only in the fungus but is closely related to sugars which are important in rust infection (Syamananda and Staples, 1963; Wynn *et al.*, 1966).

Mannitol accumulates in rust-infected bean leaves as the fungus develops, reaching a maximum when sporulation begins, and then falling off as sporulation progresses. A mycelial mannitol dehydrogenase has been partially purified from rusted leaves. It requires NADP as a cofactor and catalyzes the reversible reduction of fructose to mannitol. It is similar to polyol dehydrogenases from other organisms in that it has a low affinity for its substrate and requires a high pH for mannitol oxidation. It is suggested that mycelial mannitol synthesis may be coupled to metabolic reactions in the host cells via NADP, and an intensive research program in is progress to investigate this possibility.

*This work was sponsored in part by Grant No. GB-2975 from the National Science Foundation.

30

REFERENCES

Syamananda, Riksh, and Staples, R. C. (1963). The carbohydrate content of rusted corn leaves. *Contrib. Boyce Thompson Inst.* **22**, 1–8.
Wynn, W. K., Staples, R. C., Strouse, Blanche, and Gajdusek, Corinne (1966). Physiology of uredospores during storage. *Contrib. Boyce Thompson Inst.* **23**, 229–242.

Studies of the Biophysical Properties of Pea Enation Mosaic Virus

*R. F. Bozarth**

Earlier work on the biochemistry of plants infected with pea enation mosaic virus (PEMV) was done without any knowledge of the nature of the virus involved (Porter and Weinstein, 1962a, 1962b; Bozarth and Weinstein, 1964). At that time neither PEMV nor any virus of the circulative aphid-borne group had been purified or characterized. Our first report of the purification of PEMV (Bozarth *et al.,* 1965) was followed by a description of its biophysical properties (Bozarth and Chow, 1966).

It was found to be a small polyhedral virus with a diameter of 22 to 24 mμ. Its physical properties included a sedimentation coefficient of 113 S, a diffusion coefficient of 1.89×10^{-7} cm^2 sec^{-1}, a buoyant density in CsCl of 1.42 g cm^{-3}, and a molecular weight of 4.7×10^6 g mole^{-1}. The virus contains RNA which is apparently single-stranded (unpublished data).

Like many other small polyhedral plant viruses, PEMV occurs in concert with a slower-sedimenting "extra-virus" component. Such components have been found associated with many small spherical plant viruses. Their protein coat is identical with the virus with which they are associated, but they contain less nucleic acid than the intact virus. On occasion more than one component has been found associated with PEMV, but the only one which occurs consistently sediments at 93 S, contains about two-thirds as much RNA as whole virus, and is not infectious.

*This work has been sponsored in part by Grant No. CA-04294 from the National Institutes of Health and by the Margaret T. Biddle Foundation.

REFERENCES

Bozarth, R. F., Chow, Ching Chan, and Gross, S. (1965). Purification of pea enation mosaic virus. *Phytopathology* **55**, 127.

Bozarth, R. F., and Chow, Ching Chan (1966). Pea enation mosaic virus: Purification and properties. *Contrib. Boyce Thompson Inst.* **23**, 306–309.

Bozarth, R. F., and Weinstein, L. H. (1964). The ribonucleic acid of leaves and pods of peas infected with pea enation mosaic virus. *Phytopathology* **54**, 746.

Porter, C. A., and Weinstein, L. H. (1962a). Biochemical studies of plant virus tumors. *Trans. N.Y. Acad. Sci.* **24**, 747–749.

Porter, C. A., and Weinstein, L. H. (1962b). Alterations in biochemical patterns of the pea pod induced by pea enation mosaic virus. *Phytopathology* **52**, 25.

The Proteins of Thermophilic Fungi

Eli V. Crisan

A recent investigation (Crisan, 1964) indicates that, unlike other thermophiles, thermophilic fungi do not produce proteins of exceptional thermostability. Analysis of protein extracts of *Monotospora (Humicola) lanuginosa* by acrylamide gel electrophoresis shows the presence of 16 detectable proteinaceous bands. When examined from cultures grown at 35°, 45°, and 55°C, nine of these bands exhibit a degree of thermostability after exposure to elevated temperatures. However, only three of these bands were commonly thermostable at all incubator temperatures. Four protein bands were thermostable only in 55° cultures, while two bands were only stable in 35° cultures.

The enzyme acid phosphatase has been found to exhibit a degree of intrinsic thermostability even when extracted from mesophilic organisms. The production of detectable quantities of this enzyme has been induced in *M. lanuginosa*. Two isozymes are produced, and stability tests show that the degree of intrinsic thermostability in thermophilic extracts is no greater than that commonly exhibited by the acid phosphatases of mesophilic organisms.

The absence of detectable major differences in the degree of thermostability of thermophile proteins indicates the need for reviewing present theories proposed to explain the phenomenon of thermophilism. The capability of thermophilic growth may be a result of the expression of one or more interrelated subtle differences in metabolism rather than of a major change in the metabolic patterns found in mesophiles. This possibility is also indicated by the results of ancillary biochemical studies of the organic acids and lipids of *M. lanuginosa* which do not show patterns significantly different from those found in mesophiles.

REFERENCE

Crisan, Eli V. (1964). Isolation and culture of thermophilic fungi. *Contrib. Boyce Thompson Inst.* **22**, 291–301.

Lipids of Fungi and Their Metabolism

R. Cecil M. Jack

The years since 1957 have been a period of great activity in the study of lipids. As a result, outlines are now available of the chemistry and metabolism of lipids in many groups of organisms. The fungi are among these organisms.

Work in our laboratory, as well as others (Leegwater *et al.,* 1962; Jack, 1964, 1966; White and Powell, 1966), has shown that the major fatty acids in all fungi examined have 16 or 18 carbon atoms with variable unsaturation: 16:0, 16:1, 18:0, 18:1, 18:2, and 18:3. The major classes of lipids in all the fungi that have been studied are sterol ester, triglyceride, free fatty acid, unesterified sterol, diglyceride, phosphatidylethanoline, phosphatidylserine, and phosphatidylcholine. However, although the fungi as a group seem to contain the same major classes of lipids and the same major fatty acids, the relative amounts of these lipid classes and their component fatty acids were found to be different from the more than 40 species for which reliable data are available. In addition, there is the striking qualitative difference that, so far, γ-linolenic acid has been found only in members of the Phycomycetes (White and Powell, 1966; Shaw, 1965; Jack, 1965).

Metabolically the formation of fungal lipids occurs for the most part by the same pathways that have been discovered in plants and animals. Thus work with *Neurospora crassa* has suggested that the biosynthesis of ergosterol involves the same intermediates that lead to the biosynthesis of cholesterol in animals: acetate $\longrightarrow$ mevalonate $\longrightarrow$ isopentylpyrophosphate $\longrightarrow$ squalene $\longrightarrow$ sterol (Dauben *et al.,* 1959). Other data suggest that the biosynthesis of triglycerides and phosphoglycerides occurs via the pathway

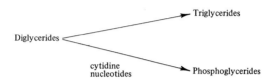

More specifically, the fatty acid patterns of *Glomerella cingulata* triglycerides and phosphoglycerides suggest that these two groups of glycerides are derived from a common pool of diglycerides (Jack, 1965), and work with *Neurospora crassa* indicates that lecithin can be formed either through the cytidine nucleotide coenzymes or by methylation of phosphatidylethanolamine (Crocken and Nye, 1964).

Investigations into the functions of fungal lipids are now in their infancy. However, the idea is already beginning to emerge that an important role of phospholipids is to control the shapes of membrane proteins and of membrane subunits.

REFERENCES

Crocken, B. J., and Nye, J. F. (1964). Phospholipid variations in mutant strains of *Neurospora crassa. J. Biol. Chem.* **239,** 1727.

Dauben, W. G., Hutton, T. W., and Boswell, G. A. (1959). The biosynthesis of ergosterol: its relationship to the squalene hypothesis. *J. Am. Chem. Soc.* **81,** 403.

Jack, R. C. M. (1964). Lipids of the conidia of *Glomerella cingulata. Contrib. Boyce Thompson Inst.* **22,** 311.

Jack, R. C. M. (1965). Relation of triglycerides to phosphoglycerides in fungi. *J. Am. Oil Chemists' Soc.* **42,** 1051.

Jack, R. C. M. (1966). Lipid patterns in the major classes of fungi. *J. Bacteriol.* **91,** 2101.

Leegwater, D. C., Young, C. G., Spencer, J. F. T., and Craig, B. M. (1962). Investigations into the production of lipids by submerged cultures of the mushroom *Tricholoma nudum. Can. J. Biochem. Physiol.* **40,** 847.

Shaw, R. (1965). The occurrence of γ-linolenic acid in fungi. *Biochim. Biophys. Acta* **98,** 230.

White, H. B., and Powell, S. S. (1966). Fatty acid distribution in mycelial lipid of *Choanephora cucurbitarum. Biochim. Biophys. Acta* **116,** 388.

Permeation of Fungus Spores

Lawrence P. Miller

Workers at the Institute have studied fungicides and fungicidal action almost from the time of its founding over 40 years ago. Some of the early work was concerned with the mode of action of sulfur (McCallan and Wilcoxon, 1931), and this has been periodically reinvestigated since that time (Miller *et al.,* 1953a; Tweedy and Turner, 1966). Emphasis was also placed on the statistical aspects of toxicity studies with fungal conidia. The staff were pioneers in the use of log-probit concepts for dosage response curves (Wilcoxon and McCallan, 1939). Within the past few months a computer has been installed, and some of the dosage response data (of which a great deal is available) are being put through a program which gives ED_{50} and ED_{95} values with their standard deviations and also the slopes with their confidence limits. When this new study is completed, it may be possible to come to some better conclusion about just how much emphasis can be put on the slopes of these curves in throwing light on the mode of action of fungitoxicants.

With the greater availability of radioisotopes the quantitative interaction between fungal conidia and various toxicants has been extensively studied. The labeled toxicants used have included ^{14}C-labeled 2-heptadecyl-2-imidazoline, 2,3-dichloro-1,4-naphthoquinone, *n*-dodecylguanidine acetate, ^{35}S-labeled ferric dimethyldithiocarbamate, ^{110}Ag, ^{144}Ce, ^{65}Zn, ^{115}Cd, ^{60}Co, and ^{203}Hg. Studies on permeability effects, both in permitting easier access to sensitive receptor sites within the conidia and in inducing an outward movement of cell contents, have also been carried out with labeled anions, such as ^{35}S-sulfate, ^{32}P-phosphate, ^{14}C-cyanide, ^{131}-iodide. The data have shown that toxicants do penetrate conidia in large amounts and that high doses are necessary to inactivate them (Miller and McCallan, 1957; Miller *et al.,* 1953b, 1954). With the exception recently noted by Westcott and Sissler that cycloheximide is toxic at low doses (ED_{50} value of 0.38 $\mu g/g$ of wet weight of cells of *Saccharomyces pasturianus*), all the fungitoxicants studied are manyfold less toxic on a weight basis than are other biocides.

Studies carried out at the Institute and elsewhere have shown that the toxicants are distributed in various cell fractions and that many earlier

35

workers who have emphasized the viewpoint that fungal cell membranes are very difficult to penetrate by foreign substances will have to reconsider this aspect of the action of fungitoxicants.

Extensive investigations of the effects of dual treatments, either simultaneous or consecutive, have shown that uptake and therefore toxicity can be markedly influenced by other cations or anions. Uptake may be increased or decreased. These results may have some practical importance since fungicides are often applied as mixtures with other pesticides.

Work on the mode of action and toxicity of fungicides both at the Institute and in other laboratories has been recently reviewed (Miller, 1968). A chapter on permeation entitled "Reaching the site of action" will appear soon in volume 2 of *Fungicides; An Advanced Treatise,* to be published by Academic Press.

REFERENCES

McCallan, S. E. A., and Wilcoxon, F. (1931). The fungicidal action of sulfur. II. The production of hydrogen sulfide by sulphured leaves and spores and its toxicity to spores. *Contrib. Boyce Thompson Inst.* **3,** 13–38.

Miller, L. P. (1966). Studies on the toxicity and mode of action of fungicides. *Intern. At. Energy Agency Tech. Rept. Ser.* **66,** 19–22.

Miller, L. P., and McCallan, S. E. A. (1957). Toxic acid of metal ions to fungus spores. *J. Agr. Food Chem.* **5,** 116–122.

Miller, L. P., McCallan, S. E. A., and Weed, R. M. (1953a). Quantitative studies on the role of hydrogen sulfide formation in the toxic action of sulfur to fungus spores. *Contrib. Boyce Thompson Inst.,* **17,** 151–171.

Miller, L. P., McCallan, S. E. A., and Weed, R. M. (1953b). Rate of uptake and toxic dose on a spore weight basis of various fungicides. *Contrib. Boyce Thompson Inst.* **17,** 173–195.

Miller, L. P., McCallan, S. E. A., and Weed, R. M. (1954). The use of radioisotopes in studying the effect of various toxicants for fungus spores. *Proc. 2nd Radioisotope Conf. Oxford, Med. Physiol.* 381–389.

Tweedy, B. G., and Turner, N. (1966). The mechanism of sulfur reduction by conidia of *Monilinia fructicola. Contrib. Boyce Thompson Inst.* **23,** 255–265.

Wilcoxon, F., and McCallan, S. E. A. (1939). Theoretical principles underlying laboratory toxicity tests of fungicides. *Contrib. Boyce Thompson Inst.* **10,** 329–338.

Some Properties of Ribosomes from Germinating Bean Rust Uredospores*

Richard C. Staples

Uredospores of the bean rust fungus [*Uromyces phaseoli* (Pers.) Wint.] germinate readily on a water surface, but the germ tube is mainly empty and devoid of protein accumulation and nuclear or cellular division. This is in contrast to conidia of saprophytic fungi in which germ tube is accompanied by the formation of new cells and protein. After germination is initiated, saprophytic conidia sythesize RNA and polysomes are formed. In germinating uredospores, however, polysomes decreased, template activity decreased, and synthesis of RNA was not observed.

Growth of most fungal conidia begins about the time of germ tube protrusion, and new cell formation is accompanied by accumulation of protein. Uredospores of the obligately parasitic rust fungi also readily germinate on a water surface, but germ tube outgrowth is not accompanied by protein accumulation and few, if any, cells are formed. Uredospore germ tubes differentiate into appressoria and other specialized cells required for host invasion if placed on an oil-bearing surface (Maheshwari *et al.*, 1967), but further development soon ceases in the absence of a susceptible host. The purpose of the present investigations was to describe the amino acid incorporation by a cell-free system derived from uredospores of the bean rust fungus [*U. phaseoli* (Pers.) Wint.] germinated on a water surface. Under such conditions the germ tubes elongate freely but do not differentiate.

Materials and Methods

Uredospores of the bean rust fungus, *U. phaseoli,* were collected from infected leaves of bean (*Phaseolus vulgaris* L. var. "Pinto") plants grown in controlled environment chambers as described previously (Staples

*Supported in part by Grant GB-5492X from the National Science Foundation.

37

et al., 1966; Staples and Bedigian, 1967). Procedures for grinding the spores, preparation of the reagents, ribosomes, and supernatant solutions of activating enzymes, steps in the incorporation reactions, and procedures for density gradient determinations were also described.

Spore Germination

When required, spores were germinated by evenly dispersing 250 mg of spores onto 400 ml of water having a surface of 555 cm^2. Dishes containing the floating spores were placed in a cold room at 4°C for 16 hr. The spores were then collected by filtration on a sintered glass funnel and redispersed at the rate of 100 mg spores/555 cm^2 of surface. These dishes were then placed on a reciprocating shaker and gently rocked at 20°C.

Assay for Template Activity

A 30,000-g supernatant fraction (S-30) was prepared from *Escherichia coli,* strain B, according to the procedure of Nirenberg (1963). The S-30 fraction was preincubated to deplete it of endogenous mRNA, dialyzed overnight against 12 liters of the required buffer, divided into 2-ml fractions, frozen with a dry ice-acetone mixture, and stored in liquid nitrogen before use. The RNA samples to be tested for template activity were added in amounts of 1.0 to 2.0 mg/ml. The S-30 fraction was added as the last component to the reaction mixture, and incubation was carried out at 37°C for 15 min.

Assay of Transferase Activity

These assays were carried out essentially as described by App and Gerosa (1966), except that the time and enzyme concentrations were reduced to achieve first-order kinetics. Furthermore, all detectable transferase activity was associated with the ribosomes; therefore the postribosomal enzyme solutions were omitted. Yeast transfer ribonucleic acid (tRNA) was esterified with ^{14}C-phenylalanine using rice supernatant solutions as described. The assay was made using two levels of ribosomes (0.5 and 0.25 mg), and 13,000 cpm of phenylalanyl-tRNA (sp. act. 25,180 cpm/mg). The reaction was started by adding the ribosomes and the reaction was stopped after 10 min by adding an equal volume (0.5 ml) of 10% trichloroacetic acid and 0.05 ml of 1% bovine serum albumin. The precipitates were washed and plated as prescribed and were counted by liquid scintillation techniques. The amounts of ribosomes were estimated spectrophotometrically by assuming that there were 50 $\mu g/\mathring{A}_{260}$ unit;

1 $\mu\mu$mole of phenylalanine gave 550 cpm on the counter. The assays were made in duplicate at each enzyme concentration.

Results

GERMINATION

A uredospore germinated overnight on a water surface is shown in Fig. 1. The germ tube is very long, mostly hollow with a bit of cytoplasm

FIG. 1. Micrograph of bean rust uredospore after germination for 16 hr on a water surface. Magnification 250×.

at the tip. The tip is simple, not forked as it occasionally may be, and devoid of new cells. Germ tube growth continues for 24 hr but is most rapid between 4 and 8 hr.

During the germination process there is no net accumulation of protein (Fig. 2A). There may even be a slight decrease in protein (Shu *et al.,* 1954). Accumulation of an exogenous isotope into protein reflects these changes (Fig. 2B) and shows that, while protein does not accumulate, protein turnover does occur. The limited protein synthesis in germinating uredospores does not appear to be a result of a restricted synthesis of amino acids. Free amino acids occur abundantly, and an analysis of protein amino acids extracted from germinating spores has shown that all amino acids are synthesized from exogenous carbon sources (Staples *et al.,* 1962; Kasting *et al.,* 1959).

AMINO ACID INCORPORATION

To initiate a study of the restraint of protein synthesis in germinating

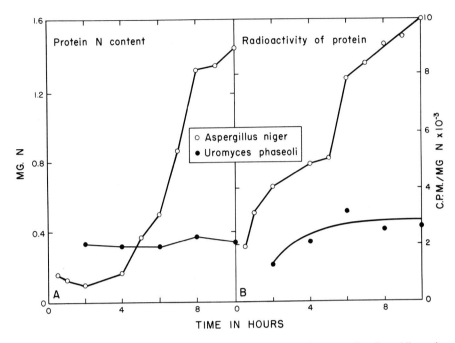

FIG. 2. Protein synthesis and assimilation of C^{14}-acetate into protein of conidia and uredospores by fungus spores during germination. (After Staples *et al.*, 1962).

uredospores, a cell-free system was developed which was active in amino acid incorporation (Staples *et al.*, 1966; Staples and Bedigian, 1967). Incorporation by the 82S ribosomes required a supernatant solution of enzymes, magnesium ions, adenosine triphosphate, and guanosine triphosphate, had a well-defined time course curve, and was extremely sensitive to ribonuclease.

POLYSOMES

Dormant uredospores were found to contain a small population of polysomes (Staples *et al.*, 1968), as demonstrated by analytical ultracentrifugation, density gradient analyses, and electron microscopy. At least half of the radioactivity incorporated by ribosomes was incorporated by the polysomes (Fig. 3A). In contrast, there was a reduction in free polysomes within 16 hr after induction of germination, as shown by loss of radioactivity in the heavy areas of the gradient (tube 17, Fig. 3B). In addition, the monosome peak contained proportionately less radioactivity, reflecting the decreased activity of the ribosomes.

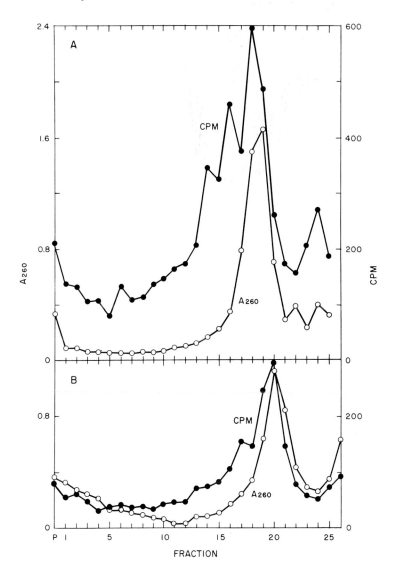

FIG. 3. Density gradient analyses of ribosomes extracted from (A) dormant spores and (B) spores germinated for 16 hr. Ribosomes were centrifuged for 15 min at 300,000 g after labeling for 40 min with a mixture of 15 radioactive amino acids (5 μc total). Meniscus is at right, pellet (P) is at left, interface of gradient and 50% sucrose indicated by arrow. Optical density peak nearest meniscus contains 82S monosomes. Gradient is linear from 15 to 30% sucrose layered on top of 0.4 ml of 50% sucrose. Total volume 4.9 ml. Fractions contained 3 drops each. Closed circles denote radioactivity; open circles denote absorbance at 260 mμ (A_{260}).

The apparent loss of polysomes after germination coincided with a decrease in the template activity of RNA prepared from germinating spores. For example, it was found that RNA prepared from uredospores 8 hr after germination had 20% as much template activity as RNA from dormant uredospores (Ramakrishnan and Staples, 1968) in an assay system prepared from *Escherichia coli* (Nirenberg, 1963). All the template activity in the RNA was located in a region between 4S and 16S on sucrose gradients. Attempts are being made to isolate and characterize this template further.

ACTIVITY OF RIBOSOMES

In contrast to the loss of polysomes and template activity during germination, the amino acid-incorporating activity of ribosomes increases (Staples, 1968). For example, ribosomes prepared from uredospores germinated for 2 hr were twice as active as ribosomes from dormant spores. However, this activity then declined, and after 8 hr of germination the ribosomes were half as active as those from dormant spores. These activities were the same whether or not polyuridylic acid was used as RNA, suggesting that enzyme activities associated with the ribosomes, rather than differences in messenger content, were responsible for the change in activity.

For this reason it was interesting that changes were found in the transferase activity of the ribosomes (Table 1). It was found that the capacity of ribosomes to accept amino acids from tRNA increased when obtained from spores floated 1 hr on water. The activity remained high during the rapid phases of germ tube outgrowth, then declined.

TABLE 1

Transfer of ^{14}C-Phenylalanine from Transfer RNA to Ribosomes Extracted from Uredospores at Various Stages of Germination[a]

Stage of spore germination	$\mu\mu M$/mg Ribosomal RNA transferred in 10 min	Stage of spore germination	$\mu\mu M$/mg Ribosomal RNA transferred in 10 min
Dormant	10.1	4 hr	36.5
Floated	22.8	6 hr	30.9
1 hr	38.4	8 hr	30.3
2 hr	27.6	16 hr	16.0

[a] Determinations were made in duplicate at two different levels of enzyme. Values are ±2.1 or better.

Discussion

Uredospores of the parasitic rust fungi and conidia of saprophytes germinate in two steps: the uptake of water and protrusion of the germ tube. However, while conidial germination is accompanied by mRNA synthesis, polysome formation and protein accumulation (see, e.g., Ono *et al.,* 1966), uredospore germination is not (Figs. 2 and 3). In a series of papers (Ono *et al.,* 1966; Yanagita, 1958; Takebe and Yanagita, 1959; Horikoshi *et al.,* 1965; Moyer and Storck, 1964), Japanese and American workers reported that on germination conidia of *Aspergillus* sp. synthesize ribosomal RNA first, then tRNA shortly afterwards. Synthesis of mRNA was observed 60 min after germ tube protrusion. At the same time polysomes appeared and protein synthesis began (Ono *et al.,* 1966). Similar findings were made, at least in part, in several other species of saprophytic fungi, notably *Neurospora* (Henney and Storck, 1963, 1964), yeast (Dietz *et al.,* 1965), and *Botryodiplodia* (Van Etten, 1968). The essence of these studies is that mRNA is not stored in conidia, but its synthesis is triggered during spore activation.

These results are in marked contrast to those of uredospores. These obligately parasitic spores apparently possess an endogenous stable mRNA and a small population of polysomes. Aside from the polysomes, evidence for the mRNA consists of assays for template activity and location of this activity on density gradients. The template has not yet been isolated, and its synthesis has never been detected. During uredospore germination, template activity decreases, polysomes decrease (Fig. 3), and net synthesis of protein is absent (Fig. 2).

As a whole, the data suggest that protein turnover in uredospores is guided by a stable, endogenous mRNA. The temporary increase in transferase activity of the ribosomes (Table 1) suggests that the machinery for protein synthesis may be turned on briefly during germ tube protrusion, but new mRNA is not synthesized in the absence of a suitable host and this early activity ceases. These ideas require supporting evidence, and they are the subject of current investigations.

REFERENCES

App, A. A., and Gerosa, Maria M. (1966). A soluble fraction requirement in the transfer reaction of protein synthesis by rice embryo ribosomes. *Plant Physiol.* **41,** 1420–1424.

Dietz, G. W., Jr., Reid, B. R., and Simpson, M. V. (1965). Ribosomes. A study of active and sluggish preparations. *Biochemistry* **4,** 2340–2350.

Henney, H. R., Jr., and Storck, R. (1963). Ribosomes and ribonucleic acids in three morphological states of *Neurospora. Science* **142,** 1675–1677.

Henney, H. R., Jr., and Storck, R. (1964). Polyribosomes and morphology in *Neurospora crassa*. *Proc. Natl. Acad. Sci. U.S.* **51**, 1050–1055.

Horikoshi, K., Ohtaka, Y., and Ikeda, Y. (1965). Ribosomes in dormant and germinating conidia of *Aspergillus oryzae*. *Agr. Biol. Chem. (Tokyo)* **29**, 724–727.

Kasting, R., McGinnis, A. J., and Broadfoot, W. C. (1959). Biosynthesis of some amino-acids from sucrose by germinating uredospores of wheat stem rust, race 15*B*. *Nature* **184**, 1943.

Maheshwari, R., Hildebrandt, A. C., and Allen, P. J. (1967). The cytology of infection structure development in urediospore germ tubes of *Uromyces phaseoli* var. *typica* (Pers.) Wint. *Can. J. Botany* **45**, 447–450.

Moyer, R. C., and Storck, R. (1964). Properties of ribosomes and RNA from *Aspergillus niger*. *Arch. Biochem. Biophys.* **104**, 193–201.

Nirenberg, M. W. (1963). Cell-free protein synthesis directed by messenger RNA. *In* "Methods of Enzymology" (S. P. Colowick and N. O. Kaplan (eds.), Vol. 6, pp. 17–23. Academic Press, New York.

Ono, T., Kimura, K., and Yanagita, T. (1966). Sequential synthesis of various molecular species of ribonucleic acid in the early phase of conidia germination in *Aspergillus oryzae*. *J. Gen. Appl. Microbiol.* **12**, 13–26.

Ramakrishnan, L., and Staples, R. C. (1968). Template activity in nucleic acids from germinating bean rust uredospores. *Phytopathology (Abstr.)* **58**, 886.

Shu, P., Tanner, Kathleen G., and Ledingham, G. A. (1954). Studies on the respiration of resting and germinating uredospores of wheat stem rust. *Can. J. Botany* **32**, 16–23.

Staples, R. C. (1968). Protein synthesis by uredospores of the bean rust fungus. *Neth. J. Plant Pathol.* **74** (Suppl. 1), 25–36.

Staples, R. C., App, A. A., McCarthy, W. J., and Gerosa, Maria M. (1966). Some properties of ribosomes from uredospores of the bean rust fungus. *Contrib. Boyce Thompson Inst.* **23**, 159–164.

Staples, R. C., and Bedigian, Dorothea (1967). Preparation of an amino acid incorporation system from uredospores of the bean rust fungus. *Contrib. Boyce Thompson Inst.* **23**, 345–347.

Staples, R. C., Bedigian, Dorothea, and Williams, P. H. (1968). Evidence for polysomes in extracts of bean rust uredospores. *Phytopathology* **58**, 151–154.

Staples, R. C., Syamananda, R., Kao, Vivian, and Block, R. J. (1962). Comparative bio-chemistry of obligately parasitic and saprophytic fungi. II. Assimilation of C^{14}-labeled substrates by germinating spores. *Contrib. Boyce Thompson Inst.* **21**, 345–362.

Takebe, I., and Yanagita, T. (1959). Origin of amino acids constituting cellular protein in germinating conidiospores of *Aspergillus niger*. *Plant Cell Physiol.* **1**, 17–28.

Van Etten, J. L. (1968). Protein synthesis during fungal spore germination. I. Characteristics of an *in vitro* phenylalanine incorporating system prepared from germinated spores of *Botryodiplodia theobromae*. *Arch. Biochem. Biophys.* **125**, 13–21.

Yanagita, T. (1958). Change in ribonucleic acid composition during the course of germination of *Aspergillus niger* spores. *Ann. Rept. Inst. Food Microbiol., Chiba Univ.* **11**, 34–35.

Chemical Changes Induced by Root-Knot Nematodes

R. Cecil M. Jack

Owens and Specht (1966) have shown that the organic acids, lipids, free amino acids, proteins, nucleotides, RNA, and DNA of galls of tomato roots caused by root-knot nematodes, *Meloidogyne* spp., are increased by large percentages when compared with healthy roots.

Using parallel analyses by cytochemical and conventional methods of analysis, it has been found (Owens and Bottino, 1966) that total cell wall components decrease in the gall tissue and that there are significant quantitative changes in the major cell wall components of gall and normal tissues. These major cell wall components are pentosans, polyhexuronates, and hexose polymers. The major quantitative differences were an increase in polyhexuronates and a decrease in cellulose. In normal roots, xylans, arabans and mannans made up most of the noncellulosic polysaccharides. In the galls, xylans and glucosans were the major polymers. The cytochemical analyses also showed that most of the wall material was removed by 17% sodium hydroxide, and a double strand of cellulose was left between syncytia. Tests for protein in the walls were negative.

Using cytochemical techniques, it was further found that nuclei pooled from host cells into the syncytial cytoplasm resume synthesis of RNA and DNA although the cells of origin have reached maturity. The renewed synthesis of RNA and DNA is accompanied by progressive hypertrophy, and the nuclei may increase in volume as much as 200-fold in tomato roots, suggesting increases in nuclear proteins, such as histones and globulins, as well as in RNA and DNA (Owens and Rubinstein, 1966).

Current work on the chemical changes induced by root-knot nematodes is addressed to two questions: When do the chemical changes first occur? In what way is mRNA involved in the observed changes in proteins?

Results indicate that the chemical differences occur as quickly as a few days after the roots have been infected with the nematodes.

REFERENCES

Owens, R. G., and Specht, H. N. (1966). Biochemical alterations induced in host tissues by root-knot nematodes. *Contrib. Boyce Thompson Inst.* **23,** 181–198.

Owens, R. G., and Bottino, R. F. (1966). Changes in host cell wall composition induced by root-knot nematodes. *Contrib. Boyce Thompson Inst.* **23,** 171–180.

Owens, R. G., and Rubinstein, J. H. (1966). Metabolic changes induced by root-knot nematodes in host tissues. *Contrib. Boyce Thompson Inst.* **23,** 199–213.

Multiplication of Plant Tumor Viruses in Insects*

Karl Maramorosch

Among the viruses proved to multiply in both plants and insects, wound tumor virus is known to cause tumors in certain susceptible species of plants. Certain other plant-pathogenic viruses are known to cause abnormal growth in plants, but few cause veritable transplantable tumors. In the group of viruses causing growth abnormalities (enations) is the pea enation mosaic virus. Similar enations are induced by certain strains of tobacco mosaic virus, but such growth abnormalities do not qualify as tumors.

Since 1965 an intensive electron microscopy study has been carried out by Shikata and Maramorosch (1965, 1966), Granados *et al.* (1967), and Hirumi *et al.* (1967) on the systemic invasion of plant and insect hosts by wound tumor virus. In ultrathin sections of plant tumors, accumulations were detected of wound tumor virus particles in the cytoplasm of necrotic, as well as non-necrotic, cells of *Melilotus alba.* Enlarged veins of crimson clover *(Trifolium incarnatum)* leaflets also contained virus accumulations. In the insect vector *Agallia constricta* virus particles were detected in blood cells, in the gut, in fatbody cells, epidermis, Malpighian tubules, mycetome, salivary gland, and recently also in the nervous system (Hirumi *et al.,* 1967). Insects that transmitted efficiently contained more virus than less efficient individuals, and a nonefficient

*The work of the author and his associates, Drs. E. Shikata, H. Hirumi, R. R. Granados, G. Streissle, J. Mitsuhashi, T. Tokumitsu, and K. Strohmaier has been sponsored in part by Grant AI-04290 from the Institute of Allergy and Infectious Diseases, Grant CA-07453 from the National Cancer Institute, U.S. Public Health Service, Bethesda, Md., and by Grants GB-1199 and GB-5444 from the National Science Foundation, Washington, D.C.

vector species, *Agalliopsis novella,* contained only small quantities of virus compared to *A. constricta.*

Mechanical injection of virus into insects permitted the study of the sequential invasion and multiplication of wound tumor virus in insects (Shikata and Maramorosch, 1967). Foci of viroplasm were found in the fatbody, gut, salivary glands, ventral ganglia, and other sites. Similar foci of viroplasm were detected in the cytoplasm of infected plants. The formation of virus microcrystals was discovered at locations somewhat removed from the foci of viroplasm, indicating that crystal formation is a secondary phenomenon, following the multiplication and accumulation of wound tumor virions. The detection of the plant-pathogenic tumor-inducing virus in the cytoplasm of nerve cells of an insect vector was unexpected. Although no deleterious effect of this virus on insects has been reported, it has now been demonstrated that wound tumor virus multiplies in the nervous system and even destroys some of the cells of its invertebrate animal host (Granados *et al.,* 1967).

The cumulative evidence from these and related studies clearly indicates that wound tumor virus infects its insect hosts as surely as its plant hosts, even though the infection of the animal is not obvious.

The pea enation mosaic virus was found by electron microscopy to be localized in the cytoplasm of plant cells in enlarged veins, and in the cytoplasm of enations of leaves and pea pods (Shikata *et al.,* 1966). In addition, the virus was demonstrated at high concentrations in cell nuclei, where it destroys the nucleolus and where it is predominant in the most active part of the nucleus (Shikata and Maramorosch, 1966). Furthermore, the virus was found in the lumen of the gut, as well as in the fatbody cells of virus-transmitting pea aphids. These results provided the first microscopic evidence of the invasion of an aphid vector by a plant-pathogenic virus.

Quantitative measurements of plant viruses have lagged behind those of bacterial and animal viruses. In an attempt to improve the quantitative measurement of wound tumor virus particles, a new density gradient method, devised by Dr. Karl Strohmaier, was applied by Dr. Gert Streissle to the study of virus concentration and multiplication in plant tumors and in insect vectors. The results indicate that plant tumors contain approximately 10^{11} particles/g, and insect vectors contain about 10^6/insect.

Approaches to the study of virus-cell interactions have been made by the use of insect tissue culture. Improved methods of invertebrate cell cultivation developed in collaboration with Drs. Hirumi, Mitsuhashi, and Tokumitsu are now being employed in the study of wound tumor and pea enation mosaic virus in invertebrate cells *in vitro* (Tokumitsu and Maramorosch, 1966).

REFERENCES

Granados, Robert R., Hirumi, Hiroyuki, and Maramorosch, Karl (1967). Electron microscopic evidence for wound tumor virus accumulation in various organs of an inefficient leafhopper vector. *Agalliopsis novella. J. Invertebrate Pathol.* **9**, 147–159.

Hirumi, Hiroyuki, Granados, R. R., and Maramorosch, Karl (1967). Electron microscope observations of a plant pathogenic virus in the nervous system of its vector. *J. Virology* **1**, 430–444.

Shikata, Eishiro, and Maramorosch, Karl (1965). Electron microscopic evidence for the systemic invasion of an insect host by a plant pathogenic virus. *Virology* **27**, 461–475.

Shikata, Eishiro, and Maramorosch, Karl (1965). Plant tumor virus in arthropod host: microcrystal formation. *Nature* **288**, 507–508.

Shikata, Eishiro, and Maramorosch, Karl (1966). Electron microscope study of plant neoplasia induced by wound tumor virus. *J. Natl. Cancer Inst.* **36**, 97–116.

Shikata, Eishiro, and Maramorosch, Karl (1966). Electron microscopy of pea enation mosaic virus in plant cell nuclei. *Virology* **30**, 439–454.

Shikata, Eishiro, Maramorosch, Karl, and Granados, R. R. (1966). Electron microscopy of pea enation mosaic virus in plants and aphid vectors. *Virology* **29**, 426–436.

Shikata, Eishiro, and Maramorosch, Karl (1967). Electron microscopy of wound tumor virus multiplication sites in insect vectors and plants. *Virology* **32**, 363–377.

Tokumitsu, Takashi, and Maramorosch, Karl (1966). Survival of aphid cells *in vitro*. *Exptl. Cell Res.* **44**, 652–655.

Mechanism of Destruction of Mosquito Larvae by the Fungus *Metarrhizium anisopliae*

D. W. Roberts

In comparison with the large volume of literature on mosquito-vectored disease organisms and on the control of mosquitoes, the terminal diseases of mosquitoes themselves have remained virtually unexplored. Exceptions among the diseases of larvae are the extensive taxonomic studies of microsporidia (protozoa) and *Coelomomyces* (fungus).

The effects of Fungi Imperfecti on mosquito larvae are particularly poorly understood. *Metarrhizium anisopliae* (a well-known entomogenous, imperfect fungus) only recently has been reported to cause death of mosquito larvae (Roberts, 1967), and current studies are directed toward determining the mode of disease induction. Larvae of all species tested to date *(Anopheles stephensi, Culex pipiens,* and *Aedes aegypti)* have proved susceptible to *M. anisopliae* spores. Spores apparently were ingested before death and, accordingly, had to be floating to induce mortality in top-feeding species and submerged for bottom-feeding species. Only viable spores were effective. Infection sometimes occurred, but in some cases no invasion of the host was detectable. The only fungus bodies in the host in the latter cases were ungerminated spores within the midgut. The culture water in which larvae had died was filtered to remove the *M. anisopliae,* and this water proved nontoxic to new larvae. Toxins were sought in the spores themselves by extracting or rupturing spores and bioassaying the products, but none was detected. It is speculated that ingested ungerminated spores, or perhaps an interaction between ingested spores and the host, produced toxins which were lethal to the host.

REFERENCE

Roberts, D. W. (1967). Some effects of *Metarrhizium anisopliae* and its toxins on mosquito larvae. *In* "Insect Pathology and Microbial Control" (P. A. van der Laan, ed.), pp. 243–246. North-Holland Publ., Amsterdam.

C. ENVIRONMENTAL HEALTH —
THE ACTIVITIES OF FUNGI

Reaction of Cellular Constituents with Fungicides

N. Joe Turner

Previous work at the Institute and elsewhere suggests that alkylating fungicides such as captan, dichlone, and dyrene are active as a result of their ability to react with sulfhydryl or amino groups of metabolites or enzymes (Burchfield and Storrs, 1956; Lukens and Sisler, 1958; Owens and Blaak, 1960; Richmond and Somers, 1966). This hypothesis is further supported by *in vitro* experiments in which it has been shown that various metabolites readily react with these fungicides (Burchfield and Storrs, 1956; Lukens and Sisler, 1958; Owens and Blaak, 1960). In some cases it has been possible to modify or reverse fungitoxic effects with compounds containing sulfhydryl groups such as cysteine and glutathione (Lukens and Sisler, 1958). Richmond and Somers (1966) have shown that the amount of captan taken up is to a large extent dependent on the concentration of sulfhydryl compounds within the spores. Pretreatment of the fungus spores with chemicals capable of reacting with these sulfhydryl groups effectively reduces the uptake of captan.

In an investigation of strains of *Aspergillus niger* resistant to mercury seed treatments, Ashworth and Amin (1964) found that resistant strains contained large concentrations of soluble nonprotein sulfhydryl compounds; fungi such as *Rhizoctonia solani,* which were susceptible to mercury fungicides, had very small reservoirs of these compounds. They also found that the concentration of nonprotein sulfhydryl compounds in fungal mycelium could be increased by supplementing the culture media with sulfates. The increase in nonprotein sulfur compounds was accompanied by a concomitant increase in resistance of the fungi to the fungicides.

Burchfield and Storrs (1956) have demonstrated *in vitro* that dyrene, 2,4-dichloro-6-(*o*-chloroanilino)-*s*-triazine, and 1-fluoro-2,4-dinitrobenzene undergo reaction with a large number of amino acids as well as proteins. They showed that the fungicides could react with amino acids having either free amino or sulfhydryl groups. However, both compounds were more reactive with sulfhydryl groups, the nitrofluorobenzene being about 500 times more reactive with sulfhydryl than amino groups. The chemical reactivity of both fungicides was attributed to the presence of active halogens which are replaced by a nucleophilic substitution reaction with sulfhydryl or amino groups.

Because of the ability of alkylating fungicides to react with a large number of different cellular constituents, it seems improbable that their mode of action can be attributed to reaction with any particular one. However, that is not to say that the reaction of a fungicide with various cellular constituents will produce an equivalent deleterious effect. Obviously the removal of a fraction of a vital enzyme system is more harmful than the removal of an equal amount of a compound such as cysteine which is not immediately needed and can be rapidly synthesized to replace the loss.

If a fungicide is effective as a result of its reaction with cellular constituents, movement into and within the cell becomes essential. In order for a molecule to penetrate to the site of action within a cell, several lipid and aqueous barriers must be penetrated. Since an increase in either lipid or aqueous solubility is often accompanied by a corresponding decrease in the other, a satisfactory compromise of lipid and water solubility is necessary. Hansch and Fujita (1964) have proposed that the movement of an organic molecule through a cell to the site of action is a random process in which the compound moves to and from various aqueous and lipid phases. The chance of its arriving at the site of action is then determined by the freedom of movement between the two phases. Thus, a partition coefficient of 1 would allow maximum diffusion of a chemical through a 1:1 emulsion of oil in water. Because of the many different cellular lipid phases, the rate of movement through the cell is greatest when the partition coefficients of the compound between each lipid phase and water is as close to unity as possible. To state it mathematically: the rate of movement is maximum when the expression $\Sigma(1 - Xn)^2$ is minimum; Xn represents the partition coefficients of the compound between water and the respective lipid phases.

Hansch and co-workers (1963, 1964) derived the following formula, which contains a factor for penetration and movement as well as the chemical reactivity factor:

$$\frac{\log 1}{C} = -a\pi^2 + b\pi + \rho\sigma K + c$$

where C is the external concentration, such as LD_{50}, π is the uptake and penetration factor derived from the logarithm of the ratio of the partition coefficients of the substituted (X^s) and unsubstituted (X^H) compounds, respectively, between 1-octanol and H_2O at room temperature; that is, $\pi = \log X^s - \log X^H$ $\rho\sigma K$ has the same meaning and value as given in the Hammett equation, and a, b, c are constants which vary for each series of compounds.

Because of the relationship of penetration and $\Sigma(1 - Xn)^2$ there is an optimum π, (π_0), for each group of compounds for each biological system; deviation above or below π_0 therefore results in reduced penetration. The ratio of aqueous to lipid fractions as well as the organization of these barriers determines the π_0 for a particular species of fungi. Using the equation above, Hansch and co-workers have successfully correlated chemical structure with biological activity for bactericidal, insecticidal, and herbicidal groups of chemicals.

In preliminary experiments with Daconil (tetrachloroisophthalonitrile), a promising new fungicide recently discovered at the Institute (Turner *et al.,* 1964), it was found that biological activity among its analogs could be correlated with the reaction rate of the fungicides with a sulfhydryl group containing the compound 4-nitrothiophenol. The reaction of 4-nitrothiophenol with halogenated benzonitriles is believed to be a bimolecular nucleophilic substitution reaction and may be represented as follows:

Because the unreacted thiophenol imparts a yellow color to the solution, the half reaction time ($t_{1/2}$) of thiophenol with the fungicides can be determined spectrophotometrically. The fungicide and thiophenol are injected in equal volumes and concentrations into a mixing cell and then into an observation cell of a spectrophotometer. As the thiophenol reacts with the fungicide, the color becomes less and less intense until finally at the conclusion of the reaction the solution is colorless. By recording the optical density at 430 μ over the time course of the reaction it is possible to obtain the $t_{1/2}$ value directly from the graph simply by locating the point at which the optical density has been reduced by 50%. The biological activity of the fungicides was determined by means of the standard slide germination test (American Phytopathological Society, 1943). Briefly, this test involves placing fungus spores into a series of test tubes containing a serial dilution of the fungicide and a suitable germination medium such as orange juice or sugar. Drops from each tube are then transferred to microscope slides which are placed in petri plates containing a moist filter paper to maintain constant 100% humidity. The spores are allowed to germinate at 20°C for 24 hr, and then the percentage inhibition of spore germination is determined by microscopic examination. The $t_{1/2}$ and ED_{50} values (50% inhibition of spore germination) for Daconil and several of its analogs are presented in Table 1. A study of the data in Table 1 indicates that biological activity is increased as the number of halogens on the ring is increased. The effect of

TABLE 1

Relationship of Fungicidal Activity to Half Reaction Rates ($t_{1/2}$) of Halogenated Benzonitriles with 4-Nitrothiophenol

Compound tested, substituents on cyanobenzene in position					Fungitoxicity, ppm, ED_{50}		Reactivity $t_{1/2}$, min
2	3	4	5	6	*Alternaria oleracoa*	*Monilinia fructicola*	
Cl	Cl	CN	Cl	Cl	>1000	>1000	14.0
F	F	CN	F	F	0.1–1	0.1–1	0.7
Cl	Cl	H	CH$_3$	CH$_3$	>1000	100–1000	>180
Cl	CH$_3$	CH$_3$	CH$_3$	Cl	>1000	100–1000	400
H	H	CN	H	H	>1000	100–1000	>400
Cl	Cl	CN	F	Cl	0.1–1	0.1–1	0.15
Cl	CN	Cl	Cl	Cl	0.1–1	0.1–1	<0.04
F	CN	F	Cl	F	0.1–1	0.1–1	<0.05
F	H	H	H	Cl	>1000	>1000	400
F	H	H	H	F	>1000	>1000	>180
CN	Cl	Cl	Cl	Cl	0.1–1	0.1–1	1.48
Cl	H	CN	F	H	100–1000	>1000	146
F	H	CN	F	H	>1000	>1000	144
Cl	Cl	F	CN	F	0.1–1	0.1–1	<0.06
F	F	F	F	F	0.1–1	0.1–1	1.30
CN	F	F	F	F	0.1–1	1–10	<0.06

the additional halogens on the ring is undoubtedly due to electronic effects which increase the lability of the active halogen in position 6.

REFERENCES

American Phytopathological Society, Committee on Standardization of Fungicidal tests (1943). The slide-germination method of evaluating protectant fungicides. *Phytopathology* **33**, 627–632.

Ashworth, L. J., Jr., and Amin, J. V. (1964). A mechanism for mercury tolerance in fungi. *Phytopathology* **54**, 1459–1463.

Burchfield, H. P., and Storrs, Eleanor E. (1956). Chemical structures and dissociation constants of amino acids, peptides, and proteins in relation to their reaction rates with 2,4-dichloro-6-(o-chloroanilino)-s-triazine. *Contrib. Boyce Thompson Inst.* **18**, 395–418.

Hansch, C., and Fujita, T. (1964). ρ-σ-π analysis. A method for the correlation of biological activity and chemical structure. *J. Am. Chem. Soc.* **86**, 1616–1626.

Hansch, C., Muir, R. M., Fujita, T., Maloney, P. P., Geiger, F., and Streich, Margaret (1963). The correlation of biological activity of plant growth regulators and chloromycetin derivatives with Hammett constants and partition coefficients. *J. Am. Chem. Soc.* **85**, 2817–2824.

Lukens, R. J., and Sisler, H. D. (1958). Chemical reactions involved in the fungitoxicity of captan. *Phytopathology* **48**, 235–244.

Owens, R. G., and Blaak, G. (1960). Chemistry of the reactions of dichlone and captan with thiols. *Contrib. Boyce Thompson Inst.* **20**, 475–497.

Richmond, D. V., and Somers, E. (1966). Studies on the fungitoxicity of captan. IV. Reactions of captan with cell thiols. *Ann. Appl. Biol.* **57**, 231–240.

Turner, N. J., Limpel, L. E., Battershell, R. D., Bluestone, H., and Lamont, D. (1964). A new foliage protectant fungicide, tetrachloroisophthalonitrile. *Contrib. Boyce Thompson Inst.* **22**, 303–310.

Studies on Structure-Activity Relationships of Biologically Active Compounds: 8-Methoxyquinolines*

Herman Gershon and Raulo Parmegiani

In an earlier report by Gershon *et al.* (1966) it was shown that on addi-

*This work was supported in part by U. S. Public Health Service Research Grant No. A1-05808.

tion of chloro, bromo, iodo, and nitro groups to the 5- and 5,7-positions of 8-quinolinol, with the exceptions of 5,7-diiodo- and 5,7-dinitro-8-quinolinol, an increase of antifungal activity was effected. Addition of amino and nitroso groups caused a loss of activity; whereas, fluorine, when placed in the 5 position, appeared to make no change in fungitoxicity over the parent 8-quinolinol. Albert *et al.* (1947) established that chelation was involved in the mechanism of inhibition of bacteria by 8-quinolinol, and that 8-methoxyquinoline, which chelates poorly, was noninhibitory.

It was of interest to determine whether nonchelating mechanisms of antifungal action could be detected, and if they could be attributed to the presence of the substituents on the quinoline ring. An approach to this problem was made by a study of the fungitoxicity of a series of correspondingly substituted 8-methoxyquinolines (Gershon and Parmegiani, 1968). Chelation was minimized in this series of compounds, with very little change in electron distribution and steric hindrance as compared with the corresponding 8-quinolinols.

Materials and Methods

TEST COMPOUNDS

Thirteen 5- and 5,7-substituted 8-methoxyquinolines prepared by methylation of the parent 8-quinolinol (Gershon and Parmegiani, 1968) are listed in Table 1.

MICROBIOLOGICAL METHODS

Antifungal activity was measured by the method described by Gershon and Parmegiani (1963). The test organisms were: *Aspergillus niger* van Tieghem, *Trichoderma viride* Persoon ex Fries, *A. oryzae* (Ahlburg) Cohn, *Myrothecium verrucaria* Ditmar ex Fries, and *Trichophyton mentagrophytes* (Robin). Activity was determined in shake flasks using Sabouraud Dextrose Broth (Difco) containing graded levels of test compound added in dimethyl sulfoxide solution. The incubation period was 6 days at 28°C.

Results

The antifungal data are summarized in Table 1. 8-Methoxyquinoline shows very little fungal inhibition. Addition of fluorine, chlorine, bro-

TABLE 1

Minimal Fungistatic Activity (mmoles/liter) of 5- and 5,7-Substituted
8-Methoxyquinolines in Sabouraud Dextrose Broth at 28°C
in Shake Flasks after 6 Days

Compound	A. niger	T. viride	A. oryzae	M. verrucaria	T. mentagrophytes
8-Methoxyquinoline	6.28	3.76	NA[a]	4.08	4.08
5-Fluoro-8-methoxyquinoline	3.38	2.82	4.80	2.82	2.54
5-Chloro-8-methoxyquinoline	1.29	0.87	1.67	0.77	0.77
5-Bromo-8-methoxyquinoline	0.94	0.41	1.15	0.33	0.33
5-Iodo-8-methoxyquinoline	NA	0.28	NA	0.38	0.28
5-Nitro-8-methoxyquinoline	NA	1.59	NA	1.47	1.47
5,7-Dichloro-8-methoxyquinoline	NA	NA	NA	NA	0.18
5,7-Dibromo-8-methoxyquinoline	NA	NA	NA	NA	0.09
5,7-Diiodo-8-methoxyquinoline	NA	NA	NA	NA	NA
5-Chloro-7-nitro-8-methoxyquinoline	NA	2.51	NA	NA	1.25
5-Chloro-7-fluoro-8-methoxyquinoline	1.06	0.47	1.18	0.89	0.36
7-Chloro-5-fluoro-8-methoxyquinoline	2.83	0.85	NA	0.66	0.56
7-Bromo-5-fluoro-8-methoxyquinoline	NA	0.58	NA	0.46	0.42

[a] NA = not active below 1000 ppm.

mine, and iodine to the 5 position of 8-methoxyquinoline caused a
marked increase in fungistatic activity in the following order: I > Br >
Cl > F, except that *A. niger* and *A. oryzae* were resistant to 5-iodo-8-
methoxyquinoline. 5-Nitro-8-methoxyquinoline did not inhibit the two
Aspergilli but was about $2\frac{1}{2}$ times as active as 8-methoxyquinoline against
the three other fungi. 5,7-Dichloro- and 5,7-dibromo-8-methoxyquinoline
were active only against *Trichophyton mentagrophytes* at $\frac{1}{20}$ and $\frac{1}{40}$ the
level of 8-methoxyquinoline. None of the organisms was inhibited by
5,7-diiodo-8-methoxyquinoline. *Trichoderma viride* and *Trichophyton
mentagrophytes* were inhibited by 5-chloro-7-nitro-8-methoxyquinoline.
The fungitoxic action of 5-chloro-7-fluoro-8-methoxyquinoline was sig-

nificantly greater than that of 5-chloro-8-methoxyquinoline. The remaining two compounds, 7-chloro-5-fluoro-8-methoxyquinoline and 7-bromo-5-fluoro-8-methoxyquinoline, were also significantly more active than the corresponding dichloro- and dibromo-8-methoxyquinolines.

Discussion

Substituted 8-methoxyquinolines, which chelate weakly, caused significant fungal inhibition. This activity, although it was weaker, paralleled that of the corresponding 8-quinolinols for the most part. This can be interpreted to mean that one or more nonchelating antifungal mechanisms exist which should also be operative in the presence of the chelating antifungal mode of inhibition. This may, in part, explain the difference in antifungal activities of the substituted 8-quinolinols as compared with the parent compound.

On introducing a fluorine atom *meta* to another halogen substituent, fungal inhibition was intensified. On the other hand, a *meta* nitro group caused depression of activity. The basis for the diminished activity of the 5,7-dichloro-, 5-7-dibromo-, and 5,7-diiodo-8-methoxyquinolines is not clear.

It appears that strategically placed substituents can modify the intensity of these antifungal mechanisms, and it is possible that synergism between these secondary mechanisms and chelation may take place.

REFERENCES

Albert, A., Rubbo, S. D., Goldacre, R. J., and Balfour, B. G. (1947). The influence of chemical constitution on antibacterial activity. Part III: A study of 8-hydroxyquinoline (oxine) and related compounds. *Brit. J. Exptl. Pathol.* **28,** 69–87.

Gershon, H., and Parmegiani, R. (1963). Antimicrobial activity of 8-quinolinol, its salts with salicylic acid and 3-hydroxy-2-naphthoic acid, and the respective copper(II) chelates in liquid culture. *Appl. Microbiol.* **11,** 62–65.

Gershon, H., and Parmegiani, R. (1968). Secondary mechanisms of antifungal action of substituted 8-quinolinols. I. 5- and 5,7-substituted 8-methoxyquinolines. *Contrib. Boyce Thompson Inst.* **24,** 33–36.

Gershon, H., Parmegiani, R., Weiner, A., and D'Ascoli, R. (1966). Fungal spore wall as a possible barrier against potential antifungal agents of the group, copper(II) complexes of 5-halogeno- and 5-nitro-8-quinolinols. *Contrib. Boyce Thompson Inst.* **23,** 219–228.

Microbial Degradation of Pesticides in Soil*

D. C. Torgeson

Almost since its inception, Boyce Thompson Institute has been concerned with various aspects of pesticide research. In addition to studies on the development of new and better pesticides and their mode of action, workers at the Institute have been interested in the effects of pesticides on the environment and, in particular, the soil environment. Vlitos and King (1952) showed that the effectiveness of 2,4-dichlorophenoxyethyl sulfate as a herbicide was due to its degradation in the soil by microorganisms to 2,4-dichlorophenoxyacetic acid (2,4-D). Other workers demonstrated that 2,4-D and a number of other pesticidal compounds were degraded to inactive compounds by soil microorganisms. Since herbicides have a potential for accumulation in soils where they may injure subsequent crops, impair the flavor, safety, and other qualities of produce, be degraded to toxic decomposition products, or disturb the balance of desirable soil microflora, a study of their degradation was started.

Two halogenated herbicides were selected for investigation to determine whether they could be decomposed by soil microorganisms and whether such capabilities of the microorganisms could be enhanced and accentuated by exposure to increasing concentrations of the herbicide. Dimethyl tetrachloroterephthalate (Dacthal), a widely used pre-emergence herbicide which was discovered and developed at the Institute, was the first compound selected for study. It was subsequently shown that Dacthal is degraded by a variety of soil microorganisms, and evidence of adaptation to increased concentration by certain bacteria was demonstrated (Tweedy *et al.,* 1967). Possible degradation products of Dacthal were also isolated from treated soil (Gershon and McClure, 1966).

Bromacil, 5-bromo-3-*sec*-butyl-6-methyluracil, a herbicide recommended for use in general weed control at relatively high rates of application, was the second compound selected for study. Fungi and bacteria were isolated from soils previously exposed to various levels of bromacil.

*This project has been sponsored in part by Grant No. WP-00750 of the U.S.P.H., Federal Water Pollution Control Administration.

Fifty-five fungus and 73 bacterial cultures were selected and their ability to degrade bromacil studied by growing them in a Czapek-Dox broth containing 20 ppm of bromacil and periodically determining the amount of bromacil present using buckwheat as the bioassay organism. None of the bacteria appeared to degrade bromacil, but four of the fungi exhibited this capability. One of the fungi, subsequently identified as *Penicillium paraherquei* Abe., was particularly active and was selected for further study. No significant amounts of bromacil could be detected 15 to 20 days after Czapek-Dox broth containing 20 ppm of the herbicide had been inoculated with this organism. Sterile soil treated with bromacil at a rate of 3.1 lb/A was still toxic to buckwheat after 56 days, but no herbicidal effects could be detected 21 days after treatment with 6.2 lb/A or 28 days after treatment with 12.5 lb/A in sterile soil inoculated with *P. paraherquei*. Herbicidal effectiveness of the 25 and 50 lb/A application was reduced to 65 and 50%, respectively, after 90 days.

A variant culture of *P. paraherquei* was obtained when the original culture was grown in a medium containing 800 to 1000 ppm of bromacil. When inoculated into a liquid mineral salt medium containing bromacil as the sole carbon and nitrogen source, the variant grew slowly, whereas the original culture failed to grow. This fungus also appears capable of degrading terbacil, 3-*t*-butyl-5-chloro-6-methyluracil, a closely related herbicide.

REFERENCES

Gershon, H., and McClure, G. W., Jr. (1966). Approach to the study of the degradation of dimethyl tetrachloroterephthalate. *Contrib. Boyce Thompson Inst.* **23**, 291–294.

Tweedy, B. G., Turner, Nikki, and Achituv, Miriam (1968). The interactions of soil-borne microorganisms and dimethyl-2,3,5,6-tetrachloroterephthalate. *Weed Sci.* **16,** 470–473.

Vlitos, A. J., and King, J. L. (1952). Fate of sodium 2,4-dichlorophenoxyethyl sulphate in the soil. *Nature* **171,** 523.

D. ENVIRONMENTAL HEALTH — AIR POLLUTION

Effects of Air Pollution on Plants*

Leonard H. Weinstein, A. E. Hitchcock, D. C. McCune,
J. S. Jacobson, D. C. MacLean, and R. H. Mandl

Air pollution research was initiated at Boyce Thompson Institute by its first Managing Director, William Crocker, in 1923. These investigations were an extension of studies begun in 1908 at the University of Chicago on the effects of illuminating gas on plants. Shortly thereafter studies were initiated on the influence of hydrocyanic acid, mercury vapors, sulfur dioxide, ammonia, chlorine, and hydrogen sulfide on plant growth and development. Preliminary investigations on the effects of hydrogen fluoride and fluorine gas started in the mid-1940s.

In 1951 an extensive program on the effects of atmospheric fluorides on plant growth and development was begun. These studies required the perfection of analytical procedures for the determination of fluorine in air and plant tissues. A number of improvements were made in analytical methods then in use. Techniques were devised and chambers were designed for controlled fumigations of plants with gaseous or particulate fluorides at concentrations below 1 $\mu g/m^3$ of air and even lower. With the availability of suitable methods the reaction of a variety of plants to measured doses of fluorides was carried out and symptoms induced by fluoride under chronic and acute conditions were catalogued. Effects of duration of exposure, intermittent exposures, and the sensitivity of plants at different stages of development received a considerable

*These studies have been sponsored in part by Grant No. AP-00189, National Center for Air Pollution Control, U. S. Public Health Service.

amount of study over a number of years. Emphasis was also placed on pathways of fluoride penetration into roots or leaves, the mechanism of translocation, and sites of intracellular binding. Although studies have continued in these areas, the scope of the program has been considerably expanded in recent years. A summary of some recent work is now described.

Tomato plants were fumigated with $H^{18}F$ to study the distribution of F in leaves, stems, and roots. Autoradiography revealed that F accumulates at the tips and margins of leaflets and in the glands along the stem. Little ^{18}F was found in stems and petioles, and practically none was translocated to roots. Once it has penetrated a leaf, F is not translocated to other leaves. These results are in agreement with the hypothesis that F moves in the transpiration stream.

The well-known toxicity of F to many metal-catalyzed enzyme reactions, especially those of the glycolytic pathway, has suggested that F damage to plants is due to the inhibition of this reaction sequence of the respiratory pathway. Many researchers, however, have shown that the rate of respiration of HF-treated plants is greatly stimulated. These results have been interpreted to mean that F in the plant cell inhibits glycolysis and, as a response to this, other pathways of respiration become more dominant. This would be especially true if the regulatory effect on respiration of adenosine di- and triphosphates were removed by uncoupling the formation of high-energy phosphate compounds from energy production of respiration. Four approaches have been used to study this problem: estimation of the levels of metabolites; direct assay of enzymes of the glycolytic pathway; estimation of the flow of carbon through the respiratory pathways; and determination of the pool size and turnover rate of soluble nucleotides.

Changes in metabolism were found to occur in HF-fumigated plants over the time course of individual experiments. Plants given a post-exposure recovery period were found to exhibit metabolic rates approaching those of nonfumigated control plants, even though the F content of the plants was not significantly affected. These results clearly demonstrated that, although F is an accumulative toxicant, plants contain a mechanism for its detoxification. The mechanism has not been clearly elucidated, but a considerable body of evidence indicates that formation of relatively insoluble F compounds with cations such as magnesium, calcium, iron, and manganese plays a role in this process. The glycolytic enzymes, enolase and pyruvic kinase, are activated by Mg^{2+} and are inhibited by added F *in vitro*. The levels of these enzymes in HF-fumigated plants, however, were found to be higher than in control plants. This finding can be interpreted two ways: F does not exert a toxic effect on glycolytic enzymes of plants *in vivo;* and enolase and pyruvic kinase are inhibited by HF, but the levels of enzymes are increased by inductive phenomena. F-sensitive steps do appear to occur in the pathways of glucose dissimilation. The pattern and rate of evolution of $^{14}CO_2$ from HF-fumigated and control plants supplied with glucose-1-, glucose-2-, glucose-3,4-, and glucose-6-^{14}C suggest that HF reduces the capacity of the cell to respond to normal metabolic changes. Pathways of synthesis and utilization of nucleotides which are required for energy transfer, synthesis of polysaccharides, and so on, appear to be less sensitive to the impact of F than are the pathways of glucose dissimilation.

The interest in fluoride toxicity stimulated the initiation of studies on the synthesis and metabolism of fluoro-organic compounds in plants. Several plant species have been reported to synthesize monofluoro-acetic acid and ω-fluoro-fatty acids from inorganic fluoride. One of these plants, *Acacia georginae,* has been used to study fluoroacetate synthesis under sterile conditions. This work established that fluoroacetate is synthesized by the plant and not by soil microflora. Experiments on the metabolism of fluoroacetate-2-^{14}C by seedlings of *A. georginae* and plants which do not synthesize fluoroacetate, such as peanut, castor bean, and "Pinto" bean, have shown that each of these species contains an enzyme system capable of cleaving the carbon-fluoride bond. This was demonstrated by measuring the evolution of $^{14}CO_2$ and the release of inorganic F.

It is now recognized that a single pollutant is rarely responsible for an air pollution problem. Therefore, investigations are under way to study the effect on plants of gaseous fluorides in combination with other pollutants in a variety of controlled environments.

GENERAL REFERENCES

Hitchcock, A. E., Weinstein, L. H., McCune, D. C., and Jacobson, J. S. (1964). Effects of fluorine compounds on vegetation, with special reference to sweet corn. *J. Air Pollution Control Assoc.* **14,** 503–508.

Jacobson, J. S., McCune, D. C., Weinstein, L. H., Mandl, R. H., and Hitchcock, A. E. (1966). Studies on the measurement of fluoride in air and plant tissues by the Willard-Winter and semiautomated methods. *J. Air Pollution Control Assoc.* **16,** 367–371.

Jacobson, J. S., Weinstein, L. H., McCune, D. C., and Hitchcock, A. E. (1966). The accumulation of fluorine by plants. *J. Air Pollution Control Assoc.* **16,** 412–417.

Ledbetter, M. C., Mavrodineanu, R., and Weiss, A. J. (1960). Distribution studies of radio-active fluorine-18 and stable fluorine-19 in tomato plants. *Contrib. Boyce Thompson Inst.* **20,** 331–348.

McCune, D. C., Hitchcock, A. E., Jacobson, J. S., and Weinstein, L. H. (1965). Fluoride accumulation and growth of plants exposed to particulate cryolite in the atmosphere. *Contrib. Boyce Thompson Inst.* **23,** 1–11.

McCune, D. C., Weinstein, L. H., Jacobson, J. S., and Hitchcock, A. E. (1964). Some effects of atmospheric fluoride on plant metabolism. *J. Air Pollution Control Assoc.* **14,** 465–468.

McCune, D. C., Weinstein, L. H., MacLean, D. C., and Jacobson, J. S. (1967). The concept of hidden injury in plants. *In* "Agriculture and the Quality of Our Environment" (N. C. Brady, ed.), pp. 33–34. American Association for the Advancement of Science, Washington, D. C.

Mandl, R. H., Weinstein, L. H., Jacobson, J. S., McCune, D. C., and Hitchcock, A. E. (1966). Simplified semi-automated analysis of fluoride. *In* Proceedings of Technicon International Symposium "Automation in Analytical Chemistry," New York City, 1965, pp. 270–273.

Weinstein, L. H. (1961). Effects of atmospheric fluoride on metabolic constituents of tomato and bean leaves. *Contrib. Boyce Thompson Inst.* **21,** 215–231.

Weinstein, L. H., Mandl, R. H., McCune, D. C., Jacobson, J. S., and Hitchcock, A. E. (1963). A semi-automated method for the determination of fluorine in air and plant tissues. *Contrib. Boyce Thompson Inst.* **22,** 207–220.

Weinstein, L. H., Mandl, R. H., McCune, D. C., Jacobson, J. S., and Hitchcock, A. E. (1965). Semi-automated analysis of fluoride in biological materials. *J. Air Pollution Control Assoc.* **15,** 222–225.

Zimmerman, P. W. (1950). Impurities in the air and their influence on plant life. *Proc. 1st Natl. Air Pollution Symp., Pasadena, Calif., 1949,* 135–141.

Zimmerman, P. W., and Hitchcock, A. E. (1956). Susceptibility of plants to hydrofluoric acid and sulfur dioxide gases. *Contrib. Boyce Thompson Inst.* **18,** 263–279.

II
Normal and Abnormal
Plant Growth

Plant Biology at The Rockefeller University

Armin C. Braun

The Rockefeller Institute for Medical Research was from its inception in 1904 until 1955, when it became a Graduate University, an Institute devoted entirely to medical research. Questions might reasonably be asked, therefore, about what plants have to do with medical research and why they should be studied at such an institution. The answers to those questions can perhaps best be found in the philosophical approach to science of Dr. Simon Flexner, the first Director. Dr. Flexner was not only a highly competent scientist and administrator but a man of great vision as well. He viewed medical research in the broadest possible manner and believed strongly that organisms of all kinds can contribute to an understanding of the principles underlying disease in man. It is not surprising to find, therefore, that certain members of his staff turned their attention very early in the history of the Institute to the use of plants as experimental test objects. One of these was Dr. Jacques Loeb who strongly believed, and was among the first to suggest, that it is the duty of science to seek a mechanistic explanation of life. His views have had a profound influence on today's thought in biology and medicine; he may, in fact, be considered to be the father of modern molecular biology. Although primarily interested in animal cells, Loeb very early carried out some classical experiments with plants as experimental test objects. As early as 1916 he demonstrated that the presence of young, vigorously growing leaves on a horizontally placed *Bryophyllum* stem increased geotropic bending as well as the number of roots that were initiated. As we now know, he interpreted his findings correctly when he suggested a hormonal explanation for his observed results. Dr. William J. Robbins, who is working at The Rockefeller University, has maintained to this day an interest in Loeb's observations and is now actively pursuing certain aspects of that work, as indicated below.

Dr. W. J. V. Osterhout also recognized quite early the advantages of working with plant material when attempting to elucidate certain complex biological phenomena. In 1920 he began to use the freshwater plant *Nitella,* which has individual cells that may be more than one inch in length. Not long afterward he turned his attention to the marine plants, *Valonia* and *Halicystis,* the cells of which may become as large as a pigeon egg. With these enormous cells he was able to obtain significant amounts of sap for analysis and was able to make electrical measurements by applying electrodes at two or more points on the cell surface. The cells of *Valonia* have the property of accumulating potassium in a far higher concentration than that in sea water, while those of *Halicystis* contain cell sap of a constitution similar to that of sea water. Such observations led Osterhout to emphasize selective permeability as a major factor in tissue function. His observations on electrical potentials in these huge plant cells led him to conclude that they result from different rates of diffusion for the sodium, potassium, and chloride ions migrating through the surface membranes. These early studies aided significantly in an understanding of similar but less accessible phenomena in animal tissues such as the conduction of nerve impulses and of muscle contraction.

It was not, however, until 1931 that work on plants began in earnest at The Rockefeller Institute. One of the great mysteries of that period was the nature of the filterable viruses and the diseases which they caused. The great influenza pandemic of 1918–1919, which destroyed more lives in a few months than did World War I in four years, did much to focus attention on the need for greater knowledge about those then mysterious disease-producing entities. The great crippler poliomyelitis and foot-and-mouth disease of animals were two other diseases among many known to be caused by viruses. It was well known during that period, moreover, that not only man and animals but also plants are afflicted with virus diseases. This, then, was an important area of study. Dr. Flexner, the man of vision, believed that perhaps work on plants and their viruses might, because of the simplicity of the system, provide an answer to the nature of viruses generally. He therefore established in 1931 a Division of Plant Pathology to be associated with an already existing Division of Animal Pathology at a beautiful site just outside of Princeton, New Jersey, to study that problem. In selecting a man to head the new Division of Plant Pathology, Dr. Flexner again made a very wise choice when he appointed Dr. Louis O. Kunkel. Dr. Kunkel selected his staff with great care, and his Division soon became the world center for plant virus research. Among Dr. Kunkel's initial appointments was Dr. Wendell M. Stanley, who was a biochemist by training and who had been Dr. Osterhout's assistant in the Laboratory of General Physiology in New York City. Within three years after the plant work had been under way in the Princeton laboratory, Dr. Stanley succeeded in isolating and characterizing the tobacco mosaic virus. The tobacco mosaic virus was found to be a crystallizable nucleoprotein that had many attributes of living organisms, such as the ability to replicate and to mutate. These findings, of course, had tremendous philosophical as well as practical implications, and in 1946 Dr. Stanley was awarded the Nobel Prize in Physiology and Medicine for his work.

Dr. Kunkel's group was small but highly productive. Among the early members of that group were Dr. Francis O. Holmes, who developed the first quantitative assay method for measuring tobacco mosaic virus; Dr. James H. Jensen, who demonstrated unequivocally that viruses, like living organisms, mutate; Dr. Lindsay M. Black, who found the first non-self-limiting tumor disease of plants caused by a virus; Dr. Philip R. White, who pioneered in plant tissue culture studies; and Dr. George L. McNew, who investigated bacterial diseases of plants.

During the period 1949–1951 the Department of Animal and Plant Pathology in Princeton was discontinued and the laboratories were integrated with those in New York. After Dr. Kunkel retired as Head of the Laboratory of Plant Pathology, work in the laboratory continued, but in new directions. Emphasis was now placed on problems of normal and abnormal growth and development in plants. Attention was focused particularly on the crown gall disease of plants which, because of its striking similarity to tumorous diseases of animals and man, might provide insight into the basic cellular mechanisms underlying tumorigenesis generally. The crown gall tumor system has been carefully analyzed, and insight has been gained into cellular mechanisms underlying tumorigenesis. The most pertinent findings have been the demonstration that nuclei of normal and tumor cells are genetically equivalent. The transformation of a normal cell into a tumor cell is thus concerned with epigenetic changes involving an alteration in the expression rather than in the integrity of the genetic information that is normally present in a cell. This means that the cellular mechanisms underlying tumorigenesis are potentially reversible; that this is true has been demonstrated experimentally not only in the crown gall disease but later by others in the case of certain malignant animal and human tumors as well. Later in this section there is a report on certain aspects of the work currently being carried out on the crown gall disease at Rockefeller University.

For a number of years the University has been interested in the biochemistry and mode of action of a specific inducer of the male sex organ or antheridium in ferns. A substance that specifically induces antheridia in many polypodiaceous fern species has been isolated in pure form. This compound is a carboxylic acid. The carboxyl group is the functional group, since esterification of that group results in loss of activity while regeneration of the free acid results in complete recovery of biological activity. The pure compound is biologically very active and can be diluted 10 billion times with water and still show antheridium-inducing activity. In a later portion of this section there is a report on work now being done at the University with that system.

In addition to the Laboratory of Plant Biology, two other laboratories at the Rockefeller University are working with plant materials. Dr. Sam Granick and his group are studying the biosynthesis of porphyrins leading, in plants, to chlorophyll formation and, in animals, to hemoglobin synthesis.

Drs. William J. Robbins and Annette Hervey, in another laboratory, are continuing their studies on the isolation and characterization of new growth-promoting factors. They are also studying the nature of phase changes in plants that result in the development of juvenile and adult forms. Such phase changes represent very interesting examples of heritable and persistent changes in the phenotype without corresponding changes in the genotype. A description of the work being done in Dr. Robbins' laboratory is presented in the next report.

Current Botanical Research

William J. Robbins

In association with Dr. Annette Hervey, Senior Research Associate at The New York Botanical Garden, and with the assistance of Mrs. Ina Wong, a number of investigations are being pursued in part at The Rockefeller University and in part at The New York Botanical Garden. They are all concerned with some aspect of plant growth and development, and they may be briefly described as follows.

A study of unidentified growth substances present in an aqueous extract of beech wood and effective on the growth of *Polyporus schweinitzii* is being continued. We have previously reported that ferulic acid or iso-eugenol combined with a mixture of fatty acids improves the growth of *P. schweinitzii* in a medium of mineral salts and sugar supplemented with various known vitamins and purine and pyrimidine bases. At least two unidentified growth factors for this fungus are present in wood extract. In cooperation with Dr. Paul Ulshafer of the Ciba Pharmaceutical Company, attempts to concentrate and isolate the unidentified substances are underway.

In cooperation with Dr. George Bistis of Fordham University, studies on the growth and development of *Morchella* sp. have been continued. Both tissue cultures and cultures from single spores are being used in this investigation.

Through the courtesy of Dr. Neal Weber of Swarthmore College a collection of fungi cultivated for food by various leaf cutting ants has been obtained. The contents of the collection is shown in Table 1. These fungi do not appear to be fastidious in their culture requirements. All grow in various natural laboratory media, though they differ in vigor of growth. We have grown some of these isolations in synthetic liquid media. Two have fruited in culture, but the others have proved recalcitrant so far.

An investigation of the juvenile and adult conditions of some seed plants has been continued. Dr. V. T. Stoutemyer of the University of California at Los Angeles reported differences in the development in tissue culture of callus obtained from the stems of the adult, seedling, and reversion stages of *Hedera helix*. We have been concerned with the growth in tissue culture of callus obtained from the stems of adult,

71

seedling, or reversion stages of *H. helix* and *H. canariensis*. We are investigating also the characteristics in tissue culture of callus from the
stems of the compound leaf and the phyllode stages of *Acacia melanoxy-
lon*. We are indebted to Dr. Stoutemyer for the material.

Dr. Jacques Loeb suggested in 1917 that the development of roots on
the stems of *Bryophyllum calycinum* Salisb. was caused by a hormone
produced by the leaf. Later he became interested in the development of
the foliar embryos present in the notches of the *Bryophyllum* leaf. These
embryos normally remain dormant as long as the leaf is attached to the
plant but grow when the leaf is removed from the plant. His interest in the
foliar embryos resulted from his concern with regeneration. Three aspects
can be distinguished in the growth of roots and the development of foliar
embryos of *Bryophyllum*. They are: the causes of the differentiation of
roots in the stem; the growth requirements of *Bryophyllum* roots; and the

TABLE 1

NUMBERING OF WEBER ANT FUNGI IN THE NEW YORK BOTANICAL GARDEN

Bot. Gar. No.	Weber No.	Ant Species	Source
W1	4260	*Trachymyrmex septentrionalis* McCook	New Jersey
W2	4312	*Atta cephalotes* L.	Trinidad, W.I.
W3	4350	*Acromyrmex octospinosus* Reich	Trinidad, W.I.
W4	4314	*Trachymyrmex urichi* Forel	Trinidad, W.I.
W5	4331	*Sericomyrmex urichi* Forel	Trinidad, W.I.
W6	4330	*Myrmicocrypta buenzlii* Borgmeier	Trinidad, W.I.
W7	4325	*Mycetophylax conformis* (Mayr)	Trinidad, W.I.
W8	4404	*Atta cephalotes* L.	Trinidad, W.I.
W9	4441	*Acromyrmex octospinosus* Reich	Trinidad, W.I.
W10	4454	*Acromyrmex lobicornis* Emery	Rio Negro, Argen.
W11	4455	*Acromyrmex (Moellerius) striatus* Roger	Rio Negro, Argen.
W12	4460	*Trachymyrmex septentrionalis* McCook	New Jersey
W13	4461	*Trachymyrmex septentrionalis* McCook	New Jersey
W14	4468	*Myrmicocrypta ednaella* Mann	Panama
W15	4469	*Apterostigma mayri* Forel	Panama
W16	4470	*Atta colombica tonsipes* Santschi	Panama
W17	4471	*Cyphomyrmex costatus* Mann	Panama
W18	4472	*Cyphomyrmex costatus* Mann	Panama
W19	4475	*Cyphomyrmex costatus* Mann	Panama
W20	4477	*Atta cephalotes isthmicola* Weber	Panama
W21	4525	*Trachymyrmex cornetzi* Forel	Trinidad, W.I.
W22	4529	*Apterostigma auriculatum* Wheeler	Trinidad, W.I.
W23	4532	*Cyphomyrmex rimosus* Spinola	Trinidad, W.I.
W24	4528	*Azteca* alien fungus	Trinidad, W.I.
W25	4546	*Trachymyrmex relictus* Borgmeier	Tobago

causes of the dormancy of the foliar embryos. These problems have interested me since the publication of Loeb's original article, and they led me to investigate the growth of excised roots of higher plants in sterile culture media. The media and methods which were successful for the cultivation of excised tomato roots have not succeeded with excised roots of *Bryophyllum*. We have, however, successfully cultivated the excised roots of *Bryophyllum* in liquid and in agar media. We are investigating the dormancy of the foliar embryos by cultivating under sterile conditions discs cut from around notches of *Bryophyllum* leaves. The growth of the foliar embryos or their failure to grow in various media may suggest the causes of their dormancy in the attached leaves. We have not succeeded in breaking the dormancy of the foliar embryos by the application of various growth substances to the attached normal leaf.

A New Class of Cell Division-Promoting Compounds Isolated from Normal and Crown Gall Tumor Cells

Henry N. Wood

It has been found that, during the transformation of a normal plant cell to a crown gall tumor cell, the biosynthetic systems concerned with cell division and growth are persistently activated, with a resulting production by the tumor cells of significant amounts of cell division-promoting substances as well as other essential metabolites. The cell division-promoting substances have been found to play a central role in the development of a capacity for autonomous growth of the crown gall tumor cell. Normal cells of the type from which the tumor cells were derived possess, on the other hand, an absolute exogenous requirement for either kinetin or another 6-substituted purine or a naturally occurring cell division-promoting substance, in addition to other metabolites, if cell growth and division are to occur. It is, then, of considerable importance to understand the chemical nature and function of these cell division-promoting compounds which assume a central place in the expression of autonomy in the crown gall tumor cell.

Two naturally occurring biologically active compounds, which differ in their physical properties, have been isolated and partially characterized chemically from rapidly growing, fully autonomous, crown gall tumor cells of *Vinca rosea* L. The evidence obtained thus far suggests that these two compounds have a nicotinamide ring, a glucose sugar moiety, sulfur in the form of sulfate or sulfonate, and one or more methyl groups. Recent studies employing gas-liquid chromatography of the postmethanolysis of the compounds indicated the presence of a straight-chain fatty acid. A mass spectrometric analysis indicated that the glucose was substituted in the 1 and 6 positions. These compounds have characteristic infrared and ultraviolet absorption spectra. Qualitative chemical tests have thus far failed to reveal any differences between the two biologically active compounds. Their final characterization will have to await further work, including a synthesis of the biologically active substances.

Kinetin (6-furfurylaminopurine) and many other 6-substituted purines have been shown to act in a number of fundamental ways as growth-regulating substances in higher plants. Such substances are of particular interest because, when used in association with an auxin, they promote cell division in many plant species. An attempt was made to learn whether kinetin, when used in association with an auxin, is itself involved in promoting cell division or whether it merely serves to stimulate the synthesis by normal *V. rosea* cells of substances that are specifically concerned in that process. Since the cell division factors isolated from *V. rosea* tumor cells are different classes of substances from those usually considered to be cytokinins, it appeared possible that the synthesis of these substances by tumor cells resulted from new genetic information that had been introduced into the cells at the time of their transformation. If this were true, then a similar type of substance should not be expected to be present in rapidly dividing normal cells. On the other hand, if such substance(s) were found in rapidly growing normal cell types, the evidence would suggest that the synthesis of such compounds by both normal and tumor cells results from the activation of that segment of the plant cell genome concerned with the synthesis of these substances. Alternatively, if no such substance were found in normal cell types stimulated to rapid growth with kinetin, then it could be assumed that kinetin itself was acting directly to promote cell division. An attempt was made to answer these questions experimentally.

In those studies normal *V. rosea* cells were grown in a tissue culture medium containing kinetin, auxin, inositol, glutamine, asparagine, cytidylic and guanylic acids. After a period of 1 month at 25°C the tissues were harvested and processed in the identical fashion as were *V. rosea* tumor cells. During the isolation procedure extreme care was exercised to prevent any production of chemical artifacts. Isolation procedures were carried out at low temperatures, and only very weak acids and bases were used. Ion exchange resins were not used. These precautions were taken to prevent the formation during the isolation procedure of non-naturally occurring compounds that have kinetinlike activity. The biological assay system using tobacco pith parenchyma cells was one that was initially suggested by the work of Jablonski and Skoog.

Experimental Results

As a final step in the purification the biologically active materials were distributed through 500 transfers in a countercurrent distribution apparatus using an *n*-butyl alcohol and water system. Two biologically active fractions with partition ratios of 1.7 and 2.7 were obtained from the tumor material. Under precisely the same conditions of isolation and countercurrent distribution, the normal tissues yielded a single biologically active substance that had a partition coefficient of 1.9 which, for all practical purposes, is identical with the first peak of activity found in the tumor tissue.

The infrared spectrum of the normal *Vinca* cell division compound taken from the 1.9 partition coefficient peak was identical with that of the *Vinca* tumor cell division compound. For purposes of chemical identification, identity of infrared spectra is unequivocal. Previous infrared analysis comparing the *Vinca* tumor cell division compounds and kinetin clearly indicated the gross differences between these compounds, as would be expected since they represent entirely different classes of compounds.

Recent work has demonstrated that tobacco-habituated tissues contain a biologically active substance that is indistinguishable by infrared analysis from cell division-promoting factors found in normal and tumor tissues of *V. rosea*. Further studies with cactus tissue have given preliminary evidence that cactus, too, contains this cell division-promoting compound. These data suggest, then, a widespread distribution of this new class of cell division-promoting compounds in higher plant species.

Discussion and Conclusions

The results obtained from this study demonstrate that both normal and tumor *V. rosea* cells, as well as tobacco and cactus tissues, contain a new class of naturally occurring cell division-promoting substances which are chemically distinct from the 6-substituted purines.

The results further suggest that kinetin merely serves to activate the synthesis of cell division-promoting substances in normal *Vinca* cell types, and that these substances rather than kinetin are specifically involved in promoting division. Since kinetin (6-furfurylaminopurine) is very different in its chemical composition from the naturally occurring cell division-promoting substances found to be synthesized by both normal and tumor cells of *V. rosea,* it appears unlikely that either kinetin or any part of the kinetin molecule serves as a direct intermediate for the synthesis of the naturally occurring biologically active substance produced by the normal cell types. It appears, then, that kinetin (6-furfurylaminopurine) acts either as an inducer of the cell division factor synthesizing systems or that it serves in some more indirect way to initiate the production by the normal cell types of the naturally occurring substances that promote cell division.

Evolutionary and Physiological Aspects of Antheridium Induction in Ferns

Bruce R. Voeller and Eric S. Weinberg

Striking a working balance between evolutionary plasticity and adaptedness to a particular environment is one of the chief problems every species faces. Organisms which reproduce by cross-fertilization provide offspring with diverse genetic constitutions, but only a few of these genetic combinations may have high adaptive value for the particular environment in which the species finds itself. On the other hand, a plant which reproduces entirely through self-fertilization, or vegetatively, is usually well adapted to its particular environment; but, should the environment abruptly change, as has repeatedly happened through evolutionary time, such a plant may not have the genetic plasticity to supply offspring which can compete in the new environments. Each species must establish a balance between these needs or risk extinction. Stebbins (1950) has referred to this balance as the plant's "compromise": "The most important feature of each genetic system is the level of compromise it establishes between the need for fitness, in order to secure immediate survival, and that for flexibility, as a means of potential adaptive response to future changes in the environment."

An extreme example of a pteridophyte which reproduces only vegetatively is the gametophyte of a species of *Vittaria* found in the Appalachians by Wagner and Sharp (1963). No sporophytes of *Vittaria* are found in the area, and the gametophytes do not produce antheridia or archegonia. Whether they are capable of producing antheridia in response to experimentally supplied antheridogens or gibberellins (see below) is unknown. In nature they reproduce vegetatively by forming thallose mats, as much as a meter across, and by producing gemmae.

A good example of striking an effective compromise is found in our common bracken fern, *Pteridium aquilinum* (L.) Kuhn. Its distribution is world-wide in temperate and tropical regions, being found nearly everywhere between the 45th parallel in the Southern Hemisphere and the 60th in the Northern. Indeed, it is so successful as widely to be considered a weed. The speed with which it can occupy a large area is closely related to the speed with which it propagates vegetatively by underground rhizomes; . . . to call them *creeping* rhizomes is almost a misnomer. Indeed, pieces as long as 200 ft have been reported (Watt, 1940). On the other hand, anyone who has looked for fertile bracken plants, bearing spores, knows how uncommon they are. Related to this rarity of spore-bearing fronds, Long and Fenton (1938) reported that at the eastern side of Britain the prothallial stage is rare or unknown. Tryon (1941) in his monograph on *Pteridium* pointed out; "In eastern North America young plants are only rarely seen," an observation with which we agree. With such a high degree of vegetative reproduction and so little evidence of sexual reproduction, it is of great interest to know how bracken manages to retain sufficient evolutionary plasticity to account for its immense abundance and success. Evidently, a great premium must be placed on cross-fertilization on those relatively infrequent occasions when an opportunity for sexual reproduction arises. Some insight into how genetic variability is assured in bracken may be inferred from work we have been carrying out on the antheridium-inducing substances in *Pteridium* and *Anemia*.

The existence of an antheridium-inducing substance in ferns was first recognized by Döpp (1950). Gametophytes of bracken produce a substance which causes newly germinated gametophytes of bracken and of *Dryopteris filix-mas* to form antheridia, the male reproductive organs. The occurrence of the substance, called antheridogen-A (Pringle *et al.,* 1960; Pringle, 1961), may be very simply demonstrated by aseptically inoculating an agar plate with bracken spores. After a culture period of several weeks, the gametophytes may be removed from the plate, the agar turned upside down to provide a clean smooth surface, and the plate reinoculated with bracken spores or those of *Dryopteris* or *Onoclea*. Within a few days the gametophytes which grow from the spores bear abundant antheridia, whereas gametophytes of control cultures remain completely vegetative during the experimental period.

Döpp (1950, 1959) showed that antheridogen-A was chiefly produced by large, heart-shaped "female" gametophytes rather than by vegetative, filamentous forms or "male," that is, antheridium-bearing, filamentous forms. Our own experiments confirm this but indicate that young, truncate *Pteridium* gametophytes, developing a meristem, also produce antheridogen. That these young two-dimensional forms produce hormone is consistent with our observation that the first antheridia appear in culture about 2 days after the first few truncate gametophytes arise. The truncate gametophytes, which quickly become heart-shaped, do not usually themselves develop antheridia, however; they remain vegetative or become archegoniate. These data are in agreement with those of Näf (1958).

Döpp also found, and we have confirmed, that the region of the heart-shaped gametophytes from which antheridogen appears to be derived, is the apical meristem and the tissues adjacent to it. This may be demonstrated by assaying surgically separated parts of gametophytes for antheridogen A. Assay gametophytes placed near isolated wings from a mature prothallus show little response, whereas those near the meristematic "notch" of the heart-shaped prothallus strongly respond.

One important additional piece of information is that the developing gametophytes of bracken, *Onoclea,* and *Anemia* lose sensitivity to antheridogen. If flasks of agar-grown gametophytes at various developmental stages are supplied with hormone and the gametophytes examined 6 days later, data such as those in Table 1 are obtained. Näf (1958) first showed this for *Onoclea* and bracken. His results, however, indicated a much sharper and more abrupt end to responsiveness. He reported that, between the 10th and 14th days after inoculation, *Onoclea* sensitivity dropped from full response to almost none. The results in Table 1 confirm that a striking decrease in sensitivity occurs, both in *Onoclea* and

TABLE 1

The Effect of Developmental Stage on Percentage of Gametophytes Bearing Antheridia 6 Days after Exposure to Antheridogen A[a] or Gibberellin A_3[b]

Days after inoculation	*Onoclea*	*Anemia*
6	99.3% (876)[c]	100% (639)[c]
8	98.4% (423)	69% (420)
10	88% (431)	59% (425)
12	61% (352)	
14	63% (192)	31% (400)
16	22% (320)	33% (400)
18	16% (316)	27% (400)

[a] Purified hormone active at 1 part per 10,000, final concentration.
[b] Concentration 10^{-4} g/ml.
[c] Number of gametophytes examined.

Anemia, but it is not so abrupt or complete as is suggested by Näf's data. Döpp (1959) also found decreased sensitivity, and on the basis of surgical experiments he concluded that the meristematic zone of prothallia produces an inhibitory substance which blocks antheridium formation.

Gametophytes appear to become insensitive to antheridogen at the same time they begin to produce antheridogen.

As was mentioned earlier, the first few bracken gametophytes which attain heart shape do not have a preceding antheridial phase. As Näf (1958) has shown with *Pteridium,* all gametophytes isolated and separately grown one per flask progress directly from filamentous form to archegoniate thallial form, bypassing an antheridial phase. We find this to be true of the gametophytes of *Onoclea sensibilis* and *Anemia phyllitidis,* as well as for those of *Pteridium.* After many additional weeks, however, antheridia may also appear on these isolated gametophytes, and sporophytes may develop. In liquid culture medium, for example, 23 of 63 isolated gametophytes of *Pteridium* developed sporophytes; in another test, 4 of 18 formed sporophytes, whereas 21 of 24 formed sporophytes when *pairs* of gametophytes were cultured. These results are in general agreement with the observations of Wilkie (1956, 1963) and of Klekowski and Baker (1966) that sporophytes form on isolated gametophytes. These sporophytes appear to arise through self-fertilization and not by apomixis.

Thus, in a population of gametophytes, it appears that the most rapidly developing individuals become two-dimensional and archegoniate and produce antheridogen. About the same time, they become insensitive to the substance. The antheridogen these gametophytes produce causes less rapidly growing gametophytes, which are still filamentous, to differentiate antheridia. Thus, through these means the fern secures greater assurance that both kinds of reproductive organs will be *present, and mature at the same time* and that they will be *on different plants and therefore provide for cross-fertilization.* If, however, sporophytes do not form through cross-fertilization, antheridia eventually form, commonly near the base of the prothallus, and self-fertilization may take place.

It is not yet clear to what extent similar control systems occur in other groups of ferns. However, we do have some information and a technique has been devised by means of which we hope many groups of ferns can be tested for their ability to form antheridogens. As evidenced by Döpp's observation of antheridium induction caused in *Dryopteris* by the substance from *Pteridium,* ferns other than bracken can respond to antheridogens. More than 50 species of ferns have been tested for their response (Voeller, 1964a) to antheridogen A (Table 2). Of these, 20 genera, from 4 separate families, possessed representatives which produced antheridia in response to the hormone. Species from 24 genera, including 4 entire families, either produced no antheridia in response to antheridogen-A, for example, the Osmundaceae and Schizaeaceae, or formed antheridia as rapidly in control cultures as in those containing the hormone, for example, species of *Polypodium.*

TABLE 2
Summary of the Responses of Fifty-two Species
of Ferns to Antheridogen A

Family	Response	No. Genera
Osmundaceae	−	2
Schizaeaceae	−	4
Cyatheaceae	−	1
Pteridaceae	−	4
	+	8
Davalliaceae	−	1
	+	1
Aspidiaceae	−	6
	+	8
Blechnaceae	−	1
	+	3
Polypodiaceae	−	5

Attempts to demonstrate the occurrence of other antheridogens, especially in species or families not responsive to antheridogen A, have led to the discovery by Näf of two additional hormones, one from *Anemia* (Näf, 1959) and one from *Lygodium* (Näf, 1960). Efforts to find other hormones in other groups have been unsuccessful. Culture filtrates from *Osmunda cinnamomea* L. or *O. claytonia* L., for example, consistently fail to induce the formation of antheridia in freshly germinating spores from the same species. Both experimental and control cultures are extremely slow to produce "spontaneous" antheridia. By contrast, *Todea barbara,* another member of the Osmundaceae, so rapidly develops "spontaneous" antheridia that it is difficult to establish whether gametophytes of this species respond to antheridogen A at all or, for that matter, to culture filtrates or agar from older *Todea* cultures. A similar problem occurs in testing most strains of *Pteridium* found in the Eastern United States for their response to antheridogen A.

To circumvent this difficulty in detection of antheridogen and, thus, to permit consideration of the phylogenetic relationship of the antheridogen control systems, a modified assay has been devised. In it the ability of the gametophyte to produce antheridogen is blocked, while the gametophyte's competence to respond to antheridogen is kept unimpaired. Assay cultures may be grown in red light by covering trays of flasks with one sheet each of red and orange Cinemoid celluloid, Nos. 5 and 6 (Davis, 1968). It will be recalled that Klebs (1917) first showed that gametophytes grown in red light remain filamentous, or one-dimensional in form, for a considerable period. Blue or white light is required for thallial, or two-dimensional, growth to occur. As has already been mentioned, only truncate or heart-shaped gametophytes appear to produce antheridogens in the species thus far studied. By inhibiting the formation of two-dimensional growth, and thence of antheridogen production, "spontaneous" antheridia do not appear. Culture filtrates isolated from bracken gametophytes raised in white light are added to coconut milk medium and inoculated with bracken spores and then incubated in red light. Under these conditions, "spontaneously" formed antheridia do not appear on filaments in control cultures, whereas the filamentous gametophytes in antheridogen-treated experimental flasks respond with great sensitivity and rapidity to added antheridogen A. In cultures supplied with the hormone, young antheridia can be recognized 4 days after spore inoculation (2 days after addition of antheridogen). By the 6th day after inoculation, essentially all of the filaments bear well-developed antheridia.

Thus, the use of red light may prove helpful in looking for antheridogens formed by species which quickly produce antheridia in culture, and for which no other assay species is known. The technique is now being tested with various ferns, for example, with *Todea barbara*.

Inasmuch as most of the studies of *Pteridium, Onoclea,* and *Anemia* have been carried out under conditions having little relationship to those prevailing in nature, the interpretation of experimental data presented above requires further careful study. Most workers have studied gametophytes grown under such unnatural conditions as continuous illumination, artificial light, *in*constant pH, and constant temperature. One of us has examined some of these conditions, including the effect of varied light intensity and photoperiod and the role of hydrogen ion concentration of culture media on the formation of antheridogen (Voeller, 1964a). More recently we have examined the effect of hydrogen ion concentration on the ability of gametophytes to respond to antheridogen, the ability of the gametophyte to overwinter out-of-doors (thence, its ability to reproduce sexually during more than one season), and the distance across which a mature archegoniate gametophyte can cause younger gametophytes to differentiate antheridia. Under conditions of constant light, for example, the "spontaneous" formation of antheridia is very much delayed in *Onoclea*. If the gametophytes are *not* grown under continuous illumination, however, they soon form antheridia. Eighty 125-ml Erlenmeyer flasks, each containing 50 ml of medium and bracken spores, were placed in the shade of a tree at Englewood, New Jersey, in the spring of 1966. The gametophytes in 75 of the flasks survived the summer. Despite 0°F weather and repeated winter freezing and thawing, 63 of the flasks still contained abundant gametophytes the following spring (1967). In the summer of 1968, after a second summer and winter, 15 flasks contained live gametophytes. Thus, under conditions at least partially simulating natural conditions, bracken can survive for periods of over 2 years.

Experiments in which spores of bracken were spread over a petri plate of agar medium bearing a single large gametophyte at its center show that antheridogen A can diffuse substantial distances from the producing plant. Antheridia formed on young sporelings several centimeters from the mature gametophyte.

In order to gain a clearer idea of the distance over which antheridogen A can influence the growth of other gametophytes, the apparatus in Fig. 1 was constructed. A glass chromatography trough 22 in. long was first aseptically filled with 100 ml of agar-gelled medium. A young heart-shaped gametophyte was placed at one end of the agar. The trough was then inserted in a sterile glass tube. At the end of a 45-day incubation period the gametophyte was removed from the end of the trough. The agar was cut into 1-in. blocks which were individually assayed for antheridogen. Under these special conditions, antheridogens could be detected as much as 10 in. from the source of production. It remains to be demonstrated whether sperms induced on a gametophyte at such a distance could reach the gametophyte which caused their formation.

Various chemical characteristics of the three known antheridogens suggested that they might possibly be related to the gibberellins (Voeller, 1964a,b). Moreover, Kato *et al.* (1962) and Muromtsev *et al.* (1964) have reported that substances with gibberellinlike activity are present in *sporophytic* tissues of several species of ferns, including species of *Alsophila, Dryopteris,* and *Athyrium.* When gibberellic acid was tested, it was found that most groups of ferns do not respond by formation of antheridia (cf. Voeller, 1964a,b). Indeed, *Onoclea sensibilis,* which is commonly used to assay antheridogen A, does not form antheridia in response to any of seven tested gibberellins, GA_1, GA_3, GA_4, GA_5, GA_7, GA_8, GA_9. *Anemia phyllitidis, A. rotundifolia,* and *Lygodium*

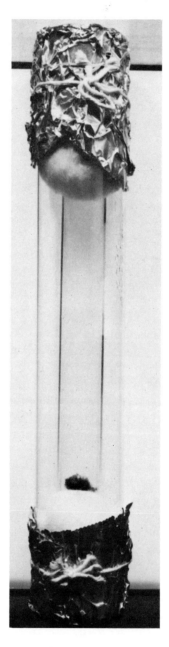

FIG. 1. Apparatus used to determine the distance which antheridogen produced by gametophytes can diffuse. Photograph taken at the end of a 45-day growth period.

japonicum, members of the Schizaeaceae, strongly respond to gibberellic acid (Schraudolf, 1962; Voeller, 1964a,b). Members of each of the four genera of the family produce antheridia on exposure to gibberellin (Table 3), and all gibberellins tested, GA_1, GA_3, GA_4, GA_5, GA_7, GA_8, and

TABLE 3
The Response of Species of the Schizaeaceae to Gibberellin A_3,
at a Concentration of 5×10^{-5} g/ml

Species	Gibberellin	Controls
Schizaea pusilla Pursh	+	−
S. robusta Baker	+	−
Lygodium japonicum (Thunb.) Sw.	+	−
L. palmatum (Bernh.) Sw.	+	−
L. scandens (L.) Sw.	+	−
L. flexuosum (L.) Sw.	+	−
Anemia hirsuta (L.) Sw.	+	−
A. pastinacaria Moritz	+	−
A. oblongifolia (Cav.) Sw.	+	−
A. tomentosa var *mexicana* (Presl) Mickel	+	−
A. tomentosa var. *anthriscifolia* (Schrad.) Mickel	+	−
A. jaliscana Maxon	+	−
A. rotundifolia Schrader	+	−
A. phyllitidis (L.) Sw.	+	−
A. phyllitidis	+	−
A. collima Roddi	+	−
Mohria caffrorum (L.) Desv.	+	−

GA_9, are biologically active (Schraudolf, 1964; Voeller, 1964a,b). GA_7 is active to concentrations as low as 5×10^{-10} g/ml.

Preliminary work involving thin-layer chromatography of the antheridogens and gibberellins indicates that antheridogen A (from *Pteridium*), and probably also antheridogen B (the natural substance from *Anemia phyllitidis*), are not identical with gibberellins 1–9 (Voeller, 1964a). However, in *A. phyllitidis* the similarities of effect between gibberellic acid and antheridogen B are striking. Both are specific in their induction of antheridia, even to the determination of such details as the number of sperms per antheridium (Voeller and Weinberg, 1967) (Fig. 2). Each is characterized by a dosage-response curve in which a fewfold increase in concentration, at the critical threshold, leads from no response in assay gametophytes to nearly full response, that is, nearly every gametophyte bearing at least one antheridium.

Furthermore, the length of the induction period required by each hormone in antheridium formation is quite similar. To demonstrate this,

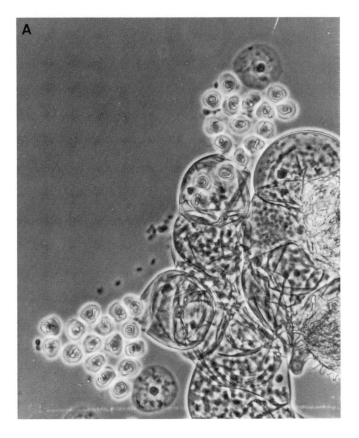

FIG. 2. Gametophytes of *Anemia phyllitidis*. Feulgen stained, phase contrast. "Squash" preparations showing 16 sperms extruded from each antheridium in (A) gibberellic acid and (B) antheridogen B-treated gametophytes.

gametophytes at the 1- to 2-cell stage were exposed for 1, 2, 3, 4, or 5 days to gibberellin or antheridogen B. After the appropriate incubation with hormone, the gametophytes were centrifuged and resuspended in sterile water and finally placed in culture solution lacking hormone. (Bioassay of the washes shows that the gametophytes are freed of all external hormone in two washes, although 6 to 10 washes are customarily used.) Twelve days after the beginning of the experiment, results such as those shown in Table 4 were obtained. Under the conditions employed, the

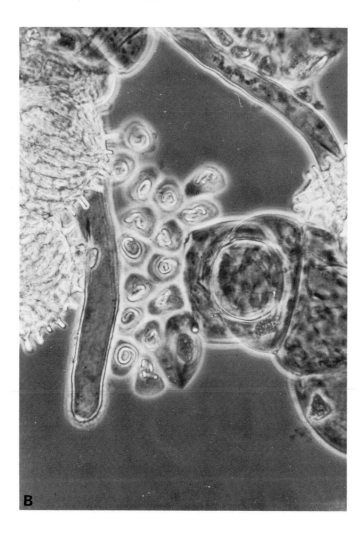

full, irreversible induction of antheridia did not take place during the 24-hr period following presentation of gametophytes to either hormone. By 48 hrs, however, significant effects were found in both types of cultures. Thus the induction periods are quite similar. The apparent difference in percent of response, however, cannot properly be compared inasmuch as the molar concentration of antheridogen B is necessarily unknown.

It was found that the pH of liquid cultures of *A. phyllitidis* often varies with the age and density of the culture. The pH of Moore's medium con-

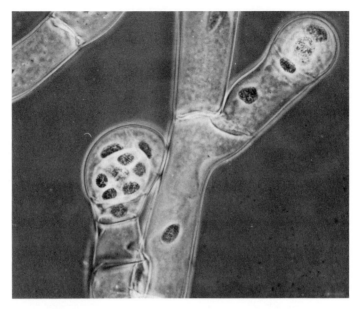

FIG. 3. Gametophytes of *Schizaea pusilla* with developing antheridia. Cells cleared with a solution of chloral hydrate in water (8:5, by weight).

taining freshly germinated spores to which gibberellic acid in a dilute sodium bicarbonate solution has been added is 5.2 to 5.4. Within 2 weeks the pH of the medium often drops to values of 3.5 to 4.0. It was thus necessary to explore the possibility of a dependence of antheridial formation on pH.

TABLE 4

Percentage of Gametophytes Bearing Antheridia after
Exposure to Induction Hormone.[a]

Induction period, days	Gibberellic acid, %	Antheridogen B, %
12	72	64
5	47	53
4	–	35
2 (48 hr)	26	6
1 (24 hr)	0	0

[a] Each percentage figure based on counts of about 300 gametophytes, except day 12, based on 100 gametophytes. Gibberellin concentration 10^{-5} g/ml.

Most of the common buffers in the pH range 3.0 to 6.0 are either toxic or they seriously inhibit the formation of antheridia in *Anemia*. However, the use of a 0.05 M solution of 2-(N-morpholino)ethanesulfonic acid·H_2O (MES) as a buffer inhibited neither growth nor formation of antheridia in response to gibberellic acid. The dependence of antheridial induction on pH is illustrated by Fig. 4. In this experiment, spores were germinated

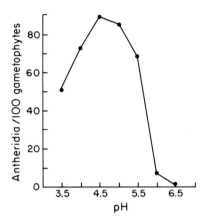

FIG. 4. Response of dark-grown *Anemia* gametophytes to 10^{-4} g/ml gibberellic acid in media buffered with 0.05 M MES at various pH values.

and grown in the dark in the presence of gibberellic acid at a concentration of 10^{-4} g/ml. Gametophytes were examined 12 days after inoculation, and the number of antheridia per 100 gametophytes was recorded for cultures grown at various pH values in MES-buffered media. Under these conditions there is some inhibition of growth at a pH of less than 4.0 but not at any of the other values tested. The decrease in response at a pH greater than 5.0 may be explained by the possibility that the cell membrane is permeable only to the acid form of the gibberellin.

Similar dependence on pH has been obtained when spores of *Anemia* were germinated and grown in the light and either gibberellic acid or antheridogen B was added at various times after germination. It is thus essential to perform experiments with *Anemia* at a constant pH. It is possible that some of the studies of various investigators on antheridium formation require reevaluation because of poor control of gametophyte density and pH.

The usefulness of expressing the activity of gibberellic acid in terms of antheridia formed by 100 gametophytes, rather than as a percentage of gametophytes bearing antheridia, is apparent from Fig. 5. Gibberellic acid at the indicated concentrations was added to cultures of *Anemia* 6 days after inoculation. Counts of antheridia were made 14 days after addition of the gibberellin. At any one time of counting, the range of an

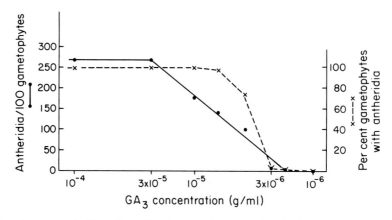

Fig. 5. Assay of gibberellic acid using actual counts of antheridia and percentage of gametophytes bearing antheridia. Details are found in text.

assay using the number of antheridia formed is much wider than that of an assay based on a percentage of responding gametophytes.

The induction of antheridia by gibberellic acid in *Anemia* provides a clear case of differentiation stimulated by a common plant hormone. It was therefore of interest to investigate the level of control of this induction. Experiments by Schraudolf (1967) have shown little effect of actinomycin D on the formation of antheridia in response to gibberellin. However, these experiments were evidently done in the light, and it is well known that such treatment leads to the breakdown of the inhibitor. Under these conditions we have seen inhibition of growth and certain characteristic growth abnormalities which may be due to the breakdown products of actinomycin rather than to the actinomycin itself.

To minimize this problem, we transferred cultures to the dark immediately after addition of actinomycin D. Spores were inoculated into an MES-buffered medium at a pH of 4.5. Actinomycin was added 4 days later, and the cultures were placed into the dark. Gibberellic acid at a concentration of 10^{-4} g/ml was added to the actinomycin D-containing cultures and to control cultures either at this time or 4 or 8 days later. This procedure allowed a comparison of the effect of preincubating the cultures with actinomycin for different times. Figure 6 shows the effect of actinomycin D at three different concentrations on the formation of antheridia. It is obvious that all concentrations show some inhibition.

The inhibition is more striking in the cultures which were preincubated with the actinomycin before addition of gibberellic acid.

The effects of actinomycin on the rate of cell division under these

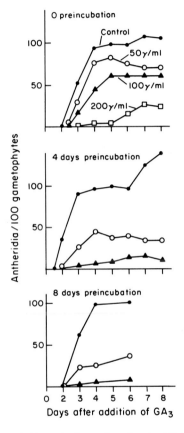

FIG. 6. Effect of actinomycin D on the formation of antheridia in *Anemia*. Gametophytes were transferred to the dark directly after addition of the inhibitor. Gibberellic acid was added at the same time as the actinomycin, 4 days later, or 8 days later.

conditions was measured in a parallel experiment. Conditions were exactly as above except that no gibberellic acid was added. Figure 7 indicates that only at the highest concentration of actinomycin D used (200 μg/ml) was there significant inhibition of cell division through the first 12 days of the experiment. Yet actinomycin at a concentration of 50 μg/ml inhibits the production of antheridia during these first 12 days, especially in cultures preincubated with the inhibitor.

The inhibition by actinomycin is never complete, even with long periods of preincubation. We have observed that, even at 200 μg/ml, actinomycin D inhibits only 40 to 50% of the incorporation of uridine into RNA. A full understanding of the action of the inhibitor in this

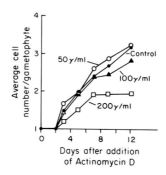

FIG. 7. Effect of actinomycin D on cell division in *Anemia*. Gametophytes were transferred to the dark directly after addition of the inhibitor. The spore cell was not included in cell counts.

system must await fractionation of the RNA of the differentiating gametophyte. The experiments presented, however, are consistent with the hypothesis of the induction of new species of RNA by the gibberellin as a limiting step in antheridial formation.

REFERENCES

Davis, Bill D. (1968). Effect of light quality on the transition to two-dimensional growth by gametophytes of *Pteridium aquilinum*. *Bull. Torrey Botan. Club* **95**, 31–36.

Döpp, W. (1950). Eine die Antheridienbildung bei Farnen fördernde Substanz in den Prothallien von *Pteridium aquilinum* (L.) Kuhn. *Ber. Deut. Botan. Ges.* **63**, 139–147.

Döpp, W. (1959). Über eine hemmende und eine fördernde Substanz bei der Antheridienbildung in den Prothallien von *Pteridium aquilinum*. *Ber. Deut. Botan. Ges.* **72**, 11–24.

Kato, J., Purves, W. K., and Phinney, B. O. (1962). Gibberellin-like substances in plants. *Nature* **196**, 687–688.

Klebs, G. (1917). Zur Entwicklungsgeschichte der Farnprothallien. Teil 2. *Sitzungsber. Heidelberg. Akad. Wiss. Math.-Naturwiss. Kl. Abhandl.* **8B**, 3.

Klekowski, E. J., Jr., and Baker, H. G. (1966). Evolutionary significance of polyploidy in the Pteridophyta. *Science* **153**, 305–307.

Long, H. C., and Fenton, E. W. (1938). The story of the bracken fern. *J. Roy. Agric. Soc. Engl.* **99**, 15–36.

Muromtsev, G. S., Agnistikova, V. N., Lupova, L. M., Dubovaya, L. P., Lekareva, T. A. (1964). [Gibberellin-like substances in ferns and mosses.] *Izv. Akad. Nauk SSSR Ser. Biol.* **5**, 727–734.

Näf, U. (1958). On the physiology of antheridium formation in the bracken fern [*Pteridium aquilinum* (L.) Kuhn]. *Physiol. Plantarum* **11**, 728–746.

Näf, U. (1959). Control of antheridium formation in the fern species *Anemia phyllitides*. *Nature* **184**, 798–800.

Näf, U. (1960). On the control of antheridium formation in the fern species *Lygodium japonicum*. *Proc. Soc. Exptl. Biol. Med.* **105**, 82–86.

Näf, U. (1961). Mode of action of an antheridium-inducing substance in ferns. *Nature* **189**, 900–903.

Pringle, R. B. (1961). Chemical nature of antheridogen-A, a specific inducer of the male sex organ in certain fern species. *Science* **133**, 284.

Pringle, R. B., Näf, U., and Braun, A. C. (1960). Purification of a specific inducer of the male sex organ in certain fern species. *Nature* **186**, 1066–1067.

Schraudolf, H. (1962). Die Wirkung von Phytohormonen auf Keimung und Entwicklung von Farnprothallien. I. Auslösung der Antheridienbildung und Dunkelkeimung bei Schizaeaceae durch Gibberellinsäure. *Biol. Zentr.* **81**, 731–740.

Schraudolf, H. (1964). Relative activity of the gibberellins in the antheridium induction in *Anemia phyllitidis*. *Nature* **201**, 98–99.

Schraudolf, H. (1967). Wirkung von Hemmstoffen der DNS-, RNS-, und Proteinsynthese auf Wachstum und Antheridienbildung in Prothallien von *Anemia phyllitidis* L. *Planta* **74**, 123–147.

Stebbins, G. L. (1950). "Variation and Evolution in Plants." Columbia University Press, New York.

Tryon, R. M., Jr. (1941). A revision of the genus *Pteridium*. *Rhodora* **43**, 1–70.

Voeller, B. R. (1964a). Antheridogens in ferns. *Colloq. Intern. Centre Natl. Rech. Sci. (Paris)* **123**, "Gif-sur-Yvette, Régulateurs Naturels de la Croissance Végétale, 665–684.

Voeller, B. R. (1964b). Gibberellins: their effect on antheridium formation in fern gametophytes. *Science* **143**, 373–375.

Voeller, B. R., and Weinberg, E. S. (1967). Antheridium induction and the number of sperms per antheridium in *Anemia phyllitidis*. *Am. Fern J.* **57**, 107–112.

Wagner, W. H., Jr., and Sharp, A. J. (1963). A remarkably reduced vascular plant in the United States. *Science* **142**, 1483–1484.

Watt, A. S. (1940). Contributions to the ecology of Bracken (*Pteridium aquilinum*). I. The rhizome. *New Phytologist* **39**, 401–422.

Wilkie, D. (1956). Incompatibility in bracken. *Heredity* **10**, 247–256.

Wilkie, D. (1963). Genetic analysis of variation in the bracken prothallus. *J. Linnean Soc. (Botany)* **58**, 333–336.

III
Aspects of Morphogenesis

On the Control of Antheridium
Formation in Ferns*

Ulrich Näf†

Döpp (1950) demonstrated that the medium and the extract from prothalli of mature cultures of *Pteridium aquilinum* hastened the onset of antheridium formation in this species by a few days, and in the prothalli of *Dryopteris filix-mas* by several weeks. Both the medium and the prothallial extracts were maximally active to a dilution of 1/100 in *D. filix-mas*. He concluded that *P. aquilinum* elaborates a hormone which specifically controls antheridium formation but fails to promote archegonium formation.

The antheridium-inducing activity was, in my studies, assayed against the prothalli of the fern species, *Onoclea sensibilis*. The prothalli of this species were ideally suited to this task for three reasons. First, most strains failed to form antheridia spontaneously under the prevailing conditions of culture (Näf, 1956, 1962c; Schraudolf, 1966c) but responded sensitively to the added antheridium-inducing hormone. Second, none of the several tested species responded to a lower concentration. Third, the assay could be read within a reasonable period of time because both germination and subsequent growth were rapid. Conditions were defined under which the extract from mature prothalli of *P. aquilinum* was mostly active to a dilution of about 1:30,000 if assayed against *O. sensibilis*. Under the same conditions the active substance accumulated to almost as high an activity in the medium (Näf, 1956, 1962a,b). Maximum activity in the medium was reached 4 to 6 weeks after inoculatiön (Naf, 1958, 1962a).

The antheridium-inducing activity is stable to boiling for 10 min at pH 2 but labile to boiling at pH 12 (Näf, 1956). It is sparingly soluble in ether

*This work was supported by Grants GB-6418 and B-12879 from the National Science Foundation. The Laboratory of Plant Morphogenesis is supported by P.H.S. Institutional Grant RC-1193 and the Christine and Alfred Sonntag Foundation.

† I am grateful to Mrs. Marie Klasser for her help with the manuscript.

(Döpp, 1950). It dialyzes, adsorbs on charcoal from which it is eluted by methanol (Näf, 1956; Pringle *et al.*, 1960), and is destroyed by oxidation (Döpp, 1950; Pringle *et al.*, 1960). The isolated substance (Pringle, 1961) contains a carboxyl group that is required for activity. The substance has been termed an antheridogen. It is active at a concentration of less than one in ten billion (Pringle *et al.*, 1961). Döpp's demonstration of an antheridium-inducing hormone (abbr. A_{Pt}*) has made available a unique model for the study of differentiation.

Specificities of Native Antheridogens

A_{Pt} does not induce antheridia in all polypodiaceous species (Döpp, 1959, Näf, 1958, 1962a; Voeller, 1964a). Unresponsive species are encountered especially in the subgroup Polypodioids (Voeller, 1964a). *Polypodium aureum* fails to respond to A_{Pt} even at a concentration 15,000 times that minimally effective in *O. sensibilis* (Näf, 1956, 1962a). Other species respond to the A_{Pt}-containing preparation only if it is added at a concentration exceeding the one minimally effective in *O. sensibilis* by a factor of 25 to 10,000 (Table 1). Pure A_{Pt} could not be used in these

TABLE 1

Concentration of A_{Pt}-Containing Preparation Needed to Induce Antheridia in Different Fern Species[a]

Species	Family and subgroup	Effective concentration	Authority
Woodsia obtusa	Woodsioids (Polypodiaceae)	25 ×	(Näf, 1959)
Dicksonia punctilobula	Dicksoniaceae	125 ×	(Näf, 1959)
Dryopteris filix-mas	Dryopteroids (Polypodiaceae)	125–300 ×	(Döpp, 1962; Näf, 1966)
Polystichum tsus-simense	Dryopteroids (Polypodiaceae)	3,000 ×	(Näf, 1966)
Aglaomorpha meyeniana	Polypodioids (Polypodiaceae)	10,000 ×	(Näf, 1966)

[a] Effective concentration expressed as multiple of that needed to induce antheridia in *O. sensibilis*.

experiments. It is possible, therefore, that the factor effective in *Aglaomorpha meyeniana,* for example, is not identical with the major component in the applied A_{Pt}-containing preparation. Such a possibility must be considered also because *P. aquilinum* elaborates a trace of an antheridogen different from A_{Pt} (Pringle, 1961). With either interpretation,

*Abbreviations: A_{Pt}, native antheridogen of *P. aquilinum;* A_{An}, of *A. phyllitidis;* A_{Ly}, of *L. japonicum;* A_{On}, antheridogen derived from *O. sensibilis;* GA_3, gibberellic acid.

Table 1 suggests that antheridium formation is controlled by different, though probably similar, substances in different subgroups of the Polypodiaceae (Näf, 1959).

Native antheridogens have been demonstrated also in the polypodiaceous species *D. filix-mas* (Döpp, 1950), *Thelypteris hexanoptera* and *Blechnum gibbum* (Näf, 1956), and *Onoclea sensibilis* (Näf, 1961, 1965). However, only the *Onoclea* antheridogen was demonstrated to differ from A_{Pt}. In *Onoclea* cultures an antheridogen could not be detected in the medium until all individuals of the gametophyte population had reached the insensitive stage (see "Antheridium formation as a function of cellular competence" below). It thus appeared that *Onoclea* prothalli failed to form antheridia under the prevailing conditions of culture because they did not begin to synthesize the antheridogen at an effective concentration until after they reached the stage at which they lack competence to respond to it. On this assumption, young prothalli that are grown together with older ones are expected to form antheridia in response to antheridogen secreted into the medium by the older prothalli. Unexpectedly, the young prothalli failed to form antheridia. The alternative thesis was proposed that an active antheridogen did not exist in the undisturbed culture medium but arose instead while the medium was being prepared for assay. It was actually demonstrated that medium from 14-day-old *Onoclea* cultures yielded antheridium-inducing activity only on heating. Low pH increased the yield. Quite likely, heating converts an inactive factor into an antheridogen, but it is not yet excluded that it destroys instead an inhibitor of antheridogen action (Näf, 1965). The active *Onoclea* factor is chromatographically distinct from A_{Pt} (unpublished data).

A_{Pt} fails to induce antheridia in the tested representatives of the fern families Osmundaceae, Cyatheaceae, and Schizaeaceae (Näf, 1959, 1960; Voeller, 1964a) even at a concentration 15,000 times that minimally effective in the assay species *O. sensibilis*. The unresponsive species *Lygodium japonicum* and *Anemia phyllitidis* (Schizaeaceae) also synthesize antheridogens. Prothalli of these species formed antheridia precociously if they were inoculated among older prothalli of the same species. *Anemia* prothalli formed male sex organs prematurely, and in great abundance, even if a single older prothallus was implanted among them. Media harvested from 5-week-old cultures of *A. phyllitidis* induced antheridia in juvenile prothalli of this species to dilutions ranging from 1/100 to 1/3000 of full-strength harvested medium. Occasionally the yield was nil, for reasons as yet unknown. The antheridium-inducing substance of *A. phyllitidis* (A_{An}) failed to induce antheridia in *O. sensi-*

bilis, the species used to assay for A_{Pt} (Näf, 1959). This, and the demonstration of different stabilities on heating at aklaline pH, led to the conclusion that A_{Pt} and A_{An} are different molecular entities (Näf, 1959; Voeller, 1964a). They have been chromatographically separated (Voeller, 1964a).

Lygodium japonicum also synthesizes an antheridogen (A_{Ly}). It is not identical with A_{Pt} (Näf, 1960). The strong indication that it also differs from A_{An} (Näf, 1960) was recently confirmed by chromatography (Näf, 1968).

More recently, Schraudolf (1962, 1966a) introduced a new note into these studies by his demonstration that gibberellic acid (GA_3) induces antheridia in the six tested species and in three genera of the family Schizaeaceae, among them *L. japonicum* and *A. phyllitidis*. Other gibberellins are also effective, some of them at an exceedingly low concentration (Schraudolf, 1964; Voeller, 1964b). Interestingly, even helminthosporic acid (Tamura *et al.,* 1963), a substance of much smaller molecular size than gibberelins, gives an antheridial response (Schraudolf, 1967a). It has been interpreted to be a stripped-down gibberellin. A_{An} appears to be chromatographically distinct from the tested known gibberellins (Voeller, 1964a). A_{Ly} is distinct from GA_3 (Näf, 1968).

A_{An} failed to induce antheridia in the investigated species of the families Polypodiaceae, Osmundaceae (Näf, 1959), and Cyatheaceae (*Alsophila australis;* Näf, 1968). Similarly, gibberellic acid failed to give an antheridial response in the polypodiaceous species *Dryopteris filix-mas* (Döpp, 1962), *Polypodium crassifolium* (Schraudolf, 1962), most of the numerous polypodiaceous species tested by Voeller (1964a), and in representatives of the Osmundaceae and Cyatheaceae (Voeller, 1964a). A weak response was seen in the polypodiaceous species *Aspidium oreopteris* (von Witsch and Rintelen, 1962), *Pteris tremula, Tectaria heracleifolia,* and *Blechnum brasiliense* (Voeller, 1964a). Several gibberellins induced an antheridial response in *Dryopteris filix-mas* and, after prolonged culture, in *Onoclea sensibilis* (Schraudolf, 1966c). Surprisingly, the observed response to gibberellin in *D. filix-mas* and *O. sensibilis* showed little dependence on gibberellin concentration. With some of the species the possibility has not been excluded that the reported response resulted indirectly from a change in the rate of vegetative growth. Where investigated, the applied gibberellin did not hasten the onset of antheridium formation in these polypodiaceous species but merely increased the percentage of antheridial prothalli.

In contrast, gibberellins (Schraudolf, 1962) and A_{An} (Näf, 1959) hasten the onset of antheridium formation in *A. phyllitidis* by more than

2 weeks. A_{Pt} hastens the beginning of the antheridial phase by several weeks in *D. filix-mas* (Döpp, 1950) and may induce male sex organs in species which do not form them spontaneously under the prevailing conditions of culture (Näf, 1956, 1962a; Döpp, 1959). Whereas gibberellins fail to hasten antheridium formation in *D. filix-mas,* the increase in the percentage of male prothalli was statistically validated (Schraudolf, 1966c). The failure of this hormone to hasten the antheridial phase in this species can be understood; for example, on the assumption that the prothallus is capable of utilizing gibberellins as precursors beginning with the developmental stage at which it starts to synthesize the native antheridogen.

The failure of A_{An} to induce antheridia in the few tested nonschizaeaceous species very closely resembles the failure of gibberellic acid to induce antheridia in the bulk of the many tested nonschizaeaceous species. A_{An} and gibberellic acid also resemble each other because both induce antheridia in schizaeaceous species. Differences become apparent, however, if the specificities of gibberellic acid and A_{An} toward species of this family are compared. Gibberellic acid is active to the same dilution toward *L. japonicum* and *A. phyllitidis* (Voeller, 1964a), or to a concentration 3 times lower in *Lygodium japonicum* (Näf, 1966). In contrast, A_{An} must be supplied to *L. japonicum* at a concentration 30 times that minimally effective in *A. phyllitidis.* More strikingly still, A_{Ly} fails to induce antheridia in *A. phyllitidis* even at a concentration 300 times that minimally effective in *L. japonicum* (Näf, 1960). Clearly, the native antheridogens of schizaeaceous species are more selective in their action than is gibberellic acid. The specificities of A_{Pt}, A_{An}, A_{Ly} and GA_3 are summarized in Table 2.

The demonstration that representatives of two schizaeaceous genera synthesize different antheridogens shows that the specificity of these substances may extend to the genus level. The question whether it reaches the species level is being investigated by comparing the antheridogens of two species within the same genus.

The demonstrated and indicated specificities of fern antheridogens suggests that antheridium formation is controlled by different, if possibly similar, substances in different groupings of ferns. The tentative assumption that fern antheridogens comprise a large number of structurally similar compounds requires the specification that the basic molecule have the minimal size and complexity which permit many structural varients. The hormonal class of gibberellins and steroids might meet this specification. Schraudolf (1962) stressed that the described properties of native antheridogens resemble those of gibberellins. The hypothesis that

TABLE 2

Specificities of Fern Antheridogens. A Summary

Antheridogen	Activity or inactivity toward		
	Polypodiaceae	Schizaeaceae	Osmundaceae and Cyatheaceae
A_{Pt}	Hastens the onset of antheridial phase up to several weeks in a majority of species; in some of them only if applied at concentration much higher than that required in the standard assay species (*O. sensibilis*); many unresponsive species in the subgroup Polypodioids.	Inactive toward tested species	Inactive toward tested species
A_{An}	Inactive toward standard assay species for A_{Pt}	Active toward the tested species of the genera *Lygodium* and *Anemia*	Inactive toward the one species tested in each family
A_{Ly}	Most A_{Ly}-containing preparations inffective toward standard assay species for A_{Pt}	Active toward *Lygodium japonicum;* inactive toward *Anemia phyllitidis*	Inactive toward tested species of Osmundaceae
GA_3	Fails to hasten onset of antheridial phase in all tested species; increases percentage of antheridial prothalli in a rare species	Active toward the tested species of the genera *Lygodium, Anemia,* and *Mohria*	Inactive

fern antheridogens are gibberellins must be considered especially for schizaeaceous species, but Schraudolf's demonstration of a clear-cut effect on *Dryopteris filix-mas* (Polypodiaceae) indicates that antheridogens in other families may also belong to this class of hormones. An A_{An}-containing preparation was active in one assay system for gibberellins (amylase induction in barley endosperm) but inactive in another (dwarf pea; Progress #9) (Näf, 1968). The failure of a substance to stimulate growth in one assay does not disprove its gibberellin nature if it is recalled that different assay systems may have a wide range of sensitivity to a given gibberellin. Nor does the positive result in the barley assay establish the gibberellin nature of A_{An}, because the pure substance could not yet be tested.

The demonstration that different fern groups have different antheridogens is of interest from a theoretical point of view. The work of Kluyver and Van Niel has pointed the way toward the discipline of Comparative Biochemistry, that is, toward the realization that many basic metabolic patterns are similar, even identical, in taxonomically widely separated organisms. As yet, little is known about the extent to which this concept may be applicable to development. Most students of this discipline prefer to think that the underlying biochemical processes, the differentiation of an antheridium for example, are basically similar in different organisms. An attempt to reconcile this postulate with the reported differences among fern antheridogens might start with the argument that the induction of an antheridium involves many different reactions and compounds. Accordingly, the nonidentity of antheridogens might lead to the postulation that their triggering action fits at different points within the sequence or network of these reactions. On this assumption, antheridium formation in species related remotely is controlled by structurally unrelated compounds. Alternatively, we might be witness to evolution at a molecular level, that is, to the phenomenon that the inducing hormone, and perhaps the acceptor site, have undergone gradual structural modification. Such a thesis permits the assumption that all fern antheridogens have the same basic structure. The assumption of gradual but ultimately far-reaching molecular change makes it plausible that antheridogens of closely related species are mutually effective to a high degree and that they are less effective and finally mutually ineffective as evolutionary relationships become more remote.

The *Anemia* Antheridogen, Gibberellic Acid, and Spore Germination

Schraudolf (1962) observed that gibberellic acid, besides inducing antheridia, also canceled the light requirement for spore germination in *A. phyllitidis*. The protonemata developed from the dark-germinated spores bore antheridia.

Liquid media harvested from 5-week-old *Anemia* cultures also induced dark germination. The dark germination-inducing activity could not be chromatographically separated from A_{An} with two solvent systems that permitted the separation of closely related fern antheridogens (Näf, 1966). In all likelihood, the dark germination-inducing factor is identical with A_{An}. It is not yet known whether light brings about germination by stimulating the synthesis of A_{An}.

The harvested *Anemia* medium induced both dark germination and antheridia on the dark-grown protonemata to a concentration of 1: 100,000, that is, to a concentration 30 times lower than it induced antheridia on the light-grown prothalli (Table 3). The studies showed that added dark germination-inducing activity or antheridium-inducing activity could be recovered almost fully from the medium of *Anemia* cultures grown in the light (Näf, 1966). The conclusion was drawn that these activities are stable in the light and that, accordingly, light decreases the sensitivity of the prothalli to A_{An}. Unlike A_{An}, GA_3 induces antheridia in the light and induces dark germination to about the same dilution (Schraudolf, 1962). This recalls the finding by Kende and Lang (1964) that GA_1 was highly active toward dwarf peas in both light and darkness. In contrast, GA_5 was 10 times more active in darkness than in light. They concluded that illumination lowers tissue sensitivity to GA_5 but not to GA_1.

TABLE 3

Induction of Dark Germination and Antheridium Formation
by Harvested "*Anemia* medium" in *A. phyllitidis* and *L. japonicum*

Dilution of *Anemia* medium	Dark germination[a]		Antheridium formation in the light[a]	
	A. phyllitidis	*L. japonicum*	*A. phyllitidis*	*L. japonicum*
1/3	–	3.5	–	29.5
1/10	–	1.5	30.0	28.0
1/30	18.0	.5	30.0	27.0
1/100	19.5	.0	30.0	4.5
1/300	18.0	.0	21.0	0.0
1/1,000	16.5	–	13.0	–
1/3,000	16.5	–	1.5	–
1/10,000	13.0	–	0.0	–
1/30,000	10.5	–	–	–
1/100,000	.5	–	–	–
1/300,000	0.0	–	–	–
Co.	0.0	0.0	0.0	0.0

[a] The numbers are averages of dark-germinated spores or antheridium-bearing prothalli in two samples of 30 observed individuals.

A_{Pt}, which fails to induce antheridia in *A. phyllitidis*, also fails to induce dark germination in this species. *Lygodium* medium regularly induces dark germination in a few *Lygodium* spores if only at the highest concentration applied; it fails to induce dark germination in *A. phyllitidis*. Thus, the specificities of the native dark germination-inducing factors are similar to, if not identical with, the specificities of the native antheridiogens.

Antheridium Formation as a Function of Cellular Competence

Antheridium formation in ferns may be described as a function of cellular competence to respond to the antheridogen. Such competence varies greatly within the tempero-spatial coordinates of development.

Prothalli of *P. aquilinum* stop forming antheridia as they attain the archegonial phase or soon thereafter. Interestingly, extracts from pro-thalli that have passed beyond the antheridial phase contain more antheridium-inducing activity than extract from still younger antheridial prothalli (Döpp, 1950). *Onoclea* and *Pteridium* prothalli were pregrown for varying periods of time on nonsupplemented medium and then exposed to medium supplemented with A_{Pt}. The results led to the conclusion that these prothalli respond sensitively to A_{Pt} during an early stage of develop-ment but lose competence to respond with antheridium formation shortly after they attain heart shape and about a week before they attain the archegonial phase (Fig. 1). Once competence is lost, the prothalli fail to respond even if A_{Pt} is supplied at a concentration 15,000 times that minimally effective in juvenile, still-sensitive prothalli. In the *Onoclea* prothallus the change from competence to incompetence occurs within less than 2 days (Näf, 1958, 1962a). The described early loss of sensi-tivity to antheridogen occurs only in prothalli not previously exposed to

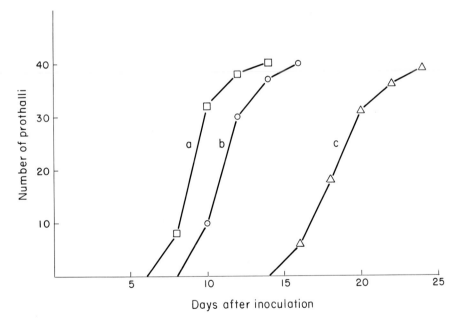

FIG. 1. Loss of sensitivity to A_{Pt} in *Onoclea sensibilis*. Numbers of prothalli out of 40 that (*a*) have attained heart shape; (*b*) have become insensitive to A_{Pt}; (*c*) have attained the archegonial phase. Loss of sensitivity assayed with A_{Pt} at concentration $600 \times$ that effective in juvenile gametophyte.

antheridogen. If prothalli are exposed to A_{Pt} at the spore stage, the loss of sensitivity to A_{Pt} is delayed to a great extent and the onset of the archegonial phase to a lesser extent (Näf, 1962c).

Czaja (1921) and Döpp (1959) demonstrated that wings excised from insensitive archegonia bearing prothalli of *Blechnum brasiliense* and *P. aquilinum,* respectively, resumed the formation of antheridia. Döpp concluded that the meristem of the maturing prothallus begins to synthesize a substance which prevents the antheridogen from inducing antheridia during the archegonial phase. His experiments further indicate that a substance antagonistic to antheridium formation may be demonstrated in the extract of archegonial *Pteridium* prothalli. He thought that the presence or absence of antheridia in *Pteridium* prothalli is determined by the interplay between the antheridogen and a substance antagonistic to its action. Wings excised from insensitive *Onoclea* prothalli also resumed antheridium formation (Näf, 1961). This is of special interest because intact prothalli of this species failed to form antheridia under the prevailing conditions of culture. The observations showed that antheridia arose only in those regions of the regenerating wings that had first undergone vegetative cell division. Perhaps something in the cell is diluted out by way of regenerative division before the cells become sensitive again.

Similar changes in competence to form antheridia occur in *A. phyllitidis.* The early application of A_{An} or GA_3 leads to the onset of the antheridial phase at the protonemal stage, more than 2 weeks before they arise spontaneously (Fig. 2). The juvenile filamentous prothallus is competent to form these sex organs throughout most of its body. As the prothallus grows into a two-dimensional cell plate, an anterior region comprising a growing portion of prothallial cells fails to respond to even the highest concentration of the hormones. Later, a new meristem is initiated laterally at the margin of the prothallus (Fig. 2, C,D). At this stage the area of competence has become contracted to a small area just behind, and on the side, of this lateral meristem (Näf, 1959; Schraudolf, 1962, 1966a), that is, the area of the prothallus described by Bauke (1878) as bearing antheridia in the natural course of events (Fig. 2,D). It is quite arresting to think that the cells given off by the lateral meristem toward the base of the prothallus are competent to respond to A_{An} while the cells given off in a forward direction lack such competence. The rhizoid-bearing region has low competence to respond to the antheridogen at all stages of development.

Inducibility of Physiological State Antagonistic to Antheridium Formation in *Anemia phyllitidis*

In *A. phyllitidis* the interval between exposure to A_{An} or GA_3 and the

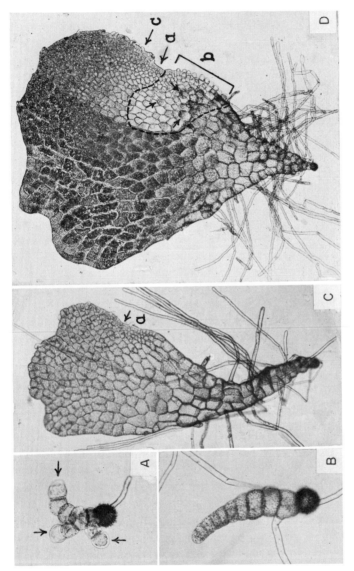

Fig. 2. Gametophyte development of *Anemia phyllitidis* in presence and absence of A_{An}. A, 12-day-old gametophyte grown in presence of A_{An} (arrows point to antheridia).B, same, but not grown in presence of A_{An}. C. 25-day-old gametophyte not exposed to A_{An}. D. 35-day-old gametophyte with area of spontaneous antheridium formation (arrow *a*, lateral meristem; *b*, row of antheridia initiated by marginal cells behind lateral meristem; *c*, papilla; stippled line demarcates area of spontaneous antheridium formation; arrows inside area point to antheridia).

appearance of antheridium initials is greater in young prothalli than in older ones (Näf, 1959; Schraudolf, 1966a). A very brief exposure to a gibberellin at low concentration led to antheridium formation at the 10-day stage but not at the spore stage (Schraudolf, 1966a). These results suggested that the events leading to antheridium formation proceed more slowly in young prothalli or, alternatively, that the juvenile prothallus is incompetent to respond to A_{An} (Näf, 1959), or that older prothalli are more sensitive to added hormone (Schraudolf, 1966a). Schraudolf also stressed that prothalli exposed to GA_3 at the spore stage attain the antheridial phase the later the hormone is added and the lower its concentration. With a given spore sample the number of vegetative cells formed on attainment of the antheridial phase was characteristic of the hormone concentration and independent of the prevailing rate of vegetative growth.

In a subsequent experiment, prothalli were exposed to a range of A_{An} concentrations at the 0-day stage, the 4-day, the 6-day, and the 11-day stages. The stages at which 7% of the prothalli had first attained the antheridial phase are recorded in Fig. 3, which discloses a startling aspect of antheridial development: In prothalli exposed to A_{An} at the 0-day stage (before or immediately after spore inoculation) the interval between the first appearance of antheridia at the highest concentration of A_{An} and the lowest one is 16 days. In contrast, the corresponding interval is 1 day, or less, if A_{An} is supplied at the 4-, 6-, or 11-day stages. With these intervals as a basis for comparison, the sensitivity of 0-day-old prothalli to differences in A_{An} concentration exceeds that of 4- to 11-day-old prothalli by a factor of at least 16.

In a subsequent experiment the numbers of vegetative cells were determined with which prothalli attain the antheridial phase when exposed at the 0-day stage and at the 11-day stage (Table 4). The results show that prothalli exposed at the 11-day stage attain the antheridial phase with nearly identical numbers of vegetative cells at all concentrations of A_{An}. In contrast, in prothalli exposed at the 0-day stage these numbers vary widely from 1.67 at the highest concentration to 60.1 at the lowest. These results reaffirm that prothalli exposed at the 0-day stage are much more sensitive to differences in A_{An} concentration than are prothalli exposed at a later stage.

With the exception of the highest A_{An} concentration, prothalli exposed at the 0-day stage attain the antheridial phase at a distinctly later stage of development than prothalli exposed at the 4-day stage (Fig. 3). This startling phenomenon led to the hypothesis that, in prothalli exposed at the 0-day stage, a physiological state antagonistic to antheridium formation

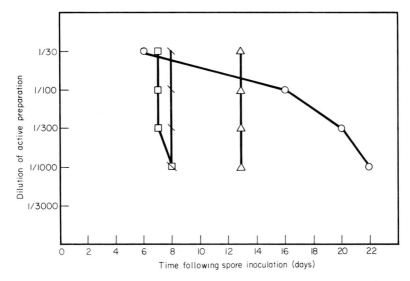

FIG. 3. Relation of A_{An} concentration to onset of antheridial phase in prothalli exposed to A_{An} at the 0-day, 4-day, 6-day, and the 11-day stages. ○, prothalli exposed to A_{An} at 0-day stage; □, at 4-day stage; ＼, at 6-day stage; △, at 11-day stage. Time after germination is plotted; at this time 7% of the prothalli have first attained the antheridial phase.

becomes operative. According to this hypothesis the antagonistic state is not an obligatory accompaniment of development but arises instead in response to a factor in the A_{An}-containing preparation. Inducibility of the antagonistic state largely decays before the prothallus attains the 4-day

TABLE 4

Number of Vegetative Cells with Which Prothalli Attain
Antheridial Phase When Exposed to Antheridiogen[a]

Anemia, medium dilution	Average number of vegetative cells in prothalli	
	Exposed to antheridogen from outset	Exposed to antheridogen at 11-day stage
1/30	1.67 ± 0.08	11.10 ± 0.66
1/100	2.93 ± 0.18	10.33 ± 0.50
1/300	35.10 ± 1.46	9.60 ± 0.56
1/1000	60.10 ± 1.75	9.93 ± 0.43
1/3000	—	9.03 ± 0.63

[a] Cell numbers were counted when a minimum of 1 out of 10 prothalli has first attained the antheridial phase. The numbers are averages of counts on 30 randomly chosen, antheridium-bearing prothalli.

stage but, once the state has been induced, its effect remains manifest beyond the stage at which it ceases to be inducible. The results of additional experiments (Table 5 in Näf, 1967a; Table 1 in Näf, 1967b) were interpreted to confirm this hypothesis. It was further shown that the physiological state antagonistic to antheridium formation is inducible at the spore stage only in the light (Näf, 1967a). A factor inducing the inhibitory state could not be chromatographically separated from A_{An} (Näf, 1967b). Thus the possibility must be considered that the inhibitory state is induced by A_{An}. Admittedly, it seems paradoxical that A_{An} should induce a physiological state antagonistic to antheridium formation at the spore stage and a physiological state promotive of antheridium formation at later stages.

In nature, germinating *Anemia* spores are probably exposed to A_{An} secreted into the substrate by maturing *Anemia* prothalli. With this in mind it might be conjectured that inducibility of a physiological state antagonistic to antheridium formation is functional in preventing the precocious attainment of the antheridial phase.

It should also be stressed that inducibility of the inhibitory state has largely decayed at the 4-day stage, 1 day after the very first spores have germinated. It is recalled in this connection that A_{An}, besides inducing antheridia, also appears to replace the light requirement for spore germination. Accordingly, inducibility of the inhibitory state might have an important regulatory function in germinating spores exposed to A_{An} that was secreted into the substrate by older prothalli. This function might consist in the prevention of hybrid metabolism, that is, the simultaneous occurrence of physiological states leading to germination and to antheridium formation.

Mode of Action of Antheridogen in *Onoclea sensibilis*

Wings excised from 16-day-old *Onoclea* prothalli formed antheridia without added antheridogen even though intact prothalli failed to form these sex organs at any stage of development under the prevailing conditions of culture. The early indication that the medium and the prothalli of 16-day-old *Onoclea* cultures contained a trace of antheridogen (Näf, 1961) was subsequently modified with the demonstration that this antheridium-inducing activity arose only on heating (Näf, 1965).

It seemed possible that the excised wings formed antheridia without the intervention of an antheridogen. In turn, this postulate led to the hypothesis that the antheridogen is functional in neutralizing a block to antheridium formation (Näf, 1961). The hypothesis is graphically illustrated in Fig. 4. It can be critically tested only with juvenile prothalli that are still at the sensitive phase.

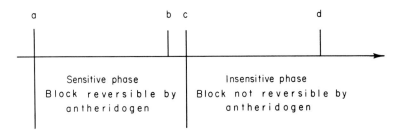

Fig. 4. Division of gametophyte development in *Onoclea* into a phase sensitive to A_{Pt} and a phase insensitive to it. *a*, Germination; *b*, attainment of heart shape; *c*, loss of sensitivity to A_{Pt}; *d*, attainment of archegonial phase.

Attempts to excise fragments from such tiny juvenile prothalli failed because most or all of the cells died. Temporary plasmolysis was chosen as an alternative technique. Plasmolysis, like the excision of the growing region, leads to regenerative growth and development (Isaburo-Nagai, 1914; Linsbauer, 1926), probably because it breaks the cytoplasmic connections between cells. Juvenile prothalli actually formed antheridia without added antheridogen on temporary plasmolysis with either mannite, calcium chloride, or sucrose (Näf, 1961). The original work was done with spores collected near Boston, Mass. Spores collected locally gave only a minimal antheridial response on plasmolysis or none at all (Näf, 1962a). However, spores obtained during 1966 and 1967 in Grassy Sprain, near New York, did give an excellent response. Probably the variability among spore samples reflects microclimatological rather than gross climatological differences. Perhaps the level of a blocking substance is lower in the well-responding strains or the reestablishment of the block following plasmolysis is more delayed. Such differences might also account for the fact that, among the several other species tested, only the juvenile prothalli of *Blechnum gibbum* formed antheridia on plasmolysis.

Most of the spontaneously formed antheridia arose in the anterior portion of the prothallus where regenerative cell division is diffuse. In the posterior region, cell division was orderly; it resulted in the formation of daughter prothalli. One or, more rarely, two antheridia could be observed to arise at the very base, and at the very earliest stage, in the regeneration of such daughter prothalli. None was formed thereafter. In contrast, in the presence of added A_{Pt}, the daughter prothalli did not stop forming antheridia until they had reached the developmental stage, at which prothalli grown from spores become insensitive to A_{Pt}. These observations are consistent with the postulate that the resumption of organized growth is followed promptly by the reestablishment of a block reversible by antheridogen and, at the normal stage, by the imposition of the block irreversible by antheridogen (Fig. 4).

Temporary plasmolysis at the 5-day stage led to the appearance of the first antheridium initials in 8-day-old prothalli. If these initials were to arise in response to antheridogen, the hormone would have had to be present at the $5\frac{1}{2}$-day stage (8 days minus the minimal lag period between the application of A_{Pt} and the appearance of the initials). If antheridogen were available to prothalli of this age in the normal sequence of events, then at least some of the individuals in a culture of (nonplasmolyzed) *Onoclea* prothalli should form antheridia, because all were then still sensitive to antheridogen. As repeatedly stressed, nonplasmolyzed gametophytes fail to form these sex organs at any stage of development. It seemed possible that plasmolysis hastened the onset of antheridogen synthesis. Regrettably, a sufficient amount of extract could not be obtained from these tiny prothalli. However, young (nonplasmolyzed) *Onoclea* prothalli failed to form antheridia if they were inoculated among temporarily plasmolyzed antheridium-forming prothalli of this species. In contrast, nonplasmolyzed *Onoclea* prothalli formed antheridia abundantly if they were inoculated among antheridium-forming prothalli of *P. aquilinum*. Clearly, the results are consistent with the postulate that plasmolyzed *Onoclea* prothalli form antheridia without the intervention of antheridogen, and with the hypothesis that the antheridogen is functional in neutralizing a block to antheridium formation. However, it was stressed that "it is difficult to demonstrate unequivocally that a developmental event can, under special conditions, take place without the intervention of the substance which normally controls this event" (Näf, 1962a). Döpp (1962) thought that the antheridogen was a sine qua non for antheridium formation.

Finally, Döpp's finding (1962), that prothalli of *D. filix-mas* formed antheridia on exposure to middle portions but not to excised wings of *Pteridium* prothalli, may be mentioned.

Investigations of the light control of antheridium formation in *Polypodium crassifolium* are also pertinent (Schraudolf, 1967c). The spore of this species is capable of dark germination; it gives rise directly to an antheridium in darkness but not in light. Control by phytochrome was indicated because these sex organs were formed also in the near red but not in red or white light. Antheridogen could not be detected while the spore cells gave rise to antheridia in darkness. Schraudolf suggested that the near red and darkness induce antheridia without the intervention of an antheridogen. Under natural conditions this species might also form antheridia without the intervention of an antheridogen in response to a particular regime of light and darkness. Alternatively, the prothalli do synthesize an antheridogen which functions by neutralizing a light-dependent block to antheridium formation.

Onoclea prothalli also formed antheridia without added antheridogen if they were transferred at the 7-day stage to near-darkness on medium supplemented with sucrose. The first antheridial prothalli were seen approximately 15 days after exposure to near darkness. Exposure to A_{Pt} hastened the onset of antheridium formation. The lag between the application of A_{Pt} and the appearance of antheridia was distinctly shorter if the antheridogen was applied 10 days after dark exposure instead of at the beginning. Perhaps a light-dependent block to antheridium formation decays in darkness (Näf, Cummins, and Sullivan, unpublished data).

Antheridogen Action and Retrieval of Genetic Information

Schraudolf (1967b) applied inhibitors of DNA duplication, DNA transcription to mRNA, and of mRNA translation to protein to learn whether GA_3 retrieves genetic information as it induces antheridia in *A. phyllitidis*.

As mentioned, this author demonstrated that prothalli exposed to gibberellic acid at the spore stage form antheridia at a developmental stage that is characteristic of the applied concentration. He expressed this characteristic stage as the number of vegetative cells formed before the onset of the antheridial phase. The number was not dependent on the prevailing rate of prothallial growth (Schraudolf, 1966a).

Most of the applied inhibitors delayed the appearance of antheridium initials. Using "the characteristic number of vegetative cells" as a criterion, he was able to conclude that this delay was due not to a specific inhibition of antheridium formation but solely to inhibited vegetative growth. His results show that delayed onset of a complex developmental event is not a sufficient criterion for the conclusion that the applied substance inhibits the event specifically. The results suggested to Schraudolf that the formation of the antheridium initial may not involve a retrieval of genetic information from DNA.

The differentiation of the antheridium initial (a semicircular outgrowth of a vegetative cell) into the mature antheridium involves 3 cell divisions with characteristic orientation of cell plates. The central cell gives rise to 8 sperm cells in *A. phyllitidis*. Whereas the inhibitors failed to interfere specifically with the formation of initials, the differentiation of these initials to the mature antheridium was drastically modified in some cases. Various teratological effects were seen. Thus the application of 5-bromo-deoxyuridine and 5-iododeoxyuridine resulted in a spectrum of all transitional stages between normal 4-celled antheridia and 3-celled vegetative lobes. These inhibitors were shown to be incorporated into the DNA of bacteria and mammals (Brockman and Anderson, 1963). Isoadenine causes reductions in the amount of spermatogenous tissue. It inhibits primarily the synthesis of purines (Booth and Sartorelli, 1961). Its incorporation into nucleic acids has also been observed (Bennett *et al.*, 1962). The results indicated to Schraudolf that the differentiation of the antheridium initial may require a retrieval of information from DNA.

REFERENCES

Bauke, H. (1878). Beiträge zur Keimungsgeschichte der Schizaeaceen. *Jahrb. Wiss. Botan.* **11,** 603–650.

Bennett, L. L., Smithers, D., Teague, C., Baker, H. T., and Sutts, P. (1962). Some effects of 4-amino-pyrazolo-(3,4-*d*)-pyrimidine on purine metabolism. *Biochem. Pharmacol.* **11,** 81–92.

Booth, B. A., and Sartorelli, A. C. (1961). 4-Amino-pyrazolo-(3,4-*d*)-pyrimidine: An inhibitor of the synthesis of purines and proteins in Ehrlich ascites cells. *J. Biol. Chem.* **236,** 203–206.

Brockman, R. W., and Anderson, E. P. (1963). Pyrimidine analogues. *In* "Metabolic Inhibitors" (R. M. Hochster and J. H. Quastel, eds.), pp. 239–285. Academic Press, New York.

Czaja, A. T. (1921). Über Befruchtung, Bastardierung und Geschlechtertrennung bei *Prothallien homosporer* Farne. *Z. Botan.* **13,** 545–589.

Döpp, W. (1959). Über eine hemmende und eine fördernde Substanz bei der Antheridien-Prothallien von *Pteridium aquilinum* (L.) Kuhn. *Ber. Deut. Botan. Ges.* **63,** 139–147.

Döpp, W. (1959). Über ene hemmende und eine fördernde Substanz bei der Antheridien-bildung in den Prothallien von *Pteridium aquilinum. Ber. Deut. Botan. Ges.* **72,** 11–24.

Döpp, W. (1962). Weitere Untersuchungen über die Physiologie der Antheridienbildung bei Pteridium aquilinum. *Planta* **58,** 483–508.

Isaburo, Nagai (1914). Physiologische Untersuchungen über Farnprothallien. *Flora N.F.* **6,** 281–330.

Kende, H., and Lang, A. (1964). Gibberellins and light inhibition of stem growth in peas. *Plant Physiol.* **39,** 435–440.

Linsbauer, K. (1926). Über Regeneration der Farnprothallien und die Frage der Teilungs-stoffe. *Biol. Zentr.* **46,** 80.

Näf, Ulrich (1956). The demonstration of a factor concerned with the initiation of antheridia in polypodiaceous ferns. *Growth* **20,** 91–105.

Näf, Ulrich (1958). On the physiology of antheridium formation in the bracken fern *Pteridium aquilinum* (L) Kuhn. *Physiol. Plantarum* **11**, 728–746.

Näf, Ulrich (1959). Control of antheridium formation in the fern species *Anemia phyllitidis*. *Nature* 184, 798–800.

Näf, Ulrich (1960). On the control of antheridium formation in the fern species *Lygodium japonicum. Proc. Soc. Exptl. Biol. Med.* **105**, 82–86.

Näf, Ulrich (1961). Mode of action of an antheridium-inducing substance in ferns. *Nature* **189**, 900–903.

Näf, Ulrich (1962a). Antheridium formation in ferns—A model for the study of developmental change. *J. Linnean Soc. (Botan.)* **58**, 321–331.

Näf, Ulrich (1962b). Development physiology of Lower Archegoniates. *Ann. Rev. Plant Physiol.* **13**, 507–532.

Näf, Ulrich (1962c). Loss of sensitivity to the antheridial factor in maturing gametophytes of the fern *Onoclea sensibilis. Phyton* **18**(2), 173–182.

Näf, Ulrich (1965). On antheridial metabolism in the fern species *Onoclea sensibilis* L. *Plant Physiol.* **40**, 888–890.

Näf, Ulrich (1966). On dark-germination and antheridium formation in *Anemia phyllitidis. Physiol. Plantarum* **19**, 1079–1088.

Näf, Ulrich (1967a). On the induction of a phase inhibitory to antheridium formation in the juvenile prothallus of the fern species *Anemia phyllitidis. Z. Pflanzenphysiol.* **56**, 353–365.

Näf, Ulrich (1967b). *Anemia phyllitidis:* Inducibility of physiological state antagonistic to antheridium formation. *Science* **156**, 1117–1119.

Näf, Ulrich (1968). On separation and identity of fern antheridogens. *Plant Cell Physiol.* **9**, 27–33.

Pringle, R. B. (1961). Chemical nature of antheridogen-A, a specific inducer of the male sex organ in certain fern species. *Science* **133**, 284.

Pringle, R. B., Näf, U., and Braun, A. C. (1960). Purification of a specific inducer of the male sex organ in certain fern species. *Nature* **186**, 1066–1067.

Schraudolf, H. (1962). Die Wirkung von Phytohormonen auf Keimung und Entwicklung von Farnprothallien. I. Auslösung der Antheridienbildung und Dunkelkeimung bei Schizaeaceen durch Gibberellinsäure. *Biol. Zentr.* **81**, 731–740.

Schraudolf, H. (1964). Relative activity of the gibberellins in the antheridium induction in Anemia phyllitidis. *Nature* **201**, 98–99.

Schraudolf, H. (1965). Einfluss von DNS-, RNS- und Proteinantimetaboliten auf die Antheridienbildung in Farnen. *Ber. Deut. Botan. Ges.* **78**, 73–75.

Schraudolf, H. (1966a). Die Wirkung von Phytohormonen auf Keimung und Entwicklung von Farnprothallien. II. Analyse der Wechselbeziehung zwischen Gibberellin-Konzentration. Antheridienbildung und physiologischem Alter der Prothallium Zellen in *Anemia phyllitidis. Planta* **68**, 335–352.

Schraudolf, H. (1966b). Die Wirkung von Phytohormonen auf Keimung und Entwicklung von Farnprothallien. III. Einfluss von Plasmolyse und Exstirpation auf die Auslösung der Antheridienbildung durch Gibberelline bei *Anemia phyllitidis* L. *Biol. Zentr.* **85**, 349–360.

Scharudolf, H. (1966c). Die Wirkung von Phytohormonen auf Keimung und Entwicklung von Farnprothallien IV. Die Wirkung von unterschiedlichen Gibberellinen und von Allogibberinsäure auf die Auslösung der Antheridien bildung bei *Anemia phyllitidis* L. und einigen Polypodiaceen. *Plant Cell Physiol.* **7**, 277–289.

Schraudolf, H. (1967a). Wirkung von Terpenderivaten (Helminthosporol, Helmintho-
sporsäure, Dihydrohelminthosporsäure und Steviol) auf die Antheridienbildung in
Anemia phyllitidis. Planta **74,** 188–193.

Schraudolf, H. (1967b). Wirkung von Hemmstoffen der DNS, RNS- und Proteinsynthese
auf Wachstum und Antheridienbildung in Prothallien von *Anemia phyllitidis* L. *Planta*
74, 123–147.

Schraudolf, H. (1967c). Die Steuerung der Antheridienbildung in *Polypodium crassifolium*
L. durch Licht. *Planta* **76,** 37–46.

Tamura, S., Sakurai, A., Kainuma, K., and Takai, M. (1963). Isolation of helminthosporol
as a natural growth regulator and its chemical structure. *Agr. Biol. Chem. (Tokyo)* **27,**
738–739.

Voeller, B. (1964a). Antheridiogens in ferns. – Régulateurs naturels de la croissance végétale, pp. 665–684. Gif s/Yvette, Paris.

Voeller, B. (1964b). Gibberellins: Their effect on antheridium formation in fern gametophytes. *Science* **143,** 373–375.

Witsch, H. von, and Rintelen, J. (1962). Die Entwicklung von Farnprothallien unter Gibber-
ellineinfluss. *Planta* **59,** 115–118.

Apospory in the Hepaticae

Edwin B. Matzke and Livija Raudzēns

Thus far, reports of apospory, apogamy, and parthenogenesis are far more numerous in other groups of plants than in the Hepaticae.

Apospory may be defined as the development of a gametophyte directly from the vegetative cells of the sporophyte, without the intervention of meiospores. Apogamy is the development of a sporophyte directly from the vegetative cells of the gametophyte, without the intervention of gametes and fertilization. Parthenogenesis is the development of an unfertilized egg into an embryo or sporophyte. Neither apogamy nor parthenogenesis has been described in the Hepaticae

Apospory and apogamy were unknown in the days of John Torrey. However, they were discovered a short time later, apogamy in a fern by Farlow in 1874, and apospory in mosses by Pringsheim and by Stahl in 1876. Subsequently, there were numerous accounts of apospory in the mosses by Correns, Marchal and Marchal, Wettstein, and other workers.

The literature on apospory in liverworts, by contrast, is quite limited. Schwarzenbach (1926) succeeded in obtaining one presumably diploid, mature, aposporous gametophyte of *Anthoceros,* while Burgeff (1937, 1943) induced apospory in a number of species of *Marchantia*. Working with *Anthoceros,* Lang (1901), Bornhagen (1926), and Rink (1935) described aposporus outgrowths, but not mature plants. Attempts at apospory in genera other than *Anthoceros* and *Marchantia* have previously failed.

To gain greater insight into the nature of apospory in the Hepaticae, a program was designed in the Laboratory of Experimental Plant Morphology at Columbia University to apply modern cultural techniques to the study of this problem.

In the initial stages of this work, *Blasia pusilla* L. proved to be experimentally suitable, since it could be grown readily in aseptic culture. Furthermore, in a previous study of elongation of excised setae of *B. pusilla,* the presence of minute, green areas in otherwise degenerating tissue had been noted by Dr. Yvonne N. Morris and the authors.

Plants of *B. pusilla* with developing sporophytes were collected in the field. Excised setae, either with or without the foot and developing capsule, were placed on modified Knop agar supplemented with microelements. The cultures were incubated in microphytotrons (Matzke, 1964) under a daily cycle of 12 hrs of low-intensity illumination at 19°C, followed by 12 hrs of darkness at 16°C.

After 3 ½ to 6 weeks in culture, the initial stages of apospory became apparent, usually as small, green, cell masses. They subsequently grew into small, characteristic *Blasia* gametophytes. From 1 to more than 20 young gametophytes appeared on individual setae. The tips of the aposporous plants were then removed, sterilized, and cultured aseptically on nutrient-agar to which 1% glucose had been added. After 2 to 3 months the tips developed into diploid gametophytes which were similar in growth pattern, rate of growth, and general vegetative characteristics to haploid plants. They produced archegonia, but no antheridia, although under similar growth conditions male haploid plants formed antheridia in abundance. The diploids had 18 chromosomes in contrast to the haploid number of 9 chromosomes. Apospory occurred in 179 setae. In every case the aposporous outgrowths developed into mature diploid gametophytes. Thus this was not an isolated phenomenon.

Subsequently to the work on *B. pusilla,* similar results have been obtained with *Pellia epiphylla* (L.) Corda and *Pallavicinia Lyellii* (Hook.) Gray. Likewise, Simone (1966), working in this laboratory, has induced apospory in the following genera and species of the Jungermanniaceae: *Lophocolea heterophylla* (Schrad.) Dum., *Radula complanata* (L.) Dum., *Scapania nemorosa* (L.) Dum., *Nowellia curvifolia* (Dicks.) Mitt., *Ptilidium pulcherrimum* (Web.) Hampe, *Jungermannia lanceolata* Schrad., and *Porella pinnata* L. In some instances the diploids of these plants did not grow so vigorously as the haploids. In *B. pusila,* on the other hand, the growth of diploids was similar to that of haploids.

That vegetative cells of sporophytes can give rise directly to diploid plants which are gametophytic in nature, tends to emphasize the fundamental similarity of the normally alternating generations.

REFERENCES

Bornhagen, H. (1926). Die Regeneration (Aposporie) des Sporophyten von *Anthoceros laevis. Biol. Zentr.* **46,** 578–586.

Burgeff, H. (1937). Über Polyploidie bei *Marchantia. Z. indukt. Abstamm. -u. Vererb-Lehre,* **73,** 394–403.

Burgeff, H. (1943). "Genetische Studien an *Marchantia."* Gustav Fischer, Jena.

Lang, W. H. (1901). On apospory in *Anthoceros laevis. Ann. Botany* **15,** 503–510.

Matzke, E. B. (1964). The aseptic culture of liverworts in microphytotrons. *Bryologist* **67,** 136–141.

Rink, W. (1935). Zur Entwicklungsgeschichte, Physiologie und Genetik der Lebermoos-gattungen *Anthoceros* und *Aspiromitus. Flora (Jena)* **130,** 87–130.

Schwarzenbach, Marthe (1926). Regeneration und Aposporie bei *Anthoceros. Arch. Julius Klaus-Stift.* Vererbungsforsch. **2,** 91–141.

Simone, L. D. (1966). Induction of apospory in seven genera of leafy hepatics. *Am. J. Botany (Abstr.)* **53,** 609.

Toward an Experimental Approach to the Systematics and Phylogeny of Leafy Liverworts

Dominick V. Basile

Mature gametophytes of leafy liverworts exhibit a truly remarkable range of form. The diversity of their leaf morphology may even rival that of the Anthophyta (Schuster, 1966, p. 475). An abundance of easily distinguishable morphological features and the apparent paucity of other reliable taxonomic criteria have contributed to the great dependence of the identification, classification, and arrangement of taxa of leafy liverworts into phylogenetic sequences on the morphology of the gametophytes. This, however, has led to some uncertainty and disagreement among students of the group. There are probably numerous reasons for uncertainty and disagreement, among which are the following:

1. The amount of detailed morphological data on which conclusions may be based is exceedingly limited. Some time ago Fulford (1948) had estimated that only 5% of the leafy liverworts had been fully investigated morphologically.

2. The same morphological data can be interpreted to support conflicting, yet logical, hypotheses. Conflicting hypotheses are rarely resolved by presenting crucial evidence or performing crucial experiments.

3. And, most importantly, there may be considerable plasticity in vegetative characteristics of gametophytes in response to different environmental conditions.

The last point is stressed because, as Schuster (1966, p. 312) put it, "The exceptionally broad range of 'somatic' adaptability has been one of the chief causes for the extreme difficulty in developing a balanced species concept for the Hepaticae." He (1966, p. 316) further states that "With even the most refined standard techniques, however, identification and circumspection of species still represent a process of theorizing *a posteriori*. Circumspection of the species is still based on static circumstantial evidence."

Over forty years ago Hans Buch (1922) clearly demonstrated that relatively small changes in the physical environment could induce morphological changes in aseptically cultured *Scapania* gametophytes which amounted to species differences. Buch's work showed particularly well the systematic importance of knowing the precise ecological conditions under which species grow and of experimentally determining the range of phenotype that may be expressed by a given genotype. In spite of this, few attempts have been made to determine experimentally the interaction of exogenous and endogenous factors on taxonomic characteristics in the leafy liverworts. Systematic conclusions are still often based on "circumstantial evidence" and "theorizing *a posteriori*."

Research in our laboratory has not been directed toward solving problens in liverwort taxonomy. Rather, we have been interested primarily in metabolic control of differentiation and morphogenesis in the leafy liverworts. Nevertheless, to the extent that the systematics of this group is based on gametophyte morphology, an experimental investigation of factors controlling their morphogenesis becomes *an experimental approach to the systematics and phylogeny of leafy liverworts.*

The following material discusses three aspects of gametophytic morphology: symmetry, branching, and leaf form, which we are investigating from the standpoint of morphogenesis; however, it emphasizes the relevance of our morphogenetical studies to liverwort systematics.

All our experiments have been conducted with the very common and widely distributed *Scapania nemorosa,* typical development of which is shown in Fig. 1.

Pattern of Development

In its general features the life cycle of *S. nemorosa* is characteristic of the majority of leafy liverworts. Particularly striking are the similarities in the pattern of germination and early development between *Scapania* and the members of most families of liverworts studied in this regard. Either the *Nardia* (cell mass) type shown in Fig. 1 or the *Cephalozia* (filamentous) type pattern (Fig. 15) is characteristic of most, if not all, families of Jungermanniales included in the suborders, Herbertinae, Ptilidiinae, and Jungermanniinae (Schuster, 1966). Both of these patterns of development may be exhibited by species of *Scapania.* In contrast, the morphology of the adult gametophyte is very distinctive. *Scapania* is representative of the only family (Scapaniaceae) of leafy liverworts with two rows of succubously complicate-bilobed lateral leaves and no trace of ventral leaves. The complete lack of a third row of leaves and the orientation of the lateral leaves results in the pronounced dorsiventral

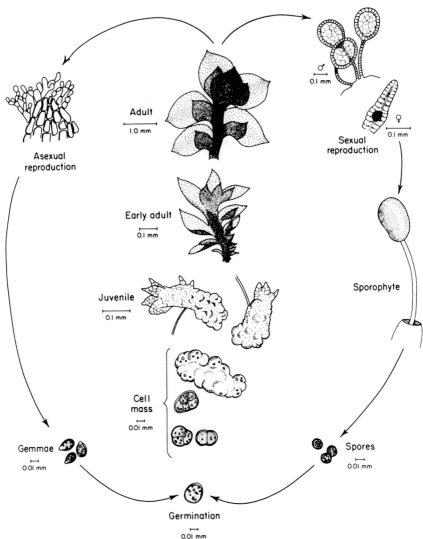

Fig. 1. Ontogeny of *Scapania nemorosa* (L.) Dum. Starting with either a spore or a uni-cellular gemma, development proceeds through a number of distinct stages. After germina-tion intercalary cell division in three planes gives rise to a globose-to-cylindrical multi-cellular protonema. Differentiation of a tetrahedral apical cell in the protonema initiates development of the leafy shoot. Early shoot development is characterized by formation of plane bifid leaves (juvenile leaves). The juvenile stages of the great majority of north temperate species of leafy liverworts are virtually indistinguishable. Gradual transition in the form of the leaves from the juvenile type to the characteristic adult type marks the early adult stage. Adult gametophytes bear two rows of complicate-bilobed lateral leaves and no ventral leaves. Unicellular gemmae produced in branching chains may develop at the shoot apex or from the margins of upper leaves. Antheridia and archegonia are formed on separate plants. Sex organs have not developed in our cultures yet.

symmetry of the gametophytes. An understanding of gametophytic symmetry is essential to modern liverwort systematics.

Symmetry

There are numerous phylogenetic systems of classification of the Hepaticae. These systems, however, fall under either of two conceptual schemes which pivot on the interpretation of symmetry. According to one scheme, bilateral symmetry is considered primitive in the Hepaticae. Evolution of the gametophyte is thus believed to have proceeded from bilaterally symmetrical thallose types through bilateral leafy types and to culminate with radially symmetrical leafy types. In the other scheme, the direction of evolution is believed to be exactly opposite with radially symmetrical leafy gametophytes representing the primitive condition.

The morphological basis for symmetry derives from the nature of the apical cell. In all leafy liverworts (exclusive of the Pleuroziaceae) the tissues of a leafy shoot originate from a single tetrahedral apical cell with three cutting faces (Fig. 2A). Segments are cut from each face in a regular sequence, although not necessarily the one shown here. If the segments (Fig. 2B) developed equally, each would give rise to a leaf of equal size and shape as well as equal portions of stem tissue. This would result in perfect triradial symmetry (Fig. 2C-D), which is found in relatively few species. If one of the segments were smaller, or if it developed less vigorously than the other two, or both, then bilateral and dorsiventral symmetry would result. Most species of leafy liverworts have a prostrate growth habit, and the segments of the apical cell closest to the substratum give rise to ventral leaves which are smaller, or are shaped differently from the lateral leaves, or both. Depending on the degree of development of the ventral segment, the symmetry of these species ranges between strict radial and strict dorsiventral. In *Scapania* the ventral segment is greatly reduced and fails to give rise to any trace of ventral leaves. Contingent on whether one conceives phylogeny in the leafy liverworts to progress from dorsiventral forms to triradially symmetrical forms or the reverse, *Scapania* would represent either a primitive type or a derived type, respectively. This is an example of how the comparative morphology of leafy liverworts may be interpreted to support either viewpoint.

Recent experimental evidence, however, strongly supports the thesis that the pronounced dorsiventral symmetry in *S. nemorosa* is a derived condition (Basile, 1967). In response to treatment with the protein amino acid hydroxy-L-proline, profound departures from the normally dorsiventral symmetry (Fig. 3) of *S. nemorosa* were induced in developing

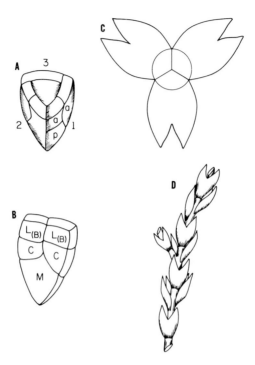

Fig. 2. Apical development and symmetry. A, Apical cell with three segments cut off in numerical order; Each new segment (cell) divides further to form first two (segment 2) then three (segment 1) cells; the two anterior cells (*a*) may divide again to form 4 cells which, with the posterior one, constitutes a 5-celled merophyte. B, Five-celled merophyte with fates of each cell indicated: M, medulla initial; C, cortex initials; L, leaf initials; (B) branch initials may differentiate from one of a pair of leaf initials. C, D, Diagrammatic representations of triradial symmetry (*C,* shoot-sector with one cycle of leaves; *D,* portion of a leafy shoot).

gametophytes. Indeed, phenovariants ran the whole range from nearly perfect triradial symmetry (i.e., three rows of isomorphic leaves), through numerous intermediate conditions (Figs. 4–6), to pronounced dorsiventral symmetry typical of *Scapania*. Changes in symmetry resulted from the formation of a third row of leaves, ventrally, and modifications in the size, shape, and arrangement of lateral leaves. The presence or absence of ventral leaves and the morphology of both lateral and ventral leaves are also important criteria for identifying and classifying leafy liverworts. This aspect of hydroxyproline-induced phenovariation and its relevance to experimental systematics are discussed later. Here the phylogenetic significance is stressed. *S. nemorosa* has been induced to form a third row of leaves without causing any permanent change in the genome.

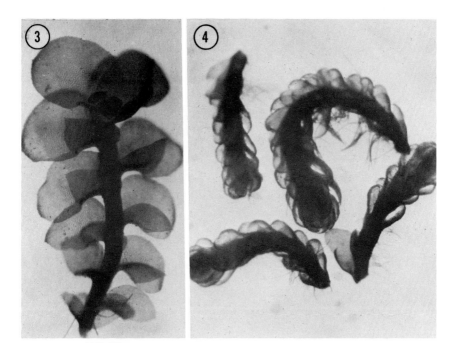

FIG. 3 TO 6. Variation in symmetry of *S. nemorosa*. FIG. 3. Portion of leafy shoot from control culture showing characteristic dorsiventral symmetry. Fig. 4. Phenovariants exhibiting bilateral symmetry due to concave-bilobed lateral leaves and entire ventral leaves. Fig. 5. Phenovariant showing bilateral symmetry but tending toward dorsiventral symmetry apically. Fig. 6. Phenovariant showing bilateral symmetry along basal third and dorsiventral symmetry along upper two-thirds of axis. (See following page.)

When the modified gametophytes were allowed sufficient time to develop subsequent to treatment with hydroxyproline, they reverted to the formation of two rows of complicate-bilobed leaves (Figs. 5, 6). These findings clearly show that it is within the genetic capacity of *S. nemorosa* to form three rows of leaves. A mutation was not induced, but a latent genetic capacity was expressed. It is therefore highly probable that the two-leaved condition presently characteristic of *Scapania* is derived from a more primitive three-leaved one. Similar experiments should determine whether this is generally true for leafy liverworts.

Branching

Another aspect of gametophytic morphology which has taken on considerable systematic and phylogenetic significance in recent years is the

FIGS. 5 and 6.

pattern of branching (Fulford, 1965; Schuster, 1966). Contemporary interpretations of branching patterns are based on the proposition that triradial symmetry represents the primitive condition in leafy liverworts. It would follow that, in primitive gametophytes, branches would have the same symmetrical distribution as leaves. Correlated with changes in symmetry which made dorsal, ventral, and lateral portions distinguishable there appear to have evolved varying degrees of specialization and restrictions in branching. The most common types of branching are shown in Fig. 7. According to Schuster (1966, p. 469), the modes of branching shown in Fig. 7, A, E occurred in the primitive leafy liverworts (i.e., exogenous, *terminal branching* from any one of the paired leaf primordia; and endogenous, *Intercalary branching* from the axils of any or all rows of leaves). In his view, a "*lack* of sharp localization of branching, and *lack* of restriction to either terminal or intercalary branching, *is a primitive trait.*" While "a sharp restriction in type (terminal vs intercalary) and localization of branching modes *represents a specialization of phylogenetic significance*" (Schuster, 1966, p. 469).

In view of the foregoing, the characteristic mode of branching in *Scapania* "represents a specialization of phylogenetic significance." For, supposedly, in the Scapaniaceae "*only* lateral intercalary branching

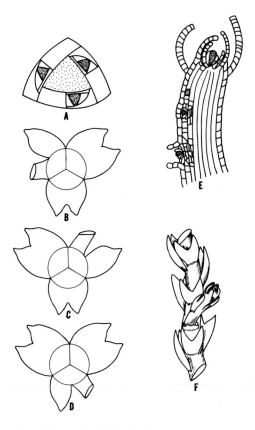

FIG. 7. Common branching modes in leafy liverworts. A–D, Terminal branching. A, Diagram of a face view of an apical cell (stippled) with three segments cut off. One of each pair of leaf initials has become transformed through a number of divisions into a branch initial. Potentially, any leaf initial may become transformed into a branch initial. B–D, Relative positions of branches in dorsiventral stems. Smaller leaves directed toward the bottom of the figure are ventral leaves, and larger leaves are lateral leaves. B, Branch developed from a ventral initial of a lateral segment and therefore replacing lower portion of the lateral leaf. This is the most common mode of terminal branching. C, Branch developed from a dorsal initial of a lateral segment. This is an uncommon type of branching. D, Branch developed from one of the leaf initials of a ventral segment. This type is of restricted occurrence. E, F, Intercalary branching. E, Diagram to show internal origin of branch. At lower left the developing branch is shown to have ruptured cortical tissue. The latter will form a sheath or collar around the base of the branch. F, Diagram to show intercalary branch arising from ventral portion of stem. Note basal collar.

is found, and generally the ability to develop terminal branches has been lost (except in the primitive genus *Blepharidophyllum*)" (Schuster, 1966, p. 470). As it turns out, the ability of *Scapania nemorosa* to develop terminal branches has not been lost at all. In the same series of experiments which revealed that *S. nemorosa* was still capable of developing three rows of leaves and displaying a wide range in symmetry, it was found that this liverwort was capable of a variety of branching modes. Endogenous branching occurred not only in axils of lateral leaves (Fig. 9) but also infra-axilary (Fig. 11) and ventrally (Fig. 12). In addition to the type of terminal branching which replaces one of a pair of leaf primordia (Fig. 8), rather specialized types of exogenous branching occurred (Figs. 10, 13, and 14). In fact, most types of branching known to occur in leafy liverworts have been induced to develop in *Scapania* simply by adding low concentrations of hydroxyproline to the culture medium.

Since the changes in branching mode, like the changes in symmetry, were not permanent, it is assumed that *S. nemorosa* had retained rather than obtained the genetic capacity to form these kinds of branches. This

FIGS. 8 TO 11. Induced branching modes in *Scapania nemorosa*. Fig. 8. Phenovariant exhibiting terminal branching; branch replaces the ventral portion of a lateral leaf. Fig. 9. Plant showing lateral intercalary branching from leaf axil; this type is characteristic of the Scapaniaceae; arrow indicates basal collar of cortical tissue. Fig. 10. Phenovariant showing terminal branching which is either dichotomous or pseudodichotomous; dichotomous branching supposedly does not occur in leafy liverworts. Fig. 11. Phenovariant with both (*a*) axillary and (*i*) infra-axillary intercalary branches; infra-axillary branches are not typical for *Scapania*. (See following page.)

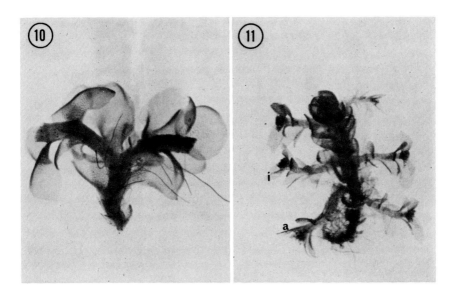

finding provides strong support for the hypothesis that restricted localized branching is derived from less restricted, unlocalized branching.

On the other hand, these results raise some questions about the reliability of present taxonomic conclusions based on branching.

Leaves

With reference to the subject of leaf morphology, it was mentioned earlier that the changes in symmetry that occurred in response to hydroxyproline treatment were due to the formation of three rows of leaves rather than two, and to changes in the form and arrangement of lateral leaves. In addition to the phylogenetic implications of these changes, there are important taxonomic ones, the most profound of which stems from the induced formation of ventral leaves.

Had these experimentally induced phenovariants been encountered in nature, they would not be included in the genus *Scapania or the family* Scapaniaceae. The presence of a third row of leaves, even though the lateral leaves were characteristic of the Scapaniaceae, would, according to modern schemes, suffice to exclude such phenovariants from this family. It so happened that ventral leaves developed in combination with a variety of forms of lateral leaves. The presence or absence of ventral leaves and specific differences in size, shape, and arrangement of leaves are important criteria for distinguishing taxa.

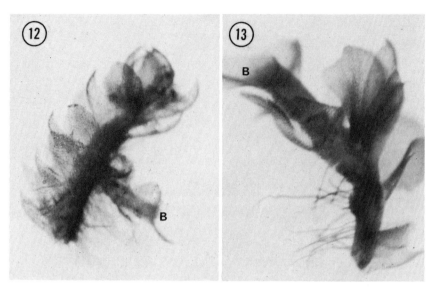

FIGS. 12 TO 14. Induced branching modes in *Scapania nemorosa*. Fig. 12. Ventral inter-calary branch (*B*). Fig. 13. Ventral terminal branch (*B*) arising just below a terminal cluster of leaves on the main axis; no half leaf is evident. Fig. 14. Two terminal (exogenous) branches (*B*) issuing laterally just below a terminal cluster of leaves in main axis. The mode of branching shown here and in Fig. 13 is reminiscent of subfloral inovation, but no sex organs are present in these cases.

It would be impossible to illustrate the almost infinite variety of size, shape, and arrangement of leaves exhibited by the leafy liverworts; it would be difficult to illustrate the permutations of shape, size, and arrangement of leaves which occurred in *S. nemorosa* in response to hydroxyproline treatment; and it would be undesirable at this time to attempt specific comparisons between the induced phenovariants and known taxa. Much more would be gained by making a few generalizations.

Despite their great number of specific differences, leaves of leafy liverworts share many basic similarities. Leaves originate at the stem apex from a 2-celled primordium and are therefore fundamentally bipartite (Fig. 2B). The bipartite nature is clearly manifest in the bilobed juvenile leaves and, in many cases, in the adult leaves of the numerous taxa having the same patterns of early development as *Scapania*. In others, the bilobed condition evident in the juvenile leaf is modified or obscured during the development of the adult leaf. Still, as Fig. 15 attempts to show, the basic leaf forms found in the majority of taxa of leafy liverworts may be derived from the bilobed condition. Similarly, for all their specific differences, the leaves of the majority of species may be seen as variations of these five general forms.

The adult leaves of the Scapaniaceae are characteristically complicate-bilobed. *S. nemorosa* is no exception. Yet, in response to the addition of hydroxyproline to the culture medium, *S. nemorosa* developed four of the five general types (Fig. 15). Truly filamentous leaves have not been observed to form, although margins of some leaves were much dissected.

The ability of *S. nemorosa* to develop these general forms with numerous variations indicates its great potential for phenocopying other species within and outside of the Scapaniaceae.

Summary and Conclusion

The introductory remarks implied that the experimental determination of factors which influence and control morphogenesis in leafy liverworts might remove some of the bases for uncertainty and disagreement regarding their phylogeny and systematics. Our experiments with *Scapania nemorosa* strongly support this thesis in three ways:

1. They have provided strong support for the hypothesis that radially erect, freely branching gametophytes represent the primitive condition in the leafy liverworts. An extension of this line of investigation to other taxa could provide the crucial evidence needed to decide whether dorsiventral or triradial symmetry constitutes the archaic condition in this group.

2. They have added considerable emphasis to Buch's pioneering work in experimental systematics. Buch clearly demonstrated that changes in the physical environment (i.e., light intensity and relative moisture) could result in phenotypic variation amounting to species differences. My experiments differ in that the phenotypic changes resulted from an

alteration of the *chemical environment* and in that *phenotypic variation exceeded genus and even family limits.* The systematic value of finding out more about both the physical and biogeochemical environment of leafy liverworts and experimentally investigating the effects of environmental parameters on phenotypic expression is clearly indicated.

3. Most important, our experiments with *Scapania* open up a completely new experimental approach to the systematics of the leafy liverworts. All the remarkable changes in symmetry, branching patterns and leaf form and arrangement occurred in responses to a single chemical compound, a protein amino acid. It should be possible to discover how

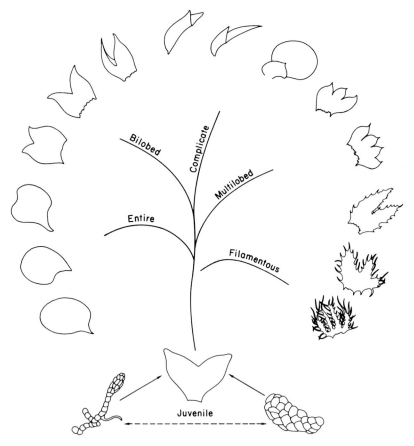

Fig. 15. Basic adult leaf forms of taxa developing *Cephalozia* (filamentous) and/or *Nardia* (cell mass) type protonemata and plane, bifid juvenile leaves. Besides the five basic forms, some transitional forms are indicated. All forms shown, exclusive of filamentous, have been induced to form in phenovariants of *Scapania nemorosa.*

this substance acts and thereby begin to explain in chemical terms the changes in morphology that serve to distinguish taxa of leafy liverworts.

REFERENCES

Basile, D. V. (1967). The influences of hydroxy-L-proline on ontogeny and morphogenesis of the liverwort, *Scapania nemorosa. Am. J. Botany* **54,** 977–983.
Buch, H. (1922). Die Scapanien Nordeuropas und Sibiriens — I. *Soc. Sci. Fennica, Commentationes Biol.* **1,** 1–21.
Fulford, M. (1948). Recent interpretations of the relationships of the Hepaticae. *Botan. Rev.* **14,** 127–173.
Fulford, M. (1965). Evolutionary trends and convergence in the Hepaticae. *Bryologist* **68,** 1–31.
Schuster, R. M. (1966). "The Hepaticae and Anthocerotae of North America," pp. 1–802. New York.

A New Look at Evolution and Phylogeny in Bryophytes

William C. Steere

New Thoughts on Old Theories of Alternation of Generations

Probably no major botanical concept has stirred up more debate, speculation, and polemic than that of alternation of generations, as first proposed by Hofmeister well over a century ago (1851, 1862).

The two major theories of alternation of generations "just grew" through the decades after their elucidation and are now therefore quite unlike what the original authors had in mind. The idea of antithetic alternation of generations suggests today that all plants arose from some algal ancestor with a diploid phase as simple as a 1-celled zygote and that, through increase in size and spore-bearing capacity of tissues produced by the zygote, the sporophyte generation arose and evolved into its present status. Both Bower (1890, 1908) and Campbell (1895, 1940) postulated that the vegetative tissues of the sporophyte developed through the "progressive sterilization of potentially sporogenous tissue," a concept widely subscribed to in the texts of my student days; many will remember the several editions and countless printings of Holman and Robbins' outstanding textbook of general botany.

In 1874, Čelakovský, in a classification of the kinds of alternation of generations in animals and plants, including seaweeds and fungi, proposed among others a somewhat metaphysical category, homologous alternation of generations. Spurred by the discovery of algae with isomorphic generations, that is, with haploid and diploid generations almost exactly similar in appearance although not in function, several algologists of this century have so modified the concept of homologous alternation of generations that even its own father could not recognize it.

Zimmerman (1932, 1955, 1959) and others have proposed that from such isomorphic algae arose the first land plants; but it seems to me that the statistical hazards of the invasion of the land by marine or freshwater algae would be increased enormously if such a step had to be taken independently by two separate generations, each of which would have to be modified for terrestrial life. Zimmerman, whether intentionally or not, has been very adept at lulling the reader's awareness of the fact that he is confusing analogies with homologies, as witness his description of an "exact homology" between bryophytes and red algae (1932). To me it is quite impossible to draw homologies between structures of higher plants and any algae, but only in function, where parallel haploid and diploid phases are produced by alternating fertilization and meiosis. The gametes of algae are not particularly similar to those of higher plants, as recent studies of their fine structure have shown, and they are not even produced in the same manner.

Too many theories concerning alternation of generations in bryophytes have been propounded, defended, and refuted. Considering the relatively small size of the Bryophyta, they have furnished a battleground for an inordinate amount of speculation over evolutionary and phylogenetic trends. I am convinced that we would be wise to give up any attempt at trying to define or adhere to the classical, orthodox categories of life cycles proposed for higher plants, which are based on long outdated and often mystical concepts. Few botanists seem to remember that Hofmeister first described alternation of generations before Charles Darwin proposed his theory of evolution, yet Hofmeister is commonly given credit for elaborating the evolutionary levels of the plant kingdom. Speculation is useful only when kept under control and recognized as such. It is far better to reexamine the facts in the light of modern knowledge and, if necessary, start over again, free of the burden of tradition and misinformation. We must do away completely with the homologous theory of alternation of generations because, as presently conceived, it has no relation to Čelakovský's original concept. Even worse, it is based largely on analogies and not homologies.

Antithetic alternation of generations, although a concept widely accepted by botanists during the first half of this century, thanks to the beneficial effect of most standard elementary textbooks and the excellent and highly influential reference works produced by Campbell (1895, 1940), Bower (1890, 1908), and G. M. Smith (1938), among others. However, the concept of antithesis between generations, and their total separation in structure, behavior, and function is wholly untenable today. Nevertheless, I must confess sadly to having taught, during my younger days, an incredibly large number of freshman students all about the antithetic alternation of generations, thanks to my own indoctrination as a student by Professor Bradley M. Davis, who had himself been a student of D. H. Campbell.

Late in the nineteenth century, Bower and other morphologists established the fiction, still perpetuated in too many texts, that the spore-

producing phase of bryophytes was entirely parasitic on the green gametophyte. In spite of the great contributions to science made possible through
Strasburger's development of microtechnical methods, his techniques
produced artifacts that were unfortunately not recognized as such by most
laboratory morphologists. Perhaps the most important of these artifacts
is the removal of chlorophyll by any alcoholic preserving solution. I am
sure that Bower, working with preserved specimens of bryophytes which
he had not seen alive, was honestly convinced that the bleached sporophytes really were parasitic on the gametophyte, as he made very clear in
his writings; also, this interpretation substantiated his own theories.

Moreover, in promoting the theory of antithetic alternation of generations to the exclusion of all others, Bower overlooked the importance of
or even dismissed as teratology much clear and persuasive evidence of
the very real homology (in the modern genetic sense) between the two
generations. For example, in 1876 Pringsheim reported his experimental
production of apospory in mosses as the result of culturing immature
sporophytes which, when they regenerated, produced not further sporophyte tissue but the filamentous protonemata normally formed by germinating spores, thereby short-circuiting spore production. This convincing experiment was soon repeated by other botanists, and the basic
technique led to the first artificial production of polyploid plants, in
mosses, by the Marchals (1907, 1909, 1911).

The same technique was used for the experimental production of apogamy, or the short-circuiting of gamete production, first described for
mosses in 1935 by Springer. The experimental production of apogamy, or
at least its recognition, came quite recently, as it had been first discovered
in ferns by Farlow in 1874, even before Pringsheim's induction of
apospory in mosses. Actually, the Marchals (1911) had observed apogamous sporophytes in their own cultures and had described them, but
for some amazing reason did not suspect their real nature. Since Springer's
pioneer work, apogamy has been reportedly reported in many species
of mosses by several workers. Wettstein (1942), in a remarkable series of
experiments elaborating those of Springer, demonstrated that the peculiar
swellings on the leaf tips of diploid plants of the moss *Phascum cuspidatum* can be induced to proceed in either of two directions simply by
changing the environmental conditions of the culture. If the diploid gametophytes are grown on a dilute culture medium and provided with an
abundance of water, the swellings produce protonemata and leafy shoots.
However, if grown on a more concentrated culture medium and provided
with less water, they develop apogamously into spore-producing structures. By alternating these two environmental conditions in a most elegant
experiment, Wettstein was able to induce a diploid leafy plant to produce

apogamous sporophytes which in turn produced leafy gametophytes from which, in turn, further apogamous sporophytes arose. Thus abundant moisture and low levels of light are conducive to the production of gametophytes, whereas lack of water, preventing fertilization from taking place, and higher light levels combine to induce apogamy and the production of typical sporophytic tissues. Wettstein's experiments are extremely enlightening in demonstrating conclusively the physiological basis for the determination of whether a diploid plant should have the external form, structure, and function of one generation or the other. I am sure that the ability of bryophytes to adjust their form and function to the conditions of the environment has had a very real influence on their evolutionary history, and vice versa. Similar experimental work in ferns, in which the difference between generations is even more remarkable, by Ralph Wetmore and his students during the 1940s and 1950s has demonstrated the essential genetical identity of the two phases as well as the physiological and, thereby, the environmental control of the phenotype expressed, whether gametophyte or sporophyte. In both bryophytes and ferns the gametophyte is delicate, easily desiccated, and fertilization occurs only in the presence of water. The sporophyte, on the other hand, is well cutinized, much firmer in texture, and produces spores of the classical land-plant type.

To summarize these remarks, the very rigid concepts that the gametophyte generation of bryophytes is haploid, gamete-producing, and the sole support of the sporophyte, and that the sporophyte must be diploid, spore-producing, and parasitic have been shown experimentally to be incorrect, perhaps best by artificially produced apospory and apogamy. The two generations are much better interpreted simply as phases with the same genetic constitution, but with different genetic drives and environmental responses under normal conditions in nature. The gametophyte, in general, is less resistant to light and drought than the sporophyte and is thereby restricted to moister habitats, as well as by the need for water for fertilization. The sporophyte, on the other hand, is adapted to a dryer habitat with more light in which the spores are most efficiently released. Finally, now that it has been shown experimentally that one phase can take the form of or produce the other phase vegetatively, the theory of antithetic alternation of generations is as dead as the homologous theory.

The Relationship between Sporophyte and Gametophyte in Bryophytes

It has been proposed by Zimmerman (1932) and others who promulgate the analogy between isomorphic algae and bryophytes that the sporophyte and gametophyte of primitive bryophytes or protobryophytes were identical but separate, and that the present-day epiphytic habit of the sporophyte is derived or secondary, and relatively recent. Although space does not permit a full discussion of the merits of the case, in my own opinion the idea is fallacious and should be discarded. In support of my heresy, I can see no logical reason or evidence to support the theory; in fact, it simply complicates matters even more, as noted earlier. On the contrary, overwhelming evidence of the long association of the sporophyte with the gametophyte phase through evolutionary time is shown by many extraordinarily complex adaptations, specializations, and modifications for an interrelationship between the two phases as they are now associated. A few examples of this large body of evidence, which has never been sufficiently emphasized, are presented here.

In *Sphagnum,* the peat moss, and *Andreaea,* the rock moss, the sporophyte consists only of the spore case or capsule and an enlarged foot or absorbing structure embedded in the gametophyte tissue at the apex of a stem or special branch. Although the capsule has no stalk or seta, when the spores are fully mature the capsule is raised well above the leafy plant by a rapid extension of the stem tip into an elongated stalk or pseudopodium — a clear case of the involvement of a gametophyte structure in the function of the sporophyte, and obviously a situation that would take a very long time to evolve.

In true mosses the calyptra is another case in point. Apparently by pressure alone it controls the growth and development of the sporophyte apex and its maturation into the capsule; without the calyptra, the capsule is malformed or even aborted. Bopp (1956, 1957) thought at first — and it it wholly logical that he should do so — that the calyptra exerted a hormonal influence on the developing capsule. He then discovered, however, that no hormonal influence exists, because he could remove, boil, and replace them, or even exchange boiled calyptras between genera of mosses, and still obtain normal capsule development!

Many other specialized and obviously ancient adaptations between sporophyte and gametophyte occur in mosses, but an even wider range of interesting structural interrelationships is to be found in hepatics (Schuster, 1966). In all bryophytes, probably through hormonal control, fertilization pulls the trigger for many changes in the gametophyte that result in structures to shelter or protect the developing sporophyte. Some of the adaptations in leafy liverworts are bizarre indeed, including marsupial pouches, hollow stem apices, subterranean sacs, and many other types of provision for the protection of the spore-producing structures. However, since the capsule is chlorophyllous during its developing stages before the spores mature, it is largely if not completely self-supporting, and no conspicuous adaptations for its nutrition seem to have evolved in the gametophyte.

The Phylogeny of Bryophytes

To turn to another topic, I would like to update some of my thinking on the evolutionary origins of the bryophytes and their position in a phylogenetic arrangement of the plant kingdom (Steere, 1958).

First of all, the bryophytes are undoubtedly polyphyletic and probably not derived from closely related groups; in fact, they represent less a close relationship than they do a level of evolution and structure. Although they all agree in the dominant gametophyte generation and epiphytic sporophyte, as well as the same general type of life cycle, there are many and substantial differences between the major groups in such basic matters as presence or absence of stomata in capsules, the chromosome number, the structure and behavior of the two phases, and many other criteria. Bryophytes certainly date back to the Devonian, and probably originated well before that (Jovet-Ast, 1967). Even the earliest fossils yet known show no approach of mosses to hepatics; their separation was very ancient indeed. The peat mosses, the rock mosses, and several other distinctive groups of mosses, likewise, are obviously very diverse and have been so for a long, long time. The Anthocerotae or horn-worts are perhaps the most remarkable and most distinctive of all in many ways.

In spite of all that has been written to the contrary in texts and the botanical literature, we have no evidence that bryophytes have evolved directly from algae, or that they present an evolutionary way station between algae and higher plants. In fact, it would seem from modern evidence that bryophytes are an offshoot of the Archegoniates, a "dead end," in an evolutionary sense, and that even so they are far more closely related to higher land plants than to algae.

The spores of bryophytes are generally cutinized and of the standard land-plant form, a type wholly unknown among algae (Erdtman, 1957, 1965). Some bryophytes have spores so highly ornamented and with such conspicuous triradiate markings that they would easily be taken for spores of living or fossil pteridophytes, and I am sure that some of the fossil spores ascribed to ancient pteridophytes really belong to primitive, extinct bryophytes.

The stomata found on the capsules of several bryophyte groups are indistinguishable in structure from those of higher land plants and in some groups have been shown to be perfectly functional, whereas in other groups they are rudimentary or nonfunctional; obviously a derived condition (Paton 1957; Paton and Pearce 1957). Paton (1957) says, "The reduction in the number of stomata may represent a change from a damp to a dry habitat. In the Anthocerotae and the Bryales the stomata probably perform a useful function, which is possibly lost in *Sphagnum,* but the absence of stomata in several highly organized but widely separated genera is confusing, and defies a simple explanation." The probability that functional stomata of exactly the same type originated independently so many times in several groups of bryophytes, and in many genera, which represent different original stocks, is as infinitesmal as it is ridiculous.

For a long time, botanists have accepted the fact that the archegonia and antheridia of bryophytes are much closer in form and function to those of higher plants than to those of algae, in spite of many attempts to show analogies. The Archegoniatae were established as a homologous group in the nineteenth century.

The tissues of bryophyte stems and capsules show some resemblance to those of higher plants (J. L. Smith, 1966; Finnochio, 1967), and some of the conducting elements must have been derived from an intermediate ancestor in the remote, pre-Devonian past. With what we know now about the interrelationship between gametophyte and sporophyte phases, it is not difficult to reconcile the occasional appearance of "sporophytic" structures in gametophyte tissues. Sporophytic vascular elements have been found in the gametophytes of ferns and their allies also.

Many early morphologists placed considerable weight on the protonema of true mosses as an indication of close relationship, in evolutionary terms, between mosses and algae. Recent studies, however, show that the structure of the protonemal cell walls is not at all of an algal nature, but precisely like that of all higher plants.

Biochemical Evidence

Today a whole new research approach furnishes even more convincing evidence of the relationship between bryophytes and higher plants than did the standard morphological criteria in the past, namely, biochemical systematics or chemotaxonomy. Within the foreseeable future we may be able to answer two questions of fundamental importance to evolutionary theory. The first is: "Are bryophytes different in their chemical constitution from other plant groups?"; the other, "With which groups of plants do bryophytes share the greatest affinity in their chemical constitution and biochemical behavior?" The answers to these questions may well revolutionize our present thinking.

From what we already know, the several groups that make up the Bryophyta have been isolated in an evolutionary sense from their ancestral stock or stocks for so long that they have evolved their own peculiar and characteristic biochemical systems which are parallel to but not always identical with those of higher plants. The cell-wall structure and constitution are different; anthocyaninlike pigments occur in bryophytes, but they are located in the cell wall itself and not as soluble compounds in the vacuole.

Ligninlike compounds occur in the cell walls of bryophytes, and lignin derivatives can be isolated from them; however, the standard lignins of higher plants have not yet been clearly demonstrated in bryophytes. It appears that flavenoid pigments do not occur in bacteria, fungi, or algae and that reports of them in these groups have been erroneous. In contrast, however, it becomes increasingly clear that these pigments do occur rather commonly in bryophytes, where no serious effort had been made to detect them until recently, because of the assumption that they would be lacking in supposedly nonlignified plants. We now know that a surprisingly wide variety of flavonoids are normal constituents of bryophytes. Alston (1967) has said of one genus of mosses, "The flavenoid chemistry of *Mnium* species examined by us is comparable in complexity to that of angiosperms, and significant interspecific differences occur. Preliminary results indicate a rich flavenoid chemistry in *Mnium* that will contribute significantly to understanding of its systematics." It is important to point out here that flavenoid pigments are, in general, restricted to lignin-producing plants, and that their structure can be directly related to the types of compounds produced from the degradation of lignin.

Finally, an area of research that will eventually lead to the solution of many problems that at present obscure the evolutionary history of the bryophytes is paleobotany. The fossil record in recent years has already provided remarkable and enlightening evidence for the relationship of bryophytes to higher plants (Jovet-Ast, 1967). However, all that has been presented here leaves us even farther from the solution of that most basic and conspicuous mystery of all: What were the primitive multicellular land plants that first appears, and from what algal stock did they originate?

REFERENCES

Alston, R. (1967). Biochemical systematics. *Evol. Biol.* **1**, 197–305.
Bopp, M. (1956). Die Bedeutung der Kalyptra für die Entwicklung der Laubmoossporogone. *Ber Deut. Botan. Ges.* **49**(9), 455–468.

Bopp, M. (1957). Entwicklungsphysiologische Untersuchungen an Moosmutanten. I. Zur Wirkung der Laubmooskalyptra. *Z. Indukt. Abst.-Vererbungsl.* **88,** 600–607.

Bower, F. O. (1890). On antithetic as distinct from homologous alternation of generations in plants. *Ann. Botany* **4,** 347–370.

Bower, F. O. (1908). "The Origin of a Land Flora: A Theory Based upon the Facts of Alternation." 727 pp. Macmillan, London.

Campbell, D. H. (1895). "The Structure and Development of Mosses and Ferns (Archegoniatae)." 544 pp. Macmillan, London (2nd edition, 1905; 3rd edition, rev. and enlarged, 1928).

Campbell, D. H. (1940). "The Evolution of the Land Plants (Embryophyta)." 731 pp. Stanford University Press, Stanford, Calif.

Čelakovský, L. (1874). Ueber die verschiedenen Formen und die Bedeutung des Generationswechsels der Pflanzen. *Sitzber. K. Böhm. Ges. Wiss. Prag* **1874**(2), 22–61.

Erdtman, G. 1957. "Pollen and Spore Morphology: Plant Taxonomy. Gymnospermae, Pteridophyta, Bryophyta [Illustrations] (An Introduction to Palynology. II)." 151 pp. Almqvist & Wiksell, Stockholm.

Erdtman, G. (1965). "Pollen and Spore Morphology: Plant Taxonomy. Gymnospermae, Bryophyta [Text] (An Introduction to Palynology. III). 191 pp. Almqvist & Wiksell, Stockholm.

Farlow, W. G. (1874). An asexual growth from the prothallus of *Pteris cretica. Quart J. Microscop. Sci. N.S.* **14,** 266–272.

Finocchio, A. F. (1967). Pitting of cells in moss gametophores. *Bull. Torrey Botan. Club* **94**(1), 18–20.

Hofmeister, W. (1851). "Vergleichende Untersuchungen der Keimung, Entfaltung und Fruchtbildung höherer Kryptogamen (Moose, Farrn, Equisetaceen, Rhizocarpeen und Lycopodiaceen) und der Samenbildung der Coniferen." 179 pp. F. Hofmeister, Leipzig.

Hofmeister, W. (1862). "On the Germination, Development and Fructification of the Higher Cryptogamia and on the Fructification of the Coniferae. Trans. by Frederick Currey. 491 pp. London, Robert Hardwicke, for the Ray Society (Revised and considerably augmented by the author from his 1851 edition.)

Jovet-Ast, Suzanne (1967). Bryophyta. Sous-règne des Embryophytes. Premier embranchement. *In* Traité de Paléobotanique" (Edouard Boureau, ed.) Tome II, pp. 17–190. Bryophyta, Psilophyta, Lycophyta. Paris, Masson et Cie.

Marchal, Él., and Marchal, Ém. (1907, 1909, 1911). Aposporie et sexualité chez les mousses. *Bull. Acad. Roy. Belg. Cl. Sci.* **1907:** 765–789; **1909:** 1249–1288; **1911:** 750–776.

Paton, Jean A. (1957). The occurrence, structure and functions of the stomata in British bryophytes. I. Occurrence and structure. *Trans. Brit. Bryol. Soc.* **3**(2), 288–242.

Paton, Jean A., and Pearce, Jean V. (1957). The occurrence, structure and functions of the stomata in British bryophytes. II. Functions and physiology. *Trans. Brit. Bryol. Soc.* **3**(2), 242–259.

Pringsheim, N. (1876). Über vegetative Sprossung der Moosfrüchte. *Monatsber. K. Akad. Wiss. Berlin* **1876,** 425–429.

Schuster, R. M. (1966). "The Hepaticae and Anthocerotae of North America East of the Hundredth Meridian." Vol. 1. 802 pp. New York, Columbia University Press.

Smith, G. M. (1938). "Cryptogamic Botany." Vol. II. Bryophytes and Pteridophytes. 380 pp. New York, McGraw-Hill (2nd edition, 1955).

Smith, J. L. (1966). The liverworts *Pallavicinia* and *Symphyogyna* and their conducting system. *Univ. Calif. (Berkeley) Publ. Botany* **39,** 1–48.

Springer, Eva (1935). Über apogame (vegetativ entstandene) Sporogone an der bivalenten Rasse des Laubmooses *Phascum cuspidatum*. *Z. Indukt. Abst.-Verebungsl.* **69**, 249–262.

Steere, W. C. (1958). Evolution and speciation in mosses. *Am. Naturalist* **92**(862), 5–20.

Wettstein, F. von (1942). Über einige Beobachtungen und experimentelle Befunde bei Laubmoosen. II. Über die vegetativ entstehenden Sporogone von *Phascum cuspidatum* und die willkürliche Änderung des Gestaltwechsels bei diesem Laubmoos. *Ber. Deut. Botan. Ges.* **40**, 399–405.

Zimmerman, W. (1932). Phylogenie. Chapter XVI, pp. 433–464. *In* "Manual of Bryology" (F. Verdoorn, ed.). 486 pp. The Hague, Martinus Nijhoff.

Zimmerman, W. (1955). Phylogenie des Archegoniaten-Generationswechsels. *Feddes Repert. (Festschr. für Theodor Herzog)* **58**(1/3), 283–307.

Zimmerman, W. (1959). Die Phylogenie der Pflanzen. Ein Überblick über Tatschen und Probleme: 2 Aufl. 777 pp. Gustav Fischer, Stuttgart.

Phytochrome and Seed Germination

Alberto L. Mancinelli

Many photomorphogenic responses of plants are under the control of a reversible photoreaction:

$$P_r \underset{\text{far red}}{\overset{\text{red}}{\rightleftarrows}} P_{fr}$$

where P_r and P_{fr} are two forms of a pigment, phytochrome (P), widely distributed in the plant kingdom from seed plant to algae.

Phytochrome, acted on by light, controls seed and spore germination (1, 2, 11, 13, 18, 19–22, 27, 29–32, 34, 39, 40, 42, 43, 45, 46, 48–52, 55–60, 62, 66–72), stem elongation (3, 15, 29–34, 36, 37, 44, 52), leaf expansion (15, 29, 30, 36, 52), flowering (16, 29, 30, 36, 52), nyctinastic movements (23, 30, 34, 35, 41), and many other responses in various kinds of plants (11, 17, 19, 25, 29, 30, 34, 52, 64).

Action spectra for phytochrome-controlled responses (29, 30, 34, 51, 52, 67), and for phytochrome photoconversion *in vivo* (56) and *in vitro* (5), have maxima in the red (R, 600–680 nm, peak around 660 nm) and far red (FR, 700–760 nm, peak around 730 nm) regions of the spectrum. Phytochrome solutions have a main peak of absorption at 660–670 nm for the P_r form and at 720–730 nm for the P_{fr} form (5, 8, 29, 30, 34, 54). The response induced by red (R) can be reversed by far red (FR) applied immediately or shortly after R; similarly, the response induced by FR can be reversed by R (2, 15, 16, 23, 26, 29, 30, 32, 34, 52, 67).

Phytochrome has been extracted and purified, and several of its physical and chemical properties have been studied (5, 6, 8, 9, 47, 54, 63, 65).

Phytochrome can be detected in tissues and in solution by spectrophotometric techniques based on the reversible changes of the absorption spectra in the red and far-red regions after R and FR irradiations, or by the reversible change of the difference in optical density ($\Delta_{O.D.}$) between 660 and 730 nm after R and FR irradiations (4, 8, 24, 56). Phytochrome content of tissue exposed to light decreases; this is probably due to an irreversible decay of P_{fr}, the unstable and physiologically active form of phytochrome (3, 7, 12, 14, 25, 29, 30, 36).

144

The mechanism of action of P_{fr} is still unknown; on the basis of some recent data an action on membrane permeability or on regulation of gene activity could be suggested (23, 30, 35, 41, 53).

Red-far red reversibility, a low-energy requirement, and action spectra with maxima in the red and far-red regions of the spectrum are characteristic of phytochrome-controlled reactions (29, 30, 34, 45, 52, 67).

This brief introduction cannot be concluded without mentioning the high-energy responses of plant photomorphogenesis (52, 62). High-energy responses are characterized by absence of photoreversibility, by action spectra with maxima in the blue and far-red regions of the spectrum, and by a requirement for prolonged periods of irradiations at fairly high intensities (52, 62). At present it is debatable whether the high-energy responses are a different type of manifestation of phytochrome action or whether they are due to a different photoreactive system (28, 30, 61).

In view of the general action of light on seed germination, seeds could be divided into two classes according to these responses: light-requiring seeds and dark-germinating seeds. This classification is not a rigid one, since a large number of external and internal factors can modify the germination response to light of many seeds (38). Other terms frequently used to indicate the response to light are positive and negative photoblastism, indicating, respectively, activation and inhibition (10) of germination by light.

Light-requiring seeds do not usually germinate in darkness. Classical examples of light-requiring seeds are the seeds of *Lepidium virginicum,* Grand Rapids lettuce, and *Arabidopsis thaliana* (1, 29, 45, 57, 61, 67, 68). The light requirement of most light-requiring seeds shows the properties of phytochrome-controlled responses: R-FR reversibility, low-energy requirement, action spectra for promotion of germination and its reversal with peaks in the red and far-red regions of the spectrum (29, 45, 67). On the basis of the experimental evidence, it is assumed that activation of germination in light-requiring seeds depends on the presence of a certain level of P_{fr}. Phytochrome is in the P_r form in light-requiring seeds. Red light, converting P_r into P_{fr}, promoties germination. Far red, applied after R, converting P_{fr} into P_r again, inhibits germination.

Germination of dark-germinating seeds could depend on a system different from phytochrome, or on the presence of a level of P_{fr} sufficient to bring about germination in darkness, or on the fact that the phytochrome-controlled reactions could have taken place at some earlier stages, for example, during the development of the seeds. Several types of physical and chemical treatments can induce a phytochrome-controlled light requirement in several dark-germinating seeds (45, 67). These results demonstrate that phytochrome is present in dark-germinating seeds, but do not prove that phytochrome is involved in the control of the dark-germination process.

In some types of dark-germinating seeds, demonstration of phytochrome control of the dark-germination process can be easily obtained, for example, in the germination of tomato seeds of the varieties Ace, Porte, and Glamour. These seeds germinate in darkness (49,51) and, at temperatures between 17° and 22°C, a single, short (1–2 min) FR irradiation inhibits germination (49,51). Red, applied after FR, repromotes germination (49,51). Action spectra for inhibition of germination and its reversal have peaks of action in the far-red and red regions of the spectrum (49). These results indicate quite clearly that sufficient P_{fr} to bring about the germination in darkness is normally present in tomato seeds. Far red, converting P_{fr} into P_r, inhibits germination; red, converting P_r into P_{fr} again, repromotes germination. Until an extensive survey is made, we cannot say if this behavior is limited to tomato seeds or is present in other seeds as well. From the limited survey we have made and from the data available in the literature (32,43,45,48,55,71), it appears that many dark-germinating seeds require prolonged irradiations for the inhibition of germination. Demonstration of phytochrome control is more difficult in these cases, since prolonged irradiations are typically required for the induction of high-energy responses. We have been able to demonstrate phytochrome control in some cases of inhibition induced by prolonged irradiations (48,49,71,72).

In tomato seeds at temperatures above 25°C, and in lettuce and cucumber seeds at temperatures around 20°C, effective inhibition of germination requires a prolonged exposure to FR radiation (48,49,50,72). It was found that a continuous FR irradiation is not required; intermittent FR, provided the dark interval between successive irradiations was not too long, was just as effective as continuous FR (48,49,50,72). This finding provided the basis for the demonstration of phytochrome control of the response induced by prolonged FR. Seeds exposed to intermittent irradiations would germinate if each FR irradiation was immediately followed by R (48,49,50,72). In these experiments on the action of alternating, cyclic R and FR, germination depends on the relative position of R and FR in each cycle (48,49,72). Thus, even in these cases in which inhibition of germination depended on a prolonged period of irradiation, it was possible to demonstrate that the dark-germination process and the response to prolonged FR are phytochrome-controlled. The necessity of continuous or intermittent far-red irradiation over a prolonged period of time indicates that P_{fr} is continuously reappearing during such a period.

The effective removal of P_{fr} before it has opportunity to act requires continuous or frequent intermittent application of FR. Eventually, a time is reached when FR is no longer required to prevent germination, indicating that further production of P_{fr} has ceased. Seeds exposed to prolonged continuous or intermittent FR do not germinate during the dark-incubation period following the exposure to FR, unless they are exposed to a short red irradiation (48, 49, 50, 72). Germination repromoted by R can be inhibited by a short FR. The seeds seem to have shifted from a physiological state requiring prolonged exposure for inhibition to a state in which a short, single FR is sufficient.

Another aspect of the germination of cucumber seeds is quite interesting. These seeds form measurable amounts of phytochrome during germination, the rate of formation being temperature-dependent. This apparent synthesis of phytochrome is inhibited by the light treatments, which inhibit germination, and is restored by the treatments which restore germination (50). At this moment we do not know if there is any cause-effect relationship between these two phenomena.

In our work we have been able to demonstrate that the control of the dark-germination process of some dark-germinating seeds is phytochrome-controlled; we have also been able to demonstrate that the response to prolonged FR irradiation is phytochrome-controlled.

Until an extensive survey is made, we cannot say if the phytochrome control of the dark-germination process of dark-germinating seeds is limited to few species of seeds or is a common feature of many seeds.

At this moment it is also very difficult to establish whether the germination responses induced by prolonged irradiations are always phytochrome-mediated, especially in cases in which sources other than far red are used. The interpretation given by us and other authors of the action of continuous white light and continuous blue on germination is not yet completely satisfactory (50, 58, 71). As with other responses induced by prolonged irradiations, it is still very difficult to determine if all the germination responses induced by prolonged irradiation are due only to phytochrome, or to a different photoreaction. Another problem in seed germination which has been studied in only very few cases is that of the action of environmental factors during the development of seeds on the photosensitivity of the germination process.

This is a very brief account of the relationships between light and seed germination. The theoretical and practical aspects of the research and of the problems in seed germination are much more complicated than what could appear from the few points made above. A complete knowledge and understanding of the actions and interactions of all the factors controlling seed germination is far in the future. The results obtained in past research have furnished enough basic information to make us feel confident that further progress will be made.

REFERENCES

1. Borthwick, H. A., Hendricks, S. B., Toole, E. H., and Toole, V. K. (1954). Action of light on lettuce seed germination. *Botan. Gaz.* **115**, 205–225.
2. Borthwick, H. A., Toole, E. H., and Toole, V. K. (1964). Phytochrome control of *Paulowina* seed germination. *Israel J. Botany* **13**, 122–133.
3. Briggs, W. R., and Chon, H. P. (1966). The physiological versus the spectrophotometric status of phytochrome in corn coleoptiles. *Plant Physiol.* **41**, 1159–1166.
4. Briggs, W. R., and Siegelman, H. W. (1965). Distribution of phytochrome in etiolated seedlings. *Plant Physiol.* **40**, 934–940.
5. Butler, W. L., Hendricks, S. B., and Siegelman, H. W. (1964). Action spectra of phytochrome *in vitro*. *Photochem. Photobiol.* **3**, 521–528.
6. Butler, W. L., Hendricks, S. B., and Siegelman, H. W. (1965). Purification and properties of phytochrome. *In* "Chemistry and Biochemistry of Plant Pigments" (T. W. Goodwin, ed.), pp. 197–210. Academic Press, New York.
7. Butler, W. L., Lane, H. C., and Siegelman, H. W. (1963). Non-photochemical transformations of phytochrome *in vivo*. *Plant Physiol.* **38**, 514–519.
8. Butler, W. L., Norris, K. H., Siegelman, H. W., and Hendricks, S. B. (1959). Detection, assay, and preliminary purification of the pigment controlling photoresponsive development of plants. *Proc. Natl. Acad. Sci. U.S.* **45**, 1703–1708.
9. Butler, W. L., Siegelman, H. W., and Miller, C. O. (1964). Denaturation of phytochrome. *Biochem.* **3**, 851–857.
10. Chen, S. S. C., and Thimann, K. V. (1964). Studies on the germination of light inhibited seeds of *Phacelia tanacetifolia*. *Israel J. Botany* **13**, 57–73.
11. Chon, H. P., and Briggs, W. R. (1966). Effect of red light on the phototropic sensitivity of corn coleoptiles. *Plant Physiol.* **41**, 1715–1724.
12. Chorney, W., and Gordon, S. A. (1966). Action spectrum and characteristics of the light activated disappearance of phytochrome in oat seedlings. *Plant Physiol.* **41**, 891–896.
13. Comming, B. G. (1963). The dependence of germination on photoperiod, light quality, and temperature in *Chenopodium* spp. *Can. J. Botany* **41**, 1211–1233.
14. DeLint, P. J. A. L., and Spruit, C. J. P. (1963). Phytochrome destruction following illumination of mesocotyls of *Zea mays* L. Meded. *Landbouwhogeschool, Wageningen.* **63**(14), 1–7.
15. Downs, R. J. (1955). Photoreversibility of leaf and hypocotyl elongation of dark-grown Red Kidney bean seedlings. *Plant Physiol.* **30**, 468–472.
16. Downs, R. J. (1956). Photoreversibility of flower initiation. *Plant Physiol.* **31**, 279–284.
17. Downs, R. J. (1964). Photocontrol of anthocyanin synthesis. *J. Wash. Acad. Sci.* **54**, 112–120.
18. Downs, R. J. (1964). Photocontrol of germination of seeds of the *Bromeliaceae*. *Phyton* **21**, 1–6.
19. Evenari, M. (1965). Physiology of seed dormancy, after ripening and germination. *Proc. Intern. Seed Testing Assoc.* **30**, 49–71.

20. Flint, L. H., and McAlister, E. D. (1934). Light in relation to dormancy and germination in lettuce seeds. *Science* **80,** 38–40.
21. Flint, L. H., and McAlister, E. D. (1935). Wavelength of radiation in the visible spectrum inhibiting the germination of light sensitive lettuce seeds. *Smithsonian Inst. Misc. Collections* **94,** No. 5.
22. Flint, L. H., and McAlister, E. D. (1937). Wavelength of radiation in the visible spectrum promoting the germination of light sensitive lettuce seeds. *Smithsonian Inst. Misc. Collection* **96,** No. 2.
23. Fondaville, S. C., Borthwick, H. A., and Hendricks, S. B. (1966). Leaflet movements in *Mimosa pudica* L. indicative of phytochrome action. *Planta* **69,** 357–364.
24. Furuya, M., and Hillman, W. S. (1964). Observations on spectrophotometrically assayable phytochrome *in vivo* in etiolated *Pisum* seedlings. *Planta* **63,** 31–42.
25. Furuya, M., Hopkins, W. G., and Hillman, W. S. (1965). Effects of metal-complexing and sulfhydril compounds on non-photochemical phytochrome changes *in vivo. Arch. Biochem. Biophys.* **112,** 180–186.
26. Goren, R., and Galston, A. W. (1966). Control by phytochrome of ^{14}C-sucrose incorporation into buds of etiolated pea seedlings. *Plant Physiol.* **41,** 1055–1064.
27. Grant-Lipp, A. E., and Ballard, L. A. T. (1963). Germination patterns shown by the light-sensitive seeds of *Anagallis arvensis. Australian J. Biol. Sci.* **16,** 572–584.
28. Hartmann, K. M. (1966). A general hypothesis to interpret "high energy phenomena" of photomorphogenesis on the basis of phytochrome. *Photochem. Photobiol.* **5,** 349–366.
29. Hendricks, S. B., and Borthwick, H. A. (1965). The physiological functions of phytochrome. *In* "Chemistry and Biochemistry of Plant Pigments" (T. W. Goodwin, ed.), pp. 405–436. Academic Press, New York.
30. Hendricks, S. B., and Borthwick, H. A. (1967). Function of phytochrome in regulation of plant growth. *Proc. Natl. Acad. Sci. U.S.* **58,** 2125–2130.
31. Hendricks, S. B., Borthwick, H. A., and Downs, R. S. (1956). Pigment conversion in the formative responses of plants to radiation. *Proc. Natl. Acad. Sci. U.S.* **42,** 19–25.
32. Hendricks, S. B., Toole, E. H., Toole, V. K., and Borthwick, H. A. (1959). Photocontrol of plant development by the simultaneous excitations of two interconvertible pigments. III. Control of seed germination and axis elongation. *Botan. Gaz.* **121,** 1–8.
33. Hillman, W. S. (1965). Phytochrome conversion by brief illumination and the subsequent elongation of etiolated *Pisum* stem segments. *Physiol. Plantarum* **18,** 346–358.
34. Hillman, W. S. (1967). The physiology of phytochrome. *Ann. Rev. Plant Physiol.* **18,** 301–322.
35. Hillman, W. S., and Koukkari, W. L. (1967). Phytochrome effects in the nyctinastic leaf movements of *Albizzia julibrissin* and some other legumes. *Plant Physiol.* **42,** 1413–1418.
36. Hillman, W. S., and Purves, W. K. (1966). Light responses, growth factors and phytochrome transformations of *Cucumis* seedling tissues. *Planta* **70,** 275–284.
37. Hopkins, W. G., and Hillman, W. S. (1966). Relationships between phytochrome state and photosensitive growth of *Avena* coleoptile segments. *Plant Physiol.* **41,** 593–598.
38. Ikuma, H., and Thimann, K. V. (1964). Analysis of germination processes of lettuce seeds by means of temperature and anaerobiosis. *Plant Physiol.* **39,** 756–767.
39. Isikawa, S. (1962). Light sensitivity against germination. III. Studies on various partial processes in light sensitive seeds. *Japan. J. Botan.* **18,** 105–132.
40. Isikawa, S., and Yokohama, Y. (1962). Effect of intermittent irradiations on the germination of *Epilobium* and *Hypericum* seeds. *Botan. Mag. (Tokyo)* **75,** 127–132.

41. Jaffe, M. J., and Galston, A. W. (1967). Phytochrome control of rapid nyctinastic movements and membrane permeability in *Albizzia julibrissin. Planta* **77**, 135–141.
42. Jones, M. G., and Bayley, L. F. (1956). Light effects on the germination of seeds of henbit (*Lamium amplexicaule* L.). *Plant Physiol.* **31**, 347–349.
43. Kadman-Zahavi, A. (1960). Effects of short and continuous illumination of the germination of *Amaranthus retroflexus* seeds. *Bull. Res. Council Israel* **D9**, 1–20.
44. Klein, W. H., Edwards, J. L., and Shropshire, W., Jr. (1967). Spectrophotometric measurements of phytochrome *in vivo* and their correlation with photomorphogenic responses in *Phaseolus. Plant Physiol.* **42**, 264–270.
45. Koller, D., Mayer, A. M., Poljakoff-Mayber, A., and Klein, S. (1962). Seed germination. *Ann. Rev. Plant Physiol.* **13**, 427–464.
46. Koller, D., Sachs, M., and Negbi, M. (1964). Spectral sensitivity of seed germination in *Artemisia monosperma. Plant Cell Physiol.* **5**, 79–84.
47. Linschitz, H., Kasche, V., Butler, W. L., and Siegelman, H. W. (1966). The kinetics of phytochrome conversion. *J. Biol. Chem.* **241**, 3395–3403.
48. Mancinelli, A. L., and Borthwick, H. A. (1964). Photocontrol of germination and phytochrome reaction in dark-germinating seeds of *Lactuca sativa* L. *Ann. di Botan.* **38**(1), 9–24.
49. Mancinelli, A. L., Borthwick, H. A., and Hendricks, S. B. (1966). Phytochrome control of tomato seed germination. *Botan. Gaz.* **127**(1), 1–5.
50. Mancinelli, A. L., and Tolkowsky, A. (1968). Phytochrome and seed germination. V. Changes of phytochrome content during the germination of cucumber seeds. *Plant Physiol.* **43**, 489–494.
51. Mancinelli, A. L., Yaniv, Z., and Smith, P. (1967). Phytochrome and seed germination. I. Temperature dependence and relative P_{fr} levels in the germination of dark-germinating tomato seeds. *Plant Physiol.* **42**, 333–337.
52. Mohr, H. (1964). The control of plant growth and development by light. *Biol. Rev.* **39**, 87–112.
53. Mohr, H. (1966). Differential gene activation as a mode of action of phytochrome-730. *Photochem. Photobiol.* **5**, 469–483.
54. Mumford, F. E., and Jenner, E. L. (1966). Purification and characterization of phytochrome from oat seedlings. *Biochemistry* **5**, 3657–3662.
55. Negbi, M., and Koller, D. (1964). Dual action of white light in the photocontrol of germination of *Oryzopsis miliacea. Plant Physiol.* **39**, 247–253.
56. Pratt, L. H., and Briggs, W. R. (1966). Photochemical and nonphotochemical reactions of phytochrome *in vivo. Plant Physiol.* **41**, 467–474.
57. Rollin, P. (1963). Observations sur la différence de nature de deux photoreactions controlent la germination des akenes de *Lactuca sativa. Compt. Rend.,* **257**, 3642–3645.
58. Rollin, P. (1964). Remarques concernent l'action de la lumiere sur la germination. *Can. J. Botany* **42**, 463–471.
59. Rollin, P. (1964). Interpretation of the different types of action of far red light on the morphogenesis of plants. *Israel J. Botany* **13**, 193–198.
60. Rollin, P. (1966). The influence of light upon seed germination. Possible interpretation of data. *Photochem. Photobiol.* **5**, 367–371.
61. Schneider, M. J., Borthwick, H., and Hendricks, S. B. (1967). Effects of radiation on flowering of *Hyoscyamus niger. Am. J. Botany* **54**(10), 1241–1249.
62. Shropshire, W., Jr., Klein, W. H., and Elstad, V. B. (1961). Action spectra of photomorphogenic induction and photoinactivation of germination in *Arabidopsis thaliana. Plant Cell Physiol.* **2**, 63–69.

63. Siegelman, H. W., and Firer, E. M. (1964). Purification of phytochrome from oat seedlings. *Biochemistry* **3**, 418–423.
64. Siegelman, W. H., and Hendricks, S. B. (1957). Photocontrol of anthocyanin formation in turnip and red cabbage seedlings. *Plant Physiol.* **32**, 393–398.
65. Siegelman, H. W., Turner, B. C., and Hendricks, S. B. (1966). The chromophore of phytochrome. *Plant Physiol.* **41**, 1289–1292.
66. Toole, E. H. (1961). The effect of light and other variables on the control of seed germination. *Proc. Intern. Seed Test. Assn.* **26**, 659–673.
67. Toole, E. H., Hendricks, S. B., Borthwick, H. A., and Toole, V. K. (1956). Physiology of seed germination. *Ann. Rev. Plant Physiol.* **7**, 299–324.
68. Toole, E. H., Toole, V. K., Borthwick, H. A., and Hendricks, S. B. (1955). Photocontrol of *Lepidium* seed germination. *Plant Physiol.* **30**, 15–21.
69. Toole, E. H., Toole, V. K., Borthwick, H. A., and Hendricks, S. B. (1955). Interaction of temperature and light in germination of seeds. *Plant Physiol.* **30**, 473–478.
70. Yaniv, Z., and Mancinelli, A. L. (1967). Phytochrome and seed germination. II. Changes of P_{fr} requirement for germination in tomato seeds. *Plant Physiol.* **42**, 1147–1148.
71. Yaniv, Z., and Mancinelli, A. L. (1968). Phytochrome and seed germination. IV. Action of light sources with different spectral energy distribution on the germination of tomato seeds. *Plant Physiol.* **43**, 1147–1148.
72. Yaniv, Z., Mancinelli, A. L., and Smith, P. (1967). Phytochrome and seed germination. III. Action of prolonged far red irradiation on the germination of tomato and cucumber seeds. *Plant Physiol.* **42**, 1479–1482.

IV
ASPECTS OF TAXONOMY

Only Ten Feet Less

Joseph Ewan

By 1867 Asa Gray had many loyal followers with an almost religious devotion. Frequent references in letters between botanists to "the Good Doctor Gray" attest to the fraternity of spirit. Gray had created a garden, a garden of living and dried plants, and by this time a garden of memories. It may fairly be said he had even built an empire. Letters I have read show him full of energies, ideas, fierce loyalties to friends abroad and up and down the streets of Longfellow's Cambridge. With bumptious competitive zeal, Asa Gray brought botanists into line in a way which, in his sincere opinion, was for the good of the botanical cause. In so doing he sometimes fiercely cut down his opposition. In today's language he was an "achiever." No single botanist in this country accomplished so much in the nineteenth century to create the image of American botany as did Asa Gray.

Many figures in the history of botany are paired off. Examples come to mind easily: Ruiz and Pavon, Humboldt and Bonpland, Bentham and Hooker, Engler and Prantl, Mathias and Constance. In the association of Torrey and Gray we know a good deal more about Gray than about his senior partner, John Torrey, botanist, chemist, and mineralogist. Torrey differed from Gray, though they had characteristics in common: both had a deeply religious turn of mind — though I have always suspected that Asa Gray attended church as a proper Bostonian whereas Torrey, a more retiring Christian, seldom mentioned his religious associations. Both took medical degrees, and both preferred the magnifying lens to the stethoscope.

Torrey was born in New York City on August 15, 1796, the son of Captain William Torrey and his wife, Margaret Nichols of New York. Little is recorded of his schooling, but of significance was his father's appointment as fiscal agent of the State Prison at Greenwich while it held a distinguished botanist, Amos Eaton, incarcerated for bad debts resulting from an unfortunate business transaction. Young Torrey was a willing pupil of the inmate, searching the countryside for fresh specimens to bring to Eaton in return for instruction on corollas and corollaries and, as Eaton wrote (February 7, 1814) to his wife from prison, supplying him

155

with all the books he wanted which were not in the State Prison Library. Later Torrey added minerals and chemistry to his interests,* and at the age of twenty-two began his medical apprenticeship under Dr. Wright Post.

Two natural historians were formative influences at this time: Dr. Samuel Latham Mitchill and Dr. David Hosack. Dr. Mitchill in 1813 delivered an excellent bibliographical essay on the literature of botany for North and South America, although his bouquets went to Fauna rather than to Flora. This was certainly known to Torrey. Dr. Hosack had worked hard to establish a botanic garden in New York and taught botany classes in the medical college (Robbins, 1964).

Torrey took his M.D. degree in 1818, hung his shingle in New York City, and practiced with moderate success, dissecting the perigynia of sedges between patients. When Asa Gray (1873) wrote Torrey's obituary, he commented that his mentor and friend "had turned his abundant leisure to scientific pursuits, especially in botany." It is, I think, evidence of Torrey's relaxed attitude toward his work that left the impression of "abundant leisure" since Torrey, in contrast, for example, to Dr. George Engelmann, was not crowding his botanical investigations between bustling house calls with drives to distant farmhouses.

Before Torrey had his medical degree, he had reported to the local Lyceum on a "Catalogue of the Plants Growing Spontaneously within Thirty Miles of the City of New York." This was published in 1819. Enthusiasm for mineralogy led to two articles published in the first volume of Professor Silliman's *Journal.* At this time he began a correspondence with Kurt Sprengel and James Edward Smith abroad, and with Nuttall, Stephen Elliott, Schweinitz, and others in this country. In 1822 Torrey and Thomas Nuttall spent the summer together in New York City, Nuttall having a lecture series scheduled that season while Torrey served as assistant to Dr. Hosack in a course of botany at Hosack's private medical school. Hosack had characteristically attempted more than he could carry through and imposed on an unwilling Torrey; yet, when he introduced Torrey to James Edward Smith of the Linnean Society, he wrote approvingly.

---

*"I will procure some of our Sirens for you if possible & also such of our Trilobites as can be procured. I have been endeavoring to procure for Dr. Hooker a set of casts in plaster of Paris of these petrifactions" [John Torrey to John Scouler, Dec. 11, 1833]. Again, "If you receive any remarkable minerals or other objects that you can spare, we should be very glad to have a share of the duplicates" [Oct. 27, 1834]. And, again, "I am as much occupied as ever in botany & mineralogy – to say nothing of Chemistry, which is my proper business & pleasure too" [August 3, 1838].

Evidently as early as 1823 Torrey planned his *Flora of North America,* since William Jackson Hooker refers to the fact in his letter of December of that year. "I am sure," wrote Hooker, "that you will do it well & consequently [do] yourself justice by it." Hooker corresponded with Torrey and apprised him of his own publication plans. In September 1824, for example, Hooker wrote, "I have been the means of sending two Botanists from Scotland to the Northwest coast of America. They are on their way to the mouth of the Columbia, whence *one* will return overland with Capt. Franklin. Another is now to go out with Dr. Richardson & spend 2 years among the rocky mountains" (Rodgers, 1942, p. 59). Tolmie and Douglas went to the mouth of the Columbia, Douglas returning overland to Hudson Bay; Drummond went with Richardson.

Torrey married Eliza Robinson Shaw of New York on April 20, 1824, and in August he began his four years teaching cadets the natural sciences at West Point. In 1825 Hooker assured Torrey that his plan for a general British flora would not interfere with Torrey's American efforts because Hooker's would "include species that could be procured by the British government and novelties would for their own credit's sake be first described in England." It was at this time that Torrey determined to adopt the Natural System of Jussieu instead of the then current Linnaean Sexual System used by Amos Eaton and others in American academies. In 1826 Torrey stood on the Great Divide between the two systems: his *Compendium of the Flora of the Northern and Middle States,* which had been in preparation for some time, began with "Monandria, Monogynia," whereas his report on the Rocky Mountain novelties of Edwin James, published the same year, followed the Natural System.

The *Flora of North America* was without doubt the *magnum opus* of Torrey and the first monument for Gray. Torrey sowed the seed for the *Flora* when he visited England six years before Gray made the trip, stirred the botanical community in England to support the project, and, most fortunately, soon discovered in Asa Gray a talented and hardworking young man and persuaded him to collaborate in the enterprise. On Torrey's visit to Glasgow in 1833 as an agent of New York University he met John Scouler, protégé of Hooker, who had gone to the Columbia and collected plants there. In 1835 Torrey wrote to Scouler:* "I am working (when not engaged in the duties of my laboratory) at my Flora of N. America. This is an extensive work which I cannot expect to

---

*For informing me of these heretofore unpublished Torrey letters, preserved in the Scouler correspondence at Mitchell Library, Glasgow, I am indebted to Dr. Blodwen Lloyd.

finish in several years. I shall not publish prematurely." On August 3, 1838, he wrote again to Scouler: "By the printed notice on the other side you will see that I am engaged with my friend Dr. Gray in printing the long promised Flora of North America. You must try to get us a few subscribers—for we print on our own account & the expenses are so heavy that we begin to be alarmed, & find that unless there are many copies of the work sold we shall be heavy losers."

When reviewing the *Flora,* William Darlington wrote: "It was exceedingly important, that whoever might undertake to prepare a North American Flora should be thoroughly acquainted with the labors of preceding botanists; and, by consulting their collections, as far as practicable, be competent to detect their errors, adjust their discrepancies, and determine their various synonyms."

In this spirit, Gray on his twenty-eighth birthday left for Europe in the fall of 1838, the first part of their *Flora* having preceded him, and Part II on its way. This was the first time an American botanist had planned to visit European countries to study type specimens essential to the North American Flora. It is clear from the almost illegible annotations I have seen in the Sherardian Herbarium at Oxford, on William Bartram specimens at the British Museum, and on the Michaux specimens at Paris, that Asa Gray worked rapidly. He always worked at a fast pace.

Before Gray left for Europe, Torrey had received plants from Leavenworth at Tampa, and from Lapham in Wisconsin, to mention only two particularly interesting lots that delighted Torrey. Torrey, like Hooker, was friendly with his botanical correspondents and field collectors, and, in contrast to Gray, considerate of their frustrations, patient, and forgiving. Barnhart aptly called it his "genial friendliness."

The team at first worked in the same city, but as early as January 1839 Gray foresaw their possible separation. Gray wrote that "of late [this fear of separation] rendered me much more anxious to obtain books and specimens, in order that I may get on by myself in case I shall be compelled to work alone" (Rodgers, 1942, p. 124). In 1842 Gray went to Cambridge, and Torrey to Princeton. With a touch of sadness, Torrey wrote to J. W. Bailey: "Now we shall probably never work together again." Torrey's words were prophetic, since six of the seven published parts of the *Flora of North America* appeared before their separation, and the eventual abandonment of the *Flora* in that format was undoubtedly due largely to their living and working apart. Torrey wrote to Scouler in Glasgow, July 20, 1847: "Dr. Gray & I are slowly working at our Flora of N. America. This is a *chronic* call. We are doing much besides—in various ways, since it was begun."

One of the multifarious activities stealing time from the progress on the *Flora* was the work on the Wilkes Expedition reports, not to mention — to use Torrey's own words — "my laboratory duties [which] are severe & take up much of my time." Much of his time was also taken up with long letters of information, and advice, particularly to young botanists. He advised Scouler in these words: "I hardly wonder at your desiring a change of residence for of all civilized ? countries, Ireland seems the last that I would select for my home . . . . It seems to me that you ought to find a better place than your professorship in Dublin." But Torrey added: "Don't be in haste to remove, unless you can decidedly better yourself" (John Torrey, 20 July 1847, to John Scouler). Scouler, it may be noted, aspired to the Glasgow botanical position vacated by Hooker.

Then there were the visitors: William Henry Harvey, algologist and student of the South African Flora, came in 1849 for the Lowell Lectures at Boston. It was evident from the letters this warm, friendly person wrote to his colleagues that he thoroughly enjoyed himself in America.

Torrey's achievements in botany were diluted by his interests in chemistry and mineralogy, whereas Gray dedicated himself to one field. When Gray wrote Torrey's obituary, he suggested one characteristic of Torrey to be "some excess of caution." One instance must suffice: When the plants collected on the Wilkes Expedition around the world awaited study, it was Gray who ventured to describe the novelties from remote places, the South Pacific and elsewhere, while Torrey demurred. In the same biographical notice, however, Gray emphasized Torrey's "scrupulous accuracy" and "remarkable fertility of mind."

To summarize Torrey's influence: he contributed to a sound taxonomy of the Cyperaceae; he fostered the work of many botanists including some, like Rafinesque, with whom he disagreed; he wrote an exemplary pioneer state flora; and he prepared many descriptions of new species for the government-sponsored Mexican Boundary Survey and the Pacific Railway Reports. Torrey was 55 when they were begun. Above all, as the senior partner of Torrey and Gray, his methods and standards did not cease with his death in 1873, but were carried forward through Gray's lifetime and into the era of Watson, Robinson, and Fernald. Torrey's link with David Hosack and the Elgin Botanic Garden of his youth was a continuum with the Torrey Botanical Club's subsequent part in the founding of the New York Botanical Garden.

Always modest, Torrey's disclaimer to his Carolina correspondent, Lewis R. Gibbes, speaks for the man: "We have endeavoured to make the best of our means — but we know full well that we shall detect many errors in the work" (Rodgers, 1942, p. 122). For the living memorial of the endemic California Torrey Pine we are indebted to Charles Christopher Parry who distinguished the tree in 1850. It was Parry who also made the felicitous suggestion of naming two 14,000-foot peaks of the Colorado Rockies, one for Gray, elevation 14, 274 feet, and the not far distant Torreys Peak, only ten feet less, 14, 264 feet — two giants in the land.

Note added in proof: Since writing this essay Christine Chapman Robbins has published: John Torrey (1796–1873), His life and times. *Bull. Torrey Botan. Club* **95,** 515–645 (1968) to which the reader should turn for a most comprehensive fresh account.

REFERENCES

Darlington, W. (1839). [Review of] A Flora of North America. *Am. J. Sci.* **35,** 180–182.
Gray, A. (1873). John Torrey: a biographical notice. *Am. J. Sci. Ser. 3,* **5,** 411–421 (also issued as a separately paged reprint).
Robbins, C. C. (1964). David Hosack. *Mem. Am. Phil. Soc.* **62,** 1–246.
Rodgers, A. D., III (1942). "John Torrey." Princeton Univ. Press. 352 pp.

Flora North America — Project '67*

Roy L. Taylor

> All this botanical work, it may be observed, has reference to the Flora of North America, in which, it was hoped, the diverse and separate materials and component parts, which he and others had wrought upon, might some day be brought together in a completed system of American botany.
>
> It remains to be seen whether his surviving associate of nearly forty years will be able to complete the edifice. To do this will be to supply the most pressing want of science, and to raise the fittest monument to Dr. Torrey's memory.
>
> From Memoir of John Torrey (1796–1873) read before the National Academy on April 15, 1873 by Asa Gray

These words, spoken by Asa Gray ninety-six years ago, still have a significant meaning as we launch our Flora North America Project. Today, we are commemorating not only the 100th birthday of the Torrey Botanical Club, but also the work of a great North American botanist, John Torrey. It was the energy and enthusiasm of this man that resulted in the development and formation of the botanical club that now bears his name.

The impetus that John Torrey gave to botany in North America is still very much in evidence today, and there is no question in the minds of the many people working on our recently initiated Flora North America Project that he must be credited with sowing the idea of just such a work.

Torrey introduced a new era to American floristics when he began the preparation of his *Flora of North America* with the help of his able associate, Asa Gray. The flora represented the first time that an indigenous effort had been made to write a continental flora based insofar as possible on all available American collections. Unfortunately, the flora initiated by Torrey and later pursued by Gray became a lifelong project for both men, but an uncompleted one. To treat all the vascular plants of North America north of Mexico, excluding Greenland, Torrey and Gray followed the natural system used by Hooker. Much progress was made between the years 1838 and 1843, and two volumes covering all the polypetalous dicotyledons and the gamopetalous dicots through

*Contribution No. 624 from the Plant Research Institute, Ottawa.

the Compositae were published. These two volumes represented the last work that Torrey was to complete of the flora, but Asa Gray, after some 35 years, resumed the publication of the flora and was finally able to issue the remaining gamopetalous dicotyledonous families after the Compositae as part of the new work entitled *The Synoptical Flora of North America*. Neither the *Flora of North America* nor *The Synoptical Flora of North America* ever reached the treatment of Apetalae, Monocotyledonae, Gymnospermae, or the vascular Cryptogamae. Although both works are now well outdated, the Torrey and Gray floras have had a profound influence on systematic botany in North America. Even today, the impact is difficult to overestimate. The great importance of these works can be attributed to the fact that Torrey and Gray developed an awareness and an esprit de corps among North American botanists, as well as an excellent working relationship with major botanical centers and scholars in Europe and Asia. The continuing work of the two great botanists gave a leadership to which the individual American collector and researcher could relate. The product of their endeavors that was so eagerly awaited both at home and abroad was a sort of grand synoptical synthesis of American floristics that every botanical practitioner and theoretician of the time needed on his shelf.

In the present century, only one attempt has been made to write a flora of North America, in this case, a truly continental flora encompassing all of North America and including a detailed treatment of all indigenous plants from the bacteria and algae through to the seed plants. This flora, initiated in 1905 by Nathaniel Britton, stands as one of the most comprehensive and ambitious taxonomic undertakings of all time. Britton's flora was conceived as a detailed monographic account of all plants found in North America. As such, the preparation of the flora necessitated exacting floristic and taxonomic research and extensive publications resulting in a very large compendium of research monographs. The project known as *North American Flora* was to consist of thirty-four volumes and the arrangement to be that of the new system of Engler. This flora, unfortunately is not complete but, under the able guidance of the staff at the New York Botanical Garden, it is hoped that the flora will be completed in its entirety.

Some question has arisen as to why we should not concentrate our efforts toward the completion of this monumental project rather than embark on a new one. I think that the answer to this question lies in the different functions that the *North American Flora* and the new Flora North America Project can play in the botanical community. The former work can aptly be called a "research flora," whereas the latter flora project is that of a concise and diagnostic manual. The distinctiveness of these two types of floras can be exemplified by the two floras of Jepson, namely, "A Manual of the Flowering Plants of California" versus his research monograph, "A Flora of California." The two different approaches to the production of floras are complementary rather than antagonistic. It is hoped that the initiation of the Flora North America Project will stimulate the completion of the *North American Flora* by reawakening the botanical fraternity to the need for the research type of flora. Both types of floras should always be available.

Apart from the work on the *North American Flora,* this century has brought an unprecedented proliferation of taxonomic research producing a stream of revisions, monographs, biosystematic papers, and floras of local, state, or regional scope. In spite of these endeavors, two information gaps keep widening. First, authorative compilation and integration and condensation, in short, synthesis and synopsis, have not kept pace with primary data gathering and, for all intents and purposes, the great wealth of accumulating information is largely unavailable to the average scientist, technologist, or layman who seeks a ready answer to a question regarding North American plants on a broad systematic and geographical scale. By patient recourse to a dozen or so individual works he can perhaps piece together the information he needs, but there is no single work to which he can turn for uniform treatment of the American flora as a whole that will give him the same kind of data for all species. The second information gap arises out of the basic capriciousness of research, which seldom follows a systematic course. Therefore, whereas the intensity and quantity of taxonomic research increases overall, the research is uneven in its coverage and the number of critical lacunae or knowledge gaps do not seem to decrease appreciably. In some ways the disparities are accentuated by further research when this research does not fit into a general scheme. For example, the publication of a new state or provincial flora can only remind us that by comparison we know less about the plants in the neighboring provinces or states. Furthermore, geographical fortuities and man-power distribution have promoted areas of feast and famine with respect to floristic studies so that, whereas plants of California, Missouri, and Illinois, the Pacific Northwest, and the Northeast have been studied extensively, those of other large regions have received relatively little attention.

The conclusion is compelling. A mechanism is needed to ensure equal chance for all geographic areas and systematic groups in North America. The Flora North America Project will be such a mechanism as to ensure coverage in a uniform style and treatment. The smaller works do not necessarily build into larger treatments, as is often assumed, and certainly not without deliberate effort. The philosophy and methods of small-scale researchers are fundamentally different from, even antagonistic at times to, the philosophy and methods of large-scale researchers, and the scale of the effort must govern the design used.

The primary tangible goal of the Flora North America Project is to produce a concise and diagnostic treatment of all vascular plants of the continental United States, Canada, and Greenland. Central America, Mexico, The West Indies, and Bermuda will be excluded. These exclusions are indeed unfortunate but, at the feasibility committee meetings, it was quite evident that the existence of innumerable poorly understood floristic elements found in these tropical or subtropical areas would have to be excluded if the Project was to realize its goal in providing the botanical fraternity with a concise treatment in a reasonable period of time. Flora North America is intended to serve both as an identification manual for plants collected anywhere within the circumscribed region, and as a systematic conspectus of the vascular plants of North America. This work will be used not only for theoretical work in taxonomy, ecology, and phytogeography but also for practical reference in biology, wildlife management, forestry, and agriculture. When completed, the Flora will include dichotomous keys, brief diagnoses, habitat and distributional summaries, pertinent synonymy, chromosome number information, and other biological observations. Tentatively the manual is projected as a four-volume work, with a fifth volume comprised of theoretical essays on the evolution, migration, and geography of the flora of North America. Some 15,000 to 20,000 species of vascular plants are thought to be found in the area as delimited. Therefore, Flora North America Project will require the cooperation of many taxonomists and other specialists. The Editorial Committee proposes to carry out the work in a series of programed and disciplined stages over a period of about 15 years. Intangible, but of no less importance, is the goal of the Project to stimulate interest in taxonomy in the higher levels of biological intergradation. As a mechanism for uncovering problems, Flora North America Project will trigger new cycles of research in systematics and floristics as well as in related disciplines. At the same time the Project will provide a scientific rationale and unifying theme for numerous isolated researches. The Flora itself is conceived as the minimum product of the 15-year effort, for it is hoped that ultimately the spin-off produce stimulated by the Project will dwarf the central publication of the scheme. In scope and duration, the Project can potentially capture the imagination of many generations of students and provide them with the systematic means of identifying the taxonomic groups most needing study. The work will be distributed in small taxonomic units to as many specialists or would-be specialists as possible. This will place the responsibility squarely on the shoulders of the taxonomic community as a whole for the treatment of the flora of North America.

The need for a Flora North America stems, on the one hand, from the challenge of past failures to complete a flora of North America, and on the other, from the ever-present and intensifying demand for an up-to-date manual and conspectus synthesizing the present state of knowledge in a useful form comparable to such twentieth-century works as *Flora SSSR* and *Flora Europaea.*

European botanists have set good examples. The monographical *Flora SSSR* was completed in 1964 after nearly 35 years of discipline and dedication. In 1956 the preparation of the concise diagnostic *Flora Europaea* was commenced, and in 1964 the first volume appeared. The second volume appeared in print in late 1968. When *Flora Europaea* is completed, our own region will be the last gap, the major one, in the full sweep of the circumboreal-circumpolar realm. Flora North America, which first received serious impetus when *Flora Europaea* appeared in 1964, is calculated to close this gap. That we will be last perhaps gives us the opportunity to be the best. The successful completion of Flora North America will bring botanists a giant step closer to the worldwide encyclopedia of plants envisaged by botanists for many years.

Conceptually, Flora North America will be modeled after *Flora Europaea* but by no means with rigid conformity. Flora North America will be a thoroughly independent and indigenous effort looking to *Flora Europaea* as a point of reference and inspiration, but also drawing on the experience of *Flora SSSR* and other long-term floristic projects such as *Flora Malayasiana* and *North America Flora.*

The early stages in the development of the Flora North America Project, including the feasibility study report to the American Society of Plant Taxonomists and the subsequent ratification by the Society, are now largely a matter of record. In January of 1967, the first meeting of the Editorial Committee was convened under the auspices of the Smithsonian Institution at Washington, and we were indeed fortunate to have Dr. Vernon Heywood, Secretary of *Flora Europaea,* attend this meeting and give freely of his wise council to the Committee. In addition to the members of the Editorial Committee, the Chairman of the Steering Committee, Dr. William Stern, and the Chairman of the Advisory Council, Dr. Robert Thorne, were both in attendance. The three-day meeting was indeed fruitful: the Project was officially launched. Many things were accomplished and initiated, but the task has just begun and much work remains to be done. The team of the Flora North America Project is working for you to provide the mechanism for the production of the Flora. The challenge is real and imposing and, on behalf of the many people who have been working toward this goal, your help is needed in meeting the challenge and providing a successful conclusion to the Project. The efforts, whether large or small, by all members of the botanical fraternity in North America will play an important role in the eventual production of the Flora. I hope that we shall achieve the exciting goal that Torrey instigated over a hundred years ago. In what better way could we honor this great North American botanist than to see his dream fulfilled?

Research Challenges in the Cyperaceae

Alfred E. Schuyler

The sedge family is one of the largest families in our North American flora, and yet the number of taxonomists conducting research in it is small. Historically, however, the Cyperaceae have received the attention of numerous North American floristic botanists and competent specialists. Henry Muhlenberg, our first North American botanist to accumulate a sizable herbarium in this country and to publish a work attempting to treat the entire North American flora, was a careful student of the family. His *Catalogus* (1813) is a valuable and carefully done, though brief, treatment of North American plants, and his *Descriptio* (1817) is invaluable to anyone interested in grasses and sedges. All this was done by a person who was also a minister and college president, and yet Torrey's tribute to him as the "*father* of American botany" (Shear and Stevens, 1921) is a deserved one. The work of a more recent floristic botanist, Professor Fernald of Harvard University, also deserves mention since, despite his broad interest in the whole flora of the northeastern United States and adjacent Canada, his treatment of the Cyperaceae in the eighth edition of *Gray's Manual* (Fernald, 1950) is the best botanists will have for Cyperaceae in much of North America for many years to come. This will probably be the case even though several sedge genera are in need of revision, including one of the largest genera of flowering plants in North America — the genus *Carex*.

The following discussion emphasizes the need for taxonomic investigation in the Cyperaceae with respect to some of the problems I have encountered in North American leafy species of *Scirpus*.

Delineation of Leafy Species of *Scirpus*

Among plants often placed in *Scirpus* there is considerable diversity, and it is difficult to delineate major groups with precision at present. It is apparent that we need to evaluate more anatomical and embryological characteristics, in addition to morphological characteristics of spikelets and flower parts, before a natural arrangement of species can be con-

167

structed. Of particular interest are the characteristics Van der Veken (1965) found in the embryos of plants in *Scirpus* and other sedge genera. The characteristics he described confirm that plants named *Scirpus cubensis* should be treated under *Cyperus* and aid in the delineation of other diverse groups treated under *Scirpus*. For example, plants similar to *S. smithii*, which usually have inconspicuous culm leaves, have mushroom-shaped embryos which differ considerably from the turbinate embryos found in plants (e.g., *S. atrovirens*) which have well-developed culm leaves. Most plants which have well-developed culm leaves are separable from other groups in *Scirpus* by the V-shaped hyaline orifice of the leaf sheath, numerous spikelets in much-branched inflorescences, achenes mostly less than 1.5 mm long with comparatively thin walls, and small embryos turbinate in outline.

Variation Patterns in Three North American Species Groups

Many North American leafy species of *Scirpus* are superficially difficult to distinguish from one another, have small differences in chromosome number from related species, and hybridize with one another to some extent. The chromosome numbers, for the most part, are consistent for a given species and provide a characteristic for distinguishing species as well as indicating relationships among them (Graph 1). Hybridization occurs among several species and is a factor to consider with respect to the variability of the group and the origin of some of the species. Three species groups are discussed below with respect to these characteristics.

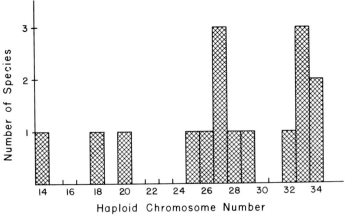

GRAPH 1. Chromosome numbers observed among North American leafy species of *Scirpus*.

Scirpus lineatus AND RELATED SPECIES

When examined on herbarium sheets, *S. lineatus* and *S. pendulus* are almost identical, and it is difficult to find consistent characteristics to distinguish them. However, the study of plants in the field, chromosome observations, and the examination of achene epidermal cells provided characteristics which support the distinctions of these species. *Scirpus lineatus* is restricted to the Atlantic and Gulf Coastal Plain in the southeastern United States and is usually found in moist, shaded localities next to streams or in swamps. At maturity the culms are lax, and the inflorescences often lop over to the ground. In addition to a terminal inflorescence, two or three lateral inflorescences are usually present. The inflorescence rays are somewhat divaricate and have axillary bulblets late in the season. The inner walls of achene epidermal cells have a wavy configuration, and a haploid number of 18 chromosomes has been determined from pollen mother cells. *Scirpus pendulus* is widespread in North America and grows in marshes, moist meadows, and ditches. At maturity the culms are nearly upright and have a terminal inflorescence only, or 1 or, rarely, 2 lateral inflorescences. The rays are pendulous (not divaricate) and lack axillary bulblets at maturity. The inner walls of achene epidermal cells are less wavy than those of *S. lineatus,* and a haploid number of 20 chromosomes has been determined from pollen mother cells.

Scirpus lineatus bears some resemblance to *S. divaricatus,* a species growing primarily in bottomland swamps in the southeastern United States which has a strongly divaricate inflorescence. Actually, *S. lineatus* is intermediate between *S. divaricatus* and *S. pendulus,* although it resembles the latter more than the former, on the basis of its habitat, inflorescence branching, and chromosome number (a haploid number of 14 has been determined for *S. divaricatus*). Both *S. divaricatus* and *S. lineatus* have lax culms and produce bulblets at maturity, although bulblets occur at nodes of the culm as well as in the inflorescence of *S. divaricatus.* It is possible that *S. lineatus* may have originated through hybridization between *S. divaricatus* and *S. pendulus,* but the only evidence for this hypothesis is the intermediate morphological status of *S. lineatus.* At the present time there are no known hybrids among these three species.

Scirpus atrovirens AND RELATED SPECIES

Scirpus hattorianus is a widespread North American species which closely resembles *S. atrovirens* and which has been identified as *S. atrovirens* var. *georgianus* by most botanists (Schuyler, 1967a). The spikelets are in glomerules at the tips of divergent inflorescence rays, and the relatively short mucronate scales are usually blackish. The achenes (Fig. 1) are about 1 mm long and usually have 5 or 6 delicate bristles at the base. The haploid chromosome number has been determined as 28. *Scirpus atrovirens* is also widespread in North America and often grows together with *S. hattorianus*. Generally, however, the localities where *S. atrovirens* grows are wetter and more lowland than those where *S. hattorianus* grows. The inflorescence rays are not so strongly divergent as those of *S. hattorianus*, and the scales are generally larger and more brownish. The achenes (Fig. 2) are larger, about 1.1 mm long, and have longer and more rigid bristles than *S. hattorianus*. Attempts to get clear meiotic figures of this species have not been successful, and it is still in need of cytological investigation. Numerous hybrids between *S. atrovirens* and *S. hattorianus* have been examined. They occur sporadically in areas where both species coexist; they can be recognized by their intermediate morphological characteristics and abortive seeds.

Scirpus ancistrochaetus also resembles *S. atrovirens* but is not likely to be confused with it so easily as *S. hattorianus* might be. It is known

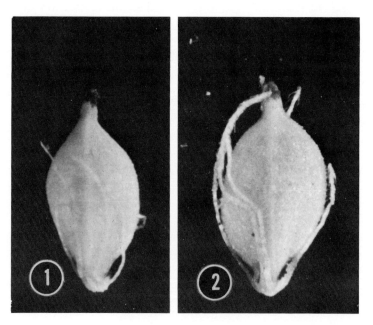

Fig. 1. Achene of *S. hattorianus* (*Wilkens 12136* PH).
Fig. 2. Achene of *S. atrovirens* (*Wilkens 12155* PH).

Fig. 3. Achene of *S. ancistrochaetus* (*Schuyler 3450* PH).
Fig. 4. Achene of *S. georgianus* (*Schuyler 3949* PH).

from only a few localities in the northeastern United States and usually grows in bogs, mud-holes, and margins of pools. The glomerules of spikelets are at tips of arching inflorescence rays, and the slightly mucronate scales are longer than those of *S. atrovirens*. The achenes (Fig. 3) are large, mostly 1.2 to 1.5 mm long, and have more rigid bristles than any of the species discussed here. The haploid chromosome number is 27. Some specimens have been examined which are hybrids between *S. ancistrochaetus* and either *S. atrovirens* or *S. hattorianus*. Because of the morphological similarity of *S. atrovirens* and *S. hattorianus,* it is difficult to be certain which of them is involved as one of the parents. The hybrids are highly sterile on the basis of seed abortion, pollen distortion, and pollen stainability. However, at the type locality of *S. ancistrochaetus* in Vermont, there is evidence of introgression among such highly sterile hybrids and *S. ancistrochaetus, S. atrovirens,* and *S. hattorianus* (Schuyler, 1967b).

It is apparent that *S. atrovirens* is morphologically and ecologically intermediate between *S. hattorianus* and *S. ancistrochaetus* and thus of possible hybrid origin. The chromosome observations of Hicks (1928) and Schuyler (1967b) also suggest that *S. atrovirens* is of hybrid origin.

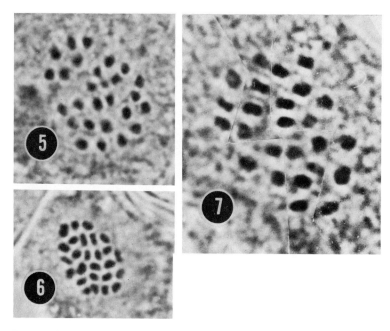

FIG. 5. Chromosomes, meiosis I, 27 units, *S. georgianus (Schuyler 3930* PH).
FIG. 6. Chromosomes, meiosis I, 26 units, *S. georgianus (Schuyler 3961,* PH).
FIG. 7. Chromosomes, meiosis I, 25 units, *S. georgianus (Schuyler 3863,* PH).

Both have reported difficulty in obtaining clear figures, and my experience in working with cytological material of *S. atrovirens* is similar to that I have encountered with other hybrids in *Scirpus*.

Another species easily confused with *S. atrovirens* and its relatives is *S. georgianus*. It is most readily distinguished from other species by the lack of bristles, or the presence of as many as 3 short ones, at the base of the achenes (Fig. 4). Three different chromosome numbers have been observed in this species and, for nine localities in which counts have been obtained, six of them had plants with 27 units in meiosis I (Fig. 5), two had plants with 26 units (Fig. 6), and one had plants with 25 units (Fig. 7). There is morphological variation among plants of *S. georgianus*, but so far it has been difficult to correlate it with the chromosome numbers. Although plants at a given locality are morphologically similar, there are differences between those from different localities, even when they have the same chromosome number. For example, plants studied from near Neffs in Lehigh County, Pennsylvania, are morphologically distinguishable from those studied from Folcroft in Delaware County, Pennsylvania, although 27 units were observed in plants from both localities. However, the plants which had 25 units from northwest of

Moorestown in Burlington County, New Jersey, are morphologically distinguishable from plants studied at all localities where 26 or 27 units were observed. Whether or not any of this variation will be of significance in delineating taxa is questionable, but further study of this species might provide a better understanding of factors related to variation.

Scirpus cyperinus AND RELATED SPECIES

Scirpus cyperinus is an extremely variable species, and hybridization between it and related species appears to be responsible for difficulty in delineating taxa in this group. Northern variants of *S. cyperinus* have spikelets in glomerules, brownish scales frequently less than 1.5 mm long, achenes which mature in late July and early August, and 33 units in meiosis I. *Scirpus atrocinctus* differs from these variants of *S. cyperinus* by having solitary spikelets at tips of pedicels, blackish scales usually longer than 1.5 mm, achenes which mature in late June and early July, and 34 units in meiosis I. Both *S. cyperinus* and *S. atrocinctus* can be found growing together throughout much of the northeastern United States, and there is evidence of abundant introgressive hybridization between them (Schuyler, 1964). Plants of apparent hybrid origin have many enlarged seeds on a numerical basis, but on a percentage basis they have a low number in view of the large number that could be produced by an individual plant if every flower produced seeds.

I suspect that *S. atrocinctus* may be of hybrid origin between *S. cyperinus* and *S. longii* (Schuyler, 1964), the latter being restricted to localities near the Atlantic Coast of the northeastern United States and in adjacent Canada. *Scirpus atrocinctus* is morphologically intermedate between *S. cyperinus* and *S. longii,* although it resembles the former more than the latter species. Both *S. cyperinus* and *S. longii* have 33 units in meiosis I, and *S. atrocinctus* has 34. Possibly this higher number originated through cytological irregularities due to hybridization.

CORRELATION BETWEEN HYBRIDIZATION AND CHROMOSOME NUMBER

The haploid chromosome numbers determined for 14 of the 18 North American leafy species of *Scirpus* range from 14 to 34 (Graph 1; a listing of species and their chromosome numbers is given in Schuyler, 1967b), and the amount and complexity of interspecific hybridization is correlated with ascending numbers. Among species with low numbers, no hybrids are known to exist; among species with intermediate numbers, hybridization is sporadic in areas where the parents coexist; and, among species with high numbers, hybridization and introgression are obviously responsible for troublesome variability confronting the taxonomist.

One hypothesis I have presented for this situation (1967b) is that this group may be an evolutionary series of hybrid complexes with plants having low chromosome numbers being more primitive than plants having high chromosome numbers. Those with low chromosome numbers may have existed longer in time, and their hybrid derivatives may have been subject to selection for a longer period of time. Among plants with high numbers, hybridization may be a more recent occurrence, and hybrid derivatives may not have been subject to selection for as long of a period of time. Thus, among plants with low numbers the only evidence of hybridization is the intermediate morphology of some of the species, while among plants with high numbers numerous hybrids with varying degrees of fertility can be found.

It may also be possible that species with high chromosome numbers can produce hybrids with greater fertility because of duplication of genetic material due to polyploidy. Stranhede (1965) reported that hybrids in *Eleocharis* with high chromosome numbers produce viable and fertile offspring despite pronounced cytological irregularities, and he suggested that polyploidy is a factor responsible for the viability of such hybrids. This may account for the apparent high degree of fertility observed in hybrids among plants of *Scirpus cyperinus* and related species which have high chromosome numbers.

REFERENCES

Fernald, M. L. (1950). "Gray's Manual of Botany." 8th edition. 1632 pp. American Book Co., New York.

Hicks, G. C. (1928). Chromosome Studies in the Cyperaceae, with Special Reference to *Scirpus. Botan. Gaz.* **86,** 295–317.

Muhlenberg, H. (1813). "Catalogus Plantarum Americae Septentrionalis Huc Usque Cognitarum Indigenarum et Cicurum." 112 pp. W. Hamilton, Lancaster, Pennsylvania.

Muhlenberg, H. (1817). "Descriptio Uberior Graminum et Plantarum Calamariarum Americae Septentrionalis Indigenarum et Cicurum." 295 pp. S. W. Conrad, Philadelphia.

Schuyler, A. E. (1964). A Biosystematic Study of the *Scirpus cyperinus* Complex. *Proc. Acad. Natl. Sci. Phila.* **115,** 283–311.

Schuyler, A. E. (1967a). *Scirpus hattorianus* in North America. *Not Nat.* No. **398,** 1–5.

Schuyler, A. E. (1967b). A taxonomic revision of North American leafy species of *Scirpus. Proc. Acad. Natl. Sci. Phila.* **119,** 295–323.

Shear, C. L., and Stevens, N. E. (1921). The correspondence of Schweinitz and Torrey. *Mem. Torrey Botan. Club* **16,** 119–300.

Stranhede, S. O. (1965). Chromosome studies in *Eleosharis*, subser. *Palustres.* III. Observations on Western European taxa. *Opera Botan.* **9**(2), 1–86.

Van der Veken, P. (1965). Contribution a l'embryographie systématique des Cyperaceae-Cyperoideae. *Bull. Jard. Botan. Bruxelles* **35,** 285–354.

Natural Hybridization in the *Scirpus lacustris* Complex in North Central United States*

S. Galen Smith†

The large, rhizomatous *Scirpus* with cylindrical, essentially leafless culms constitute a small natural group which is widespread in the Northern Hemisphere. Within this group, species delimitation is sometimes difficult. Since Chase (1904) clarified the characters of the taxa, most authors (e.g., Beetle, 1941; Fernald, 1950; Gleason and Cronquist, 1963; Hotchkiss, 1965) have recognized the three North American species *S. acutus* Muhl., *S. validus* Vahl., and *S. heterochaetus* Chase. The occurrence of morphologically intermediate plants, however, led Beal and Monson (1954) to consider *S. acutus* and *S. validus* one species. In Europe, *S. lacustris* L. and *S. tabernaemontani* C. C. Gmel. have been treated either as separate species or as subspecies of one species (Bakker, 1954; Otzen, 1962). Most recently, Koyama (1958, 1962, 1963), after extensive experience with both Asiatic and American plants, included the three American taxa as well as the Old World *S. tabernaemontani* under *S. lacustris,* which has usually been considered to be restricted to the Old World. According to this view, *S. lacustris* is worldwide in the Northern Hemisphere and includes all plants usually placed in five distinct species.

This group is herein termed the *S. lacustris* complex, following Koyama (1963), to emphasize the broad geographical scope of the problem, although the traditional recognition of three North American species and two Eurasian species is followed.

*This work was supported in part by a National Science Foundation Research Participation Fellowship at the University of Michigan and in part by a Wisconsin State Universities Board of Regents Research Grant.

†I am indebted to Edward G. Voss and William S. Benninghoff of the University of Michigan, to David L. Trauger of Iowa State University, and to Robert E. Stewart of the Northern Prairie Wildlife Research Center for valuable assistance with various phases of the work.

The three species herein considered are all widely distributed in temperate North America. Both *S. acutis* and *S. validus* occur from the Atlantic to the Pacific coasts in boreal, warm temperate, and subtropical regions. Although these two species are sympatric over large parts of North America, *S. acutis* occurs beyond the range of *S. validus* in the Southwest, and *S. validus* occurs beyond the range of *S. acutus* in the Southeast, the Pacific Northwest and perhaps in the far Northeast. The distribution of *S. heterochaetus* is both disjunct and more restricted than the other two species. It is found entirely within the ranges of both *S. acutus* and *S. validus,* in the Northeast from Ontario to New York, as well as in the Midwest and West, primarily in the central and northern prairie region.

Both *S. acutus* and *S. validus* are found in a wide range of freshwater habitats including meadows, fens, marshes, and shores and bars of lakes and streams. The relatively poorly known *S. heterochaetus* seems to occur primarily as an emergent in marshes and lakes.

Natural hybridization in the *S. lacustris* complex has been reported frequently in Europe (Bakker, 1954; Otzen, 1962), but seldom in North America. Koyama (1962) described putative *S. acutus × heterochaetus* hybrids from herbarium specimens collected in Vermont, Ontario, Quebec, and Minnesota, naming them *S. × oblongus.* The other two possible hybrid combinations have not been described. *Scirpus lacustris* and *S. tabernaemontani* are reported to hybridize with *S. triqueter* in Europe (Bakker, 1954; Koyama, 1962; Otzen, 1963).

This discussion describes putative hybrids and hybrid populations and suggests some of the factors of breeding biology and ecology that appear to control the occurrence and extent of hybridization in this complex.

Materials and Methods

Field studies were made from 1964 through 1967 in the North Central United States, principally in Michigan, Wisconsin, and North Dakota, most intensively in 1966 in the vicinity of the University of Michigan Biological Station at Douglas Lake, Cheboygan Country, Michigan.

Morphological variation of twelve populations was analyzed with the aid of hybrid indices and scatter diagrams according to the methods of Anderson (1949). For each population analyzed, 16 to 68 flowering shoots were collected at intervals of about 3 to 5 m on one or more transects made by walking through the population in approximately straight lines. As clones could not be distinguished with certainty, many samples probably include clonal duplicates.

Development of inflorescences was observed from late June to mid-August 1966 in several populations of *S. acutus* and *S. validus* in the vicinity of Douglas Lake, Michigan. Daily to weekly observations of the stage of development of about 20 tagged inflorescences of each species were made throughout the growing season.

Inflorescences for chromosome studies were fixed in acetic acid-alcohol, stored in a freezer for 1 or 2 weeks, the anthers squashed in acetocarmine, and the slides made permanent with diaphane. Voucher specimens are deposited in the herbaria of the University of Wisconsin at Madison and the University of Michigan.

Measurements of electrical conductance of water were made in North Dakota with a battery-powered portable "Solu Bridge" model RB-2 conductivity meter.

Pollen for estimations of fertility was taken from under the scales of younger spikelets that bore mature achenes in their basal florets. Pollen from more mature spikelets often appears to be highly abortive, even though abundant achenes are present.

Reproductive Biology

Members of the *S. lacustris* complex are strongly rhizomatous, the clones often spreading rapidly to cover large areas. Portions of clones broken loose by such factors as waves, ice, or muskrats may also be carried to new locations where they may form new colonies. At many localities vegetative reproduction appears to predominate over reproduction from seeds.

Sexual reproduction is probably frequent at some localities, however, for many populations I observed are strikingly variable in a way best explained by frequent outcrossing, genetic heterogeneity, and frequent seedling establishment. Also, long-distance dispersal of achenes, most probably by means of animals, would be required to establish the many isolated populations to which vegetative propagules could not readily be carried.

The following description of flowering behavior is based on my observations, primarily in the vicinity of Douglas Lake, Michigan.

1. Starting at some time from late May to mid-June in the North Central United States and adjacent Canada, the first flowering culms elongate rapidly from the base and the young inflorescences emerge from the sheaths of the inflorescence bracts. Meiosis and the first pollen mitosis occur during elongation of the inflorescence rays. Only the basal portion (ca. 5 mm in length) of each spikelet matures at this time, the apical portion remaining very short and with immature flowers.

2. New culms develop and flower successively, starting at the oldest part of a rhizome and proceeding toward its apex. New inflorescences develop over a period of several weeks, so that during the middle of the summer all stages of development from premeiosis to mature fruit may be present within one clone.

3. Within one inflorescence the stigmas of the basal flowers of all the spikelets are exerted and apparently receptive for about 3 or 4 days while the inflorescence rays are still elongating. The stigmas then turn brown and wither within about 24 hr.

4. The stamens of the flowers which have previously passed through the stigmatic stage become exerted and shed pollen in two stages, about one-half of them during the first 24 hr. following the withering of the stigmas and the other one-half during the second 24 hr. Pollen is shed primarily during the morning hours.

5. Over a period that appears to last from one to several weeks, the apical part of each spikelet elongates and its flowers progressively mature. During this period receptive stigmas as well as anthers shedding pollen are often present at the same time in the same spikelet, so that self-pollination is likely to occur. Because of the acropetal pattern of flowering, spikelets may bear mature achenes basally and unopened flowers distally.

Scirpus acutus begins flowering a few days earlier than *S. validus* at Goose Lake, Hamilton County, Iowa, and in the vicinity of Douglas Lake, Michigan. *Scirpus heterochaetus* at Goose Lake began flowering in late May 1966 about the same time as *S. acutus* in the same population.

From these observations it appears that outbreeding is favored by strong protogyny during early stages of flowering of the spikelets, whereas inbreeding is probably favored by the nearly simultaneous maturation of stamens and stigmas in the same spikelets later in development.

Chromosomes were observed during the first mitosis in young pollen grains of one collection of *S. acutus* (Douglas Lake, Cheboygan County, Michigan, *Smith* 3881) and one collection of putative *S. acutus* × *validus* from the hybrid swarm described herein at Mackinaw City, Emmet County, Michigan (*Smith* 3957-5). The *S. acutus* collection has 19 metaphase chromosomes of which 18 are very short and 1 is about three times longer. The karyotype is very similar to that reported for *S. lacustris* with $n = 19$ in Japan (Tanaka, 1940). This number is new for *S acutus* (reported as $n = 20$ from Massachusetts by Hicks, 1928) as well as for the *S. lacustris* complex in North America. In the putative hybrid, prophase chromosomes vary from 18 to 22 within the same anther, indicating that irregular meiosis has occurred. Other reports of chromosome numbers for the *S lacustris* complex are $n = 18$ for one collection of *S. heterochaetus* in Massachusetts (Hicks, 1928) and $n = 21$ for many collections of both *S. lacustris* and *S. tabernaemontani* in Europe (Otzen, 1962).

Morphological Characteristics of the Species

As there are some discrepancies among published descriptions (e.g., Chase 1904; Beetle, 1941; Koyama, 1962) and between them and my observations, a brief evaluation of the species characteristics seems desirable.

Owing both to developmental change and direct environmental modification, some characteristics vary considerably even within one clone. In all three species unfavorable environmental conditions or disease may reduce the number and size of the spikelets, and the length of the inflorescence branches (and therefore the number of solitary spikelets), and the number and size of the internal air spaces as seen in a cross section of the stem. Furthermore, the spikelets elongate during development, often for several weeks, and the inflorescence rays elongate for 1 or 2 weeks during the early stages of flowering. The reddish pigments sometimes present in the spikelet scales often fade as the spikelets mature.

The length of the achenes, generally used to distinguish the species by other authors, is very similar in all three species in several of the populations herein described. Achene length is usually shorter in *S. validus* than in *S. acutus* and *S. heterochaetus,* however.

The air spaces in the culms may be observed with the aid of a hand lens. They are measured on cross sections of the upper third of the culm (average air space width = number of spaces along a diameter divided by the diameter of the stem).

The following characteristics, based on flowering shoots with at least some mature achenes, were found to be reliable within the study area. The most reliable characteristics are italicized, and some are illustrated in Figs. 1 and 2.

Scirpus acutus. Culms hard, dark green, with *internal air spaces averaging 0.3 to 0.5 mm wide, 9 to 14 in a cross-section diameter; spikelets occasionally solitary but mostly clustered in groups of 3 to 7,* relatively few, on short, stiff rays which are scabrous on their margins; *spikelet scales* relatively thick and opaque, *dull, grayish brown prominently spotted with bright brown,* with grayish midribs, prominently long ciliate, at least the lowest prominently scabrous, *with usually crooked awns exceeding scales by more than one-half of awn length,* the awns mostly 1 to 1.5 mm long; *perianth bristles 6,* about equaling achenes; *styles bifid; achenes lenticular,* ca. one-third shorter than, and hidden by, scales.

Scirpus validus. Culms soft, pale green, with *internal air spaces averaging 1.0 to 2.5 mm wide, 2 to 4 in a cross-section diameter; spikelets solitary to clustered in groups of 2 or 3,*

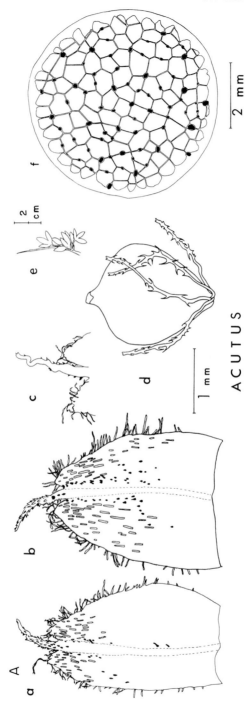

ACUTUS

FIG. 1. Morphology of *Scirpus acutus, S. validus,* and putative hybrids from Fish Creek near Ashland, Bayfield County, Wisconsin. *a, b,* Spikelet scales; *c,* spikelet scale apices; *d,* achenes and perianth bristles; *e,* inflorescences; *f,* culm cross-sections at about one-third stem length from top, showing major air spaces and vascular bundles (shown in black). On the scales, the spinelike hairs (shown in black) are reddish and the rectangular markings are bright orangish brown. Further explanation is in the text.

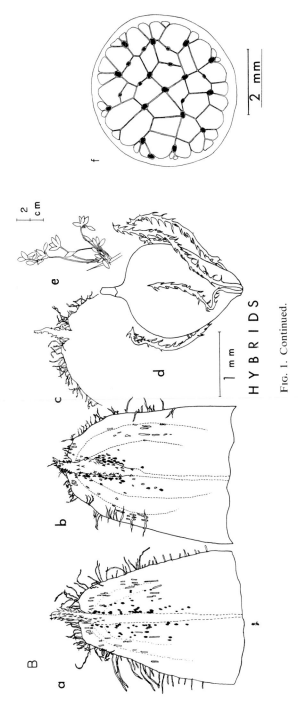

HYBRIDS

Fig. 1. Continued.

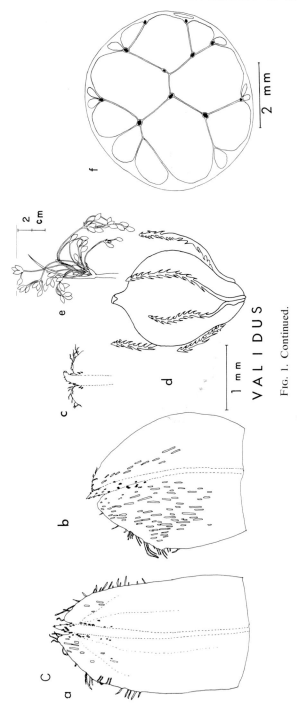

VALIDUS

Fig. 1. Continued.

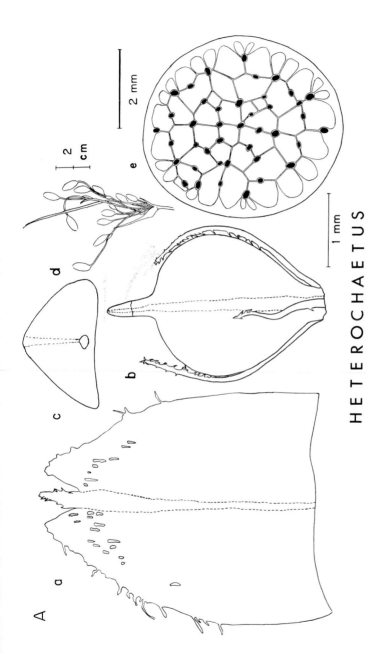

HETEROCHAETUS

Fig. 2. Morphology of *S. acutus*, *S. heterochaetus*, and putative hybrids from near Woodworth, Stutsman County, North Dakota. *a*, Spikelet scales; *b*, achenes and perianth bristles; *c*, achenes, view from apex; *d*, inflorescences; *e*, culm cross section at about one-third of stem length from top, showing major air spaces and vascular bundles (black). The awn of the *S. acutus* scale shown is unusually short and blunt; the inset (*a'*) shows a characteristic long, slender, crooked awn. The reddish spinelike hairs shown in black on the scale of the hybrid are found only on a few specimens of the hybrid and *S. acutus* in this sample. The rectangular markings are reddish brown. Further explanation is in the text.

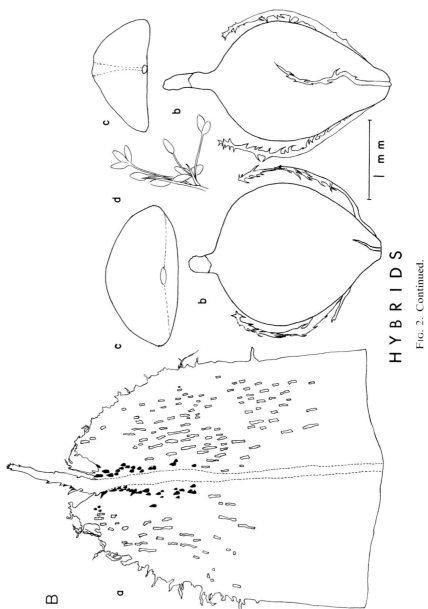

HYBRIDS

Fig. 2. Continued.

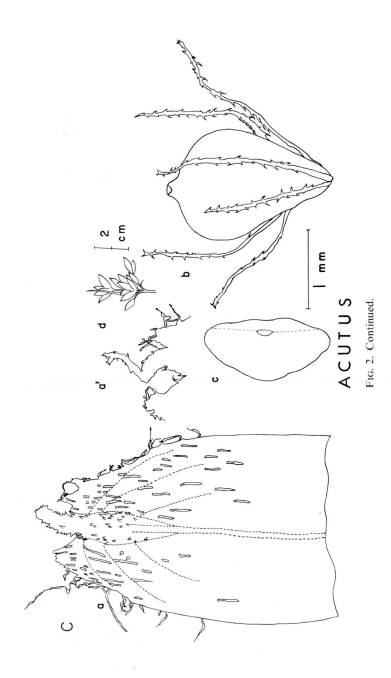

ACUTUS

Fig. 2. Continued.

relatively numerous, on long, flexible rays; *spikelet scales* thin and translucent, *bright orange-brown* with obscure darker spots and usually green midribs, prominently ciliate, scabrous on awns and midribs, *with nearly straight awns exceeding scales by less than one-half of awn length,* the awns mostly 0.2 to 0.5 mm long; *perianth bristles 6,* about equaling achenes; *styles bifid; achenes lenticular,* slightly shorter than scales, in var. *creber* partially exposed in spikelets.

   Scirpus heterochaetus. Culms usually hard but sometimes soft, with *internal air spaces averaging 0.4 to 0.9 mm wide and 6 to 9 in a cross-section diameter; spikelets all solitary,* relatively few on long, flexible rays; *spikelet scales* thin and translucent, uniformly pale gray to orange-brown, with green or grayish midrib, glabrous except for the scabrous awn and usually *a few short cilia, with straight awns exceeding scales by one-half of awn length or less; perianth bristles 2 to 4, the 2 lateral bristles prominent but shorter than achenes, the dorsal and ventral bristles often minute; styles trifid; achenes with a rounded dorsal angle,* about one-third shorter than and hidden by the scales.

Descriptions of Natural Populations

   Hybrid index computations and constructions of scatter diagrams (Tables 1 and 2) utilized only three characters, as the remaining characteristics of the species were difficult to score and trial scatter diagrams and hybrid indices based on 7 to 10 characters yielded essentially the same patterns of variations as those based on only three characters. Several other combinations of three different characters that were tried also yielded essentially the same variation patterns. The awn on the spikelet scale, although diagnostic, had been broken off on most speciments of *S. acutus* collected late in the season and so was used only for the single population containing *S. acutus* and *heterochaetus* for which the sample consists of relatively young shoots in which the spikelet awns are mostly intact. The color of the spikelet scales was scored subjectively, using spikelets typical of the extreme form of the species as a standard for comparison. Phenotypic variation, previously discussed, is doubtless responsible for some of the variation in the graphs. In spite of problems of scoring the samples, however, the analyses herein presented serve to illustrate general patterns of variation in the population studied.

POPULATIONS WITH NO EVIDENCE OF HYBRIDIZATION

   Populations containing only one species, generally either *S. acutus* or *S. validus,* were the predominant type observed, especially in northern Michigan and northern Wisconsin. These single-species populations never contained evident hybrids, although variation sometimes was suggestive of introgression.

   Scirpus acutus and *S. validus* were observed growing together with no

TABLE 1
Hybrid Index Computation for *S. acutus* and *S. validus*[a]

	S. acutus	*Intermediates*	*S. validus*
Number of air spaces in a cross-section diameter of culm	More than 9	5–8	2–4
Number of solitary spikelets out of 10	0–2	3–4	5–10
Color of spikelet scales (exclusive of brown spots)	Nearly colorless, pale grayish brown	Pale orangish brown	Bright orange-brown
Index value for each character	0	1	2
Total index value	0	3	6

[a] See explanation in the text and in the legend for Fig. 3.

TABLE 2
Hybrid Index Computation for *S. acutus* and *S. heterochaetus*

	S. acutus	*Intermediates*	*S. heterochaetus*
Achene shape	Lenticular	Weakly trigonous	Trigonous
Number of solitary spikelets out of 10	0–2	3–8	9–10
Spikelet scale awn	Long, bent	Intermediate	Short, straight
Index value for each character	0	1	2
Total index value	0	3	6

evidence of hybridization at only five localities in northern Michigan and Wisconsin. The largest of these populations, emergent in the Black River for about four miles between Cheboygan and Alverno, Cheboygan County, Michigan, serves as a standard for comparison with populations of *S. acutus* and *S. validus* in which hybrids occur. The scatter diagram and hybrid index graph (Fig. 3), based on a sample from this population, demonstrate that the species are amply distinct. Most of the scattering of spots is probably due to environmentally caused phenotypic variation, as discussed earlier. Analyses of samples of several northern Michigan and Wisconsin single-species populations of the same two species yielded patterns of variation very similar to those of the Black River sample.

POPULATIONS WITH APPARENT HYBRIDS

Of the 23 populations observed in which two or more species grew together, 17 contained apparent hybrids. The following 14 included *S. acutus, S. validus,* and hybrids between them: 8 in northern Michigan, 1 in northern Wisconsin, 2 in southeastern Wisconsin, and 3 in central North Dakota. The remaining populations containing hybrids were: 1 in central North Dakota with *S. acutus* and *S. heterochaetus,* another in central North Dakota with all three species, and one in central Iowa with all three species.

The simplest of the hybrid populations analyzed occurred on alluvial sand and clay at the mouth of Fish Creek on the shore of Chequamegon Bay on Lake Superior, Ashland County, Wisconsin. This population consisted of typical *S. acutus* and *S. validus* intermixed with several intermediate forms. A large stand of *S. validus* occupied the marshes along the creek immediately upstream. The plants typical of *S. acutus* and *S. validus* were highly fertile, the florets of the basal half of the spikelets in the samples bearing 50 to 90% mature achenes and 60 to 95% normal pollen grains (fully formed and stainable with cotton blue in lactophenol). The putative hybrids are represented in the sample by four apparent clones differing slightly from each other in spikelet color and morphology. One of these clones bears small, poorly developed spikelets which still had not shed pollen on July 22, 1966, and the others bear about 10 to 15% apparently mature achenes in the basal portion of the spikelets. The pollen in the intermediate plants in the sample is highly abortive, with only 1 to 25% apparently normal grains.

Scirpus acutus and the putative hybrids form a single group in the graphs (Fig. 3), because the *S. acutus* plants of this population have unusually brightly colored spikelets, while the apparent hybrids tend to have both clustered spikelets and small internal air spaces in their stems. The putative hybrids, however, are clearly intermediate between their parents in morphological details of spikelet scales, perianth bristles, and stem anatomy (Fig. 1).

Another population, consisting of *S. acutus, S. validus,* and a few sterile hybrid clones was located at the mouth of an unnamed creek on the south bank of the Rock River about 1¼ miles east of U.S. Highway 51, Rock County, southeastern Wisconsin (Section 14, R. 12 E., T. 4 N.).

The remaining *S. acutus* × *validus* populations included fertile hybrids and, if large, resembled hybrid swarms. Variation patterns typical of these populations may be illustrated by a sample collected about 1 mile north of Escanaba, Michigan, along the shore of Little Bay de Noc (a large northward extension of the northwest part of Green Bay in northwestern Lake Michigan), where U.S. Highway 2 traverses the landward margin of extensive marshes with sandy soil. At this locality, *S. validus* grew in scattered colonies in wet soil where water was seeping from under the highway, *S. acutus* formed extensive stands emergent in the Bay as well as with *S. americanus* in wet soil between the Bay and the highway, and the hybrids occurred at the base of the highway embankment where *S. acutus* and *S. validus* grew together. As illustrated by the hybrid index graph and the scatter diagram (Fig. 3), the Little Bay de Noc population appears to include numerous hybrids, and *S. acutus* and *S. validus* may be only distinguished arbitrarily. Although some of the hybrids are sterile, many produce abundant achenes.

Another large hybrid swarm occurred in sandy soil in water ranging from about ⅓ to 1 m on the northwestern shore of Lake Huron in the angle formed by the Straits Transit Co. Ferry slip causeway and a parking lot constructed on fill to the south, at the end of Wisconsin Highway 23 in Mackinaw City, Emmet County, Michigan. *Scirpus acutus, S. validus,* and various intermediates were scattered throughout the population, although apparent hybrids were especially abundant on fill at the edges of the parking lot and causeway. A similar but smaller population in the same county was sampled at Duncan Bay on Lake Huron about 2 miles east of Cheboygan, Cheboygan County, in the vicinity of a small boat channel dredged through evidently marly shoreline marshes with sandy soil. Here *S. acutus* was widespread with *S. americanus* in wet soil, whereas *S. validus* occurred primarily in shallow water in the vicinity of the boat channel. The hybrids at Duncan Bay occurred mostly on wet soil, apparently on fill from the dredging operation, except for one small hybrid colony growing in about ⅓ m of water with *S. validus.* Graphical analyses of samples from these two populations demonstrate the complete morphological intergradation between *S. acutus* and *S. validus* at both Mackinaw City and Duncan Bay in a manner very similar to that of the Little Bay de Noc population described above.

Other apparent *S. acutus* × *validus* populations were sampled at the following localities.

Michigan. Fill at a boat landing on the Indian River near the town of Indian River, Emmet County (two or three small hybrid clones); in artificial ponds near the headquarters of the Seney National Wildlife Refuge, Schoolcraft County (many hybrid clones scattered in very

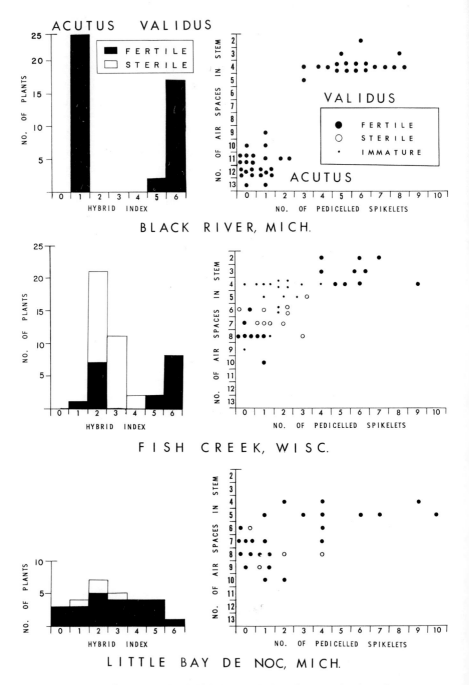

FIG. 3. Scatter diagrams and hybrid index graphs based on samples from three *Scirpus acutus-validus* populations in northern Michigan and Wisconsin showing variation typical of populations with no hybrids (Black River), a few sterile hybrids (Fish Creek), and a

shallow man-made ponds); on road fill in shoreline marshes at the head of Grand Traverse Bay about 4 miles east of Traverse City, Traverse County (a large, complex hybrid swarm similar to those described in detail above).

Wisconsin. In channels (dredged in 1871 in connection with logging) in marshes along the Peshtigo River near its mouth on Green Bay, Lake Michigan, about 7 miles south of Marinette, Marinette County (a large population incompletely studied but apparently including a hybrid swarm); around marly springs and in fens locally called "Bluff Springs" at the source of Bluff Creek, about 7 miles southwest of Whitewater, Walworth County (a small hybrid swarm).

North Dakota. Shallow ponds in the prairies of the Missouri Coteau about 4 miles east and 8 miles north of Woodworth, Stutsman County (two complex hybrid swarms similar to the Little Bay de Noc and Mackinaw City populations described above).

A population consisting of intermixed *S. heterochaetus, S. acutus,* and their apparent hybrids was located in about 0.2 to 1 m of water in a prairie pond about 5 miles east of Woodworth, Stutsman County, North Dakota. In the sample from this population (Fig. 4), most of the plants closely resemble either *S. acutus* or *S. heterochaetus* in both the number of solitary spikelets and achene shape. It is evident on careful examination with a dissecting microscope, however, that many specimens are intermediate between the species in the shape and length of the spikelet scale awn, in the number, length, and morphology of the perianth bristles, and in the shape of the achene (Fig. 2). In contrast to the *S. acutus* × *validus* populations, the variation pattern in this population suggests introgression rather than a hybrid swarm.

The only populations observed which included all three species appeared to consist of 3-way hybrid swarms. One of these populations was in a shallow prairie pond about 1 mile east of Woodworth, Stutsman County, North Dakota, and the other in a shallow prairie lake or marsh (Goose Lake) near the town of Jewell, Hamilton County, Iowa. In the North Dakota population at the time of sampling (July 16, 1966), *S. validus* was growing in water up to about 0.6 m deep in a roadside ditch at the mar-

---

hybrid swarm (Little Bay de Noc). The immature specimens from Little Bay de Noc are scored as sterile for the hybrid index graph. The number of air spaces in the stem was counted along a diameter of a cross section made about one-third of culm length from top. The number of pedicelled (solitary) spikelets is the number in 10 (multiply by 10 for percent). "Fertile" means more than 50%, and "sterile" means less than 50%, of the florets in the lower half of the spikelets bearing apparently normal achenes. The same legends apply to all three samples. Further explanation is in the text.

gin of the pond, whereas both *S. acutus* and *S. heterochaetus* were growing with various morphologically intermediate plants in about 0.6 to 1 m of water in the pond. In the Goose Lake population both on August 28,

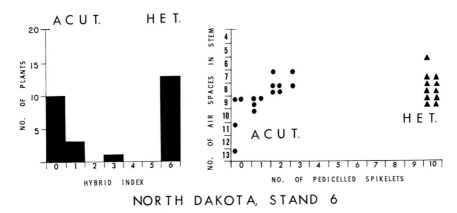

FIG. 4. Scatter diagram and hybrid index graph for a sample of a population containing *S. acutus, S. heterochaetus,* and putative hybrids. All specimens bear at least 50% apparently normal achenes in the basal half of their spikelets. Further explanation is in Fig. 3 and the text. See Fig. 5 for legend concerning dot shape.

1965, and on June 7, 1966, *S. validus* was growing primarily along the shore on wet mud, whereas *S. acutus* and *S. heterochaetus* were growing primarily in water from about 0.3 to 1 m deep in the lake, with the hybrids distributed throughout all water depths (Fig. 5). Goose Lake, in which drastic changes in vegetation and animal populations were described by Weller and Spatcher (1965), is discussed later in relation to stability of the habitat.

In samples collected from both of these apparent hybrid populations, the variation patterns are very complex and difficult to interpret. Occasional plants bearing 4 to 6 poorly developed perianth bristles (similar to those shown in Fig. 2) and about 30 to 50% solitary spikelets are probable hybrids between *S. heterochaetus* and either *S. acutus* or *S. validus* or both. Otherwise, these populations strongly resemble the *S. acutus* × *validus* hybrid swarms already described.

One apparent transgressive recombination found in almost every *S. acutus* × *validus* hybrid swarm bears a dense, spherical mass of essentially sessile spikelets that are generally intermediate between *S. acutus* and *S. validus* in pigmentation and details of scale morphology. Its stem anatomy is also intermediate between that of these species. This form, which would usually be identified as *S. acutus* because of its congested inflorescence, is very similar to the type of *S. occidentalis* var. *congestus* Farwell [*S. acutus* f. *congestus* (Farwell) Fernald] at the University of Michigan herbarium. As no other extreme recombinations were observed, the characters of the species appear to be highly correlated in the hybrid populations (e.g., very soft-stemmed plants always bear brightly colored spikelets and many solitary spikelets).

Numerous putative hybrids of the three possible parental combinations, very similar to those observed in the field, are present in herbarium collections from Wisconsin to Illinois westward through the prairie region, but they are rather scarce in collections I have seen from Michigan eastward.

Ecological Factors

Field observations in this study indicate that three ecological factors strongly influence natural hybridization in the *Scirpus lacustris* complex in the areas studied: water depth, concentration of dissolved solids, and degree of habitat stability. Although these factors are closely interrelated, they are discussed separately for the sake of clarity.

WATER DEPTH

The members of the *S. lacustris* complex appear to be partially isolated by water depth. *Scirpus acutus* was observed flowering and fruiting normally at water depths up to 3 m, at least at Douglas Lake, Michigan, whereas *S. validus* was never observed growing in water more than about 1 m deep. This apparent difference in water depth "preference" was evident in several mixed populations, such as at Goose Lake, Iowa, and two ponds in North Dakota, in which most of the *S. validus* grew on wet mud and very shallow water along the shores whereas *S. acutus* grew in deeper water and *S. heterochaetus,* when present, accompanied *S. acutus* in deeper water. The general correlation between water depth and species distribution is illustrated in Fig. 5.

In many populations, however, there seems to be no correlation between water depth and species distribution, especially along the shores of the Great Lakes. For example, *S. acutus* and *S. validus* grew completely intermixed in water varying from 0 to about 1 m in the Black River, Michigan, in Lake Huron at Mackinaw City, Michigan, and in Lake Superior at Fish Creek, Wisconsin.

In one population in a prairie pond 8 miles north and 4 miles east of Woodworth, North Dakota, *S. acutus* grew primarily in *shallower* water (about 0 to 0.1 m) and *S. validus* grew primarily in *deeper* water (about 0.1 to 0.5 m) at the time of observation on July 7, 1966. Although quantitative measurements are not available, it seems likely that concentration

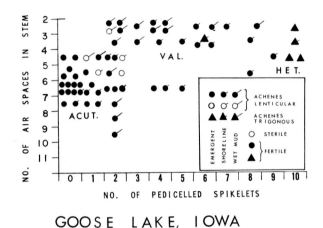

GOOSE LAKE, IOWA

FIG. 5. Scatter diagram showing morphological variation and relation to water depth in a sample from an apparent trihybrid swarm collected on August 28, 1965, at Goose Lake in Hamilton County, Iowa. "Emergent" means water about $\frac{1}{2}$ to 1 m deep; "shoreline" means water-land junction (water 0 m deep); "wet mud" means saturated soil along the uphill, relatively dry margin of the population. Further explanation is in Fig. 3 and the text.

of dissolved solutes which is high in dry seasons around many prairie ponds in the Woodworth region controls the distribution of the species at this locality, *S. acutus* growing in the more saline soil near the pond margin and *S. validus* growing in soil where the salinity is diluted by more abundant water.

CONCENTRATION OF DISSOLVED SOLIDS

My field observations indicate that *S. acutus* is generally associated with higher concentrations of dissolved solids than is either *S. validus* or *S. heterochaetus*. In central North Dakota, where concentrations of dissolved solids in the surface waters are often very high (Stewart and Kantrud, 1967), *S. acutus* is the only species of the *S. lacustris* complex associated with halophytes (e.g., *Salicornia* and *Distichlis*) in obviously saline habitats. These observations agree with conclusions based on quantitative data reported for Wisconsin by Zimmerman (1953; summarized by Curtis, 1959), and for North Dakota by Stewart and Kantrud (1967) and Trauger (1967).

At one very unusual locality in North Dakota, the relationship between species distribution and electrical conductivity (as a general
measure of dissolved solids) of the water was particularly apparent. This
locality is a small calcareous spring area near the eastern shore of the
highly saline and alkaline Salt Alkaline Lake, Kidder County. Here *S.
acutus* occurred along the shore of the lake with *S. paludosus,* adjacent
to obvious salt scalds supporting halophytes including *Distichlis* and
Salicornia, whereas *S. validus* grew with *Eleocharis erythropoda, Typha
latifolia,* and *Scirpus americanus* in small, marly springs within about 50
m of the lake. Several small colonies of probable hybrids occurred between the springs and the lake shore. Four samples collected from four
fairly discrete colonies at this locality are illustrated by the hybrid index
graphs in Fig. 6; they are arrayed with the sample most typical of *S.
acutus* at the top and that most typical of *S. validus* at the bottom. The
electrical conductivity measurements were made on water obtained from

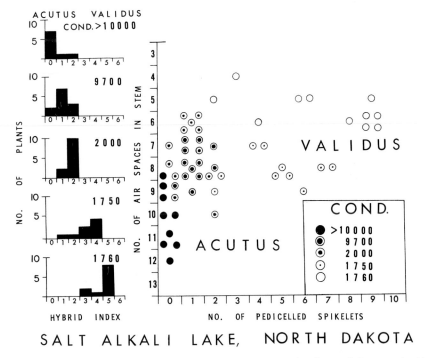

FIG. 6. Hybrid indices and a scatter diagram based on samples from a *Scirpus acutus* ×
validus population at Salt Alkali Lake, Kidder County, North Dakota, showing correlation
between electrical conductance of the water and morphological variation of the plants.
Further explanation is in Fig. 3 and the text.

the center of the colony sampled. As is evident from these graphs, the most extreme form of *S. acutus* was associated with a specific conductance of 10,000 μmhos/cm in the surface water, whereas the most extreme form of *S. validus* was associated with a specific conductance of about 1760 and the morphologically intermediate colonies were associated with conductances ranging from 1750 to 9700. Although the colony at 9700 was identified in the field as *S. acutus,* the samples resemble *S. validus* somewhat in the characters used in the analysis.

DEGREE OF HABITAT STABILITY

In northern Michigan and Wisconsin, all but one of the populations containing hybrids were associated with major earth-moving operations such as building roads, filling marshland, dredging, and constructing artificial ponds and dikes. The one apparent exception is the Fish Creek, Michigan, population. This site could have been extensively disturbed when U.S. Highway 2 was built across the creek near its mouth, however. In addition, it is probable that deposition and shifting of sediments at the mouth of the creek and along the lake shore constitute a large disturbance factor. In southeastern Wisconsin, the Bluff Springs locality has been disturbed by straightening of the creek nearby and by heavy grazing by cattle before 1962.

In sharp contrast to the localities of the Michigan and Wisconsin hybrid swarms, the prairie marshes and ponds with hybrid populations in Iowa and North Dakota appear to have been little disturbed by man. Although the water level at Goose Lake, Iowa, has long been controlled by a low dam, the water levels in ponds studied in North Dakota are not managed in any way. The shallow glacial basins in the prairie region, however, are subject to extreme and rapid fluctuations in water level due to both seasonal and long-term variations in precipitation. Water-level changes are especially large and rapid because of the small sizes of the runoff areas, the usual lack of inlets and outlets, the vagaries of precipitation in the prairie region, and the late summer drying period characteristic of the region.

In the Woodworth, North Dakota, region, water levels were unusually high in many ponds in the spring of 1966, owing primarily to runoff from heavy spring snows. Associated with this high water was a striking decrease in concentration of dissolved solids in some ponds; in an extreme example provided by Robert Stewart (personal communication) for one pond, specific conductance was 3100 μmhos/cm and water depth was $31\frac{1}{2}$ in. (ca. 0.8 m) on May 12, 1966, whereas conductance was

25,000 and water depth was only 6 in. (ca. 0.15 m) on June 21, 1965. Apparently as a result of these environmental changes, the populations of *Scirpus* dominating many of the shallower ponds in 1965 were eliminated in 1966 and replaced by either open water or the aquatic grass *Scholochloa festucacea* except around the pond margins. The seasonal and annual changes in the ponds of the Woodworth, North Dakota, region have been documented by Stewart and Kantrud (1964, 1967), Stewart *et al.* (1966), and David Trauger (1967 and personal communications).

Ecological changes in Goose Lake, Hamilton County, Iowa, were reported by Weller and Spatcher (1965). Shallow enough to support emergent aquatics over most of its area, Goose Lake was nearly completely dry in 1956 due to a series of dry years, then was gradually reflooded starting in 1957. The emergent vegetation (primarily *Typha augustifolia, T.* × *glauca, Phragmites communis,* and, reportedly, *Scirpus acutus*), which covered about 70% of the lake in 1958, disappeared almost completely during a period of high water and very dense muskrat population from 1959 to 1961, probably in part because of the muskrats' eating of the plants. Since 1961 the emergent vegetation, including much of the *Scirpus* sampled in 1965 and 1966 in the course of this study, has been gradually reestablished. (All three species and various hybrids may well have been present at Goose Lake before 1965 when voucher specimens were first collected.)

Discussion and Conclusions

ISOLATING MECHANISMS

In spite of considerable intergradation due to hybridization in some populations, morphological boundaries of the North American taxa in the *Scirpus lacustris* complex remain amply distinct within the region covered by this study. From the evidence at hand, it seems probable that the following interacting internal factors within the plants and external factors in the environment control natural hybridization.

As the species have different ecological tolerance ranges, hybridization is often prevented by physical isolation. Where their tolerance ranges overlap and they grow together in the same population, however, either the species are isolated by other factors or they hybridize so extensively that morphological boundaries are obscured.

The first stage in hybridization is interspecific pollination, apparently favored in this complex by a combination of protogyny and slight differences in the flowering time of the species. It seems probable that seeds with hybrid embryos are commonly produced but that subsequent germination and establishment of hybrid plants depends on the presence of markedly unstable habitats. Conditions most suitable for establishment of hybrids appear to be large-scale movements of soil such as are caused by construction of roads and dikes, rapid fluctuations in water level, and perhaps unusually large muskrat populations which destroy the emergent vegetation. Other disturbance factors associated with one or more hybrid populations are heavy grazing and the dynamics (e.g., movement of soil materials) associated with stream deltas. Natural disturbances such as are caused by wave and ice action on lake shores and by currents and ice in streams are apparently insufficient to allow establishment of hybrid plants under normal conditions. It is conceivable, however, that occasional catastrophic events (e.g., the formation of beach pools along the shores of large lakes) may permit establishment of hybrid *Scirpus,* although their absence at such localities observed in this study would suggest that such hybrids, if they are formed, are eliminated by natural selection during subsequent periods of relatively stable environmental conditions.

Once hybrid plants begin to flower, hybrid sterility, probably caused in part by irregularities in meiosis, operates as a partial isolating mechanism. At many localities, however, the hybrids appear to be fertile enough for the production of abundant back-cross and F_2 plants.

TAXONOMIC CONCLUSIONS

For the region included in this study, it is evident that the three North American taxa of the *S. lacustris* complex can be maintained as distinct species in spite of considerable hybridization. As herbarium specimens from parts of Western North America are often intermediate between *S. acutus* and *S. validus,* however, further studies may disclose that these two species cannot be separated in some parts of their ranges.

The question of distinctness of the American taxa from the Eurasian *S. lacustris* and *S. tabernaemontani* is beyond the scope of this discussion. From preliminary herbarium studies and published descriptions (especially Koyama, 1958, 1962, 1963), however, it is my opinion that the American plants are sufficiently distinct from their European relatives to be considered different species, but that they may not be readily separable from all Asian plants. Because of the abundance of hybrids in extensively disturbed habitats in North America, it is reasonable to postulate that hybridization is responsible for much of the taxonomic confusion in this complex in densely populated parts of Eurasia, at least where wetlands have been strongly modified by man. Although some morphological intergradation among the taxa tends to justify the treatment by Koyama (1962) of the whole complex as one wide-ranging, extremely variable species, the distinctness of the taxa in large regions of sympatry, as well as the convenience of binomials rather than trinomials or quadrinomials, makes the recognition of five species in this complex desirable until more data on variation are available.

REFERENCES

Anderson, E. (1949). "Introgressive Hybridization." 109 pp. Wiley, New York.

Bakker, D. (1954). Miscellaneous notes on *Scirpus lacustris* L. sensu lat. in the Netherlands. *Acta Botan. Neerl.* **3,** 426–445.

Beal, E. O., and Monson, P. H. (1954). Marsh and aquatic angiosperms of Iowa. *Iowa State Univ. Studies Nat. Hist.* **19**(5), 1–95.

Beetle, A. A. (1941). Species studies in the genus *Scirpus* L. III. The American species of the section *Lacustres* Clarke. *Am. J. Botany* **28,** 691–700.

Chase, A. (1904). The North American allies of *Scirpus lacustris*. *Rhodora* **6,** 65–72.

Curtis, J. T. (1959). "The Vegetation of Wisconsin." 657 pp. Univ. Wisconsin Press, Madison.

Fernald, M. L. (1950). "Gray's Manual of Botany." 8th edition. 1632 pp. American Book Co., New York.

Gleason, H. A., and Cronquist, A. (1963). "Manual of Vascular Plants of Northeastern United States and Adjacent Canada." 810 pp. Van Nostrand, Princeton, N. J.

Hicks, C. C. (1928). Chromosome studies in the Cyperaceae, with special reference to *Scirpus*. *Botan. Gaz.* **86,** 295–317.

Hotchkiss, N. (1965). Bulrushes and bulrush like plants of eastern North America. *U.S. Fish Wildlife Serv. Circ.* **221.**

Koyama, T. (1958). Taxonomic study of the genus *Scirpus* Linné. *J. Fac. Sci. Univ. Tokyo, Sect. III (Botany)* **7,** 271–366.

Koyama, T. (1962). The genus *Scirpus* Linn. Some North American aphylloid species. *Can. Jour. Botany* **40,** 913–937.

Koyama, T. (1963). The genus *Scirpus* Linn. Critical aspects of the section Pterolepis. *Can. Jour. Botany* **41,** 1107–1131.

Otzen, D. (1962). Chromosome studies in the genus *Scirpus* L., section Schoenoplectus Benth. et Hook., in the Netherlands. *Acta Botan. Neerl.* **11,** 37–46.

Stewart, R. E., and Kantrud, H. A. (1964). Relationship of waterfowl populations to water conditions in prairie potholes. *In* Annual Progress Report (for 1964), pp. 1–26. Wildlife Research Work Unit, Northern Prairie Wildlife Research Center, Jamestown, N. Dakota.

Stewart, R. E., and Kantrud, H. A. (1967). Proposed classification of potholes in the glaciated prairie region. *Trans. Wetland Seminar, Can. Wildlife Serv., Saskatoon.*

Stewart, R. E., Kantrud, H. A., and Marinaccio, J. (1966). Long-term investigations of pothole complexes on the Missouri Coteau in Stutsman County, North Dakota. *In* Annual Progress Report (for 1966), pp. 43–48. Wildlife Research Work Unit, Northern Prairie Wildlife Research Center, Jamestown, N. Dakota.

Tanaka, N. (1940). Chromosome studies in Cyperaceae, II. *Scirpus lacustris* L. *Cytologia* **8,** 515–520.

Trauger, D. L. (1967). Habitat factors influencing duck brood use of semipermanent and permanent prairie potholes in North Dakota. M.S. Thesis. Iowa State Univ., Ames.

Weller, M. W., and Spatcher, C. S. (1965). Role of habitat in the distribution and abundance of marsh birds. *Iowa State Univ. Agr. Home Economics Expt. Sta. Spec. Rept.* **43.**

Zimmerman, F. R. (1953). Waterfowl habitat surveys and food habit studies 1940–1943. *Wisconsin Conserv. Dept. Report R. R.,* Project 6-R. Mimeo.

Delimitation and Classification of the Cyperaceae-Mapanioideae*

Tetsuo Koyama

The monocotyledonous family Cyperaceae can reasonably be divided into three subfamilies, Mapanioideae, Cyperoideae, and Caricoideae. The subfamily Mapanioideae that I recognize consists of three tribes, Sclerieae, Lagenocarpeae, and Mapanieae. This concept deviates from any of the previously held classification systems, in which the genera here gathered under the Mapanioideae were scattered under various tribes belonging to the subfamilies Cyperoideae, Rhynchosporoideae, and Caricoideae. The Mapanioideae in this revised sense is characterized by the morphologically compound fruiting structures, by which it clearly differs from the rest of the subfamilies possessing the simple fruits of true achene type. The partial inflorescences in the Mapanioideae are diminutive cymes, here termed the cymelets. The main axis of a cymelet, which is terminated by a single terminal pistillate flower, bear 2 to several glumes. Some of the glumes bear an axillary staminate flower or a side branch on which lateral staminate flowers are spicately disposed. The mechanism of reduction shown in the mapanioid cymelets elucidates a phylogenetic trend among the three tribes of the Mapanioideae. The tribe Sclerieae with branched bisexual cymelets is considered to be primitive. The tribe Lagenocarpeae with simple unisexual cymelets which resulted from the reduction of staminate flowers is regarded as advanced. In the tribe Mapanieae the unbranched cymelets have a terminal pistillate flower and lateral flowers of only a single stamen. The hyaline glumes of the cymelets show morphological differentiation from the herbaceous bract subtending the cymelet. These components of the cymelet, congested on an extremely abbreviated axis, attain the condition of synanthium. The tribe Mapanieae is thus considered to be the most advanced of the three tribes concerned. On the basis of anatomical and morphological studies of the floral parts of the Mapanioideae the rela-

*Study supported by the National Science Foundation grants, GB-4012 and GB-7137, assigned to the author.

tionships of the Mapanioideae with other subfamilies were discussed briefly, and the "Synanthienhypothese" of Mattfeld was supported.

Within the family Cyperaceae the tribes Sclerieae, Lagenocarpeae, and Mapanieae belong to the least understood groups morphologically and taxonomically. Cyperologists have never agreed, for instance, about how to interpret their partial inflorescences as well as their systematic positions in the classification of the family. In the tribe Scleriae the attention of specialists has been focused on whether the pistillate flowers are lateral or terminal (Bentham and Hooker, 1883; Clarke, 1908; Mattfeld, 1935; Kern, 1961), and on whether the Sclerioid "spikelets" are homologuous to the cyperoid spikelets (Ohwi, 1944; Koyama, 1961; Kern, 1961). On the other hand, concerning the tribe Mapanieae, the main subject of argument has been whether the floral units are a hermaphrodite flower or a diminutive inflorescence (Bentham, 1877; Mattfeld, 1935; Hutchinson, 1957; Koyama, 1961; Kern, 1962), especially since Goebell (1888) introduced the concept that a single Mapanioid flower *(Scirpodendron)* is an inflorescence. A series of comparative anatomical investigations on the Cyperaceae is now under way at The New York Botanical Garden, and the results so far obtained have shed light on some of these long-standing problems. In addition, the peculiar compound fruiting structure first found in the tribe Lagenocarpeae (Koyama and Maguire, 1965) now suggests a strong taxonomic affinity among the three tribes, Sclerieae, Lagenocarpeae, and Mapanieae. The purpose of this presentation is to discuss and coordinate fully the taxonomy and the morphology of the subfamily Mapanioideae on the basis of the recent results emanating from anatomical studies.

Morphology of Partial Inflorescences

The systematic position of the genus *Scleria* and its allied genera within the family Cyperaceae can be determined largely by whether or not the pistillate flowers in these genera are terminal in a strict morphological sense. Consequently, this particular subject has long been one of the major interests among cyperologists.

Figure 3 illustrates a bisexual spikelet of *Scleria verticillata*. Figure 4 shows the arrangement of glumes as we see it. The basal two glumes (*a* and *b* in Fig. 4) are empty. A pistillate flower is located at the middle part of the spikelet between glumes *b* and *d* in Fig. 4. All upper glumes above the glume *d* bear a staminate flower at their axil. The two different interpretations of the structure of the bisexual spikelet are demonstrated in

Figs. 5 and 6. Most specialists, including Bentham (1877) and C. B. Clarke (1894, 1902, 1908, 1909), are of the opinion that the pistillate flower is laterally borne at the axil of the glume *b* on a monopodial axis, of which the upper part bears spicately arranged staminate flowers (♂ in Fig. 5). On the other hand, Mattfeld (1935) regarded the pistillate flower of *Scleria* as terminal. He stated that, "Bei den Sclerieae stehen die weiblichen Blüten terminal. Die sogenannten 'androgynen' Ährchen von *Scleria* sind (vielfach in Schraubel übergehende) Fächel aus weiblicher Priman- und männlichen Folgeblüten." Figure 6 diagrams this interpretation. Here a pistillate flower terminates an axis on which the glumes *a, b,* and *c* are borne, and the staminate portion of the spikelet is considered to be a side branch arising from the axil of glume *c.* Kern (1961) concurs in the latter view in his recent treatment of the genus *Scleria* in Malaysia. In reality, however, it is hardly possible to make a judgment without thorough comparative anatomical and morphological observations, which have been insufficiently undertaken by the investigators mentioned.

According to my anatomical investigations made on selected genera of the tribe Sclerieae, the pistillate flowers of *Scleria* and its allied genera are definitely terminal. Practically, the genus *Scleria* itself is not a good example to show this morphological evidence, because in most species of the genus *Scleria* the considerably specialized partial inflorescences tend to be unisexual through reduction of their staminate parts. The determinate nature of the partial inflorescences is best exhibited by *Becquerelia,* which is one of the genera most closely related taxonomically to *Scleria.* As shown in Fig. 1, in the partial inflorescence of *Becquerelia cymosa* the ultimate branch of inflorescences consists of a single straight monopodial axis, which is terminated by a gynoecium *(g).* The main vascular bundles *(vb),* which culminate straightly in the gynoecium, also clearly demonstrate the monopodiality of the axis. Figure 1 shows also that a few lower glumes bear a side branch *(s)* arising from their axis. These side branches are the staminate partial spikelets. The presence of a prophyll at the base of these staminate side branches demonstrates their true lateral nature. Staminate flowers are spicately arranged on the staminate side branches.

The structure of the bisexual partial inflorescences of *Scleria,* such as those of *Scleria verticillata,* is essentially the same as that of *Becquerelia.* The only structural difference between the two is that in *Scleria* the staminate side branch is generally solitary and arises from the axil of the glume immediately below the gynoecium, whereas in *Becquerelia* there are generally three such staminate branches and they are

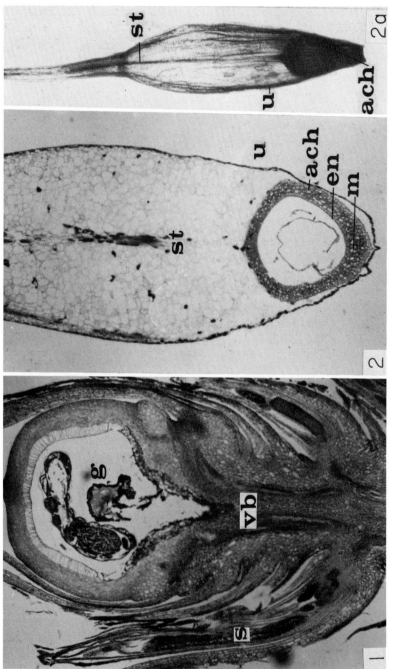

FIGS. 1 to 2a.— Fig. 1. Longitudinal section of the apical part of a young fruit-bearing cymelet of *Becquerelia cymosa*, ×75. Fig. 2. Longitudinal section of the achene-bearing portion of a mature fructification of *Hypolytrum nudum*, ×40. Fig. 2a. Young fructification of *Mapania pycnocephala*. ca ×10. *ach*, achene; *en*, endocarp; *m*, mesocarp; *s*, staminate partial spikelet; *st*, style; *u*, utricle; *vb*, vascular bundles.

borne at the axils of about three basal glumes. In the bisexual partial inflorescences of *Scleria,* when the staminate side branches become absent by reduction, the partial inflorescences become pistillate. The pistillate partial inflorescences derived through this reduction was anatomically examined in *Scleria arundinacea* in my previous contribution (Koyama,

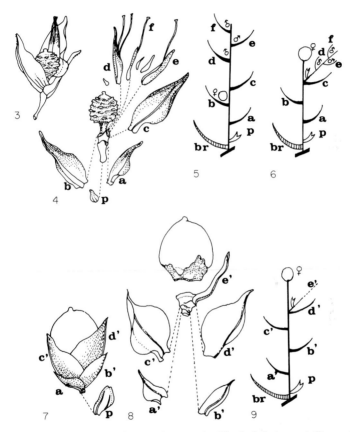

Figs. 3 to 13. Cymelets in *Scleria* and *Mapania.* Fig. 3. *Scleria verticillata,* a bisexual cymelet. Fig. 4. *Scleria verticillata,* dissection of a bisexual cymelet. Figs. 5, 6. Schematic expressions of two interpretations of the bisexual cymelets in *Scleria verticillata.* Fig. 7. *Scleria terrestris,* a pistillate cymelet. Fig. 8. *Scleria terrestris,* a dissection of a pistillate cymelet. Fig. 9. Schema showing the arrangement of glumes in the pistillate cymelets of *Scleria terrestris.* Fig. 10. *Mapania tepuiana,* cymelet. Fig. 11. Schema showing the main vascular system of the axis of cymelets in *Mapania tepuiana.* Fig. 12. Diagram showing the arrangement of glumes in the cymelets of *Mapania tepuiana.* Fig. 13. Schema showing the arrangement of glumes and flowers in the cymelets of *Mapania tepuiana. a–f, a'–e',* glumes; *br,* bract subtending a cymelet; *p,* prophyll; *s,* staminate flower. (See following page.)

1965 [Fig. 17]). Here the main vascular bundles, converging into the gynoecium without showing a trace of sympodiality of the axis, precisely follow the pattern shown by *Becquerelia* and described above. The pistillate partial inflorescences of *Scleria terrestris* retain the vestige of

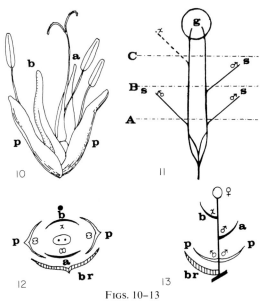

FIGS. 10–13

its staminate portion, which appears as a scaly appendage immediately below the fruiting structure (Fig. 8, *e'*). Figure 9 schematically interprets the structure of the pistillate partial inflorescence of *Scleria terrestris*, showing the evidence of the reduction of the lateral staminate side branch.

It is now appropriate to discuss the terminology of the partial inflorescences in *Scleria* and its allied genera. In the Cyperaceae the ultimate flower-bearing units of inflorescences have been described uniformly as a "spikelet" in spite of the fact that in some genera "spikelets" are not true indeterminate spicate structures, as has been mentioned above. In fact, in the tribe Sclerieae the so-called "spikelets" are not only true spikes in the strict morphological sense but are also often difficult to define clearly. For descriptive purposes it is almost impossible to designate the unit of inflorescence to be described as a "spikelet," chiefly because the inflorescences in Sclerieae are so diffuse that superficially there hardly exists a clear-cut boundary between flower-bearing and non-floriferous portions of inflorescences. For the purposes of morphological and taxonomic discussions I propose to deal with the gynoecium-bearing distal branches (Fig. 5, *b,* and Fig. 7 for instance) as the ultimate unit of inflorescences, and prefer the term "cymelet" to the term "spikelet" because the structure under discussion has a determinate axis but in no sense is of the indeterminate nature of true spikelets. The structure of the *Scleria*-type inflorescences as interpreted by Koyama (1965, 1967a) can be rephrased as follows under this revised terminology. Fruit-bearing cymelets in the tribe Sclerieae are truly determinate. The axis of the cymelets is terminated by a single terminal gynoecium (♀ in Figs. 5, 6, 9, and 24 to 27), and several glumes are borne on the primary axis of the cymelet between the gynoecium and the prophyll *(p),* which is at the base of the primary axis. When a cymelet is branched, one to few of these glumes bears a small staminate side branch (i.e., a staminate partial spikelet) arising from the axil. A prophyll (secondary) is present at the base of the staminate side branch.

Figures 24 to 27 illustrate four types of cymelets that occur in the tribe Sclerieae. The framework of the cymelets in *Becquerelia* is represented by Fig. 24. The morphological explanations for this structure were given above and therefore need not be repeated here. The cymelets of *Diplacrum* also fall under this pattern, though their glumes are two-ranked instead of being imbricated. Figure 25 illustrates the cymelet of *Bisboeckelera*. In *Bisboeckelera* the terminal gynoecium is completely enveloped in a saclike organ below which the axis of the cymelet has three staminate side branches. As fully discussed in an earlier paper (Koyama, 1965), this saclike organ was interpreted as a fusion product of the three empty glumes below the gynoecium and, therefore, it is morphologically homologous with the three subgynoecian glumes in *Becquerelia* cymelets. The cymelets of *Calyptrocarya* are schematically shown in Fig. 26. Three glumes immediately below the terminal gynoecium bear a staminate side branch, leaving the other glumes empty, a condition quite different from that of the *Becquerelia* cymelet in which the basal glumes bear such a side branch. The bisexual cymelets of *Scleria* (Fig. 27), which bear a single staminate side branch immediately below the gynoecium, constitute nothing but a specialized condition of this *Calyptrocarya*-type cymelet.

It should be noted at this juncture that the cymelets of *Scleria*-allies, as interpreted above, strikingly resemble the structure of the so-called "partial spikelets" of *Mapania* and its related genera. A comparison of Figs. 24 to 27 with Figs. 28 to 31 easily demonstrates that the framework of the "partial spikelets" of Mapanioid genera could be derived from the cymelets in Sclerioid genera when the staminate side branches of the latter are replaced with a single staminate flower, provided that the "partial spikelets" of Mapanioid genera are the true synanthia as interpreted under the "Synanthienhypothese" of Mattfeld (1938). Here, again, an opposing opinion is held by Bentham and Hooker (1883) and Hutchinson (1957): the "partial spikelets" of the genera of Mapanieae are a single bisexual flower, but are not a group of unisexual flowers. To settle the problem, serial sections of the "partial spikelets" of *Mapania, Mapaniopsis, Diplasia,* and *Hypolytrum* have been made. The anatomical observations made on these serial sections supported Mattfeld's view that the Mapanioid "partial spikelets" are a reduced inflorescence but not a single hermaphrodite flower.

Figure 10 illustrates a "partial spikelet" of *Mapania tepuiana* from Venezuela. The structure shown consists of a gynoecium surrounded by four squamellae and three stamens. The arrangement of these components is shown in Fig. 12. The outermost (or the lowest) pair of squamellae (*p* in the figures) are lateral, and each subtends a single stamen. Figures 14 to 22 show the serial cross sections of the axis of the "partial spikelet" above the point of its attachment to the main axis of the inflorescence. The behavior of vascular bundles suggests that each of the three stamens (*s*) represents a lateral branch divided from the main vascular bundles (*vb*), and that each stamen is subtended by a squamella involving no conspicuous vascular system. Figure 11 shows the vascular system based on the serial sections. The two main vascular bundles culminating in the gynoecium (*g*) deliver three branches, each ending in a stamen (*s*). Figure 14 shows the differentiation of prophylls (*p*) at the base of the "partial spikelet." The cross section made at level *C* of Fig. 11 is shown in Figs. 15 and 16, where the differentiation of the two lower stamen (*s*) is seen. In Fig. 17 the separation of the third and fourth glumes (*a* and *b* in Fig. 10) from the rhachis is seen. The cross section at level *B* of Fig. 11 is shown in Figs. 18 and 23. These two sections show the most important detail; that is, the uppermost squamella is separated from the axis distinctly above the point of attachment of the upper stamen to the rachilla. This arrangement indicates that the stamens do not belong to the gynoecium but constitute a monandrous flower axillary to each subtending squamella. The uppermost squamella (*b* in Figs. 18 and 23) becomes empty as the result of the abortion of the putative fifth stamen belonging thereto. This uppermost empty glume (*b*) is conspicuously shown in Figs. 19 and 20. Figure 11 (*x*) indicates the location of the reduced stamen. As also seen in Figs. 14 to 22, the main vascular bundles of the axis of the "partial spikelet" culminate in the bicarpellate gynoecium and show the true terminal nature of the gynoecium.

The anatomical evidence explained above sufficiently demonstrates that the "partial spikelet" of *Mapaniopsis* is an extremely reduced branch terminated by a gynoecium. The lowest pair of squamellae, which

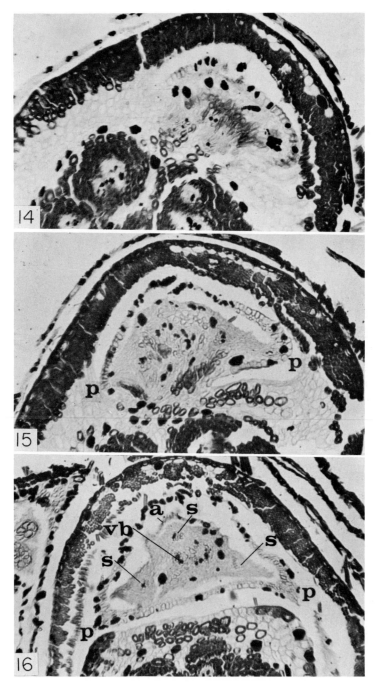

FIGS. 14 to 23. Transverse serial sections of a young cymelet in *Mapania tepuiana*. ×75. *a, b,* glumes; *g,* gynoecium; *p,* prophyll; *s,* stamen; *vb,* main vascular bundles of the axis of cymelet. For detailed interpretation see the text. (See following pages.)

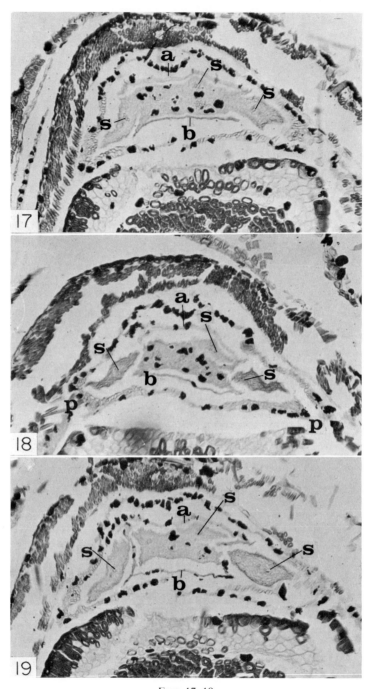

FIGS. 17–19.

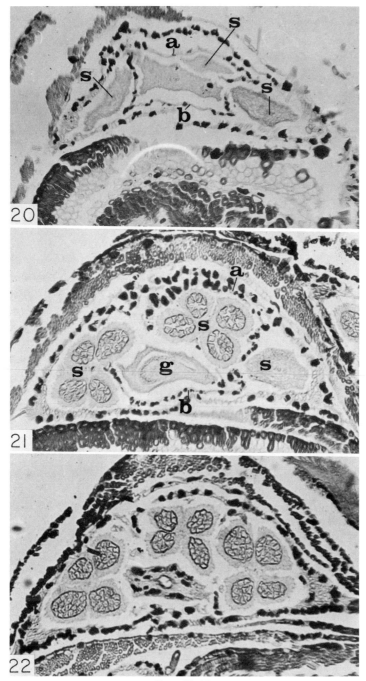

FIGS. 20–22.

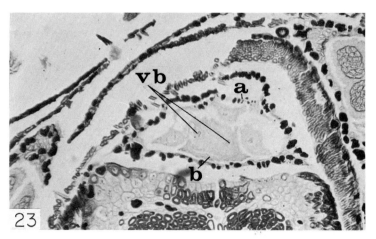

FIG. 23.

differ from the remainder in their acute keel and apparent bilateral position, are morphologically a pair of prophylls. This also coincides with
the anatomical consideration above, since in the monocotyledons such
prophylls occur at the base of the side branches. The reference slides of
the serial sections of the "partial spikelets" of *Mapaniopsis effusa* and
Diplasia karataefolia did not show any evidence to detract from the
conclusion that the "partial spikelets" of *Mapania* and its related genera
are a reduced determinate inflorescence. The "partial spikelets" of the
genera of the tribe Mapanieae are, therefore, also cymelets. Their
morphological structure is essentially identical with those of the tribe
Sclerieae. In the Mapanioid cymelets, however, the staminate partial
spikelets are replaced with a monandrous staminate flower by reduction,
as speculated above (Fig. 13).

The cymelets in the tribe Mapanieae do not show so remarkable a
structural diversity as that exhibited by the tribe Sclerieae, but they are
represented as a series of reductions of staminate flowers and their subtending squamellae. Figure 28 schematizes the cymelet of the genus
Scirpodendron as consisting of a terminal pistillate flower and a number of
lateral staminate flowers. A considerable reduction of the components of
cymelets is seen in the genus *Mapania*. The cymelets of *Mapania*
(Figs. 29 and 30) consist of only 4 to 6 squamellae the upper few of
which become empty through the abortion of their staminate flowers.
The cymelet of the genus *Hypolytrum* appears as the ultimate state in the
reduction series of the Mapanioid cymelets. As seen in Fig. 31, in the
cymelets of *Hypolytrum*, there are no squamellae between the pistil
and the prophylls.

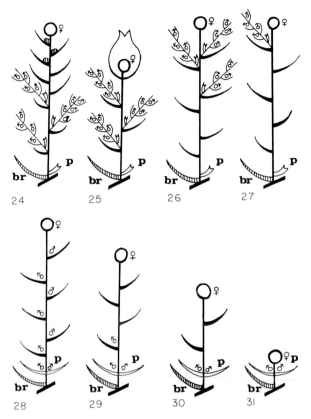

FIGS. 24 to 31. Schemata showing the arrangement of glumes and flowers in the cymelets of Mapanioideae. Fig. 24. *Becquerelia*. Fig. 25. *Bisboeckelera*. Fig. 26. *Calyptrocarya*. Fig. 27. *Scleria*. Fig. 28. *Scirpodendron*. Figs. 29, 30. *Mapania*. Fig. 31. *Hypolytrum*. *br*, bract subtending cymelet; *p*, prophyll; *s*, staminate flower; ♀, gynoecium (pistillate flower). For interpretations see the text.

The cymelets in the tribe Mapanieae are thus truly determinate. The axis of the cymelets is terminated by a single terminal gynoecium (♀ in Figs. 28 to 31). Prophylls at the base of the axis are always paired and opposite, and are different from the rest of the component glumes in having an acute keel along which the prophyll is folded. Several glumes are borne on the axis between the terminal gynoecium and the basal prophylls. At least some of these glumes bear a monandrous axillary staminate flower. In the genus *Hypolytrum* these glumes are absent.

Morphology of Fruiting Structures

Through a series of anatomical investigations (Koyama and Maguire,

1965; Koyama, 1965) I presented a concept of the morphologically compound fruiting structures in the genera of the tribes Lagenocarpeae and
Sclerieae. As these fruiting structures are not a true achene-type fruit,
the term fructification was employed to represent this peculiar structure
(Koyama and Maguire, 1965). These fructifications consist of a utricle
and an achene that is contained in or adnate to the utricle. By its morphologically compound nature the fructification of the tribe Lagenocarpeae
and the tribe Sclerieae differ greatly from the simple fruit of true achene-
type exhibited by the tribes Cypereae, Rhynchosporeae, Scirpeae, and
Cariceae. Such morphological data are not yet available for the fruiting
structures of the genera of the tribe Mapanieae. For the present study
the fruiting structures of the species of selected Mapanioid genera,
Diplasia, Mapania, and *Hypolytrum,* were sectioned. The anatomical
observations made on these materials showed that the fruiting structures
of these Mapanioid genera also fall under the same morphological category as those of the tribes Lagenocarpeae and Sclerieae.

Figure 2 shows the longitudinal section of a fructification of *Hypolytrum nudum.* A broadly obovate achene, marked *ach* in the figure, is
located at the bottom of a saclike structure *(u),* which is called a utricle
here. A slender style *(st)* extends through the large utricle and exposes
its bicleft portion, the stigmas, at the apex of the utricle, though Fig. 2
does not cover that portion of the stigmas. The relatively thick achene
wall can be differentiated into two portions: the inner membrane, consisting of one-layered, thin-walled cells *(en),* and the outer wall consisting
of several-layered sclerenchymatous cells *(m).* This arrangement recalls
those in *Scleria, Becquerelia,* and *Calyptrocarya* (Koyama, 1965). The
large utricle consisting of homogeneous parenchymatous cells closely
resembles that of *Didymiandrum* and *Lagenocarpus* (Koyama and Maguire, 1965) in every detail, and the morphological homology between
the two entities is strongly suggested. The fructifications of *Mapania
macrophylla, Mapania macrocephala,* and *Diplasia karataefolia* showed
a structure that is identical with that of *Hypolytrum nudum.* In the former
three species, however, the achene walls tend to be slightly thicker than
in *Hypolytrum nudum* and to involve more developed sclerenchymatous
tissue, while the parenchymatous tissue filling the utricle is much less
developed than in *Hypolytrum nudum.*

Such compound structure in the Mapanioid fructifications can also be
seen even at the gross morphological level under a low-power microscope. Figure 2a shows a young fructification (not dissected) of *Mapania
pycnocephala.* An achene *(ach)* is enveloped in a large hyaline utricle *(u).*
A "straightish" slender style *(st)* extends through the ellipsoid body of

the utricle and surmounts the narrow beak of the utricle. At this young stage the utricle is not filled with the parenchymatous tissue, and it appears to be semitranslucent. The later development of the utricular parenchyma tissue varies to a great extent, causing the wide range of the dimensions of Mapanioid fructifications. The remarkable inconsistency in shape and size of the fructifications noted in the tribes Mapanieae and Lagenocarpeae is thus accounted for.

Variations in the type of utricles and the degree of adnation of utricle to the enclosed achene suggest the following four types of fructifications (as illustrated in Figs. 32 to 40). These four types are tentatively called Types, A, B, C, and D.

In Type A fructification (Fig. 35), which is exemplified by the genus *Calyptrocarya* of Sclerieae, the presence of a utricle enclosing an achene is obvious even at the gross morphological level. In this type the utricle is completely free from the contained achene. The utricle *(u)* is a membranous sac open only at the apex by a small orifice, through which projects a short style *(st)*. The basal portion of the utricle is spongy and thickened, and consists of one- and, in part, two-layered parenchymatous cells *(pa)*.

Type B fructifications (Figs. 33 and 34) are represented by the genera *Becquerelia, Diplacrum,* and *Scleria.* The globose, bony achene *(ach)* is exposed over the thickened and frequently spongy bowl-like or cuplike utricle *(u)*, which has usually been described as a cupule. The cupule, consisting of multilayered parenchymatous cells, was proved to be homologous with the utricle of the fructifications in *Calyptrocarya* (Koyama, 1965). In *Becquerelia* and *Diplacrum*, cupules are adnate to the basal portion of achenes (Fig. 33), whereas, in *Scleria,* at least the marginal portion of cupules tend to be free from the body of achenes (Fig. 34).

Type C fructifications (Fig. 36) can be seen in the genera *Trilepis, Afrotrilepis, Mircodracoides,* and *Coleochloa* of the tribe Lagenocarpeae. Here a utricle surrounding an achene is conspicuous even without anatomical studies, as the utricle is free from the enveloped achene for most of its length, and hence Nees (1842) and Nelmes (1953) correctly assumed the presence of a saclike organ in their descriptions of *Trilepis* and *Coleochloa,* respectively. The utricle *(u)* is a hyaline sac without any spongy portion; in this character, type C fructification is dissimilar to any other type. The beak of the utricle is adnate to the style *(st)* of the enclosed achene.

Type D (Figs. 37 to 40) denotes a fructification in which the utricle is completely adnate to the contained achene. The fructifications of this

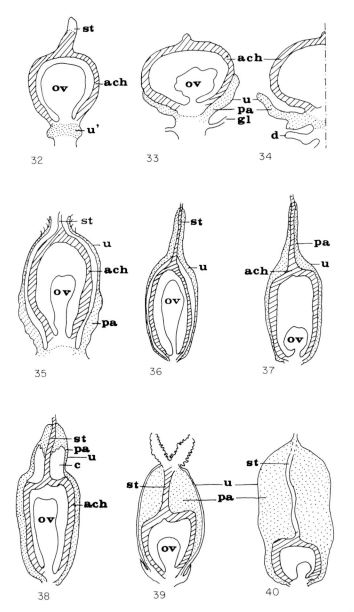

FIGS. 32 to 40. Schematic expressions of longitudinal sections of the compound fructifications in Mapanioideae. Fig. 32. *Bisboeckelera.* Fig. 33. *Becquerelia.* Fig. 34. *Scleria.* Fig. 35. *Calyptrocarya.* Fig. 36. *Trilepis.* Fig. 37. *Everardia.* Fig. 38. *Cephalocarpus.* Fig. 39. *Lagenocarpus.* Fig. 40. *Hypolytrum. ach,* achene; *c,* cavity; *d,* vestigial glume subtending a fructification; *gl,* glume subtending a fructification; *ov,* ovule; *pa,* parenchymatous tissue of utricle; *st,* style; *u,* utricle; *u',* vestigial utricle.

type are structurally divided into two parts, the lower part (body) and the upper part (beak). In the body the fructification wall consists of the epidermal layer of utricle and the sclerenchymatous pericarp of the achene. In the beak a parenchymatous tissue *(pa)* always develops between the epidermis of the utricle *(u)* and the style *(st),* which is the extension of the pericarp of the achene. So far as the anatomically examined taxa are concerned, the genera *Everardia, Cephalocarpus,* and *Lagenocarpus* of the tribe Lagenocarpeae and the genera *Displasia, Hypolytrum,* and *Mapania* of the tribe Mapanieae exhibit Type D fructification.

From this organization it is difficult to determine if Type D fructifications are compound structures consisting of a utricle and an achene. There is evidence, however, to shed light on this problem. As Marek (1959) observed, in true cyperaceous fruits of achene type, such as those of *Rhyncospora, Scirpus, Carex,* and *Cyperus,* the pericarp can be differentiated into two conspicuous portions only, without a clear boundary between the exocarp and the mesocarp. The inner wall, which is the endocarp, consists of usually one-layered, thin-walled cells. The outer portion consists of many-layered sclerenchymatous cells of which the outermost ones may be regarded as the component cells of the exocarp. The precise structural agreement of both the bony achenes of Types A and B fructification and the sclerenchymatous achenes of Type D fructification with the true achenes reported by Marek demonstrates the morphological homology between the two entities under discussion. In the fructification of a Lagenocarpeous genus, *Cephalocarpus,* the truncated apex of the sclerenchymatous achene and the base of its style are free from the utricular wall; thus there is a cavity around the style. This further suggests that the fructification is of compound origin.

Systematic Discussion

The morphological and anatomical evidence presented in the previous chapters demonstrates a definite morphological connection and close taxonomic affinity between the two tribes Sclerieae and Lagenocarpeae and the tribe Mapanieae. On this basis I propose to unite the three tribes to form a subfamily, of which the correct name should be Mapanioideae. The delimitation of Mapanioideae in this revised sense deviates from any of the previously proposed classification schemes of the Cyperaceae, in which the two tribes Sclerieae and Lagenocarpeae were considered to be only remotely related to the tribe Mapanieae, and consequently were placed under separate subfamilies.

For a better understanding of the practices in the classification of the
Cyperaceae it is advisable to review briefly the previously proposed systems of the family. The floral sexes, that is, whether the flowers of a
particular taxon are unisexual or hermaphrodite, have been considered
most important in the system of Cyperaceae. Under this concept the
tribes Sclerieae and Lagenocarpeae are most closely related to the tribe
Cariceae because of their completely unisexual flowers, whereas the
tribe Mapanieae resembles the tribe Scirpeae because of its synanthia,
which are then understood to be at least functionally equivalent to the
hermaphrodite flowers. As the most recent example of the classification
system based on the floral sexes that of Schultze-Motel (1964) can be
cited.

CYPEROIDEAE (= Scirpoideae) (flowers a synanthium in the shape of a bisexual flower)
    Tribe Hypolytreae (= Mapanieae)
    Tribe Dulichieae
    Tribe Scirpeae
    Tribe Rhynchosporeae
    Tribe Cypereae
CARICOIDEAE (flowers of true unisexual flowers and not of synanthium)
    Tribe Sclerieae
    Tribe Lagenocarpeae
    Tribe Cariceae

Schultze-Motel's system is very similar to the system of Bentham and
Hooker, which was almost solely based on the floral sexes as follows:

A. MONOCLINES (flowers hermaphrodite)
    Tribe 1. Scirpeae
    Tribe 2. Hypolytreae [= Mapanieae]
    Tribe 3. Rhynchosporeae
B. DICLINES (flowers unisexual)
    Tribe 4. Cryptangieae [= Lagenocarpeae]
    Tribe 5. Sclerieae
    Tribe 6. Cariceae

Disregarding whether the bisexual floral units are synanthia or hermaphrodite flowers, the classification systems based on the floral sexes were
followed for a long time by a number of specialists, including relatively
recent contributors such as Mackenzie (1931) and Hutchinson (1957).

Ascherson and Graebner (1902) and Ohwi (1944), on the other hand,
paid more attention to the distribution of flowers in spikes than to the
floral sexes in their classification systems. They recognized Rhynchosporoideae as the third subfamily of the Cyperaceae. In the Rhynchosporoideae only one to a few glumes of the middle portion of spikelets is

fruit-bearing, and the remainder of the glumes are empty or staminate. Ohwi placed the tribe Sclerieae in the subfamily Rhynchosporoideae as follows.

SCIRPOIDEAE
  Tribe Scirpeae
  Tribe Hypolytreae (= Mapanieae)
RHYNSCOSPOROIDEAE
  Tribe Rhynchosporeae
  Tribe Gahnieae
  Tribe Sclerieae
CARICOIDEAE
  Tribe Cariceae

Ohwi's attribution of the tribe Sclerieae to the Rhynchosporoideae depends on his interpretation that the pistillate flower of a *Scleria* "spikelet" is laterally borne at the axil of a glume of the middle portion of a spikelet, as expressed in Fig. 5 (a structure exhibited by the spikes of Rhynchosporoid genera).

The subfamily Mapanioideae that I recognize consists of three tribes, Sclerieae, Lagenocarpeae, and Mapanieae. The close systematic affinity among these three tribes rests on the structure of their fructifications and partial inflorescences, as mentioned in preceding paragraphs. Compound fructifications, which consist of a utricle containing an achene, are common to all of the genera belonging to the tribes Sclerieae, Lageno-carpeae, and Mapanieae, but such fructifications are never found in any genus of all other tribes of the Cyperaceae so far examined. The morphologically cymose partial inflorescences, here termed cymelets, occur in all the three tribes mentioned above without exception. This strongly suggests that there is a close characteristic association between the determinate cymelets and the compound fructifications. By this combination of peculiar characteristics the subfamily Mapanioideae in the revised sense can be well circumscribed, and is distinctly separable from the rest of the subfamilies in the Cyperaceae, which are characterized by the fruits of true achene type and essentially indeterminate spikelets.

Furthermore, Erdtman (1966) indicated that he had detected a considerable difference between pollen grains of the Mapanioid genera and those of other cyperaceous genera. The pollen grains of Mapanioid genera, such as *Mapania, Diplasia, Hypolytrum,* and *Scirpodendron,* are orbicular in outline and thick-walled, while the pollen grains of other genera so far examined tend to be triangular or obovoid in outline and thin-walled. More detailed pollen studies in the Cyperaceae are now under way by Tsukada and Koyama. Our recent results not only confirm

Erdtman's remarks but also disclose certain characteristic exine sculptures in pollen grains of Mapanioid genera in electron photomicrographs. The orbicular-shaped, thick-walled pollen grains were seen in the genus *Scleria* and in the genera *Everardia* and *Lagenocarpus* of the tribe Lagenocarpeae. Under the electron microscope the pattern of exine sculpture in Mapanioid pollen grains clearly differs from the usual granule type in normal cyperaceous pollen grains. This additional evidence parallels my conclusion, derived through anatomical and morphological observations, that the subfamily Mapanioideae is a taxonomically coherent group distinctly separable from any other subfamily of the Cyperaceae.

The taxonomic separation among the three tribes of the Mapanioideae can be made by the use of the characters of both fructifications and cymelets. The tribe Sclerieae differs from the other two tribes in the elongated staminate side branches of the bisexual cymelets and in the relatively poorly developed utricles of the fructifications. In the *Scleria*-type fructifications the utricles are frequently free from the achene, as seen in *Calyptrocarya* (Fig. 35), or they remain as a cupule surrounding only the basal portion of the achene, as exhibited by *Becquerelia*, *Diplacrum,* and *Scleria* (Figs. 33 and 34). Both of the tribes Lageno-carpeae and Mapanieae possess the fructifications involving a well-developed utricle in which the achene is completely contained with its pericarp adnated to the utricular wall (Figs. 37 to 40). In spite of the resemblance in the fructifications, the tribes Lagenocarpeae and Mapanieae are separable from each other by certain features of the cymelets. In the Lagenocarpeae the cymelets are always unisexual and have herbaceous component glumes which are conspicuously imbricated on a visibly elongated axis. The cymelets of Mapanieae are, however, always bisexual and have at least two basal glumes bearing a monandrous staminate flower at the axil. Their component glumes, generally called squamellae, are hyaline, and superficially they appear to be whorled rather than imbricated because of the extremely abbreviated axis. Hence the entire arrangement of the components (squamellae, monandrous staminate flowers, and a pistillate flower of a single naked pistil) substantially looks like a single hermaphrodite flower. Mattfeld's term "synanthium" applies to this particular condition of the cymelets.

In any evolutionary discussion pertaining to the Cyperaceae it is generally held that a simple structure can be derived from a complex structure by reduction, and that the connation or adnation of parts is a later result of the parts being free. Under these terms the tribe Sclerieae shows aspects that are considered to be evolutionarily primitive: the cymelets with staminate branches, and the fructifications in which the adnation of utricle to achene is incomplete. The tribes Mapanieae and Lageno-carpeae are accepted as evolutionally advanced when compared with the Sclerieae. The unbranched bisexual cymelets in the Mapanieae and the unbranched unisexual cymelets in the Lagenocarpeae would have evolved from the branched cymelets of the *Scleria* type by the pre-sumed reduction of the side branches. In the tribe Mapanieae and certain genera of the tribe Lagenocarpeae, such as *Lagenocarpus* and *Didymian-drum,* the adnation of the utricular wall to the pericarp of the contained achene is so complete that the entire organization superficially looks like a single drupe. The fructifications of *Cephalocarpus, Everardia,* and *Trilepis* (Figs. 38, 37, 36, respectively) still show a trace of adnation between the achene pericarp and the utricle; this indicates a phylo-genetic connection between the primitive *Scleria*-type fructification and the most advanced *Mapania*-type fructification (Koyama and Maguire, 1965).

The leaf anatomy of the three tribes under discussion (Metcalfe, 1963; Koyama, 1965, 1966, 1967a) supplements the foregoing interpretation of the phylogenetic interrelationships among them. In the Sclerieae, the mesophyll as seen in transverse sections of the leaf blades is sometimes not conspicuously differentiated into palisade and spongy assimilatory tissues; or, when a degree of such differentiation is noted, the compo-nent assimilatory cells do not show any significant difference in shape be-tween the palisade and spongy portions of chlorenchyma. The develop-ment of the surface-to-surface sclerenchymatous tissues, usually de-scribed as girders, is the poorest in the leaves of the Sclerieae. The swollen translucent tissue at the adaxial median costa, a tissue compara-ble to the bulliform cells in the Gramineae, is also poorly developed in the Sclerieae. In the Lagenocarpeae and the Mapanieae the transverse sec-tions of the leaf blades show that the mesophyll is clearly differentiated into three portions: the palisade, the spongy portions of chlorenchyma, and translucent parenchyma tissues, the most specialized feature of mesophyll so far observed in the Cyperaceae. Sclerenchymatous girders connecting both surfaces as well as the vascular bundles to the adaxial surface are generally well developed. In addition to such advanced features, in the Mapanieae and the Lagenocarpeae, under the adaxial epidermis, often exists a one- to three-layered hypodermis, which is com-pletely absent in the tribe Sclerieae.

The relationships of the subfamily Mapanioideae with other sub-families of the Cyperaceae must also be discussed. Holttum (1948), morphologically reviewing the structure of spikelets, treated the tribes

Sclerieae and Lagenocarpeae as the most advanced taxa comparable to the tribe Cariceae. His opinion was derived from his point of view that the strictly unisexual flowers in the Sclerieae and the Lagenocarpeae had evolved from the hermaphrodite flowers of the Scirpoid type, precisely as is usually assumed in the origin of the unisexual flowers of *Carex*. I, on the contrary, regard the tribe Sclerieae as the most primitive group represented in the evolutionary trend that is recognized in the Cyperaceae. An important fact is that a cymelet in the Sclerieae is not equivalent to a spikelet in the tribe Cypereae or the tribe Scirpeae; rather, a *Scleria* cymelet corresponds to a single hermaphrodite flower of the spikelets in the Cypereae or the Scirpeae. As already speculated above, a branched cymelet in the Sclerieae may give way by reduction to a hermaphrodite flower in the Scirpeae through a synanthium in the Mapanieae. To connect the Mapanoid synanthia with the Scirpoid hermaphrodite flowers I concur in principle with the "Synanthienhypothese" of Mattfeld (1935, 1938). Here the mechanism of reduction was explained as follows: "Unter einer weiblichen, nackten Blüte [von Mapanieae] steht eine grössere Zahl von Fächeln aus monandrischen Blüten. Diese Fächel werden reduziert auf eine Blüte. Die Zahl der Fächel unter der weiblichen Blüte nimmt ab, so dass die weibliche Terminalblüte schliesslich von mehreren Staubblättern umgeben ist, die aber jedes sein eigenes Tragblatt haben. Schliesslich ist die Zahl der monandrischen Blüten auf 3 oder 2 reduziert, so dass zwischen den Staubblättern keine Tragblätter mehr stehen können, sondern nur noch aussen von ihnen; und so ist eine von einigen Tragblättern umhüllte 'Blüte' entstanden, die von einer Zwitterblüte von *Scirpus* nicht zu unterscheiden ist." In fact, in the cymelets of *Mapania,* section *Pycnocephala,* the component four squamellae are often connate into a hyaline sac containing two stamens and a single pistil, a condition that superficially does not differ from that of a dimerous bisexual flower. A similar arrangement can be seen in the cymelets of the genus *Hypolytrum,* where there is no squamella between the lowest pair of monandrous staminate flowers and a terminal naked pistil.

The interpretation of the *Dulichium* flower by Mattfeld (1938) and Schultze-Motel (1959) further supports this hypothetical reduction trend from the Mapanioideae to the Cyperoideae (Scirpoideae). According to Schultze-Motel's anatomical observation, the hermaphrodite flowers of *Dulichium* with more or less 8 hypogynous bristles constitute a synanthium, which consists of a basal staminate and an upper pistillate flower borne on an axis arising from the axil of the subtending bract (glume). Of about 8 hypogynous bristles, the abaxial 5 (or 4) are considered to be a metamorphosed glume of the staminate flower.

The preceding discussion sufficiently elucidates the phylogenetic inter-relationships among the tribes Sclerieae, Mapanieae, and Scirpeae. The tribe Scirpeae evolved from the ancestor of the tribe Mapanieae, which had originated from the ancester of the tribe Sclerieae. This putative evolutionary trend is well reflected in the structure of partial inflores-cences. A cymelet in the tribe Sclerieae is morphologically homologous with both a synanthium in the tribe Mapanieae and a hermaphrodite flower (which is here accepted as an extremely contracted synanthium) in the tribe Scirpeae. The homology among the three phases of partial inflorescences shows that the three tribes — Sclerieae, Mapanieae, and Scirpeae — represent three stages in a consecutive reduction series of the partial inflorescences from cymelets through synanthia to hermaphrodite flowers. On the other hand, the structure of fructifications marks a con-siderable taxonomic discontinuity between the tribes Mapanieae and Scirpeae in the putative trend. Namely, the tribes Sclerieae and Mapa-nieae are characterized by the compound fructifications, as mentioned previously, while the tribe Scirpeae has the simple fruit of the true achene type. The conclusion, based on such morphological evidence, is that the subfamily Mapanioideae, which consists of the tribes Sclerieae and Mapanieae, is a natural group and is taxonomically distinct from the neighboring subfamily Cyperoideae (= Scirpoideae).

Finally, the relationship between the subfamilies Mapanioideae and Caricoideae must be discussed briefly. In the Caricoideae the genera *Schoenoxiphium* and *Kobresia* exhibit the less reduced condition of the partial inflorescences. Here the axis of partial inflorescences bears a single pistillate flower at the base and one to a few staminate flowers on the upper part. The entire spicate structure is subtended by a saclike or a spathelike prophyll usually termed a perigynium. If the axis were mono-podial and the basal pistillate flower were laterally borne (Mora, 1960, 1966; Kern, 1962), the Caricoideae would have no close taxonomic rela-tionship with the Mapanioideae because of indeterminate axes of the partial inflorescences. Kukkonen (1967a,b), on the basis of his anatomical studies of the genus *Uncinia,* interpreted the axis of the partial in-florescences in the Caricoideae as sympodial. According to Kukkonen, the main axis of the Caricoid partial inflorescences is terminated by a pistillate flower, and the so-called vestigial rhachilla is a side branch divided below the pistillate flower. The partial inflorescences in the Cari-coideae under this interpretation are cymose, and structurally they re-semble those of the Mapanioideae. In this relation I recall the partial inflorescence of the genus *Bisboeckelera* of the tribe Sclerieae (Fig. 25), in which the fructification enveloped in a closed perigynium shows at

least superficial similarity to the achene in a perigynium in the Caricoideae. It should be mentioned also that the achene of *Bisboeckelera*
has an annular vestigial utricle at its base (Fig. 32, *u'*). Since the utricles
in the Mapanioideae are believed to be the reduced glumes, it is not at all
possible that the annular vestigial utricle of the achenes in *Bisboeckelera*
might correspond to the point of attachment of the lateral branch of the
partial inflorescences in the Caricoideae. For any further discussion on
this point, anatomical investigations on the floral part of the genus
Schoenoxiphium are necessary. So far as data are available, the subfamily
Mapanioideae, on account of the compound fructifications, taxonomically
stands distinct from the Caricoideae, irrespective of whether the Caricoideae evolved from the Mapanioid ancestor or the Scirpoid ancestor.

Taxonomic Summary

DIVISION OF THE SUBFAMILIES OF THE CYPERACEAE

1. Fruiting structures compound, consisting of achene enclosed or tightly surrounded by
   utricle; utricles as a whole or in part adnate to the pericarp of inclosed achene; pistillate
   flowers terminal on a visible pedicel; ultimate unit of inflorescences involving pistillate
   flower visibly cymose. .... Subfamily 1. MAPANIOIDEAE.
1. Fruits of true achene type, not adnated to utricular structure; pistillate flowers quasi-
   lateral at the axil of glume; ultimate unit of inflorescence superficially spiciform.
   2. Fruit-bearing flowers an extremely reduced synanthium in the shape of a herma-
      phrodite flower, borne at the axil of glume, not enveloped by 2-keeled prophyll.
      .... Subfamily 2. CYPEROIDEAE.
   2. Fruit-bearing flowers a single naked pistil, enveloped in open or closed 2-keeled pro-
      phyll. .... Subfamily 3. CARICOIDEAE.

Subfamily 1. MAPANIOIDEAE C. B. Clarke in Thiselt.-Dyer, *Flora Trop. Africa* **8,** 267
        (1901), and Kew Bull. Add. Ser. **8:** 128. (1908), both as *Mapaniae.*
        Subfamily *Scleri[oide]ae* C. B. Clarke in *Kew Bull. Add. Ser.* **8,** 131 (1908).
        Type genus: *Scleria.* Syn. nov.

Inflorescentia e cymulis in panicula, capite vel raro in spica dispositis composita. Cymulae
simplices vel interdum spiculis masculis secundariis 1 ad 3 pauci-ramosae, fructificatione
unica terminatae, basi uni- vel bi-prophyllatae; glumae plures vel paucae, imbricatae interdum plus minus distichae, herbaceae vel in tribu *Mapanieae* hyalinae et nonnumquam
plus minus connatae, vacuae vel florem masculam monandrum ferentes. Fructificationes
vere terminales, achaenio et utriculo constructae; achenia in utriculo inclusa vel eo exce-
dentia; utriculi omnino vel partim cum pericarpio achaenii adnati.
        Genus typicum. *Mapania* Aublet.

The subfamily Mapanioideae in this revised sense can be subdivided into three tribes,
Mapanieae, Lagenocarpeae, and Sclerieae, which are classified as in the following key.

1. Glumes consisting cymelets herbaceous, exposed over the bract subtending cymelet; axis of cymelets elongated; cymelets bisexual or unisexual; bisexual cymelets always branched with staminate secondary spikelets; prophyll 1 to a cymelet.

    2. Fructifications not beaked, the utricle generally shorter than the subtending achene; cymelets bisexual and branched (except that in a number of species in *Scleria* the cymelets becoming unisexual and unbranched owing to the reduction of secondary staminate spikelets). . . . . Tribe 1. SCLERIEAE.

    2. Fructifications beaked, the utricle longer than the enclosed achene; cymelets unisexual, unbranched.   . . . . Tribe 2. LAGENOCARPEAE.

1. Glumes consisting cymelets hyaline, shorter than and completely covered by the bract subtending the cymelet; axis of cymelets abbreviated; cymelets always bisexual, unbranched; prophylls 2 to a cymelet.   . . . . Tribe 3. MAPANIEAE.

Tribe 1. SCLERIEAE Nees, *Linnaea* **9**, 302 (1834). Type: *Scleria* Berg.

    Caricoideae-Hoppieae Pax, *Botan. Jahrb.* **7**, 308 (1886). Type: *Hoppia* Nees.

    Caricoideae-Hoppieae-Hoppiinae Pax, *Botan. Jahrb.* **7**, 309 (1886). Type: *Hoppia* Nees.

    Caricoideae-Bisboeckelereae Pax, in Engler, *Nat. Pflanzenf. Nachr. zu II–IV Teil*, 47 (1897). Type: *Bisboeckelera* O. Kuntze.

    Caricoideae-Bisboeckelereae-Bisboeckelerinae Pax, in Engler, *Nat. Pflanzenf. Nachr. zu II–IV Teil*, 49 (1897). Type: *Bisboeckelera* O. Kuntze.

    Rhynchosporeae-Bisboeckelrinae (Pax) Engl. & Gilg., *Syll. Pflanzenf.* 1 Aufl., 128 (1912).

Ultimate units of inflorescence a bisexual cymelet, a bisexual cymelet and a staminate spikelet, or a pistillate cymelet and a staminate spikelet (only in *Scleria*); bisexual cymelets branched with one to a few staminate secondary spikelets borne at the axil of glumes on the cymelet axis; pistillate cymelets simple. Glumes consisting of cymelets herbaceous, imbricated, or 2-ranked. Pistillate flowers a terminal naked pistil; utricles subtending the pistil short, spongy (in *Calyptrocarya* the upper margins of utricles developing into hyaline sac covering entire ovary), more or less adnate to the lower portion of the ovary; achenes globose or thickly lenticular, bony, exceeding the spongy utricle; styles extremely short; stigmas 3 or 2. Staminate flowers axillary, with 1 or 2, sometimes 3, stamens.

    Five genera, mostly tropical American. 1. *Becquerelia* Brongn.; 2. *Diplacrum* R. Brown; 3. *Bisboeckelera* O. Kuntze; 4. *Calyptrocarya* Nees; 5. *Scleria* Berg.

    For the generic classification see T. Koyama (1967b).

Tribe 2. LAGENOCARPEAE. Type: *Lagenocarpus* Nees.

    Cryptangieae Bentham & Hook. f., *Gen. Pl.* **3**, 1042 (1883). Type: *Cryptangium* Schrader ex Nees.

Ultimate units of inflorescence a pistillate cymelet and a staminate spikelet; pistillate cymelets simple. Glumes consisting of cymelets herbaceous, imbricated, or occasionally somewhat 2-ranked. Pistillate flowers; a terminal compound fruiting structure consisting of a pistil completely contained in a utricle; ovary adnate to or tightly surrounded by the utricle; style adnate to the utricle for its entire length, forming the solid beak of fructification, exposing only its stigmas through the orifice of utricular beak. Fructifications subtended by 3 minute hypogynous squamellae, each ciliate with long or short hairs. Staminate flowers axillary, with 2, 3, 4 or 6 stamens.

Nine genera, mostly tropical American, some tropical West African. 1. *Coleochloa* Gilly; 2. *Afrotrilepis* Raynal; 3. *Trilepis* Nees; 4. *Microdracoides* Hua; 5. *Cephalocarpus* Nees; 6. *Everardia* Ridley ex im Thurn; 7. *Lagenocarpus* Nees; 8. *Didymiandrum* Gilly; 9. *Exochogyne* C. B. Clarke.

For the generic classification see T. Koyama and Maguire (1965). Five of the nine genera above are characterized by the peculiar woody caudices, which are epigaeous, simple, or branched and are attaining the height of 2 m in some instances. The five woody genera are *Afrotrilepis, Trilepis, Microdracoides, Cephalocarpus,* and *Everardia.*

Tribe 3. MAPANIEAE. Type: *Mapania* Aublet.
> *Hypolytreae* Nees, *Linnaea* **9,** 287 (1834). Type: *Hypolytrum* L. C. Richard.
> *Scirpoideae-Hypolytreae-Hypolytrinae* Pax, *Botan. Jahrb.* **7,** 305 (1886). Type: *Hypolytrum* L. C. Richard.

Cymelets small, borne at axils of glumes of spikes and completely covered by the subtending glume, always bisexual, consisting of a terminal pistillate flower and 2 to many scales (squamellae); squamellae hyaline, the lowest pair (prophylls) lateral and opposite, folded with an acute keel, subtending monandrous or diandrous staminate flower or empty, the other squamellae flattish, imbricated, or obscurely distichous, each subtending a monandrous staminate flower, but the upper few squamellae becoming empty by abortion of their staminate flowers. Pistillate flower a terminal compound fruiting structure consisting of a pistil completely adnate to the containing utricle. Stigmas 2 or 3, rarely up to 8.
This tribe is subdivided into the following two subtribes.

MAPANIEAE subtribe 1. MAPANIINAE. Type: *Mapania* Aublet.
Leaf and bract blades dorsiventral.

Six genera in the tropics of both hemispheres. 1. *Scirpodendron* Zippel ex Kurz; 2. *Diplasia* L. C. Richard; 3. *Exocarya* Bentham; 4. *Mapania* Aublet; 5. *Mapaniopsis* C. B. Clarke; 6. *Hypolytrum* L. C. Richard.

The genus *Principina* of Africa is regarded as a section of the genus *Mapania.** In *Principina* the partial inflorescence has a membranous sac which contains a fruiting structure and three stamens. The arrangement of these components shows that the cymelets of *Principina* consist of a terminal pistillate flower and three lateral staminate flowers below it. Three squamellae subtending the staminate flowers form the saclike structure by connation. The cymelets in *Principina,* therefore, structurally do not differ from those of *Mapania.* Since the connation of squamellae into a sac commonly occurs also in the section *Pycnocephala* of the genus *Mapania* (T. Koyama, 1967b), the saclike squamellae of

---

Mapania sect. PRINCIPINA (Uittien) T. Koyama, stat. nov.
Principina Uittien, *Rec. Trav. Bot. Néerl.* **32,** 282 (1935).
Type and sole species. MAPANIA GRANDIS (Uittien) T. Koyama, comb. nova, based on *Principina grandis* Uittien, *Rec. Trav. Bot. Néerl.* **32,** 282, *fig.* (1935). Type: *A. W. Exell 703* from Mt. Pico Papagaio, Is. Principe, Africa (BM, holotype).

Principina do not warrant its generic separation from *Mapania*. Although such an open inflorescence as seen in *Principina* is not common in *Mapania,* the sections *Tepuianae* and *Thoracostachyum* of *Mapania* exhibit a transition of infloresences from congested heads to open corymbs. The vegetative parts of *Principina* resemble those of *Hypolytrum*. However, the structure of cymelets does not support this link.

MAPANIEAE subtribe 2. CHRYSITHRICHINAE (Nees) T. Koyama, *Mem. N.Y. Botan. Garden* **17**(1), 46 (1967).

Chrysithricheae Nees, Linnaea **9**, 288 (1834). Type: *Chrysithrix* L.

Caricoideae-Hoppieae-Chrysithricinae (Nees) Pax, *Botan. Jahrb.* **7**, 309 (1886).

Leaf blades and involucral bracts terete and unifacial or ancipitous.

Two genera in South Africa, Indo-Malaysia, and Australia. 1. *Chrysithrix* L.; 2. *Lepironia* L. C. Richard (including *Chrizandra* R. Br.).

For the generic classification of the tribe Mapanieae see Pfeiffer (1925) and Koyama (1961, 1967b).

REFERENCES

Ascherson, P., and Graebner, P. (1902). "Synopsis der Mitteleuropäischen Flora," Bd. **2**, 2 Teil.

Bentham, G. (1877). On the distribution of the monocotyledonous orders into primary groups. *J. Linn. Soc. Botan.* **15**, 490–520.

Bentham, G., and Hooker, J. D. (1883). "Genera Plantarum," Vol. 3, pp. 1037–1073.

Clarke, C. B. (1894). Cyperaceae. *In* "Flora of British India," (Hooker, ed.). Vol. 6, p. 585.

Clarke, C. B. (1902). Cyperaceae. *In* "Flora of Tropical Africa." Vol. 8, pp. 266–524.

Clarke, C. B. (1908). New genera and species of Cyperaceae. *Kew Bull. Add. Ser.* **8**, 1–196.

Clarke, C. B. (1909). "Illustrations of Cyperaceae." Williams & Norgate, London.

Erdtman, G. (1966). "Pollen Morphology and Plant Taxonomy. Angiosperms." (Corrected reprint.) Hafner, New York.

Goebell, K. (1888). Über den Bau der Ährchen und Blüten einiger javanischer Cyperaceen. *Ann. Jard. Botan. Buitenz.* **7**, 120–140.

Holttum, R. E. (1948). The spikelets in Cyperaceae. *Botan. Rev.* **14**, 525–541.

Hutchinson, J. (1957). "The Families of Flowering Plants." 2nd edition. Oxford at the Clarendon Press.

Kern, J. H. (1961). The genus *Scleria* in Malaysia. *Blumea* **11**, 140–218.

Kern, J. H. (1962). New look at some Cyperaceae mainly from the tropical standpoint. *Advan. Sci.* **19**, 141–148.

Koyama, T. (1961). Classification of the family Cyperaceae (1). *J. Fac. Sci. Univ. Tokyo Sect. III,* **8**, 37–148.

Koyama, T. (1965). Interrelationships between the tribes Lagenocarpeae and Sclerieae (Cyperaceae). *Bull. Torrey Botan. Club.* **92**, 250–265.

Koyama, T. (1966). The systematic significance of leaf structure in the Cyperaceae-Mapanieae. *Mem. N.Y. Botan. Garden* **15**(1), 136–159.

Koyama, T. (1967a). The systematic significance of leaf structure in the tribe Sclerieae (Cyperaceae). *Mem. N.Y. Botan. Garden* **16**, 46–70.

Koyama, T. (1967b). Cyperaceae-Mapanioideae. *Mem. N.Y. Botan. Garden* 17(1), 23–79.
Koyama, T., and Maguire, B. (1965). Cyperaceae-Lagenocarpeae. *Mem. N.Y. Botan. Garden* 12(3), 8–54.
Kukkonen, I. (1967a). Spikelet morphology and anatomy of *Uncinia* Pers. (Cyperaceae). *Kew Bull.* 21, 93–97 (pl. 6).
Kukkonen, I. (1967b). Gedanken und Probleme zur Systematik der Familie Cyperaceae. Eine Zusammenfassung. *Aquilo, Botan.* 6, 18–42.
Mackenzie, K. K. (1931). *North American Flora* 18(1), 1–2.
Marek, S. (1958). A study of the anatomy of fruits of European genera in the subfamilies Scirpoideae Pax, Rhynchosporoideae Aschers. et Graebner and some genera of Caricoideae Pax. *Monogr. Botan.* 6, 151–177.
Mattfeld, J. (1935). Zur Morphologie und Systematik der Cyperaceae. *Proc. 6th Intern. Botan. Congr.* Amsterdam 1, 330–332.
Mattfeld, J. (1938). Das morphologische Wesen und die phylogenetische Bedeutung der Blumenblätter. *Ber. Deut. Botan. Ges.* 56, 86–116.
Metcalfe, C. R. (1963). Comparative anatomy as a modern botanical discipline with special reference to recent advancement in systematic anatomy of monocotyledons. *In* "Advances in Botanical Research" (R. D. Preston, ed.), pp. 107–147. Academic Press, New York.
Mora (Osejo), L. E. (1960). Beiträge zur Entwicklungsgeschichte und verglaichenden Morphologie der Cyperaceen. *Beitr. Biol. Pflanz.* 35, 253–341.
Mora (Osejo), L. E. (1966). Las inflorescencias parciales de último orden de *Uncinia* Pers. y la agrupación sistematica de las Caricoideae Kükenthal. *Caldasia* 9(44), 277–293.
Nees von Esenbeck, C. G. (1842). Cyperaceae. *In* Martius, Fl. Brasil. 2(1), 197–198, *t. 19*.
Nelmes, E. (1953). Notes on Cyperaceae: XXXI. The African genus Coleochloa. *Kew Bull.* 8, 373–381.
Ohwi, J. (1944). Cyperaceae-Japonicae 2. *Mem. Coll. Sci. Kyoto Univ.* B, 18, 1–182.
Pax, F. (1886). Beiträge zur Morphologie und Systematik der Cyperaceen. *Botan. Jahrb.* 7, 287–318.
Pfeiffer, H. (1925). Vorarbeiten zur systematischen Monographie der Cyperaceae-Mapanieae. *Botan. Arch.* 12, 446–472.
Schultze-Motel, W. (1959). Entwicklungsgeschichtliche und vergleichendmorphologische Untersuchungen im Blütenbereich der Cyperaceae. *Botan. Jahrb.* 78, 129–170.
Schultze-Motel, W. (1964). "Cyperaceae." *In Engler's Syllabus der Pflanzenfamilien* (H. Melchior, ed.), 2 Bd., pp. 602–607.

The Subgeneric Concept in *Eriogonum* (Polygonaceae)

*James L. Reveal**

> There comes a time in the history of nearly every genus when it becomes almost
> immoral to add new species without first having surveyed the genus as a whole.
>
> Kuijt, *Wentia* 6, 5 (1961)

The genus *Eriogonum* Michx. is composed of some 220 species that are restricted mainly to western North America from northern Mexico to Alaska. Several revisions of the genus and various species complexes have been proposed, but no study devoted solely to the subgeneric and sectional level has ever been attempted. In the past, four subgenera, *Eueriogonum, Ganysma, Oregonium,* and *Clastomyelon,* have been recognized. However, two of them *(Ganysma* and *Oregonium)* have never had the correct place of publication indicated. Two other names, *Oligogonum* and *Eucycla,* have not been used or typified. Recently a new subgenus, *Pterogonum,* was proposed. During the course of this study, the number of subgenera was increased from four to seven, and all the names mentioned above were typified where necessary and the correct place of publication determined. At the sectional level, 14 sections are usually recognized, but few of these names have been typified, nor have their boundaries been adequately defined. In this study, all the sectional names that have been proposed in the past are treated, typified where necessary, and recognized or placed into synonymy. Although some 20 additional sections are presently visualized, no new sections are proposed, pending detailed revisions of each subgenera. The possible lines of evolutionary development within the genus have been tentatively postulated. Indications show that the various subgenera have arisen at various times within the genus and in different geographical areas. The genus seems to have had its origin in the Tertiary and has always been restricted to North America. While the major center of development

* I wish to thank the Smithsonian Institution and the United States National Herbarium, which sponsored my Predoctoral Internship program in Washington, D.C., from September 1966 to February 1967; this paper was basically prepared there. I am grateful to C. V. Morton and W. R. Ernst for their helpful suggestions, and to G. J. Goodman, J. T. Howell, and G. L. Stebbins for reviewing and commenting on an early draft of this manuscript.

appears to have been in the Rocky Mountains, there are several indications of a modern south-north movement in the evolution of the more advanced species.

The genus *Eriogonum* Michx. has not been reviewed at a level above the species since 1877 when Sereno Watson proposed only three large sections instead of the several smaller and more natural ones of Bentham (1837, 1856) and of Torrey and Gray (1870). As these categories have not been typified and no recent application of the rules of nomenclature has been attempted, the purpose of this discussion is to propose a more natural system at the subgeneric rank and to typify those names.

For several years the three names proposed by Watson, *Eueriogonum, Oregonium,* and *Ganysma,* have been considered to be subgenera, and only recently has the question been raised as to what rank Watson really considered his names to be (Graham and Wood, 1965). They noted that Watson (1877) referred to his names as sections, but later, when publishing new species, would "arrange the names in such a way as to suggest that his were of subgeneric and Torrey & Gray's of sectional rank." Nevertheless, the Watson names must be accepted at the rank he designated, even though he might have implied them to be of a different rank at a later date.

The first use of the subgeneric rank was by E. L. Greene in his *Flora Franciscana* (1891), and this level was readily accepted by Kuntze (Post and Kuntze, 1903), Jepson (1913), and subsequent authors up to the present time; however, as Greene used the same names that Watson proposed, Watson has always been considered to be the author.

The various names used by Bentham, by Torrey and Gray, and by others have been considered sections, and, although Graham and Wood (1965) point out that some question may be raised as to the level these names were supposed to be, the general acceptance by monographers has been at the sectional rank.

To typify the subgeneric names it was necessary to investigate the entire genus, arranging the species within groups as I felt they should be. Once the species were grouped, the concepts of past authors were considered to determine where they placed the various species, while trying to understand on what basis they had established their sections. However, since these early authors were not working on the type concept, their types can ultimately be chosen only rather arbitrarily. Once the sectional names had been typified, they were placed into my scheme. A complete review of the literature has been carried out in several libraries during this phase of the project, and those at the New York Botanical Garden, Smithsonian Institution, U.S. Department of Agriculture, Washington, D.C., and the Gray Herbarium and Arnold Arboretum libraries have been consulted most frequently.

At present most authors distinguish four subgenera, but, from this study, seven appears to be a more realistic number. At the sectional rank 14 sections are commonly recognized, but, again from this study, the number of sections needs to be increased considerably. As the sectional arrangement is still tentative and pending further research, only the already published names are treated with the additional sections proposed in revisions to come on the various subgenera.

Eriogonum Michx. *Fl. Bor. Am.* **1**, 246 (1803).*

Espinosa Lag., *Genera Sp. Plantarum* **14**(1816), nomen dubium.†

Eucycla Nutt., *Proc. Acad. Nat. Sci. Phila.* **4**, 16 (1848).

Stenogonum Nutt., *Proc. Acad. Nat. Sci. Phila.* **4**, 19 (1848).

Pterogonum H. Gross, *Botan. Jahrb.* **49**, 239 (1913).

Annual, biennial, or perennial herbs, subshrubs, or shrubs with basal or cauline, alternate, entire, exstipulate, commonly petiolate, usually more or less tomentose leaves; flowers imperfect and these often dioecious or perfect, borne on a short axis surrounded by a membranaceous to rigid, sessile or peduncled, turbinate to campanulate, 3- to 10-lobed or toothed, erect, horizontal, or secund involucre, awnless, the few to many flowers on slender pedicels at the base of the flower, these intermixed with few to many scarious setaceous bractlets, the involucres mostly solitary and terminal or more than 1 and capitate; inflorescence simple to compoundly umbellate, more or less cymose, or racemose, subtended by whorled scalelike to foliaceous, connate bracts, occasionally in the middle of the stem or scape, 2 to several, mostly ternate; flowers hypogynous, apetalous but with a petaloid calyx, the perianth white, cream, ochroleucous, yellow, red, or purple, often tinged with pink, rose, red, or purple, 6-parted nearly or quite to the swollen basal joint or connate up to more than half the length and with either a turbinate, but not stipitate, base broader than the pedicel or with a slender, stalklike, stipitate base extending down from the perianth tube 0.5–3 (5) mm to the pedicel, this sometimes winged; tepals glabrous to glandular or pubescent within and without or both, inflated, saccate, or smooth, the outer 3 tepals (often also called "calyx

---

* In the early literature on *Eriogonum* as well as other new genera proposed in *Flora Boreali-Americana,* the author was often given as L. C. Richard in Michaux. However, in a letter to C. V. Morton, dated April 22, 1966, Madame Tardieu-Blot of Paris explains the references: "Pour la questions posée au sujet de l'Herbier de Michaux, c'est une question qui nous a curieusement déjà été posée plusieurs fois. En particulier [F. A.] Stafleu a fait des recherches sur le même sujet. A son avis il n'y a pas de raison d'attribuer à Richard les espèces de Michaux. Tout le monde répète que le Flora de Michaux a été editée par les soins de Richard, mais on ne peut pas trouver de trace écrité de ce fait. La seule preuve authentique pourrait être recherchées sur les manuscrits eux memes. Mais sur la Flore il n'y a rien . . . ."

† At my request, Dr. Lyman B. Smith of the U.S. National Herbarium attempted to locate the holotype of *Espinosa verticellata* during his visit in December 1966 to Madrid, Spain, where the type is believed to be located. He reports that the Nees specimen on which the name was based could not be found among the Eriogonoideae genera, and the specimen, he concluded, was either lost or misfiled somewhere in the herbarium.

segments") oblong or oval to obovate, the base truncate, cuneate, or cordate, similar to, narrower than, or more commonly broader than the equaling or longer, or occasionally shorter inner 3 tepals; stamens 9, inserted near the base of the perianth, glabrous or more commonly pilose at the base; pistil 3-capellary, the ovary 1-celled, 1-ovulate, 3-styled; stigmas mostly capitate, tightly rolled on immature ovaries, elongating when receptive to the round, elliptic, or oblong pollen grains; achenes triquous or rarely lenticular, glabrous to densely tomentose, winged in some; embryo straight or curved in the copious, mealy endosperm. $x = 10$.

The genus *Espinosa* was placed into synonymy under *Eriogonum* apparently first by Endlicher (1837) in his *Genera Plantarum,* but the species was not referred to any taxon until the publication *Index Kewensis* (Jackson, 1893), when it was referred to *Eriogonum tomentosum.* In reading Lagasca's original description, I noted that the description does not fit *Eriogonum tomentosum,* and, as the type locality was given as New Spain, that could only mean Mexico or California and not the eastern part of the United States where *Eriogonum tomentosum* occurs. As the specimen cannot be located and the description is not adequate to determine what species of *Eriogonum,* if indeed it is referable to an *Eriogonum,* the name *Espinosa verticellata* could be referred to, it seems best to consider *Espinosa* a nomen dubium until the type can be found.

The origin of the genus *Eriogonum* is totally unknown at present, although considerable speculation on this subject is possible, and it is presented below. The distribution of related genera and present morphological studies on members in Polygonaceae have contributed little knowledge in this situation. It is hoped that in future studies on the subfamily Eriogonoideae some information may be obtained but, as with all studies of this kind, the exact evolutionary development of the genus as well as the subfamily as a whole is lost to unrecorded history.

With the lack of fossil data, the origin of the genus can be given only by vague, speculative guesses. In view of this superabundance of lack of information, the following hypothesis is suggested as a possible area for future investigation. It is based on known relationships within other genera and families found in the western United States that have excellent fossil records and modern species distribution similar to the present trends of development in *Eriogonum.*

The origin of the genus seems to have occurred in the Tertiary or possibly slightly before, as several other western United States genera also became differentiated at this time. The climatic conditions where the genus originated must have been an arid or at least a semiarid one, and similar to the kind where most of the species occur today. The exact geographical location cannot be exactly determined, but certainly it must have been in the western part of North America. From present studies on

Tertiary floras, it is believed that the kind of flora found presently in the Great Basin grew considerably farther north, and the flora found then in Colorado, for example, was basically the kind now found in southern Mexico. Thus, during the Tertiary, the northern part of North America must have been similar to that now found in southwestern United States and adjacent northern Mexico. In the extreme northern areas, where there is slightly more moisture, the long days artifically produced a semi-arid condition.

In all these places, fossilization would have been rather unlikely. The current postulate is that, during this more northern development of the genus, the members of the new genus gradually expanded and differentiated but that the Pleistocene glaciation activities reduced or destroyed these primitive populations, although the more variable types were able to migrate southward and thus perpetuate the genus.

Today the genus is well established between the 30° and 50° latitude where long-day requirements can be met. In going northward, the days become longer, and under these conditions *Eriogonum* could exist, while to the south, where short-day conditions exist, no modern species are found, although one species does extend as far south as the state of San Luis Potosi, Mexico. This seems to indicate that the genus does not do well under short-day conditions.

If Stokes and Stebbins (1955) are correct in stating that the basic chromosome number of the genus is $x = 10$, the vast majority of the modern species are tetraploids. This, too, would indicate that the genus had originated early, and that the ancestral diploids have been lost, or at least not yet been detected.

With little more to go on than speculation, it is suggested that the early *Eriogonum* type was probably a low, woody subshrubby plant that occupied the low talus or exposed slopes where competition was reduced or almost nonexistent. It is also suggested that our modern shrubby species might have evolved from this type of plant. The annual condition, which appears to be derived, seems to have arisen several times from different perennial groups.

The present distribution of *Eriogonum* is restricted to western North America, with only a few outlying populations along the eastern coast. The reasons for this distribution seems to be the lack of an active dispersal mechanism. Most seeds in Eriogonoideae are small and smooth, and they usually fall within a few meters of the parent plants, and thus seed dispersal is slow or nonexistent if other requirements (i.e., adaphic or moisture) cannot be met. Some bird dispersal of seeds has been suggested but not demonstrated.

The related genera, *Chorizanthe* and *Oxytheca,* are believed to have evolved from *Eriogonum.* These two genera differ from *Eriogonum* in one rather unique feature; that is, their involucres are usually awned. This seems to have allowed for the far greater distribution of these genera, as they occur in both North and South America. If the suggestion is correct that *Chorizanthe* and *Oxytheca* have evolved from members within *Eriogonum,* then the separation must have occurred early, and the migration to South America must have taken place soon afterward during the Tertiary, when the great migration occurred between the two continents. Considerable work is necessary on this problem, and it is hoped that research in the future will answer many of these questions.

To return to *Eriogonum:* It seems likely that the genus has had several north-to-south migrations associated with glaciation, and thus it is possible that the south-to-north trends that are seen in several species complexes today are a result of a modern northward advance after the last glacial period, rather than a direct southern origin from an exceedingly primitive perennial species. As several groups show this pattern, the following are mentioned only as examples: *E. inflatum* Torr. & Frem. var. *deflatum* I. M. Johnst. is a strict perennial, while throughout most of its range, the var. *inflatum* is a first-year flowering perennial, but, in the northern parts of its range, var. *inflatum* is strictly an annual. *Eriogonum inflatum* is related to *E. trichopes* Torr., a strict annual. On the strictly perennial side, *E. molle* Greene of Baja California is a low, herbaceous subshrub which seems to be a primitive form of the arborescent *E. giganteum* S. Wats. of the islands off the southern California coast. A similar trend may be seen in the Rocky Mountains, where *E. jamesii* Benth. in DC. var. *undulatum* (Benth. in DC.) S. Stokes ex M. E. Jones varies into var. *jamesii,* and then to var. *flavescens* S. Wats., which in turns seems to have given rise to *E. flavum* Nutt. in Fras. While it is impossible to ascertain with absolute certainty the direction of all species trends, the vast majority at present seem to be from the south toward the north.

NATURAL KEY TO THE SUBGENERA

A. Plants biennial or more commonly perennial with essentially angled, sessile or peduncled involucres.
    B. Embryo curved.
        C. Plants with a solid or pith-filled stem, not jointed; common.   1. *Eucycla*
        CC. Plants with a hollow, jointed stem; rare.   2. *Clastomyelon*
    BB. Embryo straight, or, if curved, then the perianth stipelike.
        C. Perianth stipelike.
            D. Calyx and achene densely white – tomentose.   3. *Eriogonum*

      DD. Calyx and achene glabrous, or, if pubescent, then only sparsely
          so.   4. *Oligogonum*
    CC. Perianth not stipelike.   5. *Pterogonum*
AA. Plants essentially annual, or, if perennial, then the involucres usually peduncled and
  not angled.
    B.   Involucres mostly sessile, deeply ribbed or strongly angled.   6. *Oregonium*
    BB. Involucres mostly peduncled, not ribbed or strongly angled.   7. *Ganysma*

ARTIFICIAL KEY TO THE SUBGENERA

A.   Perianth abruptly stipelike at the attenuated base, the stipe not at all winged; bracts
    foliaceous, indefinite in number (2 to several).
    B.   Tall, erect perennials with a single, rarely more, leafy stem arising from a short,
        branched caudex or a deep, soft taproot; perianth white with long, dense, white
        hairs, the stipe mostly 2–5 mm long, the outer segments of the perianth narrower
        than the inner, or nearly similar; plants of the southeastern United States, ranging
        from Texas eastward to Florida, and northward to North Carolina. 3. *Eriogonum*
    BB. Low, spreading caespitose to shrubby, branched perennials arising from a hard,
        usually highly branched, woody caudex; perianth mostly yellow, glabrous, or, if
        pubescent, the hairs mostly short and not at all dense, the stipe up to 3 mm long,
        the outer segments of the perianth as wide as or wider than the inner segments;
        plants of the western United States from northern Mexico to Alaska, with a
        single species *(E. allenii)* in Virginia and West Virginia.   4. *Oligogonum*
AA. Perianth not attenuated at the base nor usually stipelike, but, if stipelike, then the
  stipe winged; bracts foliaceous or reduced to scalelike, connate bracts, mostly ternate.
    B.   Plants caespitose or tall and erect perennials to large arborescent shrubs, or, if
        annual or biennial, then the stems normally single from the base and tall and erect
        with leafy stems.
      C.   Plants caespitose perennials to large arborescent shrubs, or, if annual or
         biennial, then stems single from the base, tall and erect, leafy; plants wide-
         spread and common from the northern part of the western United States
         south to northwestern Mexico.   1. *Eucycla*
      CC. Plants tall and erect perennials mostly with a single stem arising from a
         caudex.
        D.   Involucres 3 at a node, sessile in the axils of the bracts, not angled,
          becoming ruptured at maturity with numerous expanding flowers;
          stems internally jointed; narrow endemic known only from Death
          Valley, California.   2. *Clastomyelon*
        DD. Involucres single, peduncled, usually angled, not ruptured by the few
          flowers; stems not internally jointed; plants mainly of northern Mexico
          and adjacent southern Texas northward to Nebraska and westward to
          Utah and Arizona.   5. *Pterogonum*
    BB. Plants annual, or, if perennial, then the involucres usually peduncled and not
      angled.
      C.   Involucres strongly ribbed or angled, strongly appressed and sessile to the
         stems for the most part especially in young plants; plants mainly along the
         Pacific Coast, but extending eastward as far as Texas and northeastern
         Mexico.   6. *Oregonium*

CC. Involucres smooth, not ribbed or angled, usually peduncled or, if sessile, the involucres not pressed to the stems; plants mainly of northwestern Mexico northward to Oregon, usually east of the Sierra Nevada, eastward to North Dakota and western Texas.   7. *Ganysma*

1. Subgenus Eucycla (Nutt.) Kuntze, in Post and Kuntze, *Lexicon Gen. Phan.* **204** (1903). *Eucycla* Nutt., *Proc. Acad. Nat. Sci. Phila.* **4,** 16 (1848). Lectotype: *Eucycla ovalifolia* (Nutt.) Nutt. = *Eriogonum ovalifolium* Nutt. Vide: Reveal, in Reveal and Spevak (1967).

Low, spreading caespitose perennial herbs to large arborescent shrubs arising from branched, hard, woody caudices, mostly caespitose but up to 3 m high; glabrous to tomentose; leaves various, borne basally or along the stems or at each node, mostly alternate, glabrous, ciliate, glandular to densely tomentose, often more so below than above; flowering stems erect or spreading, bearing virgated, racemose, cymose-paniculate, or capitate inflorescences; bracts ternate, connate at the bases, seldom foliaceous, mostly acute and linear, scalelike; involucres sessile or peduncled only from the forks of the branches, the peduncles, when present, erect and stout; involucres turbinate to campanulate, solitary or clustered, angled at least at the base of the involucral tube, not ribbed, mostly 5- to 6-lobed, the teeth shallow, acute to obtuse, erect; perianth abruptly narrowing to a rounded or acute base, narrowed to the point of attachment or, if with a stipelike base, then the stipe winged, the calyx segments accrescent, white to yellow, pink or red, glabrous, glandular, or pubescent, the outer whorl of segments slightly to exceedingly larger than the inner whorl of segments; achenes inserted or slightly exserted, not winged, triquous; embryo curved.

Sections within the Subgenus Eucycla

Section Lachnogyna Torr. & Gray, *Proc. Am. Acad. Arts Sci., Daedalus* **8,** 163 (1870).
    Lectotype: *E. lachnogynum* Torr. ex. Benth. in DC.
Section Fasciculata Benth., *Trans. Linn. Soc. London* **17,** 411 (1837).
    Lectotype: *E. fasciculatum* Benth.
        Sect. *Fascicarium* Kuntze, in Post & Kuntze, *Lexicon Gen. Phan.* **204** (1903). Based on Sect. *Fasciculata* Benth.
Section Corymbosa Benth. in DC., *Prodr.* **14,** 17 (1856).
    Lectotype: *E. microthecum* Nutt.
        Sect. *Corymbarium* Kuntze, in Post & Kuntze, *Lexicon Gen. Phan.* **204** (1903). Based on Sect. *Corymbosa* Benth. in DC.
Section Capitata Torr. & Gray, *Proc. Am. Acad. Arts Sci., Daedalus* **8,** 165 (1870).
    Lectotype: *E. pauciflorum* Pursh, as to type, not as to concept of all present authors. Vide: Reveal (1967).
        Sect. *Capitarium* Kuntze, in Post & Kuntze, *Lexicon Gen. Phan.* **204** (1903). Based on Sect. *Capitata* Torr. & Gray.
Section Latifolia Benth., *Trans. Linn. Soc. London* **17,** 412 (1837).
    Lectotype: *E. latifolium* Sm.
        Sect. *Desmocephala* Benth. in DC., *Prodr.* **14,** 12 (1856).
            Lectotype: *E. latifolium* Sm.
        Sect. *Capitellata* Torr. & Gray, *Proc. Am. Acad. Arts Sci., Daedalus* **8,** 167 (1870).
            Lectotype: *E. nudum* Dougl. ex Benth.
Section Elata Rydb., *Fl. Rocky Mts.* **213** (1917).
    Type: *E. elatum* Dougl. ex Benth.
Section Racemosa Rydb., *Fl. Rocky Mts.* **215** (1917).
    Lectotype: *E. racemosum* Nutt.

Section Eucycla

Sect. *Heterosepala* Torr. & Gray, *Proc. Am. Acad. Arts Sci., Daedalus* **8**, 164 (1870). Based on *Eucycla* Nutt.

Sect. *Hetarium* Kuntze, in Post & Kuntze, *Lexicon Gen. Phan.* **204** (1903). Based on Sect. *Heterosepala* Torr. & Gray.

Sect. *Dichotoma* Rydb., *Fl. Rocky Mts.* 213(1917). Lectotype: *E. strictum* Benth.

Section Micrantha Benth., *Trans. Linn. Soc. London* **17,** 413 (1837). Lectotype: *E. annuum* Nutt.*

Sect. *Annua* Rydb., *Fl. Rocky Mts.* 217(1917).

Type: *E. annuum* Nutt.

The subgenus *Eucycla* is the largest and most difficult in the genus. At present it is considered to contain nearly 100 species of which several are undescribed, and certainly the discovery of more can be expected. The subgenus is tentatively divided into 14 sections, of which the 8 listed above are presently described.

This subgenus has gone under the name *Oregonium* for several years, but the typification of this name by Roberty and Vautier (1964) in their essay on Polygonaceae with *Eriogonum vimineum* makes it necessary to restrict the name *Oregonium* to those annual species centering around this species and to revive *Eucycla* for this large group of perennials. It is somewhat unfortunate that *E. ovalifolium,* a highly evolved species, should be the type species of this subgenus, which is generally composed of primitive species.

The differentiation of *Eucycla* from the ancestral *Eriogonum* types must have occurred early. It is presently visualized that the early species would fit in *Eucycla,* and within these early groups there were several subsequent finer divisions which ultimately led to the formation of the other subgenera, as well as of the several sections within *Eucycla.* The separation of the various subgenera probably occurred in early Tertiary, or slightly before, and during the following periods the subgenus *Eucycla* has differentiated into several sections which have differences that are often as great as or greater than some of those between the subgenera. However, the sections are held together by a series of intermediate sections or species, and only by considering the entire subgenus in relation to the whole genus has it been possible to see the overall trends of relationships, even though the extremes are quite distinct.

The most primitive species in this subgenus, as well as the genus, probably were woody, perennial subshrubs or shrubs with astipitate

---

*Recent studies have shown this section to represent a new subgenus, subgenus *Micrantha* (Benth.) Reveal, stat. nov., containing two species. It will be discussed in a later paper.

flowers deposed on a cymose inflorescence. Within *Eucycla,* after its early and basic divergences from the primitive buckwheats, several lines of modern species development have occurred and can be seen to represent three major lines of development.

The large shrubby or arborescent species (i.e., *E. fasciculatum, E. giganteum,* etc.) moved slowly out of northern Mexico into the Pacific Coast chaparral belts of California, where several species have gradually become differentiated into coastal and insular form. These species have become somewhat isolated from each other, and, possessing enough variation to continue to evolve, they became highly specialized rather rapidly. Thus the present-day species are not necessarily like the ancient types, but both probably still share some common features.

The low herbaceous subshrubs (i.e., *E. microthecum, E. brevicaule,* etc.) occupy much of the western United States and have expanded particularly in the Intermountain Region. This group has had several north-south movements possibly associated with glaciation, and thus considerable variation is found in the present distribution of related species groups. In some areas, notably in the Green-Colorado river drainages, several species have become differentiated by strict edaphic isolation, and thus several micropopulations exist where little or no gene flow has occurred. This reduction in gene flow has resulted in several distinct species which occupy a relatively small area.

To a great degree the pronounced differentiation seen in the morphology of the various species in this part of the subgenus has occurred without the evolution of any obvious genetic incompatibility barrier. The reproductive isolation barriers which are normally responsible for the divergence of the various species does not seem to be genetic, but rather edaphic, ecologic, and geographic. Thus, with these weak barriers, the species are probably vulnerable to any sudden changes, whether natural or artificial. Field observations of the several species seems to indicate that, when a particular type is isolated from its related kinds, the isolate rapidly evolves in its new habitat, usually with a substantial loss of individuals and with a rapid change in morphology.

Certainly some scientists will readily question a species concept that would allow the existence of morphologically distinct species which, apparently, have not become genetically separated owing to the lack of an internal isolation barrier. However, in this genus such species are excellent and will not readily invade new areas where closely related species occur. Where sympatric species occur, rarely is hybridization seen, and this seems to be where the various species have developed genetic isolation barriers due to this sympatric condition.

The low caespitose species (i.e., *E. pauciflorum, E. ochrocephalum,* etc.) can be traced directly to the low herbaceous group noted above. The caespitose species occur mainly in the high mountains of the Far West, with a few scattered species being found on the foothills east of the Rocky Mountains. These species occupy a great variety of habitats, in low elevations down to 6000 ft and also to an elevation of over 12,000 ft. Unlike most of the other subgenera, the members in this part of *Eucycla* are highly restricted, often to a single mountain range and, in some cases, to only part of a range. Not only is the distribution highly restricted, but also the distances between the various species are usually great, and thus the chances for gene flow is greatly reduced or gene flow has not been possible for a considerably long period of time.

The origin of the endemics in the herbaceous and caespitose groups seem to be distinctly different. In the first group the species appear to have evolved from small, yet variable species; thus the related species occur rather close together. This seems to be due to the occurrence of these species at low elevations, where the species are separated by edaphic or ecologic rather than geographic barriers. Also, in looking into other genera mainly from the Intermountain Region, the species of these genera also seem to have a southern origin with a northward-moving pattern of development.

On the other hand, the caespitose group seems to have been one in which only a small number of species existed in the past but each population was rather highly variable. At least in the western United States, glaciation must have caused a great reduction in the overall distribution of these primitive species, leaving only a few, widely scattered populations behind on the higher mountain peaks above the effects of the glaciers or in areas south of the glacial action. This reduction in the various intermediate populations allowed for a gradual differentiation of the isolated forms which evolved independently of each other. The species which exemplify this development best in the Intermountain Region may be found in the genus *Primula* and in parts of *Astragalus* and *Eriogonum*. All these groups appear to have come from the north, as the species all occur at higher elevations.

The overall evolution in this subgenus seems to have been rapid. The species barriers are often external rather than internal, yet they are real and the flow of genetic material is restricted. The whole story for this group is not known, nor is it even discussed here because of the multitude of species; thus, only a few general statements are made at this time.

2. Subgenus Clastomyelon Coville & Morton, *J. Wash. Acad. Sci.* **26,** 304 (1936). Type: *E. intrafractum* Cov. & Mort.

Tall, erect, perennial herbs with a single stem arising from a hard, woody, caudex, 8–12 dm high, glabrous or nearly so; leaves strictly basal, oblong-ovate, densely pilose-tomentose on both surfaces; flowering stems erect, with virgatedly branched inflorescences, the stems divided into many transverse articulations which become externally obvious at maturity, the divisions ringlike, 3–10 mm long; bracts 3- to 6-parted, connate at the bases, acute; involucres mostly in clusters of 3 at a node, each sessile in the axils of the bracts, campanulate, not strongly angled, 5-lobed, becoming ruptured by the many expanding flowers and bractlets; flowers rounded at the base, astipitate, yellow, tinged with rose at maturity, pubescent without, the segments about equal, oblong-oblanceolate; achenes inserted, flask-shaped, the bases prominently 3-lobed, tapering abruptly to strigose, 3-angled beaks.

The subgenus *Clastomyelon* has only a single species which is very rare and highly restricted to limestone outcrops in the area of Death Valley, California.

This subgenus was next to the last to be proposed, and, when it was described by Coville and Morton, their discussion and descriptions were exact; thus little can be added at this time. The species has only been infrequently found since the collections made by M. F. Gilman, then associated with the Death Valley Museum, and his collections are somewhat fragmentary. From the little information that it has been possible to obtain, the species still represents a distinct subgenus, but what its origin might have been is unknown. Allowing for a proper amount of speculation, the subgenus must have come from a part of *Eucycla,* and possibly near the *Eriogonum nudum* group.

3. Subgenus Eriogonum. Type: *E. tomentosum* Michx.

Tall, erect perennials with a single stem (rarely more) arising from a soft, woody caudex, (0.3) 1.5–1.5 (2) m high; leaves basal and whorled, or cauline and alternate or whorled, lanceolate to obovate, glabrate to densely long pubescent; stems erect, glabrate to silky pubescent; bracts ternate, connate at the bases; cauline leaves more reduced above, narrower than the basal leaves; inflorescences elongated, opened, and long-branched paniculate cymes; involucres sessile or short-peduncled, peduncles erect; involucres turbinate to campanulate, smooth or angled, mostly 5- to 8-lobed, the lobes shallow or, if deeply dividing the tubes, then the lobes spreading and reflexed, lanceolate; flowers long stipitate, thinly pubescent to densely white-tomentose with long, matted hairs, yellowish or whitish, the inner whorl of calyx segments wider than the outer whorls of calyx segments, or the segments nearly equal; achenes long exserted, usually densely white-pubescent; embryo straight.

Sections within the Subgenus Eriogonum

Section Eriogonum
  Sect. *Eriantha* Benth., *Trans. Linn. Soc. London* **17,** 406 (1837). Lectotype: *E. tomentosum* Michx.

Sect. *Epinosa* (Lag.) Kuntze, in Post & Kuntze, *Lexicon Gen. Phan.* **204** (1903), as to its application to Sect. *Eriantha* and *Eriogonum tomentosum*, not *Espinosa* Lag., nom. dubium.
Section Trachytheca Nutt., *J. Acad. Nat. Sci. Phila.* II, **1**, 166 (1848). Type: *E. longifolium* Nutt.

The subgenus *Eriogonum* (in the past referred to *Eueriogonum*) is presently considered to include only two species, each in a section of its own.

This subgenus has been considered to include what is here called subgenus *Oligogonum* but, in this investigation of the subgeneric relationships using the distinctive morphological features and the proposed evolutionary developments within the two subgenera, it seemed to call for a separation at a higher taxonomic rank than section, in which the groups have been placed in the past. With the exclusion of the winged achene species which are now placed in *Pterogonum,* and the placement in *Oligogonum* of the low, spreading to shrubby, branched perennials which have a hard, woody caudex, basically yellowish perianth that is glabrous or, if pubescent, then with sparse and usually shorter hairs, and only sparsely pubescent achenes, the subgenus *Eriogonum* takes on a more natural appearance.

Both *Eriogonum tomentosum* and *E. longifolium* are distinct species, although the latter may be separated into three geographical varieties. *Eriogonum longifolium* seems to have had its origin from an ancestral type somewhat similar to the *Eriogonum* type that may have been associated with the evolution of *Pterogonum,* while *E. tomentosum* may have originated from an early form of *E. longifolium*. The subsequent disjunct populations of *E. longifolium* from Texas to Arkansas, and then to Florida, indicate that the intermediate populations probably have been eliminated by the Cenozoic inundation of much of the Coastal Plain during the last glaciation periods. This could certainly explain the absence of the Coastal Plain species, *E. tomentosum,* along the Gulf Coast. James (1961) has discussed several related incidences of a similar nature in other genera.

4. Subgenus Oligogonum Nutt., *J. Acad. Nat. Sci. Phila.* II, **1**, 166 (1848). Lectotype: *E. umbellatum* Torr. Vide: Reveal, in Reveal and Spevak (1967).

Low, spreading caespitose to shrubby branched perennials arising from a branched, hard, woody caudex, mostly caespitose or up to 1.2 m high; leaves borne on the ends of the caudices usually in tufts of 3–15 leaves, or whorled at the base of the stems, mostly oblanceolate, linear to ovate, glabrous to glabrate or densely tomentose, often more so below than above; flowering stems often scapelike and capitate or a simple or compound branched umbellate cymes, bractless or with a whorl of 2 to several foliaceous bracts near the center of the stems or at the base of the umbel; umbel simple or compound, bearing a single involucre at the end of each ray or congested into capitate or subcapitate heads by the lack or shortening of the rays; involucres turbinate, not angled or ribbed, mostly 4- to 8-lobed, the teeth acute to obtuse, shallow and erect or deeply dividing the tubes and spreading to reflexed, mostly lanceolate; calyx narrowed to a short, slender, stipelike base which is jointed to, and only slightly if at all thicker than, the pedicel, the flowers accrescent, cream to whitish, yellow to reddish, glabrous or pubescent, the hairs mostly short and not densely matted, the outer whorl of calyx segments slightly wider than the inner whorl of segments; achenes inserted to exserted, triquous, glabrous to sparsely pubescent mostly at the apices; embryo straight or more commonly curved.

Sections within the Subgenus Oligogonum

Section Oligogonum

    Sect. *Umbellata* Benth., *Trans. Linn. Soc. London* **17,** 407 (1837). Lectotype: *E. umbellatum* Torr.

    Sect. *Umbellogonum* Kuntze, in Post and Kuntze, *Lexicon Gen. Phan.* **204** (1903). Based on Sect. *Umbellata* Benth.

Section *Flava* Rydb., *Fl. Rocky Mts.* **212** (1917). Lectotype: *E. flavum* Nutt. in Fras.

Section *Caespitosa* Rydb., *Fl. Rocky Mts.* **212** (1917). Lectotype: *E. caespitosum* Nutt.

Section Pseudo-umbellata Torr. & Gray, *Proc. Am. Acad. Arts Sci., Daedalus* **8,** 161 (1870). Lectotype: *E. pyroliifolium* Hook.

    Sect. *Pyroliifolia* Rydb., *Fl. Rocky Mts.* **212** (1917). Lectotype: *E. pyroliifolium* Hook.

The subgenus *Oligogonum* is presently considered to include 29 species in about 7 sections of which only the four noted above are described.

This subgenus, the first proposed in the genus *Eriogonum,* was limited to all species of *Eriogonum* which have "outer segments of the perianth, which increase a little in size, and are either larger and erect, or all nearly equal." By this definition, given by Nuttall (1848b), and accounting for the species which he had placed into different genera, Nuttall was placing all the species except *E. tomentosum* and *E. longifolium* into his subgenus. As the selection of *E. umbellatum* as the lectotype for this subgenus was not explained in the recent paper in *Taxon* (Reveal and Spevak, 1967), it is now discussed.

Eriogonum umbellatum was selected for two reasons. First, the selection of a species included in one of Greene's subgenera would have led to the synonymizing of one of those names long associated with the genus, and I have tried to avoid supplanting any well-known name whenever possible. As the distinction between the subgenera *Eriogonum* and *Oligogonum* became obvious, it was felt that, instead of proposing a new subgeneric name, the typification of the Nuttall name to limit the new subgenus as now conceived would be best. Second, by considering the characteristics on which Nuttall had established the subgenus, *E. umbellatum* seemed to fit. The outer segments are nearly equal in anthesis, but they enlarge slightly in fruit. Also the name, "oligogonum," means "few nodes" and, in this respect, *E. umbellatum* certainly fits.

The evolutionary development of the species in *Oligogonum* seemed to have occurred in three distinct geographical areas. In the Rocky Mountains, the first center of speciation, several forms within *Eriogonum umbellatum* have originated, and the several diverse forms within *E. umbellatum* indicate that this species is still a highly variable and a rapidly evolving species.

Eriogonum sphaerocephalum and its related species had their origin in the second center, which is now located in southeastern Oregon and adjacent Idaho. In this area several species have evolved and have become rather widespread in the Pacific Northwest and the northern part of the Intermountain Region. From the species which originated in this area, several forms moved southward into the third center of differentiation, California, where several small, isolated endemics have resulted.

The most highly evolved species are the polygamo-dioecious plants, *Eriogonum marifolium, E. incanum,* and *E. polypodum.* Not only do these species have a unique reproductive feature, but also they are apparently aneuploids derived from *E. umbellatum* forms or some near relative.

5. Subgenus Pterogonum (H. Gross) Reveal, *Sida* **3,** 82 (1967). *Pterogonum* H. Gross, Botan Jahrb. **49,** 239 (1913). Lectotype: *P. atrorubens* (Engelm. in Wisl.) H. Gross = *E. atrorubens* Engelm. in Wisl. Vide: Roberty and Vautier (1964).

Tall erect perennials mostly with a single stem arising from a deep, soft, woody, caudex, (0.3) 0.5–2 m high; leaves basal and whorled or cauline and alternate, mostly spathulate to narrowly oblanceolate or ovate, glabrous to densely pubescent or glandular-pubescent, often with ciliated leaf margins; stems erect or nearly so, glabrous or glabrate to silky pubescent or glandular-pubescent; bracts ternate, connate at the bases; cauline leaves, when present, becoming reduced above, usually narrower than the basal ones; inflorescences mainly elongated, open, long-branched paniculate cymes or di- or trichotomously branched cymes or cymes which are suppressed on one side; involucres pedunculate or rarely sessile, the peduncles curving upward, stout; involucres turbinate to campanulate, not angled or ribbed, mostly 4 to 5- (8) lobed, the teeth shallow, erect, acute to obtuse to truncate; flowers astipitate, pubescent or glabrous, yellow to red or purple; achenes winged or slightly ridged, glabrous or pilose, usually long exserted; embryo straight.

Sections within Subgenus *Pterogonum*

Section *Pterogonum*
  Sect. *Alata* Benth. in DC., *Prodr.* **14,** 6 (1856). Lectotype: *E. alatum* Torr.
  Sect. *Alarium* Kuntze, in Post and Kuntze, *Lexicon Gen. Phan.* **204** (1904). Based on Sect. *Alata* Benth. in DC.

The subgenus *Pterogonum* is presently considered to include 8 species which may be grouped into two sections, although only one is now described (Hess, 1967; Reveal, 1967).

This subgenus was revived recently as a distinct genus by Roberty and Vautier (1964), but their fundamental differences, winged versus non-winged achenes and nonexpanding versus expanding perianth segments, for separating *Pterogonum* from *Eriogonum* do not take into consideration the exceedingly close relationship between the two groups. If their concept was followed, *E. atrorubens* would be placed in the genus *Pterogonum,* and the closely related *E. rupestre* S. Stokes in the genus *Eriogonum,* as the latter species lacks a distinctly winged achene. To base the distinction between two genera on this single character ignores the several similar features shared by the two species and by the various subgenera and *Pterogonum.* It should also be noted that, when Gross proposed the genus, he had an additional character which was the straight versus curved embryo. However, as other species also have straight embryos (as in *Pterogonum*) which occur mainly in the subgenera *Eriogonum* and *Oligogonum,* this feature is not so unique as first thought by Gross (1913).

From a historical point of view, species with winged achenes have been placed generally in the subgenus *Eriogonum,* while those without winged achenes were generally placed in the subgenus *Ganysma.* The present treatment follows the work of Stokes (1936), the last monographer of the genus, who placed all these species in her Section 1A.

All the species in *Pterogonum* are basically plants of northeastern Mexico which have been gradually moving northward since the last glacial periods. The center of this subgenus seems to have been northeastern Mexico.*

6. Subgenus Oregonium (S. Wats.) Greene, *Fl. Frans.* **146** (1891). Lectotype: *E. vimineum* Dougl. ex Benth. Vide: Roberty and Vautier (1964).

Low decumbent to erect annual herbs with one to several stems arising from the taproots, up to 8 dm high; leaves basal, sheathing up the stems or, at each lower node, various, glabrous to densely tomentose; stems bearing inflorescences of elongated virgated branchlets which bear involucres at the nodes, the lateral ones appressed to the stems, or inflorescences with short branchlets usually composed of a single internode which is terminated by a solitary involucre and the lateral ones appressed to the stems; involucres cylindric-turbinate, turbinate, or prismatic, sessile, and subtended by ternate bracts which are connate at the bases, the bracts scalelike or occasionally foliaceous; involucres distinctly

*The assistance provided by the use of the doctoral dissertation of William J. Hess is gratefully acknowledged.

5- to 6-angled or deeply to strongly ribbed, the teeth short and erect; calyx rounded at the base, astipitate, accrescent, white, yellow, or pink, glabrous to hispid or glandular, the outer whorl of calyx segments slightly wider than the inner whorl of segments; achenes inserted to slightly exserted, triquous, with a long, 3-angled, beak; embryo curved.

Sections within the Subgenus Oregonium

Section Oregonium

Sect. *Oregonium* S. Wats., *Proc. Am. Acad. Arts Sci., Daedalus* **12**, 262 (1877).

Subsection Virgata (Benth. in DC.) Reveal, stat. nov.

Sect. *Virgata* Benth. in DC., *Prodr.* **14**, 14 (1856). Lectotype: *E. virgatum* Benth. in DC. = *E. roseum* Dur. & Hilg.

Subsection Oregonium

Section Divaricata Rydb., *Fl. Rocky Mts.* **211** (1917). Lectotype: *E. divaricatum* Hook.

Sect. *Puberula* Rydb., *Fl. Rocky Mts.* **217** (1917). Type: *E. puberulum* S. Wats.

The subgenus *Oregonium* is presently considered to include 25 species in 6 or 7 sections, of which only the two above are currently recognized.

There may be some question about why I have proposed to make a division at the subgeneric level to separate the annuals from the perennials in what had been considered a single subgenus in the past, a separation seemingly based on only this single character. Unlike the subgenus *Ganysma*, in which closely related species may be annual or perennial (i.e., *E. inflatum* versus *E. trichopes*), there are no such similar species relationships between *Oregonium* and *Eucycla*. The annuals are basically a California group in which aneuploidy has run rampant. Counts are known to be $n = 9, 11, 12, 17, 18$, and 20, whereas, in *Eucycla,* the numbers are $n = 20$ or 40, a few species having $n = 16$ or 18. Although several species remain to be counted, the trends seems to be well established within both groups, and the two subgenera seem to have been independent of one another in their evolutionary development for some time. It is felt, however, that *Oregonium,* like the other subgenera, probably had its origin from some ancestral group in *Eucycla* but, unlike most of the other subgenera, this separation has been somewhat more recent.

The major proliferation of species has been in southern California, where the group has undergone rapid evolution. The small microclimates of California and the resulting aneuploidy have evolved several distinct species with only slight morphological differences; therefore a key to the species of this area is often difficult to use (see Reveal and Munz, 1968). From this center the various species have radiated outward, basically northward along the Pacific Coast and eastward into the Great Basin, the exception being *E. polycladon* Benth. in DC. of Mexico, northward into Texas to Arizona and extreme southern Utah.

The distinction between *Oregonium* and *Ganysma* is not a sharp one, and there seem to be some species in one subgenus which are more closely related to species in the other than to species within their own subgenera. The section *Divaricata* has been placed in both *Ganysma* and *Oregonium,* but, according to the involucral characters, it belongs to *Oregonium.* An unnamed section of four species from the Inner Coast Range of California which are all related to *Eriogonum vestitum* J. T. Howell bridges the gap between the two subgenera, as these species have involucres similar to those in *Ganysma,* but they are often closely appressed to the stems and thus similar to those in *Oregonium.* As I had reported previously (1966), *E. collinum* S. Stokes ex M. E. Jones of the subgenus *Ganysma* is closely related to *E. salicornioides* Gandg. of *Oregonium* (reported as *E. demissum* S. Stokes, a synonym) in having the same chromosome count and flower construction but, as *E. collinum* has peduncled involucres and *E. salicornioides* does not, they are placed in separate subgenera. While there may be some readjustments within these two subgenera with certain species or even sections, the subgenera as typified are excellent and distinct.

7. Subgenus Ganysma (S. Wats.) Greene, *Fl. Frans.* **151** (1891). Lectotype: *E. angulosum* Benth.

   Annual or perennial herbs with one to several stems arising from a thin, soft taproot or a hard, woody caudex, up to 1.5 m high; leaves basal, sheathing up the stems, or at each lower node, mostly cordate, glabrous to densely tomentose or hirsute; stems more or less repeatedly dichotomous or trichotomous cymes of filiform to stout, glabrous, glandular, scabrellous, pilose, or tomentose branches with scalelike or foliaceous, ternate, bracts, connate at the bases; involucres turbinate to campanulate to hemispheric, sessile or, more commonly, long peduncled, erect, horizontal, or deflexed, of two whorls of 3-foliaceous lobes or 4–5 (8) lobes or teeth, the teeth short and erect or slightly turned in, not distinctly angled and never ribbed; flowers rounded at the base, astipitate, accrescent, white, yellow, pink, or red, glabrous, hispid, pustulose, or glandular, the outer whorl of calyx segments often wider than the inner whorl of calyx segments; achenes inserted to slightly exserted, triquous or rarely lenticular, with short to long, 3-angled beaks; embryo curved.

Sections within the Subgenus Ganysma

Section Stenogonum (Nutt.) Kuntze, in Post and Kuntze, *Lexicon Gen. Phan.* **204** (1903), the earliest combination, not Roberty and Vautier (1964).

   Stenogonum Nutt., *Proc. Acad. Nat. Sci. Phila.* **4,** 19 (1848). Type: *S. salsuginosum* Nutt. = *E. salsuginosum* (Nutt.) Hook.

Section Foliosa Benth. in DC., *Prodr.* **14,** 21 (1856). Lectotype: *E. abertianum* Torr.

   Subsection Foliosa

   Subsect. *Rumiciflora* Torr. & Gray, *Proc. Am. Acad. Arts Sci., Daedalus* **8,** 189 (1870). Type: *E. abertianum* Torr.

   Subsection Spergulina Torr. & Gray, *Proc. Am. Acad. Arts Sci., Daedalus* **8,** 189 (1870). Lectotype: *E. spergulinum* A. Gray.

       Sect. *Spergulina* Rydb., *Fl. Rocky Mts.* **216** (1917). Type: *E. spergulinum* A. Gray

Section Pedunculata Benth. in DC., *Prodr.* **14,** 19 (1856). Lectotype: *E. cernuum* Nutt.

Section Gomphotheca (Nutt.) Reveal, in Reveal and Spevak, *Taxon* **16,** 412 (1967).

Oxytheca Nutt. sect. *Gomphotheca* Nutt., *Proc. Acad. Nat. Sci. Phila.* **4,** 19 (1848). Type: *Oxytheca glandulosa* Nutt. = *E. glandulosum* (Nutt.) Nutt. ex Benth. in DC.

Section Ganysma

Sect. *Stipulata* Benth., *Trans. Linn. Soc. London* **17,** 406 (1837). Type: *E. angulosum* Benth.

Sect. *Substipulata* Benth. in DC., *Prodr.* **14,** 22 (1856). Based on Sect. *Stipulata* Benth.

Sect. *Pseudo-stipulata* Torr. and Gray, *Proc. Am. Acad. Arts Sci., Daedalus* **8,** 187 (1870). Based on Sect. *Stipulata* Benth.

Sect. *Bracteolata* Curran, *Bull. Calif. Acad.* **1,** 273 (1885). Lectotype: *E. angulosum* Benth.

Sect. *Pseudostiparium* Kuntze, in Post and Kuntze, *Lexicon Gen. Phan.* **204** (1903). Based on Sect. *Pseudo-stipulata* Torr. & Gray.

The subgenus *Ganysma* is presently considered to include 55 species which are placed in seven sections of which the four above are described.

This distinctive subgenus is here recognized as it has been for several years, the one exception being the removal of the northeastern Mexican *Eriogonum ciliatum* complex to the subgenus *Pterogonum.*

The evolutionary development in this subgenus is most enlightening because here a species by species evolution is often possible to see. In the section *Pedunculata* it is possible to trace the development of the *Eriogonum deflexum* complex from its perennial Baja California, Mexico, ancestors to its highly evolved, desert annuals of the western United States (Reveal, 1968). A similar development can be seen in the section *Gomphotheca,* where the perennial *E. inflatum* var. *deflatum* gradually passes into *E. trichopes* as noted before.

Throughout *Ganysma* it is possible to trace a Mexican origin of the major species lines, with a division of species occurring in the south western United States. Unlike *Oregonium,* whose species developed in the mountains, the *Ganysma* species have developed primarily in the deserts, and therefore a far lesser degree of aneuploidy is present. Chromosome counts for *Ganysma* are $n = 16$, 18, and 20, with one known polyploid of $n = 40$ (Reveal, 1965, 1966, 1967c, 1968).

The nomenclatural problems associated with the names *Oregonium* and *Ganysma* should be explained. When Watson proposed the sections *Oregonium* and *Ganysma,* they were both superfluous substitutes for the several already proposed sectional names of Bentham and Torrey and Gray. However, the epithet of a subgenus cannot be superfluous because it was superfluous as the epithet of a section as stated in Article 60 of the present Code (1966). Specifically that article states: "When the rank of a genus or infrageneric taxon is changed, the correct name or epithet is the earliest legitimate one available in the new rank. In no case does a name or an epithet have priority outside its own rank." Thus, even though the

Watson names were superfluous when proposed, Greene was perfectly free to use the epithets *Ganysma* and *Oregonium* in the subgeneric rank.

The typification of *Oregonium* has already been discussed. In regard to *Ganysma* it is necessary to select a lectotype for the subgenus based on the protologue of Greene and, on this basis, *Eriogonum angulosum* is selected because it comes closest to the features given by him. By selecting this species, the subgenus continues to be defined as it has been for several years.*

At the generic level is the problem of *Oxytheca* Nutt. This genus seems to be composed of species that have been derived from two genera, *Eriogonum* and *Chorizanthe,* although to what degree remains to be determined only by critical research. As the type species, *O. dendroidea* Nutt. is closely related to *E. spergulinum* A. Gray, a transfer of the type species from *Oxytheca* to *Eriogonum* would place the genus into synonymy. As some *Oxytheca* species seem still to form a distinct genus, a new genus would have to be proposed and, in the herbarium, Dr. George J. Goodman of the University of Oklahoma has proposed such an arrangement. However, it seems to me, as long as the genus *Oxytheca* can be defined and rather easily maintained, it should be retained and simply recognized that the genus is probably not natural but includes derived elements from two genera. However, within the genus there are still a few elements which have evolved to a point at which they could be maintained as a distinct genus, although that genus would be weakly defined and difficult to maintain.

REFERENCES

Bentham, G. (1837). On the Eriogoneae, a tribe of the order Polygonaceae. *Trans. Linn. Soc. London* **17,** 401–420.

Bentham, G. (1856). *In* "Prodromus . . ." (A. de Candolle, ed.). **14,** 5–28.

Coville, F. V., and Morton, C. V. (1936). *Eriogonum intrafractum,* a new species and new subgenus from Death Valley, California. *J. Wash. Acad. Sci.* **26,** 209–213.

Curran, M. K. (1885). Botanical notes. Classification of the Eriogoneae as affected by some connecting forms. *Bull. Calif. Acad. Sci.* **1,** 272–275.

Endlicher, S. (1837). "Genera Plantarum Secundum Ordines Naturales Disposita, Vindobonae."

Graham, S. A., and Wood, C. E., Jr. (1965). The genera of Polygonaceae in the southeastern United States. *J. Arnold Arb.* **46,** 91–121.

Greene, E. L. (1891). "Flora Fransicana." San Francisco.

Gross, H. (1913). Bietrage zur Kenntnis der Polygonaceen. *Botan. Jahrb.* **49,** 234–339.

---

* In regard to these nomenclatural problems, I acknowledge the helpful assistance of C. V. Morton, H. W. Rickett, and F. A. Stafleu.

Hess, W. J. (1967). A taxonomic study of the subgenus Pterogonum in the genus *Eriogonum* (Polygonaceae). Unpublished Ph.D. Dissertation, University of Oklahoma, Norman.

Jackson, B. D. (1893). "Index Kewensis Plantarum Phanerogarum," Oxford Univ. Press.

James, C. W. (1961). Endemism in Florida. *Brittonia* **13**, 225–244.

Jepson, W. L. (1913). "A Flora of California." Vol. 1, pp. 376–428.

Kuijt, J. (1961). A revision of *Dendrophthora* (Loranthaceae). *Wentia* **6**, 1–145.

Lagasca, M. (1816). "Genera et Species Plantarum, quae aut novae . . . ." Madrid.

Michaux, A. (1803). "Flora Boreali-Americana." Parisiis.

Nuttall, T. (1848a). Descriptions of plants collected by Mr. William Gambel in the Rocky Mountains and Upper California. *Proc. Acad. Nat. Sci. Phila.* **4**, 7–26.

Nuttall, T. (1848b). Descriptions of plants collected by William Gambel, M.D., in the Rocky Mountains and Upper California. *J. Acad. Nat. Sci. Phila.* II, **1**, 149–189.

Post, T. von, and Kuntze, O. (1903). "Lexicon Generum Phanerogamarum." Stuttgart.

Reveal, J. L. (1965). *Eriogonum. In* Documented chromosome counts of plants. *Madroño* **18**, 124.

Reveal, J. L. (1966). On the specific distinction of *Eriogonum nutans* and *collinum*. *Madroño* **18**, 167-173.

Reveal, J. L. (1967a). Notes on *Eriogonum* – II. Variations in *Eriogonum atrorubens*. *Sida* **3**, 82–86.

Reveal, J. L. (1967b). Notes on *Eriogonum* – III. On the status of *Eriogonum pauciflorum*. *Great Basin Nat.* **27**, 102-117.

Reveal, J. L. (1967c). Documented chromosome numbers of plants. *Madroño* **19**, 134-136.

Reveal, J. L. (1968). Notes on Eriogonum – IV. A revision of the *Eriogonum deflexum* complex. *Brittonia* **20**, 13-33.

Reveal, J. L., and Munz, P. A. (1968). *Eriogonum. In* "Supplement to A California Flora." Univ. Calif. Press, Berkeley.

Reveal, J. L., and Spevak, V. (1967). Publication dates and current names of 144 names proposed in two 1848 Thomas Nuttall articles. *Taxon* **16**, 407–414.

Roberty, C., and Vautier, S. (1964). Les genres de Polygonacees. *Boissiera* **10**, 7–128.

Rydberg, P. A. (1917). "Flora of the Rocky Mountains and Adjacent Plains." Publ. by author, New York.

Stokes, S. G. (1936). "The genus *Eriogonum*." San Francisco.

Stokes, S. G., and Stebbins, G. L. (1955). Chromosome numbers in the genus *Eriogonum*. *Leafl. Western Botany* **7**, 228–233.

Torrey, J., and Gray, A. (1870). A revision of the Eriogoneae. *Proc. Am. Acad. Arts Sci., Daedalus* **8**, 145–200.

Watson, S. (1877). Descriptions of new species of plants with revision of certain genera. *Proc. Am. Acad. Arts Sci., Daedalus* **12**, 246–278.

V
The Role of Botanical Gardens in Plant Research and Education

Research and Education at the New York Botanical Garden

William C. Steere

The New York Botanical Garden was chartered in 1891 by the Legislature of the State of New York, although its historical origins go back considerably further. Dr. David Hosack, a distinguished medical teacher and practitioner who was also one of the prominent botanists of his day, founded the Elgin Botanic Garden at his own expense in 1801. This new botanic garden was an important attraction to notable botanists and medical men of the day, and brought many visitors, both American and foreign. Dr. Hosack eventually found his public garden too expensive to maintain privately, and decided to sell it to the State of New York, in 1811. Long after the sale of his botanic garden, Dr. Hosack eloquently defended the concept of and the need for a botanic garden in New York City — even though the State allowed his to fall into ruin.

As boy and young man, John Torrey was exposed to the multiple benefits of a public botanic garden, not only from his own visits to the Elgin Botanic Garden, but also from continued close association with Dr. Hosack, first as his student at the College of Physicians and Surgeons (from which Torrey received his Doctor of Medicine degree in 1818) and as his assistant in a course on botany in 1822. At a supper held in 1867 in honor of Torrey, the impact of the Elgin Botanic Garden on him at an impressionable age became very evident, as indicated by the tribute he gave to it. The Torrey Botanical Club carried on the tradition of the desirability of a major botanical garden in New York City, and so responded immediately and sympathetically when the idea of going ahead with such a plan was proposed to it some twenty years later. Nathaniel Lord Britton, an instructor in botany at Columbia University, took his new wife to spend the summer of 1888 at the Royal Botanic Garden at Kew, near London, and both of them came back with the firm conviction that New York must finally develop its long-needed botanic garden. Inspired by the Brittons' enthusiastic and vigorous statements, the Torrey

Botanical Club issued in 1889 a clear and persuasive statement of the urgent need for such an institution, whose purposes were included in the following paragraph.

"The uses of a botanic garden may be reckoned as of four sorts. First and foremost is the purely scientific and education use. Subsidiary to this, but still of a marked degree of importance, are the pharmaceutical and horticultural uses, and, lastly, the general use as a place of agreeable resort for the public at large." This appeal, "unanimously adopted and ordered to be printed for general circulation, at a regular meeting of the Torrey Botanical Club, held January 8, 1889," was successful in attracting the attention and arousing the enthusiasm of a group of prominent citizens who in 1891 founded the New York Botanical Garden as a corporation chartered by the State, with the aims already expressed by the Torrey Botanical Club, but in more legalistic terms.

"Erected for the New York Botanical Garden by the City of New York for the advancement of botanical knowledge – 1897–1899," appears on the cornerstone of the present museum building, and sets in focus the basic and historic commitment of this institution to botanical research. The founder of The New York Botanical Garden, Professor Nathaniel Lord Britton of Columbia University, originally a geologist, became one of the most productive plant taxonomists of his generation, yet, in staffing his new institution around the turn of the century, one of his early appointments was a plant physiologist. Britton's concept of a much wider spectrum of botanical research than was customary in the major botanical gardens of the world has been adhered to. In fact, the scope of research activities is broader today than it was seventy years ago.

Today The New York Botanical Garden places a greater emphasis on the public use of its facilities then might be gathered from the last place relegated to it in the 1889 statement issued by the Torrey Botanical Club, quoted above. As a quasi-public institution supported in part by the City of New York, which furnished funds especially for such functions as gardening and maintenance, the Botanical Garden has a responsibility to the public much greater than that of a wholly private institution. However, the dedication to public service comes from a deeper wellspring than simply a *quid pro quo* obligation for support from the City of New York. The New York Botanical Garden recognizes its broader responsibilities to disseminate information about plants to all levels of the public. The transcendental importance of green plants as primary sources of food energy and of oxygen is too little known generally, as well as all the other essential aspects of plants. The welfare of contemporary civilization depends on exploring and studying the botanical resources of the world and in clarifying the role that plants play in all human activities. To attain this end several kinds of educational activities are offered for the public.

Educational Activities for the Public

Educational activities for the public are arranged at all levels, from the very simplest observation by a visitor of labeled plants both outdoors and under glass, to serious formal courses for adults. Outdoors, the extensive botanical collections of trees and shrubs and other plants are arranged in such a way as to be of interest to the public as well as of importance to the botanist and horticulturist who wants to see species for his own professional reasons. The same policy is followed in the Conservatory. In addition, handsome plantings of horticultural varieties outdoors and exhibited in flower shows in the Conservatory are successful in focusing public attention on plants. Participation in the International Flower Show is another important step in the same direction, as the exhibits set up by The New York Botanical Garden are invariably of an educational nature and usually win the major educational medals and other awards. The educational exhibits in the museum building of plants of economic importance to man, as well as of the various groups of plants, are very attractive to the general public, especially to groups of grade school and high school students, who learn much that would not otherwise be presented to them.

Formal course work for the public is very diverse, ranging from single courses of one to eight sessions to formal two-year programs that lead to certificates in Botany, Horticulture, or Garden Design. Especially effective in a great metropolitan area is a Children's Gardencraft Program by which children between the ages of nine and fifteen spend Saturday morning during the spring semester and mornings on other days during the summer learning, on a very practical basis, how to grow vegetables and flowers. Other activities are arranged for children, but one of the great lacks in the activities of our educational department is a more formal program for school children, simply because of lack of funds. However, an outstandingly successful activity has been the Trainee-Gardener Program, by which high school students receive a two-year apprentice-style training in all the aspects of gardening throughout the seasons. Since there are few if any other training programs of this type, a tremendous lack of personnel for the whole spectrum of professional, industrial, and commercial fields related to gardening exists, and each trainee who graduates has his choice of several jobs.

In its effort to bring scientifically accurate information about plants to the general public, in addition to the classes and exhibits, the Botanical Garden has embarked on a major program of publication, first with a series of five volumes, *Wild Flowers of the United States,* of which two volumes have already appeared, covering the northeastern and the southeastern United States. These books, magnificently illustrated by color photographs, have been written in clear, nontechnical English by a highly qualified expert, H. W. Rickett, long a member of the staff. The *Garden Journal* is a magazine published largely for members of the Botanical Garden, and contains nontechnical, yet accurate, articles about plants. We plan for it eventually a much greater role in our public education program, with a much wide distribution than membership.

Research

Research at The New York Botanical Garden is supported by income from endowment, special gifts, and in recent years by grants from federal agencies, especially the National Science Foundation and the National Institutes of Health. Occasional support has also been obtained from the Office of Naval Research, the Atomic Energy Commission, the Arctic Institute of North America, and others.

SYSTEMATIC BOTANY

With a herbarium of 3.5 million specimens and one of the finest botanical libraries under one roof in the Western Hemisphere, The New York Botanical Garden presents outstanding facilities for research in systematic botany to its staff, graduate students, and numerous visiting investigators. As in most great botanical gardens, the research emphasis has been more on taxonomy, floristics, and phytogeography than other fields.

Nathaniel Lord Britton, the first Director of the Botanical Garden, who was responsible for its founding, was interested first in the flora of the temperate United States, and the work of his associates reflected this interest, especially that of John K. Small, who became the great professional expert on the flora of the southeast United States, and Per Rydberg, who published extensively on the floras of the Plains and Prairies of the central United States, as well as on Rocky Mountain flora.

Once he had seen the temperate flora under control, Britton turned his attention to tropical America, with special attention to the West Indies. The result was the publication of the only definitive flora of Puerto Rico and the Virgin Islands. For more than twenty years, Bassett Maguire, Assistant Director (Botany), has continued the interest of the Botanical Garden in tropical botany begun by Britton, and has specialized in the flora of many parts of tropical America, but with especial attention to the great, flat-topped mountains of the Guayana Highland of northeastern South America. He has made or arranged more than one hundred expeditions to these Mt. Roraima-type mountains, each with its unique flora. Maguire also conducts monographic research on the plant families Guttiferae, Rapateaceae, Theaceae, and Ochnaceae. The field investigations of Howard S. Irwin, Head Curator, of the Planalto of Central Brazil, and of Ghillean T. Prance, Krukoff Curator of Amazonian Botany, of the Amazon Basin, are neatly coordinated in their geography with those of Maguire. In addition, Irwin carries on monographic studies of the Leguminosae, especially of the genus *Cassia,* whereas Prance is a specialist on the tropical family Chrysobalanaceae. Brother Alain Liogier, Honorary Curator of West Indian Botany, is occupied in field work on the island of Hispaniola, for which he is writing a major flora. Caroline K. Allen, Research Associate, who is a leading authority on the Lauraceae, has traveled extensively in tropical America to see several genera of laurels in their native environment, as well as to the major herbaria in Europe to investigate original and type specimens. Otto Degener, Collaborator in Hawaiian Botany, and his wife, Isa Degener, continue botanical collecting and research for their *Flora Hawaiiensis.* Eugene Jablonski, Honorary Curator of Tropical Botany, has recently completed a definitive study of the Euphorbiaceae of the Guayana Highland and is now extending his work to the Amazon Basin and adjacent areas. Tetsuo Koyama, Curator, has brought to his monographic studies of tropical American sedges, the Cyperaceae, the current techniques of cytology, palynology, and anatomical studies. He has also collected and made field studies of Cyperaceae in Venezuela and Ceylon.

Work on the flora of various parts of the United States has continued through the years, in spite of the increased tempo of research on tropical American floras. Henry Allan Gleason's revision of a major publication by Britton appeared in 1952 as *New Britton and Brown Illustrated Flora,* in three volumes. A shorter version, *A Manual of Vascular Plants,* appeared in 1963 under the joint authorship of Gleason and Arthur Cronquist. Arthur Cronquist, Senior Curator, has worked for many years on the flora of the western United States and has contributed extensively to two major multivolume publications that are approaching completion, *Flora of the Pacific Northwest* and *Flora of the Intermontane Region.* His monographic interests lie in the Compositae, which he has studied in the field throughout the United States as well as in Mexico and Central America.

CRYPTOGAMIC BOTANY

In the Cryptogamic Herbarium, Clark T. Rogerson, Senior Curator, conducts morphologic, cultural, and monographic studies on hypocreaceous fungi, the Hypocreales. William C. Steere, Director, continues his field studies and research on bryophytes, with especial reference to the geographical distribution of Arctic and Antarctic mosses. He also looks forward to the resumption of cytological research on mosses. Mulford Martin, Honorary Curator of the Moss Herbarium, works assiduously at keeping the collections in order, in the time at his disposal. The Cryotogamic Herbarium is in serious need of full-time curators for algae, bryophytes, ferns, and other groups.

Historically, cryptogamic botany has been an important aspect of the total research program of the Botanical Garden since its founding. Mrs. Elizabeth Gertrude Britton, wife of the first director, was an able bryologist in her own right; she built up one of the best working collections in the world. She had as an associate another able bryologist, Robert S. Williams. L. M. Underwood, who worked on the fern collections, was one of the outstanding specialists of his time. For the fungi, William A. Murrill published extensive revisions of the fleshy Basidiomycetes in *North American Flora,* and Fred J. Seaver became one of the most distinguished mycologists of his time, known not only for his productive research but also as the founder of *Mycologia.*

PALEOBOTANY

Herman F. Becker, Curator of Paleobotany, in addition to his responsibility for the paleobotanical collections, has done extensive field work and research on several Tertiary floras he discovered in Montana. Paleobotany has been historically an important research field at The New York Botanical Garden since the days of Arthur Hollock, a prominent earlier paleobotanist.

ECOLOGY

Pierre Dansereau, Senior Curator of Ecology, aided by Virginia Weadock, Senior Research Assistant, and several graduate students and research assistants, carries on, as one of several long-term investigations, functional analyses of vegetation of several parts of the world, from New

Zealand through the Azores to Baffin Island. Dansereau, who came to The New York Botanical Garden from the University of Montreal on April 1, 1961, returned to the University of Montreal July 1, 1968, as Professor of Ecology in a new Faculty for Environmental Studies, especially concerned with cities.

PLANT PHYSIOLOGY

Even though Nathaniel Lord Britton was one of the most productive plant taxonomists of his generation, he was very anxious to establish a broad spectrum of botanical research and teaching in his new institution. As a consequence, one of his early appointments was a plant physiologist, Daniel Trembly MacDougal, who became a most outstanding expert in this field. Plant Physiology at The New York Botanical Garden was greatly reinforced by the appointment of William Jacob Robbins as Director in 1937, the first plant physiologist to hold this post. For the twenty years of his tenure, Robbins built up a strong program of research in plant physiology. He also negotiated the establishment of the Alfred H. Caspary Curatorship of Plant Physiology, the first incumbent of which was Richard M. Klein, appointed in 1953, who held the post until 1967, when he resigned to accept a Professorship in Botany at the University of Vermont. Although the Caspary Curatorship of Plant Physiology is vacant (at the time of this writing) and a replacement for Klein is needed, related fields, especially microbiology and biochemistry, are growing at a rapid pace.

Annette Hervey, Senior Research Associate, has maintained for many years a large collection of fungus cultures housed at the Botanical Garden and has assisted William J. Robbins, Director Emeritus, in his research on tissue cultures from higher plants, largely at the Rockefeller University.

MICROBIOLOGY

Alma W. Barksdale, Senior Research Associate, has been working for some years on sexual reproduction in the water mold *Achlya bisexualis,* especially on the hormonal control of production of sex organs. After several years she completed the herculean task of isolating an amount of hormone A, which is produced by the female plant and stimulates the male plant, sufficient for chemical study and identification by Trevor C. McMorris, Senior Research Associate. In 1967, McMorris and Barksdale published a report showing that hormone A, designated "antheridiol," is a steroid.

BIOCHEMISTRY

Marjorie Anchel, Senior Research Associate, works on the chemistry of metabolic products of Basidiomycetes, especially the mushroom, *Clitocybe illudens*. From this fungus, Anchel has isolated and identified several remarkable compounds including polyacetylenes. Trevor C. McMorris, Senior Research Associate, has worked with Anchel and Barksdale in the actual determination of structure of interesting compounds produced by various fungi, a research program greatly facilitated by the recent acquisition of a nuclear magnetic resonance spectrometer. McMorris spent several months at the University of London during 1967 working on the synthesis of antheridiol. The program in biochemistry is reinforced by visiting postdoctoral investigators.

PLANT PATHOLOGY

The first plant pathologist at The New York Botanical Garden, Bernard O. Dodge, was appointed in 1928. His brilliant work in recognizing mutations in the mold fungus *Neurospora* and his pioneer work in crossing strains with different mutations laid the foundation for the whole field of genetical microbiology. Dodge retired in 1947 but continued to work in his laboratory until a few months before his death in 1960. P. P. Pirone, Senior Plant Pathologist, who replaced Dodge, is investigating new diseases of several trees on New York streets, especially *Ginkgo biloba* and the Norway maple, *Acer platanoides*. David Davis, Research Associate, is occupied with an investigation of the basic causes of selective pathogenicity in the *Fusarium*-wilt disease.

Graduate Student Program

The research program of The New York Botanical Garden is much enhanced by the presence of graduate students in residence as well as many postdoctoral visitors. The Director of the Botanical Garden is ex-officio Professor of Botany at Columbia University, and several other staff members hold the title of Adjunct Professor. As many as fifteen graduate students, registered at Columbia University, do their doctoral research at the Botanical Garden under the supervision of qualified staff members. Occasionally students come from Fordham University, Rutgers University, and other institutions in the New York area to work on master's level or doctoral programs. Arrangements have just been made for a similar program through the City University of New York with Lehman College.

Publications

As part of its activities in botanical research and education, The New York Botanical Garden publishes *North American Flora,* the *Memoirs of The New York Botanical Garden,* and *Botanical Review.* In addition, it publishes *Mycologia* for the Mycological Society of America, *Brittonia* for the American Society of Plant Taxonomists, and *Economic Botany* for the Society for Economic Botany.

The Brooklyn Botanic Garden

Warren Balgooyen and George S. Avery

The Brooklyn Botanic Garden is one of the few institutions in the home territory of The Torrey Botanical Club that is acting in the dual role of offering people popular-level educational opportunities in horticulturally slanted botany and gardening and, through its outreach stations, serving as a conservator of the wild. The Garden is one of about fifteen popular cultural institutions affiliated with the City of New York. It was founded in 1910 by people of foresight as an arm of the Brooklyn Institute of Arts and Sciences, a private eleemosynary corporation, and is dependent on the City of New York for about half of its financial support. As a membership society, its family of private supporters extends to forty-four states and several other countries.

Title to the fifty acres of park land that constitute the Botanic Garden is held by the City.

In the first ten years of the Botanic Garden's existence, until 1920, there were approximately 2 million visitors in all. In the 1950s and 1960s there were approximately 1½ million visitors annually — not only from New York and its immediate environs, but from all states and many countries. The Botanic Garden ranks fourth high in numbers of visitors to the popular cultural institutions affiliated with the City of New York; only the Metropolitan Museum, the American Museum of Natural History, and the Bronx Zoo presently have greater numbers. The Garden's fifty acres are the busiest of their kind on earth.

While the Garden provides a tranquil retreat for the harried urbanite, education, research, and the dissemination of horticultural and scientific information provide the largest measure of its public service. About 10,000 telephone calls seeking horticultural and gardening information (and an equal number of inquiries by mail) are received each year.

Nearly 100,000 handbooks on various horticultural and conservation practices are distributed annually throughout the world. They are issued quarterly as *Plants and Gardens,* a magazine, and three of the four issues each year are reprinted as handbooks. Forty of the most popular issues are kept continuously in print as low-cost ($1.00 or $1.25 per copy), paperback publications available to all who are interested. The subjects of the handbooks include plant propagation, conservation, pruning, gardening with native plants, breeding ornamental plants, landscape design, flowering trees and shrubs, origins of American horticulture, orchids, and other special families of plants. Among the currently most popular titles are herbs, house plants, dye plants and dyeing, Japanese gardens, and two books on bonsai.

A film series is now in production with the objective of further dissemination of horticultural information. The first one, completed in 1966, carries the title "Pruning Practices at the Brooklyn Botanic Garden." It received four awards for excellence (three national and one international) and is presently being distributed throughout the United States. The second film in the series, completed in 1969, is "Planting and Transplanting at the Brooklyn Botanic Garden."

There is no better way to remind the city dweller of Nature's simple truths and fragile beauty than to provide him with a living exhibit. In carrying out this function, the Brooklyn Botanic Garden has acquired some 10,000 species and varieties of plants since its founding in 1910. Of these the succulents (about 2000) comprise the largest single collection, orchids (1000) and bromeliads are runners-up. These collections, of course, are under glass. Impressive collections of begonias and gesneriads, an abundance of ferns, and a host of tropical economic and ornamental plants are also on display in the conservatories.

On the grounds are some thirty species and cultivars of Japanese flowering cherries, a representative collection of flowering crabapples, and the Cranford Memorial Rose Garden with nearly 700 species and varieties; 250 species and cultivars of rhododendrons, a systematic collection of trees and shrubs, and two delightfully interesting herb gardens have considerable popular appeal. The hill-and-pond style Japanese Garden, one of the most popular of all the special gardens, is a spot of extraordinary beauty. It was constructed in 1914–1915. A replica of the 500-year-old Ryoanji Temple Stone Garden (Kyoto, Japan) was completed in 1963; although it is an abstract Zen garden — neither horticultural nor even a garden in the western sense of the word — it provides an unusual esthetic experience for those who view it. Other special areas include the rock garden, fragrance garden for the blind, iris garden, garden of naturally dwarf trees and shrubs, and the "Dewpath" garden completed in 1969 — yet another Japanese garden inspired by the traditional Tea Garden style.

Although there is no entrance fee for the Botanic Garden as a whole, the policing problem has been simplified by charging a nominal admittance fee to a few of the special gardens on Saturdays, Sundays, and holidays. Legislation is being sought to permit charging a small entrance fee to the overall Garden.

The Instruction Department offers courses of one to several sessions at both the child and adult levels. The Adult Education courses currently attract about 2500 students annually in some 75 to 80 learn-by-doing courses. The subjects are as varied as "Gardening with Ferns," "Japanese Flower Arranging," "Bonsai for Beginners" and "Dyeing with Natural Plant Dyes." Fees for the courses range from $3.00 to $24.00.

In a cooperative program with New York City schools, approximately 20,000 children come to the Garden each year for instruction by staff teachers. A leisure-time program on Saturdays and in the summer attracts more than 1000 additional children. In-service courses for teachers are still another educational offering. Practically all courses are filled to capacity.

One of the most specialized public services provided by the Garden is its liaison as interpreter of gardening and horticultural aspects of Japanese culture. The several Japanese gardens and the bonsai collection, started in 1925, are evidence of this special sphere of activity. At this time the bonsai collection is the most outstanding one on public view anywhere in this hemisphere.

The Botanic Garden's reference library is one of the outstanding special collections in the United States. Among its 50,000 volumes is a magnificent collection of incunabula, pre-Linnaean, Linnaean, and post-Linnaean books of scientific historical interest.

One of the most important developments since the founding and early growth of the Botanic Garden has been the establishment of three suburban branches. The first one, the 223-acre Kitchawan Field Station, is on Kitchawan Road in Westchester County, about 40 miles from New York and 5 miles from Mt. Kisco. It was acquired in 1956 through the generosity of the Jeremiah Van Brunt family. A fully equipped research laboratory was completed there in 1958 at a cost of $391,000. Nearly $200,000 of this money came from gifts through a special committee of the Botanic Garden Women's Auxiliary, some $90,000 from the Federal Government through the National Institutes of Health, and the balance from general funds. A greenhouse connecting with the laboratory was completed in 1968 — built from funds raised by the Kitchawan Women's Auxiliary.

In addition to housing the Research Department of the Garden (for which there was no longer adequate space in the Brooklyn building) this new facility is used for public gatherings of horticultural and garden-slanted organizations, and groups like the Torrey Botanical Club. Here, also, has been formed a satellite adult education program offering many courses similar to those given in Brooklyn; approximately 600 people enrolled in such courses in the fiscal year 1967–1968. The property itself is to be kept in its natural state for outdoor education and research. About 6 miles of foot trails have been developed, along some of which are labeled plants—the native flora. Nature study groups and conservation-oriented individuals are admitted by appointment.

The second "outreach" station to be acquired (1963) is on Spring Valley Road, about 2½ miles from the Field Station; it has been named the Teatown Lake Reservation. It was a gift of the conservation-minded family of the late Gerard Swope, Sr. This tract presently comprises 225 acres and there are possibilities of further expansion. Included within the property is the 33-acre Teatown Lake and two buildings that are being used for educational and residential purposes. About 8 miles of marked and unmarked trails are open to the public. To date, the main activity at the Reservation has been the development of a conservation education program for children. An enthusiastic response to this idea from the local community has led to a rapidly expanding program which has not yet caught up with the public demand. An adult education program has been started there also, and nature walks are frequently arranged. Various other cultural events are scheduled there from time to time. As at Kitchawan, the property is to be kept in its natural state with maximum protection of its flora and fauna; no development or activities hostile to the natural surroundings are planned.

The third and most recent outreach station to be acquired (1966) is in Albertson, Long Island, 20 miles from New York. It is located on I. U. Willets Road, adjacent to the Long Island Railroad station, and has been named the Fanny Dwight Clark Memorial Garden in memory of an ardent horticulturist—the first wife of the late Mr. Grenville Clark of Dublin, New Hampshire, donor of the property. There are 11 beautiful acres of lawn and woods and two houses. Mr. Clark gave $125,000 for development and maintenance of the property, and $90,000 as a "guarantee fund," the nucleus of an endowment. It was the donor's wish that this Memorial Garden be essentially self-supporting by means of an entrance fee and a modest charge for parking. The 100-car parking area is now in operation.

Three shallow ponds to attract water birds have been completed and the Garden was opened to the public in 1969. When it is in full operation, the well-known Brooklyn Botanic Garden courses of instruction will be offered for adults, and it is now planned to have a junior educational offering including summer gardens for children. The Botanic Garden is particularly pleased to extend its activities to Albertson, for this 11-acre parcel is one of the last "green islands" in a sea of suburban housing. It also offers a practical test of whether such a garden can be virtually self-supporting.

A less recognizable, more indirect, but far-reaching public service is continually performed by the Brooklyn Botanic Garden through the patient progress of its Research Department at the Kitchawan Field Station. The research staff publishes the results of its findings in various scientific journals. Research activities are supported in part by Federal funds through grants from the National Science Foundation and other government agencies.

At a Torrey Centennial celebration held at the Botanic Garden on May 6, 1967, current scientific investigations of the Research Department staff were presented. The following is a digest of current scientific investigations in the fields of air pollution, nematology, forest pathology, microbiology, mycology and soil micro-ecology. A project on air pollution recently completed involved the growing of various test plants known to be sensitive to specific gaseous pollutants in the urban environment of the Botanic Garden in Brooklyn. Two glass chambers housed the experimental plants. One was equipped with a carbon filter, and both were continually flushed with ambient urban air. The results were striking. A marked difference in plant vigor and growth between the filtered (control) chamber and the nonfiltered test chamber was accentuated by the appearance of visible symptoms of localized leaf injury on many of the test plants. The type and cellular location of injury produced showed that oxidants, a component of smog, are major phytotoxic constituents of the atmosphere. Experimental exposures of plants to known concentrations of ozone, one type of oxidant, indicated that this gas occurs naturally in sufficient concentrations in "city air" to cause plant injury.

The effect of air pollution on bacteria and fungal spores is also being studied. Chronic exposure to toxic gases could alter the ecology of microbes in natural habitats. The resistance of microbes in pure culture to gases depends on the type of pollutant. Some microbes remain dormant while in contact with the gases but resume growth when removed. Others appear to adapt to some gases. Bacteria and fungi tolerate short exposures to 13,000 ppm sulfur dioxide, 10,000 ppm hydrogen sulfide, or 200 ppm ozone. These microbes are several hundredfold more resistant to sulfur dioxide than are nematodes, but both types of organisms appear equally sensitive to ozone. In general, microorganisms appear to be considerably more resistant to toxic gases than higher plants and animals. The mechanisms whereby air pollutants damage microorganisms are being defined.

Nematological studies are under way to find a biological control for some of the plant parasitic nematodes. It has been discovered that the incorporation of various organic mulches in the soil has some nematocidal effects. Isolation of these compounds and determination of their nematocidal effects may lead to a biological solution to the long-standing serious problem of controlling plant parasitic nematodes. A nematode-air pollution project is also in progress. It has been discovered that viviparity can be induced in an egg-laying nematode after exposure to chronic levels of SO_2.

In forest pathology the possibility of air pollution, specifically ozone, as a contributing factor to the decline of the sugar maple has been investigated, and studies are presently under way that may implicate a virus as part of the "dieback disease" riddle of the native American ash (*Fraxinus americana*). One and possibly several viruses have so far been transmitted to herbaceous test plants from the foliage and woody tissues of "declining" ash. They have been identified as belonging to a group of viruses that are common plant pathogens.

In soil micro-ecology the biochemical composition and biological activity of root exudates are being studied. Various plant species are grown under controlled conditions of light, temperature, and humidity in chambers with special equipment that permits periodic and quantitative collection of materials liberated by sterile roots. A variety of sugars, amino acids, proteins, and compounds have been detected which differentially stimulate or inhibit growth of various microbes. The amounts and types of materials liberated depend on the plant species and its stage of growth. Only 1 to 3 proteins have been detected in exudates of various species by disc gel electrophoresis, whereas the roots appear to contain as many as 17 proteins. Techniques have been developed for removing inorganic salts from the exudates, without significant losses of organic materials. This purification of the exudates is necessary for both biochemical and biological assays.

Respiration of axenic intact roots is also being studied with an integrated system of flow and pressure controllers, solenoid valves, program times, and infrared CO_2 analyzer. Root respiration and possibly also root exudation of a wide variety of plants appear to exhibit a noncircadian periodicity superimposed over light-influenced circadian rhythms which change with the stage of plant development.

These studies may have relevance to the biological control of soil-borne root-infecting pathogens.

Because clay minerals appear to be important determinants of the activity, ecology, and population dynamics of microorganisms in natural habitats, the influence of clay minerals on microorganisms is being studied on various levels of experimental complexity. In pure culture, some 2:1 minerals, especially montmorillonite, markedly stimulate respiration of bacteria, whereas other 2:1 minerals, 1:1 minerals, and particles which possess some of the characteristics of clays have relatively little influence. This stimulation is, in part, related to the clays maintaining the pH of the environment suitable for sustained growth, and to the cation exchange capacity, possibly the specific surface, but not the particle size distribution of the minerals. Fungal respiration and spore germination are not significantly influenced by clays at low concentrations, but respiration is substantially reduced at high concentrations, especially by montmorillonite, apparently as a result of impaired gas exchange caused by increased viscosities. In soil, heterotrophic (substrate decomposition) and autotrophic (nitrification) activities are altered by augmenting the soil with montmorillonite or kaolinite. The growth of bacteria, as determined by the replica plating technique, is faster through soils containing clay minerals similar in x-ray characteristics to montmorillonite, whereas growth of fungi is faster through soils not containing such clays. The rate of spread of *Fusarium* wilt of banana is also generally faster, *in situ*, in the latter type of soils. Similarly, most soils from which *Histoplasma capsulatum* has been isolated do not contain expanding three-layer aluminosilicates, whereas the geographic distribution of another soil-borne human pathogen, *Coccidioides immitis*, does not appear to be related to soil mineralogy.

Sorption between microorganisms and clay minerals, both of which have a net negative charge at the pH of most microbial habitats, depends primarily on pH and on the type of cations present in the ambient solution. Sorption occurs *in vitro* only at pH values below the isoelectric point of the microbial cells, or in the presence of polyvalent cations which either decrease the electrokinetic potentials or result in a differential charge reversal of the particles. Similar relationships appear to be involved in the flocculation of clay minerals by microbial metabolites. The isoelectric point of bacteria shifts to higher pH values as the valence and concentration of the cations present in the ambient environment increase.

Studies of the affinity of clay minerals for organic substances and water show that montmorillonite homoionic to various mono-, di-, tri-, and tetravalent cations has no affinity for glycine and only slight affinity for dimethylamine. Montmorillonite homoionic to hydrogen exhibits a strong affinity for dimethylamine and a limited affinity for glycine. The glycine, however, can be removed from the clay by repeated washings with water.

The retention of water by montmorillonite is greatly influenced by the type of cation saturation and is greatest with hydrogen, followed by other monovalent cations, followed by di- and then by tri- and tetravalent cations. Glycine does not alter the relative retention of water, whereas dimethylamine does.

VI
Phytopharmacology in Modern Medicine

Plant Flavor and Aromatic Values in Medicine and Pharmacy

George M. Hocking

Flavors and aromas have been, and will continue to be, important in pharmaceuticals (medicinals), perfumes, foods, and beverages. Attractive odors and tastes are conferred by many but by no means all essential oils and odoriferous compounds. Also furnishing flavor/odor values are such diverse materials as oleoresins, balsams, glycosides, sugars and sugar alcohols, and organic acids and their esters.

The current importance of such materials is indicated by the large number of items of this category which are officially monographed in the latest edition of the two outstanding American medicinal compendia, the *United States Pharmacopeia* and the *National Formulary*. The *U.S. Pharmacopeia* XVII (1965) has a total of 898 monographs, of which 154 are plant drugs or their derivatives or preparations and, of these 154 items, 38 or nearly a quarter are aromatic or flavoring materials or both. In N.F. XII, with its 763 total monographs, 196 may be considered plant derivative products (even though the commercial source of some may be by synthesis). Of these 196, 44 can be classed as aromatic/ flavor products or preparations of plant origin which represents about 22.4%. To summarize, the official compendia show about one-quarter of their plant products as flavor and aroma donors.

It should be clear that the line between aroma and taste is not a hard and fast one. Thus vanilla has value both as a flavor in medicines and foods and as an aroma as in cosmetics. In addition, the aroma plays a large part in the total flavor impression. Methyl salicylate, wintergreen oil, is a strongly odorous flavor. In cinnamon, onion, sassafras, and many other substances, flavor and aroma freely mingle, aroma being the more important in some cases, the flavor in others. To prove the importance of odor in flavor, it is necessary only to hold the nose between finger and thumb and then taste cinnamon: the characteristic flavor is found lacking (Zotterman, 1962).

There are considerable differences in the aroma/flavor ratios in most essential oils, since some individual compounds are more readily volatile than others. Hence, with time and the loss of the more volatile components, the nature of an oil generally changes, and there actually results a whole series of oils differing in aroma and flavor, depending on which compounds have been lost and which remain.

Many flavor materials are almost entirely lacking in aroma; for example, tamarind, a flavor popular and ubiquitous in the bazars of eastern Asia, has almost no aroma, and the same is true of the shredded endosperm meat of the coconut, and the pulp of *Cassia fistula* (cassia pods), used much like tamarind and prunes as flavor, food, and mild laxative.

Since about the turn of the century there has been a continuing contest between two primary groups of aromatic/flavor materials: the essential or volatile oils, derived from natural plant sources, known and used for centuries, and the aromatic principles or compounds, essentially of recent origin, and mostly known only for the past few decades. Many of the latter, of genuine synthetic type, are not found in nature.

Essential Oils

The essential oils represent a group of secondary plant substances (along with the alkaloids, flavones, waxes, etc.) in which there is much current interest on both the academic and the practical or manufacturing fronts. By use of the newer separation techniques, especially chromatography, the presence of new compounds is constantly being reported in one or other of the approximately 9000 oils now known. With new, precise, analytical procedures, the elucidation of structure of many individual compounds is proceeding rapidly. Another major activity is in the study of the biosynthesis of essential oils, their role in the plant economy, and their taxonomic significance; these data often provide information about the position of the originating plant in the phylogenetic scheme.

Aromatics

The other group, the so-called aromatics, have become ever more popular as a result of increasing efficiency and economy of manufacture and of proof of their value and relative safety.

The aromatic compounds are readily available and relatively inexpensive. Unlike the essential oils, the aromatics are dependent neither on climatic conditions, the soil, the political situations in many small foreign countries, nor on the other difficulties of agricultural or forest production. To cite an extreme instance, methyl salicylate is the chief (98–99%) component of wintergreen oil, which is produced by distillation in remote areas of Tennessee and some other states. In recent years the price of synthesized methyl salicylate was of the order of 50c a pound, while the so-called "southern wintergreen oil" (true oil from *Gaultheria procumbens*) has been costing as much as $20.00 a pound, some forty times more than the easily synthesized aromatic compound (Guenther, 1962). (Many physicians consider the natural oil superior, hence its use continues.)

With this increasing production and use of aromatics, the preparation of essential oils has undergone some readjustments. Thus, at present, approximately equal volumes of the two great groups are said to be marketed.

Despite the popularity (especially among manufacturers!) of the aromatics, natural flavors and perfume materials based on essential oils, and so on are generally regarded as having greater intrinsic value and usefulness, mostly because of their more adequate or more complex flavor/odor values.

An aromatic compound cannot usually replace the essential oil of which it is an active (or *the* active) constituent. Hence, for instance, vanillin, although it may deceive some people, is quite definitely inferior to the much richer flavored crude vanilla fruit as exhibited in its various preparations. Only a person with deficient or untrained senses of smell and taste would be unable to notice the difference.

Another, clearer example of this is the synthesized form of cinnameldehyde, active principle of cinnamon oil, which was introduced on the market and officially recognized in N.F. VIII and IX (1947 and 1955) during a period when the natural cinnamon (or cassia) oils were almost unobtainable. Cinnamaldehyde was eventually found to be quite unsatisfactory as a flavor and was dropped from the compendium.

History of Use

Flavors and perfumes have played an important part in cultural history from the earliest known times. Through the ages they have been fundamental commodities which have endowed life with more pleasure and comfort.

A great monetary value was placed on the spices, particularly, and for centuries the people of western Europe were willing to pay exorbitant prices for these essential oil commodities that were brought from the Pacific and Indian ocean areas by boat and camel caravan across thousands of miles of the Asian mainland and adjacent ocean.

Something of the eastern appreciation for flavors and their importance in the traditional medicine of Indo-Pakistan may be witnessed in the name "attar," which is applied to the druggist who prepares the essence or essential oil or perfume also called "attar." (The word is often altered to "otto" in the west, and specifically applied to otto of rose, rose oil.)

Chemistry

The composition of essential oils is now known to be much more complex than it was previously throught to be. With the use of gas-liquid chromatography, the known components of peppermint oil have increased from approximately 12 to between 80 and 90. Commonly, essential oils examined have 40 to 60 components (Guenther, 1962). Recent examination of Bourbon vanilla revealed 13 constituents present (Bohnsack, 1967). Coffee has been shown to have at least 96 odorous compounds, of which 37 have been identified, and potato shows about 34 compounds.

By using various types of chromatography to separate constituents, and various types of spectrophotometry to determine molecular structure, it has been possible in recent years to catalog and characterize the detailed make-up of many essential oils.

Evaluation by chemical means alone has not proved sufficient, however. The best judgment of quality of many products in which correct flavor/aroma is most essential comes from the senses of a trained and sensitive individual, the professional taster. Even better than dependence on a single person is the use of flavor (or taste) panels composed of several individuals whose collective opinion is more likely to be considered reliable and valid. Other refinements, such as the taste (or flavor) profile, also increase the accuracy of such determinations.

Medicinal and Pharmaceutical Uses

A primary use of the essential oils and aromatic materials is for flavoring oral preparations, such as antacid tablets and powders, elixirs, cough syrups and drops, tonics, laxatives, antiseptics and germicides, vitamin preparations, orally administered antibiotics and sulfonamides, and many combinations, including prescriptions.

Strictly speaking, the aromatics are less important as a separate group than the flavors. They play their largest part in the perfuming of ointments, creams, lotions, liniments, inhalants, room and hospital sprays, soaps, and so on.

However, there are many other applications of essential oils besides those for taste-smell.

Medicinally, some oils are applied clinically or in the home as skin irritants—as rubefacients (as in liniments), vesicants (e.g., capsicum), counterirritants (e.g., turpentine oil), as stimulants of hair growth (in hair tonics), as hyperemics to increase local blood flow, as local anesthetics (e.g., cloves), as antipruritics for aggravated itching, and in the relief of muscular rheumatism (volatile mustard oil in mustard plasters). Sometimes, in topical application, these products are useful antiseptics (or bacteriostats), germicides, antimycotics (antifungal agents), and ectoparasiticides (to destroy insects, etc.), also as insect repellents (e.g., citronella oil). Some of the essential oil drugs and derivatives have striking anti-inflammatory or antiphlogistic values, as *Matricaria chamomilla* (with chamazulene), methyl salicylate, and (recently) *Aristolochia clematitis* (*Fortschritte der Botanik,* 1963).

Another important medicinal use is in treatment of bronchial disorders as expectorants to stimulate the mucous secretions and flow, often by applications in inhalants (e.g., eucalyptus oil) and in nasal ointments and sprays (e.g., peppermint oil and menthol).

For the gastrointestinal tract, essential oils and their drugs serve as stomachics (to aid digestion in the stomach), as aromatic bitter tonics (e.g., angelica), as carminatives to reduce discomfort (e.g., coriander oil), as antispasmodics (or spasmolytics) to relieve muscular contractions of stomach and intestines (e.g., calamus) (Maj *et al.,* 1966), as cholagogs and choleretics (e.g., Indonesian turmeric), as correctives (or corrigents) with strong cathartics (e.g., anise oil), and as general stimulants of the functioning of the entire system or organism. Formerly, some oils were used as anthelmintics to control worm infestations in the alimentary tract, a declining use and, at least in the United States, a declining problem.

Some essential oils and oil drugs were formerly applied to the urinary tract as diuretics (e.g., juniper oil), but in recent years they have been displaced to a large extent by less irritant types of diuretics; however, some oils are still used as urinary antiseptics. Sometimes essential oil products have been used as emmenagogs (e.g., pennyroyal oil), but unfortunately they have also sometimes been misused in higher dosages. Products of this category play a minor part in the control of central nervous system disorders when compared with those of several other medicinal groups. However, a number have sedative or even mild hypnotic effects (e.g., valerian and asafoetida), some promote diaphoresis or perspiration flow (e.g., pimpinella), and others are said to be analeptic, stimulating the basic functions of the body, respiration and circulation.

Some volatile oil products, such as nutmeg, *Myristica fragrans,* have been used as popular hallucinogens. Nerve stimulation by these agents and others is also thought to play a part in improved functioning of the various endocrine organs, such as the thyroid gland.

In the recent past, one member of the group had a high reputation for treatment of some cardiac complaints, namely, camphor, formerly often referred to as "German digitalis."

Because of such uses as these and the inevitable development of new applications in future years, flavors and aromas, though still playing a dominant role in the rather elementary function of rendering medicaments and pharmaceuticals more palatable and more likely to be used "just as the doctor ordered," constitute an important group in positive medical treatment. There is increasing appreciation of these complex materials, and fuller utilization in many areas of health retention and disease control is to be expected.

In addition to bodily applications, the essential oils and related products may often be used with value as germicides and preservatives. As a matter of fact, this was the principal use of spices in medieval days; at that time, before refrigeration was available, meats and other foods were so preserved. For this reason, some spices were worth more than an equal weight of gold.

Other Uses

The essential oils and aromatics are used in food flavoring (as in pickles, candy, bread, cakes, jellies, confectionery), in beverages (as in wines, gins, soft drinks), in masticatories (notably chewing gum), in fumitories (such as tobacco*), in toilet goods (as dentifrices), and in alcohol denaturation. The aromatics and oils are very important industrial deodorants, for which special use they are applied to rubber, textile, leather, plastic, paper, and other products. Of course, the single biggest use of the floral type of essential oils and aromatics is in the area of perfumery and cosmetics.

An important utilization of both essential oils and aromatics is as precursive materials in the synthesis of various organic compounds, often of medicinal interest. As an example, citronella oil is used in the synthesis of vitamin A.

---

*It may be noted here that the world's biggest user of rose oil is said to be the American Tobacco Company.

Tastes or Related Sensations Produced by Flavors

Flavors can be classified according to the dominant type of taste sensation produced but, because combinations of tastes are usually involved, they are generally too complex to be placed under a single heading. Some of the dominant groups follow.

1. *Pungency* or "bite": Notable in radish, horseradish, and other members of the mustard family (Cruciferae); due in this group chiefly to isothiocyanates.
2. *Bitterness:* Found with alkaloids and some glycosides and many crude drugs, such as chicory, gentian, and galanga ("bitter principles") (see later discussion).
3. *Sourness:* Noted in acids and acid salts; one of the more attractive flavors, especially in combination with sweetness, aroma, etc.
4. *Sweetness:* Pronouncedly attractive for infants and children (this is the first developed taste manifestation in man); most, though not all, sugars are sweet (e.g., gentianose is bitter); dextrose (a monose) (as found in grapes) and sucrose (a diose) (as seen in carrots) are the most common sweetening agents. Some glycosides are sweet: glycyrrhizin has fifty times the sweetness of sucrose.

Jaggery, the sugar from the juice of a palm, is said to be very delicious, somewhat like maple sugar. Fairchild (1947) once said that no one had had sufficient imagination to import this into the United States.

5. *Aroma:* is chiefly a smell sensation noted generally with spices (discussed later), such as fennel, celery, and garlic.
6. *Acridity:* Represents a stinging taste sensation, actually more of a feeling than a taste. It is often caused by the mechanical effect of calcium oxalate crystals in plant tissues; e.g., in unprocessed *Arisaema triphyllum,* Indian turnip; *Manihot* spp., cassava, or yucca; and *Colocasia antiquorum,* taro. Other taste characters recognized are astringency (e.g., unripe persimmons), coolness (e.g., peppermint oil), and warmth (e.g., ginger).

Desiderata for Flavoring in Medicinals

The physician requires that the medicine gain patient acceptance and not discourage him from continuing the prescribed dosage. To this end, the flavor must be complex (e.g., acid and sweet), full, with a "quick and clean cut-off of after-taste" (Sjostrom, 1967).

Use of a nauseating or otherwise disagreeable medicine with a flavor

of medium attractiveness may produce in the patient a continuing re-
vulsion thereafter when he tastes the flavor in the same or other combinations or even alone. For example, some of the old-fashioned dis-
agreeably griping senna or castor oil laxatives used sassafras or cinnamon flavors, which thereafter became utterly distasteful to the patient.

Flavor-Altering Materials

Both natural and synthetic additive compounds are extensively used at
present in medicine, foods, and so on. These compounds include flavor
additives or improvers, flavor potentiators, flavor enhancers, flavor
blenders, and flavor inhibitors.

1. *Flavor additives* represent new flavors added (e.g., anise or lemon
oil, paprika oleoresin).

2. *Flavor potentiators* add nothing really new but accent the natural
flavors (Solms, 1967). For example, monosodium glutamate (MSG) has
been a popular agent for bringing out a meaty flavor. Lately certain
nucleotides have also been popular, often in combination with MSG. The
great problem is to develop as strongly as possible the innate flavor of the
product so as to be able to label it, as one manufacturer has done in
recent advertising, "the very" flavor.

3. *Flavor enhancers* include maltol, sodium chloride, sugars, food acids,
yeast extract, and so on. Ammoniated glycyrrhizin (AG) has long been
known and has been used to intensify greatly the sweetness of sucrose
and chocolate and reduce the flavor potentiator costs of these materials
(Morrish and Muller, 1965; Anon, 1965a,b).

4. *Flavor blenders* are used to reduce conflicts or incompatibilities
between flavors (e.g., oil of onion, tarragon oil).

5. *Flavor inhibitors* are used to reduce undesirable flavors; one of the
best known is *Gymnema sylvestre*. The juice of the "miracle fruit" from
Nigeria and Ghana, reported recently (Inglett, 1965) is said to sweeten
sour flavors; thus it is a kind of taste inhibitor.

Specific Medicinal Flavors

In medical practice it is customary to use certain specific flavors in
particular types of medication. For children's medical formulas, chocolate
and raspberry have been preferred; the former, however, is now found
often contraindicated because of the frequent occurrence of allergy to
chocolate among children. For cough syrups, wild cherry bark (*Prunus*

serotina) syrup is customarily used. Licorice and cherry traditionally mask bitter and saline tastes. Lemon is also widely used for masking bitter flavors of alkaloids, glycosides, and similar substances. Dental preparations, such as mouth washes and dentifrices, are often flavored with peppermint oil. To conceal the unpleasant flavors of salicylates and ammonium chloride (among others), cinnamon is often admixed.

In consequence of its large usage, the leading medicinal plant crops in the United States are the aromatic plants peppermint, from *Mentha piperita* (first introduced from England 150 years ago), and spearmint, from *Mentha spicata* and *M. cardiaca*. These crops are grown in the Midwest and Far West over large areas.

One of the most popular flavoring materials is vanilla beans; Europeans learned about this material from the Aztecs. The active principle, vanillin, is now made on a factory scale very cheaply from such inexpensive materials as the lignin available in vast tonnages from wood pulp manufacture. Synthetic vanillin currently costs only about $9 per kilogram, whereas, if vanillin were extracted from the expensive vanilla beans (which cost around $10 per pound), 1 kilo of this natural vanillin would cost about $1000 — over a hundredfold more costly than the synthetic product. Despite the high price of vanilla, however, the annual production is about 1000 metric tons or about 2¼ million pounds, valued at about 20 million dollars.

Wine is an important flavor additive in liquid forms of many medications. Its use goes back into history, for the growing of grapes and the fermenting of juice is recorded by many of the oldest classical writers.

Among the flavoring and aromatizing materials widely used in medicine and pharmacy are the various and distinctive members of the citrus group: lemon, bitter and sweet orange (Wolford and Attaway, 1967), grapefruit, lime, bergamot, tangerine, petitgrain, and others. Both the juice and the peel oil have been used in medicines, foods, and beverages.

In recent work (Berry *et al.*, 1967) the compound that is perhaps chiefly responsible for the characteristic aroma and flavor of grapefruit oil has been identified. The compound is a ketone called nootkatone, and it is also found in lemon, orange, lime, and bergamot oils. An important part of orange oil fragrance is now known to be due to the compound ethyl-3-hydroxyhexanoate.

In recent research work (Koch and Schiller, 1964) the fragrant aroma of apple juice is claimed to be due chiefly to hexanal, a rather simple aliphatic aldehyde.

Passion fruit is used as a source of wine with an especially pleasant flavor and aroma (Muller *et al.*); in some parts of the world, *Passiflora* species supply flavor to ice cream. Eventually, passion fruit may become a useful pharmaceuticomedical flavor.

Balsamic flavors, including balsam of Peru, balsam of tolu, and benzoin, constitute a group of their own. In this group also is styrax or sweet gum, a balsam produced mostly in subtropics of the old world but also in our own hemisphere (it is produced in the state of Alabama). This balsam is used as an expectorant and in perfumes, but chiefly to "desharpen" tobacco flavors.

Trilisa or deer tongue is another product of southeastern United States; the carefully cured leaves of *Trilisa odoratissima,* exhibiting the strong aroma of coumarin, are used. Coumarin has been disallowed in foods and medicines but is still permitted in the aromatization of cigars, cosmetics, and so on, where there is little or no oral ingestion.

Other flavors which should be mentioned are nutmeg and its aril, mace, both popular condiments in very wide usage.

A most familiar flavor is artificial maple, but few know that it is prepared from fenugreek seed (*Trigonella foenum-graceum*), a field crop from California and elsewhere. Other flavors with drug connotations are figs, prunes, and tamarinds. Manna, an exudation from the manna ash of southern Italy is mostly a simple sweet flavor without character, rarely used in the United States (at present), but still quite popular in Europe. Several other mannas have been used medicinally.

Closely related flavoring substances are the categories of spices, bitters, and herbs.

Spices

An important group of specialized flavoring materials which also have medicinal value as carminatives (to relieve gastrointestinal distress) are the condiments or spices. In view of their physiological effect, they must be viewed as more than mere food adjuncts, although this is how they are now generally regarded. The group illustrates the difficulty of drawing a hard and fast line between foods and medicines. In the olden days, spices were considered an important part of the medical armamentarium.

The primary use of spices is to stimulate appetite, and thus in this way often also indirectly benefit the health. Part of this effect derives from stimulation of the stomach mucous secretions, for which a need is more commonly found in tropical areas, where in fact most of the spices grow. Perhaps the chief spice today is, as it has been for centuries, pepper, both black and white, the white representing merely an unripe, macerated, and peeled black pepper. The pungency of pepper is attributed more to piperine and chavicine (isomeric alkaloids) than to the oil. Many other peppers are known and used; there are no less than 600 recognized species of *Piper;* and they include *P. longa, P. betle* (used in making betel chew), and *P. methysticum* (used to prepare the South Sea beverage called kava kava).

Another spice, often called "red pepper" but not a true pepper at all, is *Capsicum.* This native American product is now popularly used throughout the world. Some forms such as African "Cayenne pepper" are especially hot spices. The genus *Capsicum* is a small one but has many variations and is known by many names, such as the chile of Latin America, the relatively mild paprikas and pimentos, and so on. "Capsaicinoid" is the name now applied to the combination of capsaicin and its dihydro derivative, the active principles.

Turmeric, or curcuma, is often used in foods and medicines; a food in which it is used is the famous curry or "rice table" (Dutch rijsttafel) of Asia. Curry (from "khura," palatable) is a most attractive food. Turmeric has many medicinal uses abroad.

Ginger, which may be regarded as a stronger form of turmeric, is widely used in the home medicine of Germany and elsewhere in breast teas and "ginger teas," but is not popular in the United States for such uses except among immigrants. The active principles are the closely related keto compounds, zingerone and gingerole.

A spice commonly used is cinnamon. The best pharmaceutical cinnamon is the Ceylon, with Saigon the most commonly employed, although cassia bark (or Chinese cinnamon) is often used in the household spice, sometimes to replace the more expensive Ceylon and Saigon cinnamons.

Pimenta, also called allspice or Jamaica pepper, is very popular; the name allspice refers to the flavor, which is reminiscent of several other products. It is used mostly to spice sausages.

Saffron was very popular among medieval peoples. In addition to its brilliant yellow color, saffron has a strong flavor which may be repulsive when first tasted; however, this flavor tends to become more palatable with repeated use. In earlier centuries, this product was considered the best medicine and was always included in the very complex formulas so prevalent in those days, medicines often containing scores of components. In several European countries, saffron was so highly regarded that adulteration or sophistication of saffron was punished by the death penalty.

Mustard, both black and white, is rich in both an essential and a fatty oil, the former being developed in an enzymatic hydrolytic reaction involving grinding of the seed with water, then separation by distillation.

Actually the essential oil is no longer used to any great extent, whereas the seeds are widely used to make mustard condiment or household mustard, mustard plasters, and so on. The mustard flour mixed with lukewarm water is an important emergency emetic in the home, and it also serves as an excellent household poultice.

Similar properties are found in horseradish, the root of which is peeled, grated with vinegar, then packed in jars. Horseradish is notably rich in vitamin C; hence it may be thought of as a medicinal food.

There are many umbelliferous spices in use today. They include anise and fennel, which both date from the times of ancient Egypt; caraway, coriander, chervil, dill, celery, parsnip, masterwort (*Peucedanum ostruthium*), angelica (notable for its use in Benedictine liquor), levisticum (or lovage), pimpernel, black caraway (*Nigella sativa*), parsley, cow parsley (*Anthriscus silvester*), garden carrot fruit, cummin, and others.

A popular spice in the United States and almost everywhere is clove, the flower bud from the tropical tree, *Eugenia caryophyllus*. A clove appears on the Zanzibar flag, this country being the only one with a spice as its chief export product.

Among other condiments available and used is caper; caper flowers are pickled with salt and vinegar and used in the cuisine. *Capparis spinosa* of Europe is the most popular but the Asian species are similar.

Habitually masticated in many parts of south Asia and the Pacific islands is betel nut, together with numerous spice materials, such as cardamom, capsicum, pepper, and turmeric. Betel or "pan," as it is often called in Asia, is cherished by most of the people in these warm countries of the Old World and, with its richness in spice materials, suggests (the) chutney or sauce of curry.

Bitters

The quality of bitterness has been of great importance in medicine in the past and continues to be important in the medical practice of extra-American areas up to the present time. Bitter substances (or bitter agents), referred to in German works as "Amara," have been in popular use for centuries. Thus, of the 263 medical agents of Hippocrates (ca. 500 B.C.), 30 were bitters (Lauer, 1954).

One consulting the pages of any herbal dating from the 1400s to 1600s finds that many bitters occupied an important place in the botanical medicine of that era. They were especially recommended for reducing fever (i.e., as antipyretics). Eventually this led to the belief that only a bitter-tasting medicine would relieve fever. This false notion has persisted in many areas up to the present day; indeed, in the rural regions of southeastern United States the notion has been extended to include almost any medicine.

The most recent edition of the *U.S. Pharmacopeia* has no representatives of the class of bitters, gentian and cinchona having been dropped over the last few years. The current edition of *National Formulary* apparently has only one bitter, a half-synthetic: sucrose octaacetate. The current edition of the German *Pharmacopeia* (the 6th), however, has monographs for 12 bitter drugs, but it is expected that there will be only 5 in the forthcoming 7th edition. The following bitters are considered to be the best available at present: gentian root, pomegranate peel, centaury herb, wormwood, and cinchona bark.

Although modern medicine shows little interest in bitters*, the layman has continued to partake of them freely in the form of beers, wines, liqueurs, and cocktails. Quantities of these are self-administered perorally by patient laymen who no doubt experience some degree of appetite stimulation. The rotundity of many a beer drinker is probably due to a hearty appetite and not to the brew he has imbibed.

It is said that in Europe the bitter types of beer (like Pilsener) are most in demand, and the highest prices are paid for those with the highest bitter strength (Brieskorn, 1966).

Bitter-tasting agents have two primary effects: stimulation of the digestive activity, and production of nausea and distaste. From the psychic standpoint, bitters have a wide range of effect on the individual, producing, on the one hand, pleasurable sensations and, on the other hand, disgust and aversion. Strong doses of bitters, such as sucrose octaacetate or brucine, when added to alcohol render it so horrible as to be nonpotable; hence these and other bitters are useful as denaturants.

The obnoxious effects of bitters may be offset by dilution and by the use of appropriate added flavors. Ingenuity has been applied to mask bitter taste with sweet and aromatic flavors, as in the elixirs or (as a better example)in the universal cola drinks and similar beverages, since the latter contain bitter substances, including caffeine, in a rather complex mixture. (For instance, Coca-Cola is said to contain ten essential oils.)

Thus the beverages consumed daily by millions of Americans for comfort, relaxation, and congeniality are really comparable to the bitter medicines of the past; they represent a sort of modern bitter medicinal (Silvestro, 1962).

---

*A considerable decrease in the discussion of bitter substances in or as medicinals is shown in some of the newer pharmacology textbooks, such as Goodman and Gilman.

Many modern synthetic medicinals are bitter-tasting, sometimes extremely so. Pharmaceutical manufacturers are compelled to overcome this objectionable feature insofar as possible; this is generally done by preparing the medicinal in tablet form. When they use taste correctives or masking substances without actually eliminating the bitterness, it might well be conjectured that part of the therapeutic benefits of their product may lie in the bitter-principle effect (Luckner, 1965).

By reflex action, bitters produce a stimulation of the salivary and gastric glands and, by central projection of the stimulation to cortical areas of the brain, there develops the attractive sensation of appetite or, in more extreme cases, the aggravated pains of hunger. Of course, other organoleptic messages may participate in this stimulation, especially the sight of food and the feel of food in the mouth.

Bitter principles are common in several vegetable families, especially Burseraceae, Compositae, Rutaceae, Simarubaceae, Menispermaceae, Meliaceae, and Cucurbitaceae. In some other families there may be individual species with bitter substances in relatively high concentration.

Chemically, most bitter principles are mono-, sesqui-, di-, and triterpenoids or are derived from them by degradative processes. Others are glycosides (e.g., picrocrocin of saffron); saponins (soybean saponin), depsides, and tannins (e.g., chocolate bitter). Though there is considerable diversity in the molecular structure of bitter compounds, compounds of considerable similarity occur in various families, for example, columbin in the Menispermaceae (*Calumba*) and picropolin in the Labiatae (*Teucrium polium*) (Pfeuffer, 1966). Many aromatics (such as hops) also furnish useful bitter agents. Some plant materials, such as true origanum, contain two or more distinctive bitter principles.

On the whole, little has been done to study molecular structures of bitter principles, much less in perfecting the synthesis of these compounds; consequently, for nearly all members of the group the galenical preparations are used, rather than the isolated principles, in preference to the crude material itself.

Herbs

In addition to the bitters and spices, as distinctive classes of aromatic and flavoring materials, there is another group of plant products which is popular in household medicine and for which the odor-taste properties are paramount. They are the so-called "herbs" or "garden herbs." Included, among many others, are: Hyssop, the herb of *Hyssopus offici-*

nalis: mostly used in bronchial disorders; Sage, from *Salvia officinalis:* an important condiment; Thyme, the herb of *Thymus vulgaris:* popular for cough preparations, (so used with a well-known proprietary, Pertussin); Hypericum, called sometimes St. John's wort: the essential oil used in recent times in cosmetics (Bergwein, 1967); Tarragon: the herb used as a condiment, often combined with mustard; Marjoram: *Majorana hortensis,* a flavor and seasoning with miscellaneous medicinal uses; Wild margoram: *Origanum vulgare,* a flavor and diaphoretic with other uses; an essential to pizza making.

Conclusion

The appropriate use of flavors and perfumes to improve oral and local medication is a continuously evolving science and art in which plant material sources still predominate. The objective of much scientific research in this field is to render medicines more pleasant for the patient. Flavors and aromas also play a very important part in almost every other phase of human activity.

REFERENCES

Anon. (1965a). *Food Process. Marketing* **26,** 86.
Anon. (1965b). *Food Eng.* **37,** 99.
Bergmark, M. (1958). Lust und Leid durch Drogen, pp. 170ff. Wissenschaftl. Verlagsges, Stuttgart.
Bergwein, K. (1967). *Perfumery Essent. Oil Rec.* **58,** 164–165.
Berry, R. E., *et al.* (1967). Nootkatone, one of chief flavor compounds of grapefruit juice. *J. Food Sci.* **32,** 75–78.
Bohnsack, H. (1967). *Riechstoffe* **17,** 133–135.
Brieskorn, C. H. (1966). *Planta Med.* **14,** Suppl. 1–4.
Fairchild, David (1947). "The World Grows Round My Door," p. 265.
Fortsch. Botan. **1963,** 405.
Guenther, Ernest. (1962). Speech at Auburn University, Auburn, Alabama.
Inglett, G. E. (1965). *J. Agr. Food Chem.* **13,** 284–287.
Koch, J., and Schiller, H. Z. (1964). *Lebensmittel-Untersuch.* **125,** 364. (Through Am. Perf. Cosm., Feb. 1967.)
Lauer, A. (1954). *Deut. Apotheker-Zt.* **24,** 326.
Luckner, M., *et al.* (1965). Evaluation of bitter drugs. *Pharmazie* **20,** 20–21.
MacLeod, W. D., and Buigues, N. M. (1964). *J. Food Sci.* **29,** 565.
Maj, J., *et al.* (1966). Pharmacological properties of the native calamus, *Acorus calamus.* III. Spasmolytic action of the volatile oil. *Acta Polon. Pharm.* **23,** 477–482.
Morrish, R. J., and Muller, R. E. (1965). *Food Process. Marketing* **26,** 74.
Muller, C. J., *et al.* (1964). *J. Food Sci.* **29,** 569–575.
Pfeuffer, T. (1966). Teucrium. *Planta Med.* **14,** Suppl, 117.

Silvestro, M., *et al.* (1962). Medicinal herbs and bitter tonics and liqueur production. *Riv. Ital. Essenze-Profumi* **44,** 548–552.

Sjostrom, L. B. (1967). "Trends in Flavor Preferences." A. D. Little, Cambridge, Mass.

Solms, J. (1967). Flavor enhancing compounds in foods. *Chimia* **21,** 169–175.

Weicker, Hermann. (1944). Conversation (S. B. Penick & Company, New York).

Wolford, R. W., and Attaway, J. A. (1967). Orange aroma and flavor. *J. Agr. Food Chem.* **15,** 369–377.

Zotterman, Y. (1962). Olfaction and Taste. Vol. 1. Pergamon, London.

Microbial Biodynamic Agents*

Nestor Bohonos

One hundred years ago, when the Torrey Botanical Club was founded, it would have been difficult, even inconceivable, to discuss active agents from microorganisms, but much has transpired in the interim. At that time botanicals constituted the bulk of available drugs. Today, microbially derived agents are the major natural products in modern pharmaceutical practice. Since bacteria, yeasts, fungi and algae are lower forms of plants, and since there is much interplay with research on biodynamic agents from higher plants, this subject can, and logically should be, included in the present-day activities of the Torrey Botanical Club.

To discuss this subject in the limited space available and to avoid being too general, specific examples have been selected to illustrate procedures, products, or activities which reflect the characteristics of this area of endeavor. It is, of course, necessary to omit many important observations. Reports of activities in animal or clinical trials do not necessarily indicate therepautic utility. These activities should be regarded as leads which require intensive evaluation of such products and related compounds for efficacy and toxicity characteristics.

The critical significance of antibiotics in modern medical practice is well known, and even the elementary school pupil knows that a mold is used to produce penicillin. What is frequently not appreciated is that developments such as the antibiotics are the culmination of efforts of numerous scientific disciplines and that a long, arduous sequence of investigations is required from the initial observation to the clinical acceptance of a product. The spectacular development of antibiotics may be attributed to the critical significance of infectious diseases in medicine and to the relative simplicity and directness of test systems.

*The preparation of this review was supported in part by Research Grant No. FR05526 from the Division of Research Facilities and Resources, National Institutes of Health.

289

A large variety of other types of biodynamic agents exist which may be said to be direct or indirect developments of microbial product research. The constantly increasing effort in this area is undoubtedly due to recognition of the accomplishments to date and appreciation of the advantages of dealing with microbial systems. The following are some of the attractive features of microbial product research:

1. Availability of culture.
2. Cultures may be preserved.
3. Cultures may be grown in laboratories.
4. Short generation time – rapid multiplication.
5. Fermentation conditions and mutations may lead to new products.
6. Available technology for scale-up.
7. Large spectrum of products already demonstrated.

Between 1935 and 1950, major contributions were made as a consequence of the realization that microorganisms require growth factors; in many instances they were found to be vitamins. Other strains of microorganisms were found to be excellent sources of these growth factors or vitamins; thus they were used to produce these compounds in research or commercial quantities. During World War II a good deal of the riboflavin was made by fermentation. A contaminant *Corynebacterium* was isolated from one of these riboflavin fermentations and found to be an unusually good source of folic acid activity (Hutchings *et al.*, 1944). This discovery facilitated the isolation of sufficient crystalline material for chemical and biological studies. Folic acid (see Fig. 1) was demonstrated to have vitamin activity (Hutchings *et al.*, 1941). In the course of chemical studies on analogs, the antimetabolite aminopterin was prepared (Seeger *et al.*, 1947) which was subsequently found to be clinically effective in the treatment of acute leukemia (Farber *et al.*, 1948). A microbiological assay (Shorb, 1947) facilitated the isolation of crystalline vitamin B_{12} (the antipernicious anemia factor) in the United States. The commercial production of this important complex vitamin is entirely dependent on microbial processes.

Before the development of the riboflavin, folic acid, and penicillin fermentations, there was relatively little technology in large-scale aerobic fermentations. This technology has now been extended to the management of such difficult fermentations as the growth of mushrooms, ergot alkaloid-producing organisms, algae, and animal cells. Biologists have been crucial in the development of mutants which result in higher yields or more readily processed mashes, or which form superior chemically related products.

In the development of large-scale penicillin operations it was necessary to obtain cultures which produced high yields of penicillin G (Fig. 1) in commercially practical tank fermentations. Currently, a number of

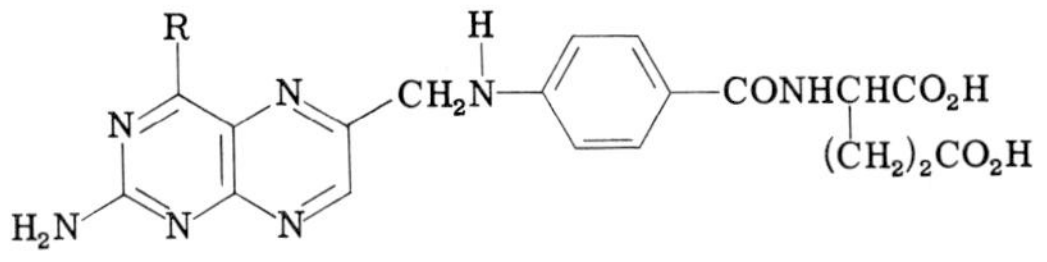

Pteroylglutamic acid
(folic acid), R = OH
4-aminopteroylglutamic acid
(aminopterin), R = NH$_2$

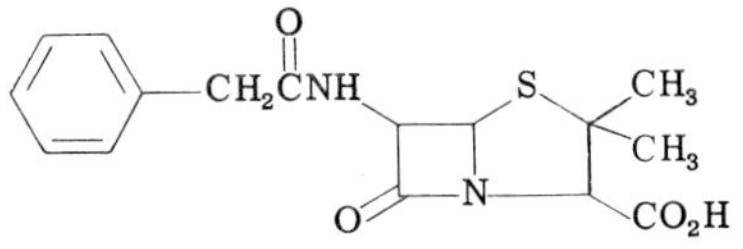

Benzylpenicillin (penicillin G)

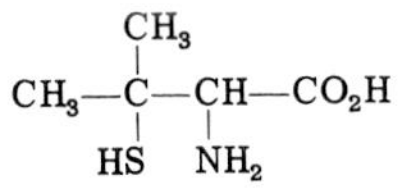

Penicillamine

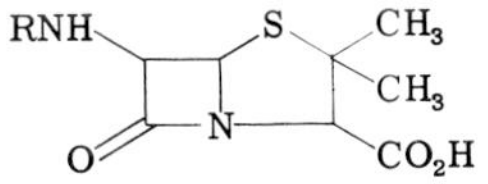

6-Aminopenicill-
anic acid (R = H)
semi-synthetic
penicillins (R = Acyl)

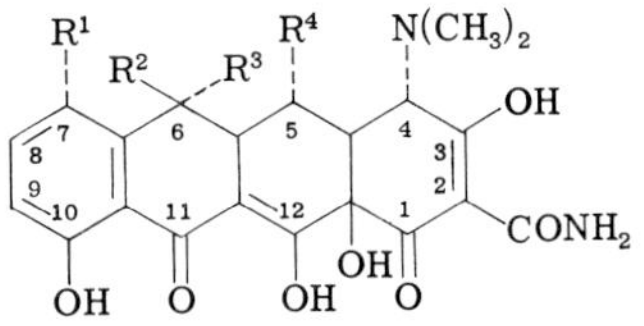

	R^1	R^2	R^3	R^4
Tetracycline	H	OH	CH$_3$	H
7-Chlortetracycline	Cl	OH	CH$_3$	H
6-Demethyl-7-chlortetracycline	Cl	OH	H	H
5-Hydroxytetracycline	H	OH	CH$_3$	OH
6-Methylene-5-hydroxytetracycline	H	—	=CH$_2$	OH
α-6-Deoxy-5-hydroxytetracycline	H	H	CH$_3$	OH

FIG. 1.

superior semisynthetic penicillins are made chemically from microbially derived 6-aminopenicillanic acid (Fig. 1). Another spin-off from penicillin research has been the degradation product penicillamine (Fig. 1). It has a diversity of pharmacological properties which are attributed to its chelating capacity, sulfhydryl-reducing activity, or its vitamin B_6 antagonism. D- or DL-Penicillamine has been reported to be effective in the treatment of Wilson's disease (Walshe, 1960), lead poisoning (Goldberg et al., 1963), cysteinuria (Crawhall et al., 1963), macroglobinemia (Ritzmann et al., 1960; Block et al., 1960), and in schizophrenia (Nicolson et al., 1966). It can influence immune response (Allman and Tobin, 1965), the level of circulating rheumatoid factor (Jaffe, 1963), and collagen metabolism (Nimini and Bavetta, 1965). Although this drug is being used clinically, it is implicated in severe side reactions and there is considerable controversy regarding its use.

The structures of the five commercially available tetracyclines differ in substituents on the 5, 6, and 7 positions (Fig. 1). 7-Chlortetracycline, tetracycline, and 6-demethyl-7-chlortetracycline are produced by *Streptomyces aureofaciens*. Tetracycline was discovered on hydrogenolysis of chlortetracycline (Boothe et al., 1953; Conover et al., 1953) and in fermentations (Martin et al., 1954–1955; Minieri et al., 1954–1955). Because chlortetracycline fermentation technology was highly developed, it was easier to produce tetracycline commercially by this chemical conversion than to develop the tetracycline fermentation. In recent years this fermentation process has been made commercially feasible. In the course of developing high-yielding chlortetracycline strains, a mutant was obtained which could no longer introduce the methyl in the 6 position; thus the discovery of 6-demethyl-7-chlortetracyline (McCormick et al., 1957). 5-Hydroxytetracycline was first obtained from a *Streptomyces rimosus* fermentation (Finlay et al., 1950); and it serves as precursor for the chemical synthesis of 6-methylene-5-hydroxytetracycline (Blackwood et al., 1961) and α-6-deoxy-5-hydroxytetracycline (Stephens et al., 1958). All five tetracyclines have a qualitatively similar antibacterial spectrum, but they differ in pharmacological properties. 7-Chlortetracycline and 5-hydroxytetracycline have individual characteristics which theoretically, if present in the best combination, might be expected to result in a superior product. The postulated 5-hydroxy 7-chlortetracycline (Mitscher et al., 1966) was obtained as a result of knowledge gained in biogenetic studies on the tetracyclines. Unfortunately, the extreme instability of this product precluded any potential for it. A new tetracycline, 7-dimethylamino-6-deoxy-6-demethyltetracycline, is active against some bacteria resistant to the commercial tetracyclines (Redin, 1966); thus it is possible that new tetracyclines with broader activity may be developed.

Griseofulvin (Fig. 2), a clinically effective antifungal agent, may be said to have been developed as a consequence of an observation that

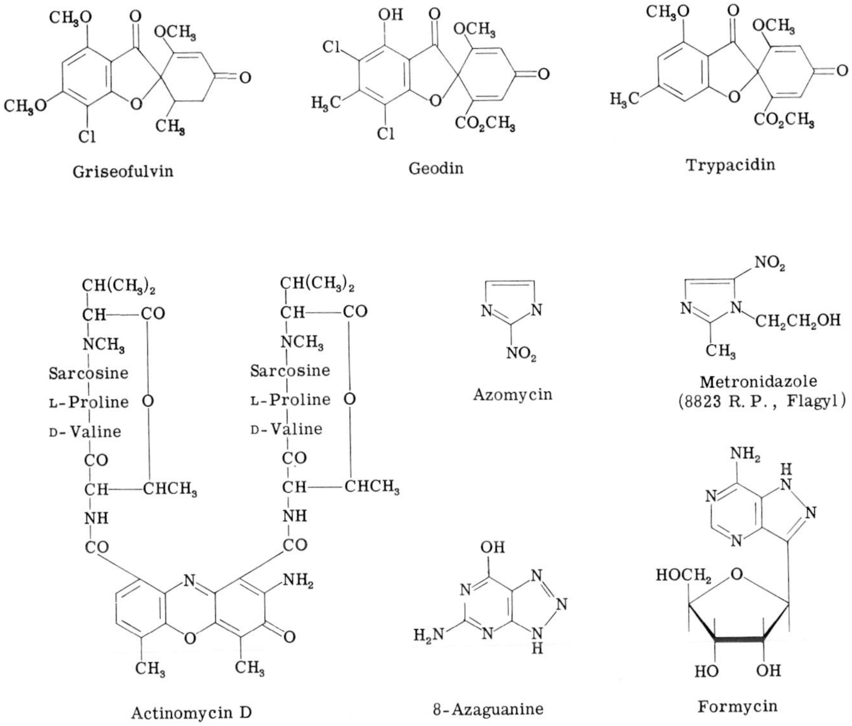
Griseofulvin
Geodin
Trypacidin
Azomycin
Metronidazole
(8823 R. P., Flagyl)
Actinomycin D
8-Azaguanine
Formycin

FIG. 2.

conifers would not grow on a certain heath soil (Brian *et al.,* 1945). The predominating fungus in the soil was found to produce "curling factor," so named because of the distortion it caused in hyphae of *Botrytis allii* (Brian *et al.,* 1946). After isolation and chemical characterization, this product was found to be identical with griseofulvin first isolated in studies on the biochemistry of fungi (Oxford *et al.,* 1939). Observations on the systemic antifungal activity in plants (Brian *et al.,* 1951) were followed by reports that orally administered griseofulvin was effective in the treatment of ringworm in guinea pigs (Gentles, 1958) and cattle (Lauder and O'Sullivan, 1958). Nineteen years after its discovery, it was reported to be clinically effective in human therapy (Williams *et al.,* 1958; Blank and Roth, 1959). A large number of penicillia were found to produce griseofulvin, and the dechloro and bromo analogs were obtained from fermentations. Griseofulvin and a large number of related compounds were chemically synthesized. Although much is known about structural requirements for activity, to date none of these products has been accepted as clinically more effective in the treatment of dermatomycoses.

Anti-inflammatory activity of griseofulvin was observed in the course of treatment of dermatophytic infections of guinea pigs (Gentles, 1958) and man (Cochrane and Tullett, 1959) and, subsequently, in the conventional cotton pellet and tuberculin skin sensitivity tests (D'Arcy et al., 1960). This activity has been attributed to the hydrolysis of the antibiotic to 3-chloro-4,6 dimethoxysalicylic acid (Logeais et al., 1966). Nonfungal therapeutic uses of griseofulvin in gout, inflammatory reactions, rheumatology, peripheral vascular diseases, and in coronary dyscrasias have been reported by numerous investigators (Blank, 1965). Griseofulvin can, however, exhibit various toxicities; for example, disturbed porphyrin excretion in man (Rimington et al., 1963), alteration in prothrombin time in patients on "warfarin" therapy (Cullen and Catalano, 1967), hepatocarcinogenicity in mice (Barich et al., 1960; Hurst and Paget, 1963; De Matteis et al., 1966; Epstein et al., 1967). This broadly active compound has recently been reported to inhibit cuticle formation and morphogenesis in mosquitoes (Anderson, 1966).

Microorganisms produce many compounds that have structural features in common with griseofulvin and which have had little or any biological testing. Geodin (Raistrick and Smith, 1963) is one of numerous such compounds isolated in studies on chemical constituents of fungi. In common with many dienones, it is antifungal but it lacks the systemic activity of griseofulvin. Trypacidin (Fig. 2), another closely related product, was isolated in a screening program for antiprotozoal antibiotics (Balan et al., 1963). It has been found to be highly effective in the control of *Toxoplasma gondii* infections in mice (Ebringer et al., 1965).

Azomycin (Fig. 2) was first reported as an antibacterial antibiotic of high nitrogen content (Maeda et al., 1953; Okami et al., 1954), and it was subsequently found to have antitrichomonal activity (Horie, 1956). The independent discovery of azomycin as an antitrichomonal antibiotic (Despois et al., 1956) led to a synthetic program on nitroimidazoles and the discovery of the clinically important drug metronidazole (Fig. 2), which is more active as an antitrichomonal drug and far less toxic (Cosar and Julou, 1959). A great deal of work is being done currently on the synthesis of nitroimidazole compounds.

Microorganisms have been extensively used in test systems and as sources of products in the search for anticancer agents. The discovery of the antimetabolite activity of aminopterin is an example of how micro-organisms can be utilized in test systems. In many instances an anti-biotic is first identified as a new biodynamic agent, purified, and sub-sequently tested in animal tumor systems. Actinomycin D (Fig. 2) was first observed as an antibiotic active against gram-positive bacteria (Manaker *et al.,* 1954–1955), and it was subsequently found to be active against transplanted tumors in mice (Farber, 1955). This was the first antibiotic to have important clinical effects in cancer (Farber, 1966). A number of other antibiotics have selective efficacy in the clinical treatment of cancer. Since anticancer agents may inhibit cell multiplication by inter-fering with nucleic acid metabolism, it is not surprising that many synthetic and natural product leads are purine or pyrimidine derivatives. An inter-esting observation was that the anticancer agent 8-azaguanine (Fig. 2), first obtained chemically, was later reported as an antibiotic from a streptomyces (Anzai and Suzuki, 1961). In this compound, modification of the imidazole ring was sufficient to make it function as an antimetabo-lite. The recently announced antitumor and antiviral antibiotic formycin (Hori *et al.,* 1964; Koyama *et al.,* 1966; Ishizuka *et al.,* 1968) (Fig. 2) has a different type of alteration in the imidazole ring. Coformycin, an un-usual product, inhibits the enzymatic conversion of formycin to the less active 6-hydroxy analog, formycin B (Sawa *et al.,* 1967). It is possible that further studies on coformycin or related compounds may result in products which may stabilize amino groups in other anti-neoplastic agents and thus increase their activity.

Because virus particles contain nucleic acids, it is not surprising that virus multiplication, particularly in *in vitro* test systems, can be inhibited by anti-neoplastic agents. A number of high molecular weight products with no *in vitro* activity against bacteria or fungi have been observed to have activity in mouse tumor or virus tests. Compounds such as actino-mycin D, puromycin, and mitomycin C have been used to decrease im-mune response or organ transplants.

Because antibiotics are biodynamic agents, it is not surprising that in complex mammalian systems some affect neuromuscular activity (Straw *et al.,* 1965), loss of memory (Flexner *et al.,* 1967), lipolysis (Mehta *et al.,* 1967), liver regeneration (Gershbein, 1967), contraction of smooth muscle (Eliasson, 1958; Arai *et al.,* 1964), vascular permeability (Harada *et al.,* 1967), and so on.

Microbially produced glucocorticoids constitute an important segment of ethical pharmaceuticals. Until it was observed that the chemically difficult hydroxylation of steroids in the 11 position could be readily performed by microorganisms, microbial transformations were primarily of academic interest. Since then many complex molecules, such as steroids, antibiotics, alkaloids, and terpenoids, have been microbially modified (Iizuka and Naito, 1967). In the commercial production of the glucocorticoid triamcinolone (see Fig. 3), the 11- and 16-hydroxyls and

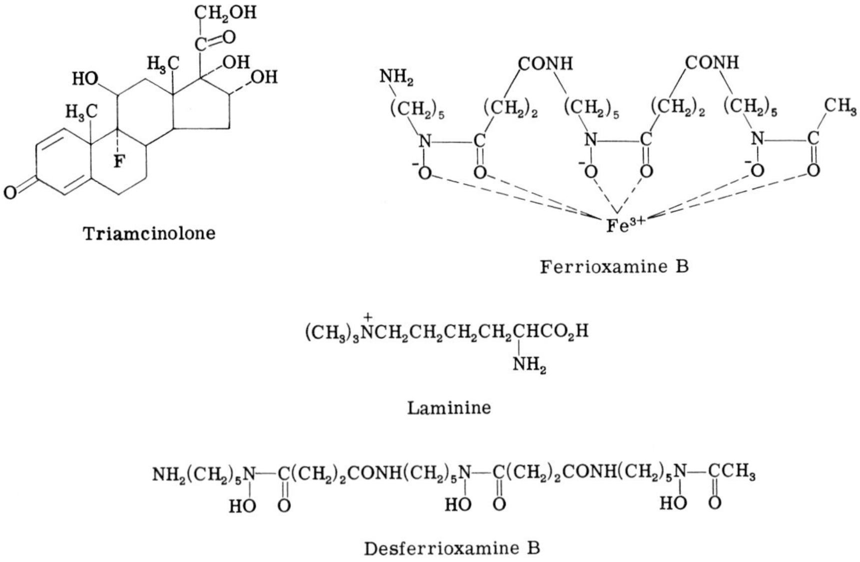

Triamcinolone

Ferrioxamine B

$$(CH_3)_3 \overset{+}{N}CH_2CH_2CH_2CH_2CHCO_2H$$
$$\underset{NH_2}{|}$$

Laminine

$$NH_2(CH_2)_5N—\underset{\underset{O}{\parallel}}{C}(CH_2)_2CONH(CH_2)_5N—\underset{\underset{O}{\parallel}}{C}(CH_2)_2CONH(CH_2)_5N—\underset{\underset{O}{\parallel}}{C}CH_3$$
$$\quad\ \ \underset{HO}{|} \qquad\qquad\qquad\quad \underset{HO}{|} \qquad\qquad\qquad\ \ \underset{HO}{|}$$

Desferrioxamine B

FIG. 3.

the unsaturation in the 1,2 position are introduced by microbial action. Morphine and codeine can be hydroxylated in the 14 position by a basidiomycete to form more active analgesic agents. The anticoagulants "dicoumarol" and "warfarin" were developed as a consequence of the investigation of the hemorrhagic factor produced on microbial spoilage of hay and silage (Stahmann et al., 1941). The production of this hemorrhagic factor is attributed to microbial transformation of o-coumaric acid (Bellis et al., 1967). Physiologically active amines, such as cadaverine, putrescine, tryamine, histamine, and serotonin, are products of the decomposition of amino acids.

Desferrioxamine B (Bickel et al., 1960) (Fig. 3) is derived from the naturally occurring growth factor ferrioxamine B, which contains tightly complexed iron. The desferro compound is an excellent iron scavenger which has been found useful in the treatment of primary and secondary hematochromatosis (Wöhler, 1962) and acute iron poisoning (Moeschlin and Schnider, 1963).

Microbial enzymes, such as streptokinase, streptodornase, penicillinase, amylases, cellulases, diastases, and proteinases, are used clinically. Interesting observations have been reported with keratinases, fungal fibrinolytic enzymes, platelet aggregating enzymes, "clearing factor" like lipases, and L-asparaginase, which is currently being evaluated in cancer chemotherapy.

The ergot alkaloids are another type of important biodynamic agent of microbial origin. They exert characteristic effects on the contraction of smooth muscles, serotonin antagonism, adrenergic blockade, and the central nervous system. All the therapeutically important ergot alkaloids are lysergic acid derivatives. As indicated previously, it is now possible to produce ergot alkaloids by submerged fermentations.

A broad range of products from an equally diverse spectrum of microorganisms exhibit activity in various hematological phenomena. In addition to the previously mentioned compounds, anticoagulant activity has been obsefved with bacterially derived dextran sulfate and vitamin K_2, algal fucoidin (Springer *et al.*, 1957), and atrometin obtained from a mushroom (Euler *et al.*, 1965). The common meadow mushroom *Agaricus campestris,* produces a highly active hemagglutinin (Sage and Vazquez, 1967). Dextran sulfate and fucoidin also have heparinlike properties in inducing the presence of clearing factor in blood (Stewart, 1958; Schuler and Springer, 1957). Laminine (Fig. 3) is a hypotensive agent isolated from an alga (Takemoto *et al.*, 1964).

Many phytotoxic or plant growth agents of varied chemical structures have been isolated from studies with plant pathogens or from screening programs using plant growth test systems. Gibberellic acid (Fig. 4) was isolated as the active principle involved in the "Bakanae byo" or "foolish seedling" disease of rice, a disease in which plants grow unusually tall and then die. This "toxic" principle has been found useful in plant growth regulation and in the production of barley malt. In addition to its activity in plants, gibberellic acid has been reported to influence insect metabolism (Carlisle *et al.*, 1963; Ellis *et al.*, 1965; Nation and Robinson, 1966), to affect mammalian resistance to ascites tumor (Schwartz, 1961) and multiplication of *Mycobacterium tuberculosis* (Schwartz, 1963). Phytodynamic agents as a group have had relatively little evaluation in animal systems.

Much attention has been focused on toxins produced in spoiled foods or feeds. Aflatoxins (Fig. 4), responsible for significant losses in the poultry industry, have been found to be highly carcinogenic. Dicoumarol and the ergot alkaloids can, in fact, be considered mycotoxins. A particularly interesting product, zearalenone, was isolated from corn infected by *Gibberella zeae* (Stob *et al.*, 1962; Urry *et al.*, 1966). This compound has anabolic and estrogenic properties, and it as well as related compounds are being evaluated for utility. Decumbin (Fig. 4) was first pro-

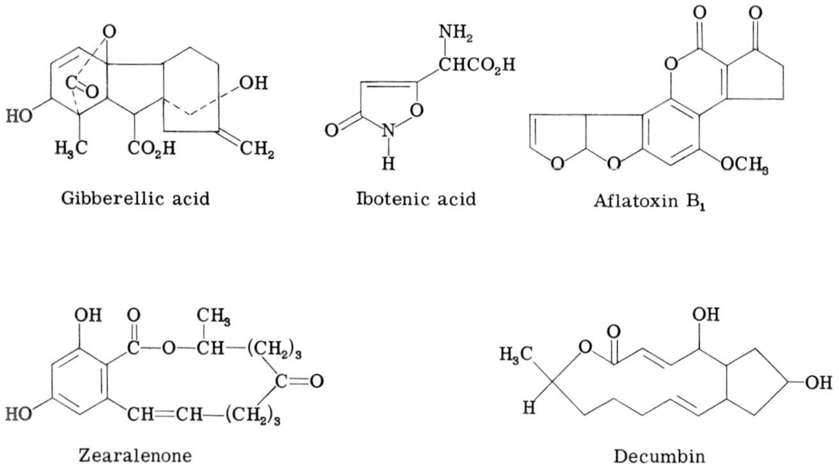

Gibberellic acid   Ibotenic acid   Aflatoxin B$_1$

Zearalenone   Decumbin

FIG. 4.

duced by a penicillium isolated from spoiled corn (Singleton *et al.*, 1958). It was subsequently isolated as the antibiotic cyanein (Betina *et al.*, 1962) and as brefeldin A (Harri *et al.*, 1963). The broad scope of biological activities of decumbin (Betina *et al.*, 1966) may be associated with the unsaturated lactone structure. A particularly unique activity is the salivation caused by slaframine, an alkaloid isolated from *Rhizoctonia leguminicola* (Rainey *et al.*, 1965; Aust and Broquist, 1965).

Microbial products with a range of chemical structures exhibit insecticidal activities. Ibotenic and tricholomic acids are isoxazole compounds isolated from flycidal or agaric mushrooms (Takemoto and Nakajima, 1964; Takemoto *et al.*, 1964). Piercidin, a product from a streptomyces, has a structure containing a pyridine nucleus and isoprenoid side chain (Takahashi *et al.*, 1965). The destruxins are peptide anhydrides (Tamura *et al.*, 1964). Toxins from the commercially important insecticidal *Bacillus thuringiensis* have properties of a protein (Cooksey, 1968) and a nucleoside or nucleotide (Beng, 1966). Novobiocin was found to be the most active of twenty-seven antibiotics tested against the female colding moth (Harris, 1967).

As should be apparent, many biological test systems have been successfully utilized in the detection or evaluation of microbial products. New methods can be expected to lead to new types of agents. Differences in strains or growth conditions of bacteria, fungi, algae, protozoa, insects, plants, and so on, can result in new characteristics in test systems and thus in the detection of new active compounds. Morphological changes of microbial, plant or animal cells may be the basis of test systems for biodynamic agents. The serotonin antagonist HO_{2135} was detected in a program in which the Magnus test with isolated guinea pig intestines was adapted to evaluating microbial filtrates (Arai and Hayama, 1962). Adipose tissue metabolism has recently been used for the detection of biological activity of microbial products (Kuo *et al.,* 1966). In the development of screening systems to be applied to crude extracts, it is important to have systems that depend on processes which are expected to be of significance in chemotherapy, require little material, can be performed readily and economically, and can be reliably quantified. A very critical aspect in the search for new active agents is the development of identification procedures to determine, as soon as possible, the novelty of an observation. This generally requires the availability of reference samples and a knowledge of their characteristics.

Frequently, after the initial work on a natural product, a limited supply precludes intensive and random biological evaluation or use for chemical manipulations. With microbial products this is generally a problem which can be resolved with additional manpower and facilities. Universities are now becoming active in the formation of centers in which research quantities of microbial products can be prepared. Previously isolated compounds should be studied and considered as candidates for biological testing and/or for conversion to new products which would be evaluated for activity. It would not be unusual if a long-known chemical oddity were to be important in a drug of the future.

Summary

Microbial products constitute the major segment of natural products used in modern medical practice. Some of the advantages and characteristics of the use of microbial systems for the detection or production of biologically active agents have been discussed. Examples have been selected to illustrate the large variety of compounds obtained from bacteria, yeasts, fungi, and algae; the diversity of activities which individual products may have in plant, animal, and insect systems; the use of these products for chemical modification studies; and the desirability for broad screening of natural products.

REFERENCES

Allman, K., and Tobin, M. S. (1965). *Proc. Soc. Exptl. Biol. Med.* **118,** 554.

Anderson, J. F. (1966). *J. Econ. Entomol.* **59,** 1476.

Anzai, K., and Suzuki, S. (1961). *J. Antibiotics (Tokyo)* **A14,** 253.

Arai, T., and Hayama, T. (1962). *Japan. J. Med. Progr.* **49,** 813.

Arai, T., Kuroda, S., Koyama, Y., Miyaki, K., and Onodera, K. (1964). *Ann. Rept. Inst. Food Microbiol. Chiba Univ.* **17,** 31.

Aust, S. D., and Broquist, H. P. (1965). *Nature* **205,** 204.

Balan, J., Ebringer, L., Nemec, P., Kovak, S., and Dobias, J. (1963). *J. Antibiotics (Tokyo)* **A16,** 157.

Barich, L. L., Nakai, T., Schwarz, J., and Barich, D. J. (1960). *Nature* **187,** 335.

Bellis, D. M., Spring, M. S., Stoker, J. R. (1967). *Biochem. J.* **103,** 202.

Beng, G. (1966). *Experientia* **22,** 81.

Betina, V., Fuska, J., Kjaer, A., Kutkova, M., Nemec, P., and Shapiro, R. H. (1966). *J. Antibiotics (Tokyo)* **A19,** 115.

Betina, B., Nemec, P., Dobias, J., and Barath, Z. (1962). *Folia Microbiol. (Prague)* **7,** 353.

Bickel, H., Hall, G. E., Keller-Schierlein, W., Prelog, V., Vischer, E., and Wettstein, A. (1960). *Helv. Chim. Acta* **43,** 2129.

Blackwood, R. K., Beereboom, J. J., Rennhard, H. H., Schach von Wittenau, M., and Stephens, C. R. (1961). *J. Am. Chem. Soc.* **83,** 2772.

Blank, H. (1965). *Am. J. Med.* **39,** 831.

Blank, H., and Roth, F. J., Jr. (1959). *Arch. Dermatol.* **79,** 259.

Block, H. S., Prasad, A., Anastasi, A., and Briggs, D. B. (1960). *J. Lab. Clin. Med.* **56,** 212.

Boothe, J. H., Morton, J., II, Petisi, J. P., Wilkinson, R. G., and Willimas, J. H. (1953). *J. Am. Chem. Soc.* **75,** 4621.

Brian, P. W., Curtis, P. J., and Hemming, H. G. (1946). *Brit. Mycol. Soc. Trans.* **29,** 173.

Brian, P. W., Hemming, H. G., and McGowan, J. C. (1945). *Nature* **115,** 637.

Brian, P. W., Wright, J. M., Stubbs, J., and Way, A. M. (1951). *Nature* **167,** 347.

Carlisle, D. B., Osborne, D. J., Ellis, P. E., and Moore, J. E. (1963). *Nature* **200,** 1967.

Cochrane, T., and Tullett, A. (1959). *Brit. Med. J.* **2,** 286.

Conover, L. H., Moreland, W. T., English, A. R., Stephens, C. R., and Pilgrim, F. J. (1953). *J. Am. Chem. Soc.* **75,** 4622.

Cooksey, K. E. (1968). *Biochem. J.* **106,** 445.

Cosar, C., and Julou, L. (1959). *Ann. Inst. Pasteur* **96,** 238.

Crawhall, J. C., Scowen, E. F., and Watts, R. W. E. (1963). *Brit. Med. J.* **1,** 588.

Cullen, S. I., and Catalano, P. M. (1967). *J. Am. Med. Assoc.* **199,** 150.

D'Arcy, P. F., Howard, E. M., Muggleton, P. W., and Townsend, S. B. (1960). *J. Pharm. Pharmacol.* **12,** 659.

De Matteis, F., Donelly, A. J., and Runge, N. J. (1966). *Cancer Res.* **26,** 721.

Despois, R., Pinnert-Sindico, S., Ninet, L., and Preud'homme, J. (1956). *Giorn. Microbiol.* **21,** 76.

Ebringer, L., Balan, J., Catar, G., Horakaua, K., and Ebringerova, J. (1965). *Exptl. Parasitol.* **16,** 182.

Eliasson, R. (1958). *Experientia* **14,** 460.

Ellis, P. E., Carlisle, D. B., and Osborne, D. J. (1965). *Science* **149,** 546.

Epstein, S. S., Andrea, J., Joshi, S., and Mantel, N. (1967). *Cancer Res.* **27,** 1900.

Euler, K. L., Tyler, V. E., Jr., and Brady, L. R. (1965). *Lloydia* **28**, 203.
Farber, S., Diamond, L. K., Mercer, R. D., Sylvester, R. F., Jr., and Wolff, J. A. (1948). *New Engl. J. Med.* **238**, 787.
Farber, Sidney (1955). *Am. J. Pathol.* **31**, 582.
Farber, Sidney (1966). *J. Am. Med. Assoc.* **198**, 826.
Finlay, A. C., Hobby, G. L., P'an, S. Y., Regna, P. P., Routien, J. B., Seeley, D. B., Shull, G. M., Sobin, B. A., Solomons, I. A., Vinson, J. W., and Kane, J. H. (1950). *Science* **111**, 85.
Flexner, L. B., Flexner, J. B., and Roberts, R. B. (1967). *Science* **155**, 1377.
Gentles, J. C. (1958). *Nature* **182**, 476.
Gershbein, L. L. (1967). *Antibiotics (Tokyo)* **A20**, 25.
Goldberg, A., Smith, J. A., and Lockhead, A. C. (1963). *Brit. Med. J.* **1**, 1270.
Harada, M., Takeuchi, M., and Katagiri, K. (1967). *J. Antibiotics (Tokyo)* **A20**, 369.
Harri, E., Loeffler, W., Sigg, H. P., Stahelin, H., and Tamm, Ch. (1963). *Helv. Chim. Acta.* **46**, 1235.
Harris, H. F. (1967). *J. Econ. Entomol.* **60**, 7.
Hori, M., Ito, E., Takita, T., Koyama, G., Takeuchi, T., and Umezawa, H. (1964). *J. Antibiotics (Tokyo)* **A17**, 96.
Horie, H. (1956). *J. Antibiotics (Tokyo)* **A9**, 168.
Hurst, E. W., and Paget, G. E. (1963). *Brit. J. Dermatol.* **75**, 105.
Hutchings, B. L., Bohonos, N., Hegsted, D. M., Elvejhem, C. A., and Peterson, W. H. (1941). *J. Biol. Chem.* **140**, 681.
Hutchings, B. L., Stokstad, E. L. R., Bohonos, N., and Slobodkin, N. H. (1944). *Science* **99**, 371.
Iizuka, H., and Naito, A. (1967). "Microbial Transformation of Steroids and Alkaloids," Univ. of Tokyo Press, Tokyo, and University Park Press, State College, Pa.
Ishizuka, M., Sawa, T., Hori, S., Takayama, H., Takeuchi, T., and Umezawa, H. (1968). *J. Antibiotics (Tokyo)* **A21**, 5.
Jaffe, I. A. (1963). *Ann. Rheumatic Diseases* **22**, 71.
Koyama, G., Maeda, K., Umezawa, H., and Itaka, Y. (1966). *Tetrahedron Letters,* 597.
Kuo, J. F., Holmlund, C. E., Dill, I. K., and Bohonos, N. (1966). *Arch. Biochem. Biophys.* **117**, 269.
Lauder, I. M., and O'Sullivan, J. G. (1958). *Vet. Record* **70**, 949.
Logeais, J., Maillard, J., Vincent, M., Delaunay, P., and Vo-Van-Tri. (1966). *Compt. Rend.* **262D**, 933.
McCormick, J. R. D., Sjolander, N. O., Hirsch, U., Jensen, E. R., and Doerschuk, A. P. (1957). *J. Am. Chem. Soc.* **79**, 4561.
Maeda, K., Osato, J., and Umezawa, H. (1953). *J. Antibiotics (Tokyo)* **A6**, 182.
Manaker, R. A., Gregory, F. J., Vining, C., and Waksman, S. A. (1954–1955). Antibiotics Annual, p. 853.
Martin, J. H., Shay, A. J., Pruess, L. M., Porter, J. N., Mowat, J. H., and Bohonos, N. (1954–1955). *Antibiotics Ann.,* p. 1020.
Mehta, S. K., Weser, E., and Sleisenger, M. H. (1967). *Proc. Soc. Exptl. Biol. Med.* **125**, 905.
Minieri, P. P., Firman, M. C., Mistretta, A. G., Abbey, A., Bricker, C. E., Rigler, N. E., and Sokol, H. (1954–1955). *Antibiotics Ann.* p. 81.
Mitscher, L. A., Martin, J. H., Miller, P. A., Shu, P., and Bohonos, N. (1966). *J. Am. Chem. Soc.* **88**, 3647.
Moeschlin, S., and Schnider, U. (1963). *New Engl. J. Med.* **269**, 57.

Nation, J. L., and Robinson, F. A. (1966). *Science* **152,** 1765.

Nicolson, G. A., Greiner, A. C., McFarlane, W. J., and Baker, R. A. (1966). *Lancet* **1,** 344.

Nimini, M. E., and Bavetta, L. A. (1965). *Science* **150,** 905.

Okami, Y., Maeda, K., and Umezawa, H. (1954). *J. Antibiotics (Tokyo)* **A7,** 53.

Oxford, A. E., Raistrick, H., and Simonart, P. (1939). *Biochem. J.* **33,** 240.

Rainey, D., Smalley, E. B., Crump, M. W., and Strong, F. M. (1965). *Nature* **205,** 203.

Raistrick, H., and Smith, G. (1963). *Biochem. J.* **30,** 1315.

Redin, G. S. (1966). *Antimicrobial Agents Chemotherap.* p. 371.

Rimington, C., Morgan, P. N., Nicholls, K., Everall, J. D., and Davies, R. R. (1963). *Lancet* **2,** 318.

Ritzmann, S. E., Coleman, S. I., and Levin, W. C. (1960). *J. Clin. Invest.* **39,** 1320.

Sage, H. J., and Vazquez, J. J. (1967). *J. Biol. Chem.* **242,** 120.

Sawa, T., Fukagawa, Y., Homma, I., Takeuchi, T., and Umezawa, H. (1967). *J. Antibiotics (Tokyo)* **A20,** 227.

Schuler, W., and Springer, G. F. (1957). *Naturwiss.* **44,** 265.

Schwartz, E. (1961). *Naturwiss.* **54,** 371.

Schwartz, E. (1963). *Bratislav. Lekarske Listy* **43,** 317.

Seeger, D. R., Smith, J. M. Jr., and Hultquist, M. E. (1947). *J. Am. Chem. Soc.* **69,** 2567.

Shorb, M. S. (1947). *J. Biol. Chem.* **169,** 455.

Singleton, V. L., Bohonos, N., and Ullstrupp, A. J. (1958). *Nature* **181,** 1072.

Springer, G. F., Wurzel, H. A., McNeal, G. M., Jr., Ansell, N. T., and Doughty, M. F. (1957). *Proc. Soc. Exptl. Biol. Med.* **94,** 404.

Stahmann, M. A., Huebner, C. F., and Link, K. P. (1941). *J. Biol. Chem.* **138,** 513.

Stephens, C. R., Murai, K., Rennhard, H. H., Conover, L. H., and Brunings, K. J. (1958). *J. Am. Chem. Soc.* **80,** 5324.

Stewart, G. T. (1958). *Brit. J. Exptl. Pathol.* **39,** 109.

Stob, M., Baldwin, R. S., Tuite, J., Andrews, F. N., and Gillette, K. G. (1962). *Nature* **196,** 1318.

Straw, R. N., Hook, J. B., Williamson, H. E., and Mitchell, C. L. (1965). *J. Pharm. Sci.* **54,** 1814.

Takahashi, N., Suzuki, A., and Tamura, S. (1965). *J. Am. Chem. Soc.* **87,** 2066.

Takemoto, T., Daigo, K., and Takagi, N. (1964). *J. Pharm. Soc. Japan* **84,** 1180.

Takemoto, T., and Nakajima, T. (1964). *Yakugaku Zasshi* **84,** 1230.

Takemoto, T., Yikobe, T., and Nakajima, T. (1964). *Yakugaku Zisshi* **84,** 1232.

Tamura, S., Kuyama, Y., Kodaira, Y., and Higashikawa, S. (1964). *Agr. Biol. Chem. (Tokyo)* **28,** 137.

Urry, W. H., Wehrmeister, H. L., Hodge, E. B., and Hidy, P. H. (1966). *Tetrahedron Letters,* 3109.

Walshe, J. M. (1960). *Lancet* **1,** 188.

Williams, D. I., Marten, R. H., and Sarkany, I. (1958). *Lancet* **2,** 1212.

Wöhler, F. (1962). *Med. Klin. (Munich)* **57,** 1370.

The Alkaloids of *Catharanthus roseus* G. Don (*Vinca rosea* L.) in Cancer Chemotherapy

Gordon H. Svoboda

Interest in a phytochemical screening program can reasonably be based on the fact that no pharmacological prototype presently utilized in modern medicine has been found outside of the plant or animal kingdoms. Because of the author's interest in and work with the higher plants, this report is so restricted.

The pitfalls inherent in a randomized selection from the more than 500,000 plant species available are obvious. While restriction of a program to one involving a randomized selection from folkloric usage decidedly narrows the scope, pitfalls are also herein inherent. It hardly seems reasonable to presume that the aborigine with his overall primitive culture would necessarily be the possessor of a sophisticated medical knowledge. Furthermore, it will soon become obvious that most of these plants would be classified as panaceas, being used in countless conditions which could not be duplicated in animals, a criterion so essential to a successful study. Consequently, only plants reported to be useful in the human situation, where conditions could be simulated in the experimental animal, would be collected.

A program may be further limited by restricting activity to the field of alkaloids. However, in the author's laboratories no such restriction has been made, even though the alkaloids allow for a seemingly more rational approach to isolation and purification problems. It is the nature of the pharmacology that determines the desirability as a medicinal product; the chemistry is incidental.

Selection of the extract to be submitted for testing also becomes an important consideration. It is the author's contention that no pure medicinal of higher plant origin elicits any overt pharmacological response other than that shown by a defatted ethanolic extract of the plant whence came the pure entity. Of course, it can always be argued that a subtle activity can be overlooked, but this is a risk, calculated or otherwise, which must be taken in even a modest screening effort.

A very likely candidate for collection was the pantropical, erect, ever-blooming herb or subshrub, *Catharanthus roseus* G. Don. Reported usage of various galenicals prepared from this Madagascan periwinkle as an oral hypoglycemic agent (Garcia, 1954) prompted its phytochemical examination in two separate laboratories, independently and unknown to each other. Neither group could substantiate this reported activity in either normal or experimentally induced hyperglycemic rabbits. However, the Canadian group, Noble, Beer, and Cutts observed a peripheral granulocytopenia and bone marrow depression in rats associated with certain fractions (Beer, 1955; Cutts *et al.*, 1957). Continued investigation led to their preparation of vincaleukoblastine (VLB) sulfate,* an alkaloid capable of producing severe leukopenia in rats (Noble *et al.*, 1958a,b; Cutts *et al.*, 1960).

The observation of experimental oncolytic activity, primarily that against the P-1534 leukemia, a transplanted acute lymphocytic leukemia, in DBA/2 mice, associated with certain extracts and fractions thereof (Table 1), prompted an intensive phytochemical research effort for the responsible principles (Svoboda, 1958; Johnson *et al.*, 1959; Svoboda *et al.*, 1959; Johnson *et al.*, 1960). Leurosine, a new dimeric alkaloid closely related chemically to VLB, was eventually obtained, along with VLB sulfate. The activity of both of these alkaloids against the P-1534 leukemia in DBA/2 mice was first demonstrated in these laboratories.

Isolation and Purification

The isolation of any alkaloid is an individual problem, but several standard techniques exist for the preliminary extraction from the crude drug and for its subsequent purification. Unfortunately, however, few plants yield single alkaloidal entities and, as a result, the main problem becomes one of separation from complex alkaloidal mixtures which are overwhelmingly contaminated with nonalkaloidal materials.

Most approaches fail to take full advantage of the relative basicities of the alkaloids during extraction, treating the problem as two separate and distinct processes, that is, isolation and purification. Consequently, classical extraction and purification techniques proved of little value in solving the problem at hand. The problems of isolation and purification

---

*The scientific names and abbreviations designated by the discoverers of these alkaloids are vincaleukoblastine (VLB), leurosine (L), leurocristine (LC) and leurosidine (LD). Their respective generic names are vinblastine (VLB), vinleurosine (VLR), vincristine (VCR) and vinrosidine (VRD).

TABLE I

ACTIVITY OF ORIGINAL EXTRACT OF WHOLE PLANT (*Catharanthus roseus*) AND
CRUDE FRACTIONS AGAINST P-1534 LEUKEMIA

Material	Dosage, mg/kg/day	Av. wt. change g, T/C	Av. survival time, days, T/C	% Increase in survival time[a]	% Indefinite survival
Defatted whole plant extract	120.0	+0.1/+2.7	25.6/14.8	73	0
Fraction A	0.5	−0.6/+1.2	26.5/19.2	38	20
Fraction B	30.0	−1.2/+1.2	24.0/19.0	25	40
Total alkaloids	6.0	+0.8/+2.9	27.7/17.2	61	20
	7.5	+0.2/+0.6	29.8/13.4	122	0
	15.0	−2.3/+0.6	20.3/13.4	51	60
	15.0	+0.3/+0.5	30.0/13.0	130	0
	75 (oral)	−1.5/+0.6	20.6/13.4	53	0

[a] P-1534 mouse leukemia in DBA/2 mice. Ten mice are intraperitoneally implanted with a suspension of malignant cells and, after 24 hr, five of these receive IP injections of the drug daily for 10 days. The maximum tolerated dose is given as predetermined using Swiss white mice. The experiment is designed so the control animals live about 15 days, and a percent prolongation due to drug is calculated. When the mice live three times the life span of the controls (about 45 days), they are considered indefinite survivors and are rechallenged without treatment to prove their susceptibility to the malignancy.

are inherently related, and the initiation of purification procedures as early as possible during extraction can usually be advantageous. Therefore the new technique of selective or differential extraction was devised (Fig. 1) (Svoboda, 1958; Svoboda et al., 1959).

As cited earlier, both leurosine and VLB were obtained during a single purification phase (Table 2). This separation was indeed a fortuitous circumstance. Leurosine was obtained by direct crystallization of a number of chromatographic fractions from methanol, while VLB base rarely crystallized from this solvent. VLB sulfate, however, readily crystallized from ethanol, while leurosine sulfate, formed from the residual base present, did not crystallize from ethanol under the conditions which prevailed.

Since the very early stages of this investigation, extensive experimental evaluation of other chromatographic fractions produced an unusually high percentage of "indefinite" survivors (Table 3). It was recognized that this activity was due to neither of the two alkaloids nor to any therapeutic combination thereof. Subjecting these fractions to any of the known purification techniques proved to be a futile experience.

Consequently, another new procedure was devised, namely, the gradient pH technique (Svoboda, 1961). Its uniqueness lies in the fact that alkaloidal separation is effected under acidic conditions, yielding leurocristine and leurosidine. The actual yield of leurocristine is approximately $3 \times 10^{-4}\%$, thereby making it the lowest of any medicinally useful compound ever produced on a commercial basis. Dose response data for the four oncolytic alkaloids are presented in Table 4.

The utilization of the new techniques of selective or differential extraction and gradient pH technology, in conjunction with column chromatography on alumina, has resulted in the isolation of some 61 alkaloids (Tables 5 to 9). While some 26 new dimeric alkaloids have been obtained, only 6, which are indole-indoline in character, have shown experimental oncolytic activity. They are vincaleukoblastine (VLB), leurosine, leurocristine, leurosidine, leurosivine (Svoboda, 1963; Svoboda et al., 1963), and rovidine (Svoboda et al., 1964). The activities of the last two alkaloids are of a relatively low order of magnitude, and their further discussion is not warranted at this time. Of these, only VLB* and leurocristine* are commercially available at present for chemotherapeutic management of human neoplasms.

---

*Vincaleukoblastine is supplied as VELBAN (vinblastine sulfate, Lilly) and leurocristine is supplied as ONCOVIN (vincristine sulfate, Lilly).

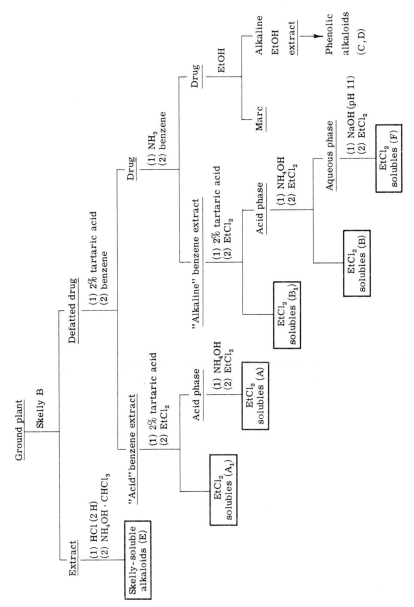

FIG. 1. Extraction scheme for *Catharanthus roseus* G. Don.

TABLE 2

CHROMATOGRAPHY OF FRACTION A

Fraction, 500 cc ea.	Eluting solvent	Compound	Wt, g	Crystallizing solvent
1	Benzene	Catharanthine	0.250	Methanol
2	Benzene	Vindolinine (as dihydrochloride)	0.210	Methanol-ether
3–19	Benzene	Ajmalicine	0.798	Methanol
20–21	Benzene	Vindoline	0.820	Ether
34–42	Benzene-chloroform (1:1)	Leurosine	0.234	Methanol
43–45	Benzene-chloroform (1:1)	Vincaleukoblastine (as sulfate)	0.126	Ethanol
46	Chloroform	Virosine	0.010	Acetone
47–52	Chloroform-methanol	Amorphous residues	—	—

TABLE 3

ANTI-P-1534 ACTIVITY OF AMORPHOUS FRACTIONS FREE OF VLB AND LEUROSINE

	Dose, (mg/kg/day)	Toxic deaths	% Prolongation	Indefinite survivors
1	15.0	5/5	0	0
	6.0	5/5	0	0
	3.0	0/5	?	5/5
2	3.0	2/5	?	3/5
3	0.6	2/5	181	0/5
4	4.5	0/5	151	1/5
5	9.0	1/5	147	2/5
6	6.0	0/5	123	4/5
7	30.0	0/5	238	4/5
8	6.0	2/5	198	2/5
9	1.9	0/5	203	4/5
10	3.8	0/5	85	4/5

Chemistry

Preliminary studies of these alkaloids shows that they were unrelated to other naturally occurring oncolytic agents, namely, podophyllin and colchicine, and that they were essentially indole and dihydroindole in character (Gorman *et al.,* 1959). Examination of such physical data as electrometric titration values, ultraviolet, infrared, and nuclear magnetic resonance spectra of the four active alkaloids indicated that they were closely related chemically and were unsymmetrical dimeric compounds. Microanalysis of leurosine and VLB, their sulfates, dihydrochlorides, and quaternary salts indicated that they were $C_{46}H_{56\text{-}58}N_4O_9$ compounds (Neuss *et al.,* 1959).

Comparison of these spectral data with those of the other naturally occurring alkaloids, particularly catharanthine and vindoline, indicated a close interrelationship between the dimers and these monomers. Furthermore, comparison of the infrared spectrum of an equimolar solution of catharanthine and vindoline with those of leurosine and VLB showed them to be virtually superimposable from 2 to 8 μ and extremely similar up to 16 μ. This observation then allowed the postulation that the dimeric alkaloids leurosine and VLB were composed of catharanthine- and vindolinelike moieties, with minor molecular modifications, linked together in some unique, heretofore unknown manner. It therefore became possible to investigate the structures of these more readily available smaller molecules and then relate this information to the dimeric compounds (Neuss and Gorman, 1961; Gorman *et al.,* 1962).

TABLE 4

DOSE RESPONSE DATA FOR ACTIVE ALKALOIDS

Alkaloid ($\cdot$ H$_2$SO$_4$)	Dosage, mg/kg/day	Toxic deaths	% Increase in survival time[a]	Indefinite survivors
Leurosine	7.5	0	0	0
	10.0	0	32	0
	11.25	0	41	0
	20.0	1	76	1
	150.0 (oral)	0	46	0
Vincaleukoblastine	0.05	0	41	0
	0.10	0	53	0
	0.30	0	70	0
	0.45	0	98	0
	0.45	1	131	0
	0.60	1	150	0
	1.5 (oral)	0	70	0
Leurocristine	0.06	0	24	0
	0.09	0	32	0
	0.12	0	49	0
	0.15	0	55	2
	0.20	1	110	2
	0.25	0	226	3
	0.30	2	?	3
	0.35	2	30	1

Leurosidine			
2.0	0	21	0
3.0	0	30	0
4.0	0	75	0
5.0	0	127	0
7.5	0	?	5
10.0	1	?	4

[a]The response of this neoplasm, maintained in the laboratories, to leurosine and VLB changed during the period 1958–1962. Leurosine now gives a more consistent activity than formerly (80% prolongation), while VLB currently gives a lower order of activity (50% prolongation) at the maximum tolerated dose. The response to leurocristine and leurosidine during the period from 1960 to the present has remained unchanged.

TABLE 5

ALKALOIDS PREVIOUSLY REPORTED

Name	Empirical formula	M.P., °C
Ajmalicine	$C_{21}H_{24}N_2O_3$	253–254
Tetrahydroalstonine	$C_{21}H_{24}N_2O_3$	230–231
Serpentine	$C_{21}H_{22}N_2O_3$	156–157
Lochnerine	$C_{20}H_{24}N_2O_2$	202–203
Reserpine[a]	$C_{33}H_{40}N_2O_9$	264–265
Akuammine[a]	$C_{22}H_{26}N_2O_4$	258–260

[a]Not encountered in the studies reported here.

TABLE 6

MONOMERIC ALKALOIDS

	Formula	pK$'_a$	M.P.,°C	Source[a]
Indoles				
1. Ammorosine	—	7.30	221–225	R
2. Catharanthine	$C_{21}H_{24}N_2O_2 \cdot H_2O$	6.8	126–128	L, R
3. Cathindine ($\cdot$ ½ H_2SO_4)	—	7.25	239–245 (dec.)	R
4. Cavincidine ($\cdot$ ½ H_2SO_4)	—	7.85	236–239 (dec.)	R
5. Cavincine ($\cdot$ ½ H_2SO_4)	$C_{20}H_{24}N_2O_2 \cdot$ ½ $H_2SO_4 \cdot$ ½ H_2O	6.90	275–277 (dec.)	L, R
6. Dihydrositsirikine	$C_{21}H_{28}N_2O_3$	—	215	L, R
7. Isositsirikine ($\cdot$ ½ H_2SO_4)	$C_{21}H_{26}N_2O_3 \cdot$ ½ H_2SO_4	—	—	L, R
8. Sitsirikine ($\cdot$ ½ H_2SO_4)	$C_{21}H_{26}N_2O_3 \cdot$ ½ H_2SO_4	7.6	239–241 (dec.)	L, R
9. Vinaspine	—	7.85	235–238	L
2-Acyl Indoles				
1. Perividine	$C_{20}H_{22}N_2O_4$	Neutral	271–279 (dec.)	L
2. Perivine	$C_{20}H_{24}N_2O_3$	7.5	180–181	L, R
3. Perosine ($\cdot$ ½ H_2SO_4)	—	7.60	219–225	L, R
Oxindoles				
1. Mitraphylline	$C_{21}H_{26}N_2O_4$	6.20	269–270	L, R

[a] R, roots; L, leaves.

TABLE 7

MONOMERIC ALKALOIDS

	Formula	pK$'_a$	M.P.,°C	Source[a]
α-Methylene indolines				
1. Akuammicine	$C_{20}H_{22}N_2O_2$	7.98	181–182	R
2. Lochnericine	$C_{21}H_{24}N_2O_3$	4.2	190–193 (dec.)	L
3. Lochneridine	$C_{20}H_{24}N_2O_3$	5.5	211–214 (dec.)	L
4. Lochnerinine	$C_{22}H_{26}N_2O_4$	—	168–169	L
5. Lochnerivine	$C_{24}H_{28}N_2O_5$	Neutral	278–280	R
6. Lochrovicine	$C_{20}H_{22}N_2O_3$	4.50	234–238	L
7. Lochrovidine	$C_{22}H_{26}N_2O_4$	5.60	213–218	L
8. Lochrovine	$C_{23}H_{30}N_2O_3$	Neutral	258–263	L
Dihydroindoles				
1. Maandrosine ($\cdot$ ½ H_2SO_4)	—	6.90	160–173	R
2. Vincolidine	$C_{23}H_{26}N_2O_3$	5.45	165–170	L
3. Vincoline	$C_{21}H_{24}N_2O_4$	6.1	230–233	L
4. Vindoline	$C_{25}H_{32}N_2O_6$	5.5	154–155	L
5. Vindolinine ($\cdot$ 2HCl)	$C_{21}H_{24}N_2O_2 \cdot$ 2HCl	7.1	210–212 (dec.)	L
6. Vindorosine	$C_{24}H_{30}N_2O_5$	—	167	L

TABLE 7 *(Continued)*
MONOMERIC ALKALOIDS

	Formula	pK'$_a$	M.P., °C	Source[a]
Miscellaneous				
1. Ammocalline	$C_{19}H_{22}N_2$	7.30	>335 (dec.)	R
2. Pericalline	$C_{18}H_{20}N_2$	8.05	196–202	R
(Tabernoschizine)				
(Apparicine)				
(Gomezine)				
3. Perimivine	$C_{21}H_{22}N_2O_4$	Indeterminate	292–293 (dec.)	L
4. Virosine	$C_{22}H_{26}N_2O_4$	5.85	258–261 (dec.)	R

[a] R, roots; L, leaves.

TABLE 8
DIMERIC INDOLE-INDOLINE ALKALOIDS

	Formula	pK'$_a$	M.P., °C	Source[a]
1. Carosine	$C_{46}H_{56}N_4O_{10}$	4.4, 5.5	214–218	L
2. Catharicine	$C_{46}H_{52}N_4O_{10}$	5.3, 6.3	231–234 (dec.)	L
3. Catharine	$C_{46}H_{52}N_4O_9 \cdot CH_3OH$	5.34	271–275 (dec.)	L
4. Desacetyl VLB ($\cdot H_2SO_4$)	$C_{44}H_{56}N_4O_8 \cdot H_2SO_4$	5.40, 6.90	>320 (dec.)	L
5. Isoleurosine	$C_{46}H_{60}N_4O_9$	4.8, 7.3	202–206 (dec.)	L
6. Leurocristine	$C_{46}H_{56}N_4O_{10}$	5.0, 7.4	218–220 (dec.)	L, R
7. Leurosidine	—	5.0, 8.8	208–211 (dec.)	L, R
8. Leurosine	$C_{46}H_{58}N_4O_9 \cdot 8H_2O$	5.5, 7.5	202–205 (dec.)	L, R
9. Leurosivine ($\cdot H_2SO_4$)	$C_{41}H_{54}N_3O_9 \cdot H_2SO_4$	4.80, 5.80	>335 (dec.)	R
10. Neoleurocristine	$C_{46}H_{56}N_4O_{12}$	4.68	188–196 (dec.)	L
11. Neoleurosidine	$C_{48}H_{62}N_4O_{11}$	5.1	219–225 (dec.)	L
12. Pleurosine	$C_{46}H_{56}N_4O_{10}$	4.4, 5.55	191–194 (dec.)	L
13. Rovidine ($\cdot H_2SO_4$)	—	4.82, 6.95	>320 (dec.)	L
14. Vinaphamine	—	5.15, 7.0	229–235	L
15. Vincaleukoblastine	$C_{46}H_{58}N_4O_9 \cdot (C_2H_5)_2O$	5.4, 7.4	201–211	L, R
16 Vincathicine ($\cdot H_2SO_4$)	—	5.10, 7.05	>320 (dec.)	L

[a] L, leaves; R, roots.

The structures of VLB and leurocristine (Fig. 2) were eventually elucidated, this having been accomplished by utilization of a combination of chemical and physical techniques, the latter mainly involving the use of mass spectrometry (Neuss *et al.,* 1964). The complete molecular structure, including the stereochemistry and the absolute configuration of leurocristine methiodide dihydrate, has recently been determined by the

TABLE 9

MISCELLANEOUS DIMERIC ALKALOIDS

	Formula	pK'$_a$	M.P., °C	Source[a]
1. Carosidine	—	Indeterminate	263–278, 283 (dec.)	L, R
2. Vincamicine	—	4.80, 5.85	224–228 (dec.)	L
3. Vincarodine	$C_{44}H_{52}N_4O_{10}$	5.8	253–256 (dec.)	L
4. Vindolicine	$(C_{25}H_{22}N_2O_6)_2$	5.4	248–251 (melts, recryst)	L
			265–267 (dec.)	
5. Vindolidine	$C_{48}H_{64}N_4O_{10}$	4.7, 5.3	244–250 (dec.)	L
6. Vinosidine	$C_{44}H_{52}N_4O_{10}$ (?)	6.80	253–257 (dec.)	R
7. Vinsedicine	(Mol. wt. 780)	4.45, 7.35	206	S
8. Vinsedine	(Mol. wt. 778)	4.65, 7.0	198–200	S

[a] L, leaves; R, roots; S, seeds.

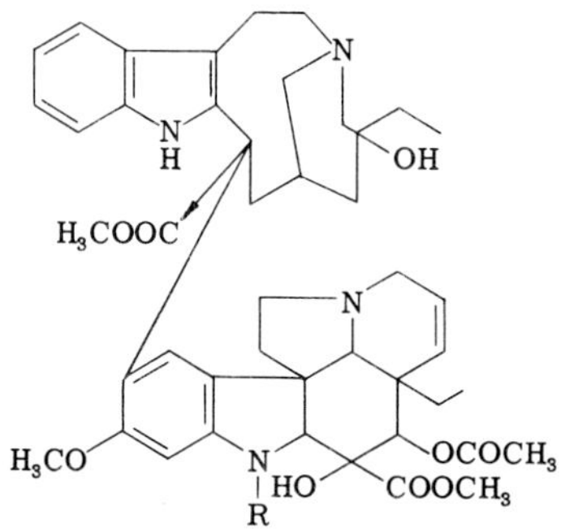

VLB: R = CH$_3$ Leurocristine: R = CHO

FIG. 2. Structures of vincaleukoblastine and leurocristine.

combination of two crystallographic methods based on the anomalous scattering of x-rays. The structures of both leurocristine and VLB have therefore been unequivocally established (Moncrief and Lipscomb, 1966). The only overt difference between these two compounds is seen in the substituent grouping on the N in the dihydroindole portion of the molecule; in the case of VLB it is N-methyl and in the case of leurocristine it is N-formyl. This minor difference in chemical structure is responsible for the differences observed in the treatment of human neoplasms.

A structure for leurosidine, C$_{46}$H$_{58}$N$_4$O$_9$, isomeric with VLB, has recently been proposed (Neuss *et al.*, 1967). The hydroxyl is at C-3′ and is probably α-oriented, rather than at C-4′ as in VLB.

This structure of leurosine has yet to be elucidated; work in this direction continues in this and other laboratories.

Biochemical and Mechanism Studies

The *in vitro* effect of the four active oncolytic alkaloids on cells appears to be that of producing metaphase arrest, and this phenomenon has been observed in varying degrees *in vivo* (Palmer *et al.*, 1960). However, differences have been observed with regard to the potency and exact type of action of the various alkaloids. Vincaleukoblastine and leurocristine produce a typical C-mitotic effect, micronuclei being frequently observed, while leurosine and leurosidine appear to produce so-called ball-metaphase rather than the classical C-mitotic effect.

The mechanism by which these alkaloids inhibit tumor growth remains unknown. The effects above-cited can be seen both *in vitro* and *in vivo* in the absence of therapeutic response, and it seems unlikely that these cytological effects alone can explain therapeutic activity.

In the Lilly Laboratories neither inhibition nor stimulation of respiration nor glycolysis of drug-sensitive tumor cells was affected by any of the active oncolytic alkaloids at levels approaching physiological concentrations. Some inhibition was realized at very high concentrations, but this was not considered particularly meaningful. Using drug-sensitive tumor systems, no interference was noted with either RNA or DNA synthesis (Johnson *et al.*, 1963).

Richards and co-workers, studying the *in vivo* effect of VLB on nucleic acid metabolism of rat bone marrow and thymus cells, observed inhibition of DNA synthesis. Little effect on RNA synthesis was noted (Richards *et al.*, 1963; Richards and Beer, 1964). Studying the effect of VLB on synthesis of nucleic acid precursors showed that it may slightly stimulate formate utilization. They also found an extensive accumulation of labeled serine and a decrease in the specific activity of adenine- and guanine-containing nucleotides. However, under similar conditions they found no such marked effect on Ehrlich ascites cells. This then poses the question of the relationship of results with normal tissue to the mechanism of inhibition with neoplastic cells. Beer had previously found that VLB was essentially ineffective in inhibiting RNA or DNA synthesis in rapidly regenerating rat liver (Beer, 1961).

Creasey and Markiw (1964a,b) noted inhibition of soluble RNA synthesis in Ehrlich ascites tumors with no interference in the synthesis of ribosomal RNA. They further found that vincaleukoblastine, leurocristine, and colchicine were alike in this respect. The latter observation might well indicate that they are studying the biochemistry of mitotic arrest and not the oncolytic mechanism. To date, no definitive solution to the problem of the mechanism of action of these alkaloids can be given (Creasey, in press).

Clinical Studies

Only two of the active dimeric alkaloids, vincaleukoblastine and leurocristine, have undergone extensive clinical trial. Both have been found to be effective in the treatment of a number of human neoplasms, and information about their possible usefulness has been more completely reviewed elsewhere (Johnson *et al.*, 1963). To date, there is no clinical evidence of cross-resistance with radiation or with the other oncolytic agents presently in use. Despite only minor structural differences, the clinical utility of these agents seems to differ. A summary of the comparison of their clinical characteristics as understood in December, 1966, is presented in Table 10; neoplasms responsive to treatment are shown in Tables 11 and 12.

Vincaleukoblastine has been shown to be effective in the treatment of chorionepithelioma, Hodgkin's disease and other lymphomas, as well as in a variety of other neoplasms. The most striking feature observed for leurocristine is its ability to induce complete hematological remission of the acute leukemias of childhood, both lymphocytic and myelogenous. Another interesting response is that reported for carcinoma of the cervix, a neoplasm singularly nonresponsive to chemotherapy.

It has been demonstrated that combinations of chemotherapeutic agents produced a higher initial complete remission rate as well as remissions of longer duration, particularly in children with acute leukemia (Frei, 1964; Freireich *et al.*, 1964, 1965). In contrast to other chemotherapeutic compounds, leurocristine usually has little depressive effect on the bone marrow, and it is thought to be an ideal agent to use in combination therapy. It has been used in full therapeutic doses in combination with such myelosuppressive agents as amethopterin and 6-mercaptopurine in acute leukemia and with the antimetabolities and alkylating agents in Hodgkins' disease and metastatic carcinoma. Combinations of four antileukemic agents, leurocristine, amethopterin, 6-mercaptopurine, and prednisone, have been reported as having reduced the leukemic cell population in patients with acute leukemia to unprecedently low levels.

Clinical experience in the United States with leurosine has been limited (Neuss *et al.*, 1964; Gailani *et al.*, 1966). Therapeutic effect without toxicity has been demonstrated in one case of Hodgkin's disease. Of 41 other patients with various neoplastic conditions treated to date, only 2 have exhibited partial tumor shrinkage with clinical improvement, but in neither case was the response of sufficient extent or of a long enough duration to be considered significant by the usual criteria. These limited clinical data do not allow for any decision to be made regarding whether or not useful activity can be expected with significant frequency.

The experience in France has involved some 50 patients (Mathe *et al.*, 1965; Amiel *et al.*, 1966). They included Hodgkin's disease, 15; mycosis fungoides, 1; acute lymphoblastic leukemia, 19; lymphoblastosarcoma, 15. This study indicated that leurosine did not appear to possess any pronounced specificity for a particular cellular series. Two apparently complete remissions of 3-month duration were observed in Hodgkin's disease. One apparently complete remission of 45 days duration was observed in acute lymphoblastic leukemia. The best indication for the use of leurosine was in the treatment of lymphoblastosarcoma, good re-

TABLE 10

COMPARISON OF THE CLINICAL CHARACTERISTICS OF VINCALEUKOBLASTINE SULFATE AND
LEUROCRISTINE SULFATE AS UNDERSTOOD IN DECEMBER 1966

	VLB sulfate	Leurocristine sulfate
Weekly intravenous dose for solid tumors	0.10–0.30 mg/kg, average 0.15 mg/kg	0.01–0.05 mg/kg, average 0.025 mg/kg
Weekly intravenous dose for acute childhood leukemia	Benefit reported in some cases	Approx. 0.10 mg/kg
Leukopenia	Dose limiting factor	Uncommon Rarely limits dosage
Anemia and thrombocytopenia	Rarely occur	Rarely occur
Neuromuscular manifestations	Rarely occur Reversible	Dose limiting factor Reversible
Constipation	Rarely occurs	Almost invariable if preventive medication not used

TABLE 11

NEOPLASMS REPORTED RESPONSIVE TO TREATMENT WITH VINCALEUKOBLASTINE SULFATE

Monocytic leukemia
Lymphomas
    Hodgkin's disease
    Lymphosarcoma
    Mycosis fungoides
    Reticulum cell sarcoma
Carcinomas
    Carcinomas of the breast which are unresponsive to appropriate endocrine surgery and hormonal therapy.
    Carcinomas of the bronchus
    Some carcinomas of the skin and mucosae, including those of the mouth, palate, tongue, paranasal sinuses, anus, vagina, bladder, and
        urethra
Seminoma and embryonal tumors of the testis
Methotrexate-resistant choriocarcinoma
Letterer-Siwe disease (Histiocytosis x)

TABLE 12

NEOPLASMS REPORTED RESPONSIVE TO TREATMENT WITH LEUROCRISTINE SULFATE

Acute leukemia
Lymphomas
  Hodgkin's disease
  Lymphosarcoma
  Reticulum cell sarcoma
Carcinomas
  Carcinomas of the breast which are unresponsive to appropriate endocrine surgery and
    hormonal therapy; response usually more rapid than with VLB
  Carcinomas of the cervix
  Carcinomas of the prostate
Choriocarcinoma
Primary brain tumors (Astrocytomas)
Neuroblastoma
Rhabdomyosarcoma
Wilm's tumor

---

sults having been achieved in one-third of the cases, one patient having been in complete remission for more than a year. On the whole, however, the frequency and duration of remission in the diseases treated were distinctly inferior to those which can be achieved, depending on the nature of the cases, with VLB, leurocristine, or the other antimitotic agents.

Noble and co-workers have made the observation in tissue culture studies that leurosine is capable of lysing a culture of malignant cells and is superior to both VLB and leurocristine in this activity, this phenomenon having been observed when the alkaloidal sulfates were added to the culture in saline. However, in the presence of adult human plasma the lytic activity of leurosine was completely inhibited, while that of VLB and leurocristine was unaffected. Fetal plasma did not inhibit the activity of leurosine. Noble has found that the inhibitory factor of plasma resided in the globulins of the adult human plasma. Obviation of this protein inactivation in the human situation has not been accomplished; this task presents a real clinical challenge.

Structural Modifications

The elucidation of the structures of VLB and leurocristine allows for a rational and systematic approach to their synthesis from some of the more abundantly occurring alkaloids, either by modification of other dimers or by condensation of the appropriate monomeric entities. Structure-activity relationships can also now be logically pursued.

Figure 3 illustrates the approach which has been taken to provide various derivatives of VLB. Reduction of the double bond in the dihydroindole portion of the molecule yields dihydro VLB, which, though it is less toxic than VLB, is also less potent, being only approximately one-third as active as the parent compound against the P-1534 leukemia. Noble *et al.* (1967) found it to possess a relatively low order of antitumor activity against the Ehrlich and L5178Y ascitic tumors. The response differed from VLB, suggesting that this derivative may possess a different mechanism of action. Further reduction yields the hexahydro derivative which is devoid of oncolytic activity. The other derivatives shown are also inactive. However, it may be of interest to state that, while desacetyl VLB is inactive, it is also approximately ten times as toxic as VLB.

Certain aspects of this work had indicated that the acetyl group was important for activity in our animal screens. Varying the ester function in the dihydroindole portion of the VLB molecule has resulted in the preparation of several interesting series of compounds (Hargrove, 1964; Johnson *et al.*, 1965); their activities are presented in Tables 13 and 14.

In the series of 4-acyl analogs of VLB the chloroacetyl derivative appeared to possess the most desirable experimental oncolytic activity and consideration was given to its being tested clinically. However, when

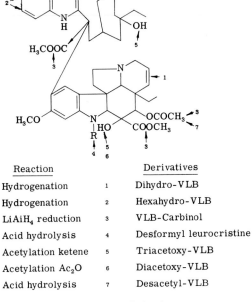

Reaction		Derivatives
Hydrogenation	1	Dihydro-VLB
Hydrogenation	2	Hexahydro-VLB
LiAiH$_4$ reduction	3	VLB-Carbinol
Acid hydrolysis	4	Desformyl leurocristine
Acetylation ketene	5	Triacetoxy-VLB
Acetylation Ac$_2$O	6	Diacetoxy-VLB
Acid hydrolysis	7	Desacetyl-VLB

FIG. 3. VLB derivatives.

the halogen atom was replaced with an amine, yielding a series of α-aminoacetyl analogs, a number of compounds with even greater oncolytic activity were produced. The most interesting compound of this series is desacetyl VLB-4 (N,N-dimethylaminoacetate). As can be seen from the data in Table 14, it is capable of equaling the absolute result of leurocristine, although its optimum dosage is 20-fold greater. It does, however, possess a better therapeutic index.

Experiments indicate that it is apparently equally effective by either oral or parenteral routes. Furthermore, it is effective against intracranial P-1534 leukemia. While the intracranial implant resembles but is not identical with CNS leukemia, this system can serve as an experimental model in which the possibility of crossing the blood-brain barrier exists.

While the derivatives studied represent α-aminoacetyl analogs, data are presently unavailable for the β-analogs.

TABLE 13
4-ACYL ANALOGS OF VLB

Derivative	Dose, mg/kg/day	% Prolongation
Propionyl	0.55	77 + 1 survivor
Butyryl	0.50	30
Isobutyryl	0 90	35
Phenylacetyl	2.0	25
Benzoyl	0.75	32
Chloroacetyl	0.35	127
Dichloroacetyl	0.30	37
Cyanoacetyl	0.30	31
Acetyl (VLB)	0.35	25–30

TABLE 14
4-AMINOACETYL ANALOGS OF VLB

Derivative	Dose, mg/kg/day	% Prolongation
Methylaminoacetyl	3.0	187 + 3 survivors
Dimethylaminoacetyl	5.0	5 survivors
Methylcyclopropylaminoacetyl	3.75	201 + 4 survivors
Diethylaminoacetyl	1.5	Ineffective
Pyrrolidinoacetyl	7.5	100
Piperidinoacetyl	3.0	24
Morpholinoacetyl	15.0	127
Piperazinoacetyl	1.5	Ineffective
N-Methylpiperazinoacetyl	15.0	30
N-Phenylpiperazinoacetyl	1.5	Ineffective
β-Hydroxyethylpiperazinoacetyl	15.0	78

The four naturally occurring oncolytic alkaloids and the dimethylglycyl derivative (vinglycinate sesquisulfate) have similar experimental tumor spectra but with some differences, the most striking being the activity of leurocristine and leurosidine against several AKR tumors (Table 15).

Early clinical observations with this derivative revealed some therapeutic efficacy (Armstrong *et al.*, 1965, 1967). However, in further clinical studies (59 patients were treated) nothing dramatically or uniquely beneficial was observed. On the other hand, stability problems were encountered. In addition, serious eye problems (corneal and lens changes) were observed in 2 patients on long-term therapy. Although causal relationship was not definitely documented, clinical trial with this compound has been discontinued (Jansen, personal communication).

Diuretic Activity

A high degree of diuretic activity in saline-loaded rats has recently been established for two of the monomeric alkaloids, catharanthine and vindolinine, lesser activity being observed with two others (Svoboda *et al.*, 1964a). Comparison of their activity with that of the thiazides is shown in Table 16.

This discovery prompted an extension of this investigation to related alkaloids, as well as to certain derivatives of the parent active compounds (Gorman *et al.*, 1964). The activity was found to be quite specific for the ring systems of the compounds listed in Table 17 and to be defined by rigid structural requirements within a given series.

Although the activity of many of the alkaloids investigated compares favorably with that of the thiazides, they are structurally unrelated. This then uncovers a new class of compounds which should be investigated either *per se* or via structural modifications to discover new utilizable diuretic agents.

Hypoglycemic Activity

The elusive hypoglycemic activity has recently been reported in these laboratories as being associated with a number of the pure alkaloids (Svoboda *et al.*, 1964b). In the past, both experimental and limited clinical investigations of various alkaloidal and nonalkaloidal fractions have proved to be disappointingly negative (Farnsworth, 1961). Evidently because of the inherent toxicities of the crude extracts or fractions tested, it was not possible to obtain experimental verification.

TABLE 15

COMPARISON OF ANTITUMOR ACTIVITY OF ACTIVE ALKALOIDS AND DERIVATIVE

Tumor	Host	Compounds[a]				
		VLB	L	LD	LC	DMG
Lilly mammary	DBA/1	−	−	−	+[b]	−
Sarcoma 180	CAF₁	−	−	−	−	−
Adenocarcinoma 755	C₅₇BL/6	−	−	−	+	−
C-1498 leukemia	C₅₇BL/6	−	−	−	−	−
P-1534 leukemia	DBA/2	+[b]	++	+++[b]	+++	++
L-1210 leukemia	DBA/2	−	+	−	−	+
Ridgeway osteogenic sarcoma	AKR	−	−	++	++	−
Mecca lymphosarcoma	AKR	−	−	−	−	−
AKR leukemia	AKR	−	−	−	++	+
Ehrlich ascites	Cox std	+++	++	−	+++	+++
Freund ascites	CAF₁	++	+	++	+++	+++
S-180 ascites	CAF₁	+++	++	+	+++	+++

Tumor	Host	VLB	L	LD	LC	VLB-4
B-82A leukemia	C58	++	++	-	++	++
Walker carcinosarcoma 256	Rat	+	+	-	+	+
Lilly mammary	C3H	-	-	-	-	-
Gardner lymphosarcoma	C3H	-	-	-	+	+
S-91 melanoma	DBA/1	-	-	-	-	-
X-5563 myeloma	C3H	-	-	-	-	-
High malignancy clone	C3H	-	+	-	-	-
Lilly rhabdomyosarcoma	Rat	++	+	-	+	++
EO-771 adenocarcinoma	$C_{57}BL/6$	N.D.	-	N.D.[c]	N.D.	++
Friend leukemia[d]	DBA/2	N.D.	-	++	+	N.D.

[a] VLB, vincaleukoblastine (·sulfate); L, leurosine (·sulfate); LD, leurosidine (·sulfate); LC, leurocristine (·sulfate); DMG, dimethyl glycyl derivative, desacetyl VLB-4 (N,N-dimethylaminoacetate) (·sesquisulfate).

[b] +, 30–50%; ++, 50–100% inhibition of solid tumors or prolongation of survival time in leukemias; +++, 100% inhibition of solid tumors or > 100% prolongation of survival time in leukemias.

[c] N.D., not done.

[d] Atypical virus-free line.

TABLE 16

DIURETIC RESPONSE TO ALKALOIDS AND THIAZIDES[a]

Compound	Dose mg/kg	Urine volume, ml	Increase over controls		
			Na	K	Cl
				μ equivalents	
Vincolidine	36	0.85[b]	263.5	Insignificant from controls	273.0
Catharanthine (·HCl)	5	0	0	0	—
	50	4.20	326.8	102.0	355.5
Lochrovicine	3.6	1.77	146.8	170.4	195.4
	36.0	8.32	634.3	379.4	708.6
Vindolinine (·2HCl)	5	1.72	184.0	53.7[b]	209.3
	50	10.78	1156.0	544.8	1344.2
Chlorothiazide	5	1.35	210.9	66.1[b]	240.8
	50	3.57	655.3	141.2	666.5
Dihydrochlorothiazide	0.5	2.90	390.0	58.5[b]	444.0
	5.0	4.55	861.5	256.7	933.8
Cyclothiazide	0.05	1.65	337.8	47.8[b]	345.8
	0.50	4.96	799.1	195.0	912.8
	5.0	11.00	1735.4	520.8	1825.7

[a] Female rats, weighing 180–250 g and fasted overnight, were orally loaded with normal saline solution, 15 mg/kg. Included in this solution, the test compound was administered as a suspension in 1% acacia. Control animals received only the 1% acacia in saline. The animals were then placed into metabolism cages, and the urine was collected over a 5-hr period. Eight rats, housed two per cage, were used for each dose level. At the end of the test period the urine volume was recorded for each cage. Sodium and potassium were determined on the urines of each cage by flame photometry utilizing an internal lithium standard. Chloride was determined amperometrically by means of a Cotlove chlorido-meter.

[b] Values not significant at the 95% limits of confidence.

TABLE 17

DIURETIC RESPONSE TO DERIVATIVES AND RELATED ALKALOIDS

Name	Dose, mg/kg	Urine volume, ml	Increase or decrease from control		
			Na	K	CL
			μ equivalents		
Ajmalicine	5.0	−0.85	−18.5	−80.5	−99.0
	50.0	−0.55	−220.8[a]	−78.8	−303.5[a]
Ajmaline · HCl	5.0	−0.60	−22.2	−25.2	−13.2
	50.0	3.40[a]	429.0[a]	50.0	445.2[a]
N-Allylperivinol	5.0	−2.75	−116.2	−158.5	−70.5
	50.0	−4.25[a]	−177.5[a]	−265.0[a]	−310.8[a]
Ammorosine	36.0	−2.20	−256.2[a]	−114.2	−311.8[a]
Carbomethoxy dihydrocleavamine · HCl	50.0	1.80	259.5[a]	47.0[a]	329.8[a]
Cleavamine · HCl	5.0	−1.45	−119.0	−31.8	−124.2
	50.0	−2.75[a]	−317.8[a]	−66.2	−384.0[a]
Conopharyngine · HCl	5.0	0.73	−92.2	103.5	−38.5
	25.0	0.30	−111.2	54.0	−31.2
Coronaridine · HCl	5.0	0.53	135.7	17.4	163.2
	50.0	11.71[a]	1228.4[a]	302.7[a]	1627.7[a]
Descarbomethoxy catharanthine	5.0	−1.25	−148.5[a]	−52.5[a]	−59.2
	50.0	−2.20[a]	−495.8[a]	−113.8[a]	−575.8[a]
Dihydrocatharanthine · HCl	5.0	1.45	170.0	24.0	99.0
	50.0	All animals died on test			
Dihydrovindolinine · HCl	3.8	0.60	192.0	−12.8	186.2
	37.5	7.80[a]	1132.8[a]	111.2	1098.8[a]
Epi-ibogamine	5.0	−0.20	−31.5	−8.5	21.5
	50.0	1.30	−133.2	11.8	−171.5

TABLE 17 (continued)

Name	Dose, mg/kg	Urine volume, ml	Increase or decrease from control		
			Na	K	CL
				μ equivalents	
N-Ethyl-O-acetylvindolininol	0.9	-1.35	-186.5[a]	-79.0[a]	-190.2[a]
	9.0	-1.60	-253.2[a]	-90.5[a]	-204.0[a]
Ibogamine	5.0	0	49.0	0.8	13.2
	50.0	9.45[a]	461.0[a]	154.2[a]	134.5
Isoperivine · HCl	2.9	-3.5	-318.2[a]	-254.0	-222.8
	29.0	-0.15	62.8	-160.2	-50.2
Isoperivinol · HCl	5.0	-0.10	54.2	-33.0	11.8
	50.0	4.35[a]	368.8[a]	95.5	289.0[a]
Isovindolinine · 2HCl	5.0	-2.2[a]	-136.2[a]	16.8	-141.8[a]
	50.0	2.2	159.2	221.8	248.2
Isovindolininol	3.75	0.15	-2.25	2.0	-26.0
	37.5	1.0	175.0	91.8	157.2
Lochnerine	3.6	-1.32	-35.2	-5.6	-46.4
	36.0	-2.2[a]	-210.7[a]	-89.7[a]	-268.0[a]
Lochrovidine	3.6	-0.23	65.8	20.7	-5.2
	36.0	0.82	56.6	21.7	-2.7
Mitraphylline	36.0	0.40	195.2	-152.2[a]	156.8
N-Methylvindolininol	3.75	0.60	58.0	36.8	49.5
	37.5	2.0	98.0	139.8	186.8
Perivine sulfate	5.0	-0.15	-27.5	-0.8	-54.0
	50.0	0	-168.2[a]	190.5[a]	-132.8
Quebrachidine	5.0	0.80	17.2	2.8	83.5
	50.0	0.32	-141.3	-28.4	-183.8

	Dose				
Sitsirikine · ½ H_2SO_4	5.0	1.60^a	-263.1^a	-37.6	-273.6^a
	50.0	-2.05^a	-334.5^a	-62.2^a	-344.2^a
Tabernanthine	5.0	-2.00	-124.5	-76.0	-116.2
	50.0	13.95^a	1076.5^a	482.8^a	832.5^a
Tetrahydroalstonine	5.0	-0.20	27.8	-10.0	45.2
	50.0	-0.90	44.0	87.8	60.5
Vindoline	1.0	-0.35	99.0	20.2	54.8
	10.0	0.15	56.2	-8.8	54.5
Vindolininol	3.75	-1.93^a	-250.3^a	22.9	-239.0^a
	37.5	-2.25^a	-285.5^a	-49.8	-237.0^a
Virosine	3.6	-0.97	-44.2	-12.1	-103.2
	36.0	-0.97	42.4	-13.6	-51.7
Voachalotinol	5.0	-0.25	20.8	47.5	-15.0
	50.0	0.70	236.8^a	23.8	203.2^a
Voacangine · HCl	5.0	2.0^a	-40.5	395.8^a	47.5
	25.0	11.85^a	586.0^a	1790.8^a	830.0^a
Vobasinol · HCl	5.0	0.70	111.8	9.2	3.8
	50.0	-0.25	7.2	-73.0	-124.2

[a]Values which show a difference from controls significant at 95% limits of confidence.

TABLE 18

HYPOGLYCEMIC ACTIVITY OF *C. roseus* ALKALOIDS AND STANDARDS[a]

Alkaloid	Mean change in blood glucose, mg/100 ml					Activity[b]
	1 hr	2 hrs	3 hrs	5 hrs	7 hrs	
Ajmalicine	+16	+21	+28	+ 4	+15	—
Catharanthine (·HCl)	+20	+ 5	+ 6	−11	−14	±
Leurosine (·H$_2$SO$_4$)	+ 6	− 7	−22	−28	−31	++
Lochnerine	+ 2	− 3	−10	− 9	−20	+
Perivine	+ 4	+ 4	+14	+11	− 3	—
Sitsirikine (·½ H$_2$SO$_4$)	+57	+58	+32	+18	+10	—
Tetrahydroalstonine	+15	+ 3	0	− 8	−17	±
Vincathicine (·H$_2$SO$_4$)	+ 1	− 3	+12	− 4	+ 2	—
Vindoline	−11	−21	−15	−17	−12	+
Vindolinine (·2HCl)	+11	− 3	−12	−24	−30	++
Acetohexamide[c]	−30	−39	−37	−31	−26 (18 rats)	+++
Tolbutamide[d]	−28	−30	−25	−10	+ 2 (18 rats)	+

[a] The alkaloids were tested for hypoglycemic activity in six normal rats. The rats were fasted for 18 hr and, after a control blood sample had been taken for glucose determination, the compound was administered orally in a dose of 100 mg/kg. Blood glucose was then measured with a Technicon AutoAnalyzer at 1, 2, 3, 5, and 7 hr after administration, the mean changes in blood glucose from the control values being recorded.

[b] Activity: (−) inactive; (±) questionable; (+) slight; (++) moderate; (+++) strong.

[c] *N*-ϕ-acetylphenylsulfonyl-*N′*-cyclohexylurea (Dymelor, Lilly).

[d] *N*-(Toluenesulfonyl)-*N′*-*n*-butylurea (Orinase, Upjohn).

TABLE 19

HYPOGLYCEMIC ACTIVITY OF DERIVATIVES AND RELATED ALKALOIDS

Alkaloid	Mean change in blood glucose, mg./100 ml.					Activity[a]
	1 hr	2 hrs	3 hrs	5 hrs	7 hrs	
Ajmaline (·HCl)	+ 8	+ 4	+ 1	− 2	− 7	−
Allyl perivinol	+15	+11	+ 2	+ 2	−10	−
Cleavamine	+11	+ 6	+11	−10	− 6	−
Coronaridine (·HCl)	+ 9	+11	− 2	−21	−33	+
Desacetylvindoline	+ 6	+ 5	+ 3	−15	−20	±
Dihydrocatharanthine	+ 8	+ 4	−19	−23	−31	+ (toxic)
Dihydrovindolinine (·2HCl)[b]	− 3	− 2	−10	−21	−20	+
Epi-ibogamine	+27	+23	+15	+27	+11	−
Ibogamine[c]	+ 8	+17	+ 5	− 4	−19	±[a]
Isovindolinine (·2HCl)[c]	−11	−23	−25	−28	−34	++[a]
Reserpine	+11	+20	+30	+47	+50	−

[a] Activity: (−) inactive; (±) questionable; (+) slight; (++) moderate.
[b] Kindly supplied by Dr. Jean Le Men, l'Ecole Nationale de Medecine et de Pharmacie, Reims (Marne), France.
[c] 50 mg/kg.
[d] Toxic at 100 mg/kg.

Our preliminary results have indicated that catharanthine ($\cdot$ HCl), leurosine ($\cdot$ H$_2$SO$_4$), lochnerine, tetrahydroalstonine, vindoline, and vindolinine ($\cdot$ 2HCl) produce varying degrees of blood-sugar lowering (Table 18). This activity is characterized by its slow onset but relatively long duration of action. A number of related alkaloids and derivatives were subsequently tested, and the results are given in Table 19.

It is interesting to note that several of the alkaloids and derivatives which effect a hypoglycemic response also produce significant diuresis, namely, vindolinine ($\cdot$ 2HCl), dihydrovindolinine ($\cdot$ 2HCl), and coronaridine ($\cdot$ HCl). With the exception of lochnerine, which is antidiuretic in action, the others exert no diuretic response. No physiological correlation or explanation is presently forthcoming.

These alkaloids are all structurally different from the sulfonylureas and therefore represent new leads in this area of research. It is highly probable that the continued use of various galenical preparations of *Catharanthus roseus* in indigenous medicine as oral hypoglycemic agents is not completely without merit.

Summary

An intensive phytochemical investigation of the pantropical plant *Catharanthus roseus* G. Don (*Vinca rosea* L.) has resulted in the isolation of six new alkaloids which possess demonstrable experimental oncolytic activity. Two of these complex indole-indoline alkaloids, vincaleukoblastine (VLB) and leurocristine (LC), are commercially available for the chemotherapeutic treatment of a variety of human neoplasms.

The successful isolation and purification of these entities resulted from two new contributions to alkaloid technology — selective or differential extraction and the gradient pH technique. The scope of utility of these new procedures is not presently known.

The P-1534 leukemia, a strain-specific, transplantable, acute lymphocytic leukemia, carried in DBA/2 mice, served not only as a bioassay for obtaining these alkaloids but also for predicting clinical activity.

The metabolic pathways by which these compounds work are presently unknown. It is quite probable that their mechanisms of action differ not only from those of other known antineoplastic agents but from those within the group as well.

Structures for VLB, leurocristine, and leurosidine have been defined, allowing for a rational approach to structural modification and an understanding of structure-activity relationships.

Two other experimental pharmacological activities, diuretic and hypoglycemic, have been found to be associated with a number of alkaloids obtained from this plant. Thus the common Madagascan periwinkle appears to be a cornucopia of the plant kingdom.

Acknowledgments

The author would like to thank Messrs. A. T. Oliver and D. R. Bedwell for technical assistance and Miss E. D. Liljeblad for aid in preparing the manuscript. The biological work described was done in cooperation with Drs. I. S. Johnson, J. P. Burnett, Jr., R. H. Tust, and M. A. Root; the chemical work in cooperation with Drs. M. Gorman, N. Neuss, and W. W. Hargrove. Clinical data were provided by Drs. J. G. Armstrong and C. J. Jansen, Jr.

REFERENCES

Amiel, M., Bernard, J., Bessis, M., Dreyfus, B., Najean, Y., Seligmann, M., and Pequignot, H. (1966). Acquisitions recentes dans la chimiotherapie des cancers. *Presse Med.* **74**, 1683–1686.

Armstrong, J. G., Dyke, R. W., Fouts, P. J., Hawthorne, J. J., Jansen, C. J., Jr. and Peabody, Initial clinical experience with a modified vinblastine molecule. *Proc. Am. Assoc. Cancer Res.* **6**, 3.

Armstrong, J. G., Dyke, R. W., Fouts, P. J., Hawthorne, J. J., Jansen, C. J., and Peabody, A. M. (1967). Initial clinical experience with vinglycinate sulfate, a molecular modification of vinblastine. *Cancer Res.* **27**, 221–227.

Beer, C. T. (1955). The leucopenic action of extracts of *Vinca rosea. British Empire Cancer Campaign, 33rd Ann. Rept.* pp. 487–488.

Beer, C. T. (1961). Biochemical studies with vincaleukoblastine. Canadian Cancer Conference, Vol. 4, pp. 355–361. Academic Press, New York.

Creasey, W. A. (In press). Modifications in biochemical pathways produced by the *Vinca* alkaloids.

Creasey, W. A., and Markiw, M. E. (1964a). Biochemical effects of the Vinca alkaloids. I. Effects of vinblastine on nucleic acid synthesis in mouse tumor cells. *Biochem. Pharmacol.* **13**, 135–142.

Creasey, W. A., and Markiw, M. E. (1964b). Biochemical effects of the Vinca alkaloids. II. A comparison of the effects of colchicine, vinblastine and vincristine on the synthesis of ribonucleic acids in Ehrlich ascites carcinoma cells. *Biochem. Biophys. Acta* **87**, 601–609.

Cutts, J. H., Beer, C. T., and Noble, R. L. (1957). Effects on hematopoeisis in rats of extracts of *Vinca rosea. Rev. Canad. Biol.* **16**, 476.

Cutts, J. H., Beer, C. T., and Noble, R. L. (1960). Biological properties of vincaleukoblastine, an alkaloid in *Vinca rosea* L., with reference to its antitumor action. *Cancer Res.* **20**, 1023–1031.

Farnsworth, N. R. (1961). The pharmacognosy of the periwinkles: *Vinca* and *Catharanthus. Lloydia* **24**, 105–138.

Frei, E., III (1964). Vinca alkaloids in the treatment of neoplastic disease in man. *Lloydia* **27**, 364–367.

Freireich, E. J., Karon, M., Flatow, F., and Frei, E., III (1965). Effect of intensive cyclic chemotherapy (BIKE) on remission duration in acute lymphocytic leukemia. *Proc. Am. Assoc. Cancer Res.* **6,** 20.

Freireich, E. J., Karon, M., and Frei, E., III (1964). Quadruple combination therapy (VAMP) for acute lymphocytic leukemia of childhood. *Proc. Am. Assoc. Cancer Res.* **5,** 20.

Gailani, S. D., Armstrong, J. G., Carbone, P. P., Tan, C., and Holland, J. F. (1966). Clinical trial of vinleurosine sulfate (NSC-90636): a new drug derived from *Vinca rosea* Linn. *Cancer Chemother. Rept.* **50,** 95–103.

Garcia, F. (1954). A botany symposium on medicinal plants. *Proc. 8th Pacific Sci. Congr. Natl. Res. Council Philippines* **IVA,** 182–194.

Gorman, M., Neuss, N., and Biemann, K. (1962). Vinca alkaloids. X. The structure of vindoline. *J. Am. Chem. Soc.* **84,** 1058–1059.

Gorman, M., Neuss, N., and Svoboda, G. H. (1959). *Vinca* alkaloids. IV. Structural features of leurosine and vincaleukoblastine, representatives of a new type of indole-indoline alkaloids. *J. Am. Chem. Soc.* **81,** 4745–4746.

Gorman, M., Tust, R. H., Svoboda, G. H., and Le Men, J. (1964). Alkaloids of *Vinca rosea* (*Catharanthus roseus*). XXVI. Structure-activity studies of some alkaloids and their derivatives. *Lloydia* **27,** 214–219.

Hargrove, W. W. (1964). Preparation and activities of chemically modified dimeric Catharanthus alkaloids. *Lloydia* **27,** 340–345.

Jansen, C. J., Jr. Personal communication.

Johnson, I. S., Armstrong, J. G., Gorman, M., and Burnett, J. P., Jr. (1963). The Vinca alkaloids: a new class of oncolytic agents. *Cancer Res.* **23,** 1390–1427.

Johnson, I. S., Hargrove, W. W., and Wright, H. F. (1965). Selection of a clinically active substance from a series of chemically produced ester analogs of vinblastine. *Proc. Am. Assoc. Cancer Res.* **6,** 33.

Johnson, I. S., Wright, H. F., and Svoboda, G. H. (1959). Experimental basis for clinical evaluation of anti-tumor principles derived from *Vinca rosea* Linn. *J. Lab. Clin. Med.* **54,** 830.

Johnson, I. S., Wright, H. F., Svoboda, G. H., and Vlantis, J. (1960). Antitumor principles derived from *Vinca rosea* Linn. I. Vincaleukoblastine and leurosine. *Cancer Res.* **20,** 1016–1022.

Mathe, G., Schneider, M., Band, P., Amiel, J.-L., Schwarzenberg, L., Cattan, A., and Schlumberger, J. R. (1965). Leurosine sulfate (NSC-90636) in the treatment of Hodgkin's disease, acute lymphoblastic leukemia and lymphoblastic lymphosarcoma. *Cancer Chemother. Rept.* **49,** 47–49.

Moncrief, J. W., Lipscomb, W. N. (1966). Structure of leurocristine methiodide dihydrate by anomalous scattering methods; relation to leurocristine (vincristine) and vincaleukoblastine (vinblastine). *Acta Cryst.* **21,** 322–331.

Neuss, N., and Gorman, M. (1961). The structure of catharanthine, a novel variant of the Iboga alkaloids. *Tetrahedron Letters* **6,** 206–210.

Neuss, N., Gorman, M., Hargrove, W., Cone, N. J., Biemann, K., Büchi, G., and Manning, R. E. (1964). *Vinca* alkaloids. XXI. The structures of the oncolytic alkaloids vinblastine (VLB) and vincristine (VCR). *J. Am. Chem. Soc.* **86,** 1440–1442.

Neuss, N., Gorman, M., Svoboda, G. H., Maciak, G., and Beer, C. T. (1959). Vinca Alkaloids. III. Characterization of leurosine and vincaleukoblastine, new alkaloids from *Vinca rosea* Linn. *J. Am. Chem. Soc.* **81,** 4754.

Neuss, N., Huckstep, L. L., and Cone, N. J. (1967). *Vinca* alkaloids. XXIX. Structure of leurosidine (vinrosidine, VRD), an oncolytic alkaloid from *Vinca rosea* Linn. (*Catharanthus roseus* G. Don). *Tetrahedron Letters* **9**, 811–816.

Neuss, N., Johnson, I. S., Armstrong, J. G., and Jansen, C. J., Jr. (1964). The Vinca alkaloids. *Advan. Chemotherapy* **1**, 133–174.

Noble, R. L. Personal communication.

Noble, R. L., Beer, C. T., and Cutts, J. H. (1958a). Role of chance observation in chemotherapy. *Ann. N.Y. Acad. Sci.* **76**, 882–894.

Noble, R. L., Beer, C. T., and Cutts, J. H. (1958b). Further biological activities of vincaleukoblastine — an alkaloid from *Vinca rosea* L. *Biochem. Pharmacol.* **1**, 347–348.

Noble, R. L., Beer, C. T., and McIntyre, R. W. (1967). Biological effects of dihydrovinblastine. *Cancer* **20**, 885–890.

Palmer, C. G., Livengood, D., Warren, A., Simpson, P. J., and Johnson, I. S. (1960). The action of vincaleukoblastine on mitosis *in vitro. Exptl. Cell Res.* **20**, 198–201.

Richards, J. F., and Beer, C. T. (1964). Some effects of Vinca alkaloids on nucleic acid metabolism. *Lloydia* **27**, 346–351.

Richards, J. F., Jones, R. G. W., and Beer, C. T. (1963). The effect of vinblastine on the nucleic acid metabolism of thymus cell suspensions. *Proc. Am. Assoc. Cancer Res.* **4**, 57.

Svoboda, G. H. (1958). A note on several new alkaloids from *Vinca rosea* Linn. I: Leurosine, virosine, perivine. *J. Am. Pharm. Assoc. (Sci. Ed.)* **47**, 834.

Svoboda, G. H. (1961). Alkaloids of *Vinca rosea (Catharanthus roseus)*. IX. Extraction and characterization of leurosidine and leurocristine. *Lloydia* **24**, 173–178.

Svoboda, G. H. (1963). Alkaloids of *Vinca rosea* Linn. (*Catharanthus roseus* G. Don). XVIII. Root alkaloids. *J. Pharm. Sci.* **52**, 407–408.

Svoboda, G. H., Neuss, N., and Gorman, M. (1959). Alkaloids of *Vinca rosea* Linn. (*Catharanthus roseus* G. Don). V. Preparation and characterization of alkaloids. *J. Am. Pharm. Assoc. (Sci. Ed.)* **48**, 659–666.

Svoboda, G. H., Oliver, A. T., and Bedwell, D. R. (1963). Alkaloids of *Vinca rosea (Catharanthus roseus)*. XIX. Extraction and characterization of root alkaloids. *Lloydia* **26**, 141–153.

Svoboda, G. H., and Barnes, A. J., Jr. (1964). Alkaloids of *Vinca rosea* Linn. (*Catharanthus roseus* G. Don). XXIV. Vinaspine, vincathicine, rovidine, desacetyl VLB and vinaphamine. *J. Pharm. Sci.* **53**, 1227–1231.

Svoboda, G. H., Gorman, M., and Root, M. A. (1964b). Alkaloids of *Vinca rosea (Catharanthus roseus)*. XXVIII. A preliminary report on hypoglycemic activity. *Lloydia* **27**, 361–363.

Svoboda, G. H., Gorman, M., and Tust, R. H. (1964a). Alkaloids of *Vinca rosea (Catharanthus roseus)*. XXV. Lochrovine, perimivine, vincoline, lochrovidine, lochrovicine and vincolidine. *Lloydia* **27**, 203–213.

The Unfolding Panorama of the
New World Hallucinogens

*Richard Evans Schultes**

Knowledge of plants and knowledge of healing or treating disease have been closely linked from man's earliest social and cultural gropings. What may be termed *botany* and *medicine* are still intimately intertwined in primitive societies that have persisted to the present time. From all sources, it may be inferred that the shaman or witch doctor, who represents the oldest professional man in the evolution of human culture, was usually an accomplished botanist.

But what does history itself — human social development since the advent of written records — tell? The answer is the same: botany and medicine were so close that for a great part of man's historical period they were, for most practical purposes, one and the same discipline. And it was so until, about 1500, when the two began to separate from their long wedlock, and to the advantage of both sciences.

Yet the tendency toward some kind of union was hard to break, and even in comparatively recent times there are indications of the persistance of this union. Linnaeus, it is recalled, was a medical doctor. Even a century later, some of the leading botanists were medically trained and practiced their medical profession. Asa Gray, founder of Harvard's Gray Herbarium, and John Torrey, were medical doctors.

With the gradual sophistication of chemistry in the last half of the last century, and the exaggerated abuse, especially in the United States, of "folk medicines," "Indian remedies," and other therapeutic quackery, there set in a countercurrent, a tendency to disparage any ethnobotanical data concerning physiologically active plants and to exalt and exaggerate the potentialities of synthetic chemistry for progress in therapeutics.

Then the revolution set in about thirty-five years ago: the discovery of so many startlingly effective drugs, mostly of plant origin, that there has crystallized the realization that the Plant Kingdom, variously estimated as between 200,000 and 500,000 species, represents virtually an untapped

---

*See also "Hallucinogens of Plant Origin." *Science* **163,** 245–254.

reservoir of unknown chemical structures, many with extraordinarily interesting physiological properties. There has come about, once again, a drawing together of the botanical, pharmaceutical, and medical sciences, albeit a healthier alliance than the one that existed throughout most of man's cultural history (Schultes, 1963c).

Although there have been striking evidences of this *rapprochement* in numerous aspects of recent developments in pharmaceutical chemistry, nowhere perhaps has the evidence been more challengingly provacative than in the study of hallucinogenic or psychotomimetic drugs (Schultes, 1961b, 1963a,b).

Though primative man tried to find direct palliatives or remedies for his ailments, the psychic effects of drugs were far more important to him than the purely physical. This is readily understandable when it is remembered that most, if not all, primitive cultures attribute sickness and death to supernatural forces. Witchcraft, aided by communion with the spirit world, was the principal tool in the treatment of disease. For this reason, primitive man sought and put an extraordinary value on plants that had sundry strangely unreal, psychic effects that were capable of transporting him beyond the prosaic confines of this mundane environment to exciting worlds of indescribably ethereal wonder. The narcotics, especially those inducing visual and other hallucinations, were primitive man's "medicines" *par excellence* and early secured a firm place in his magic and religious practices, which, though often indistinguishable, were the basis of his medical practice. How did this condition come to pass? Faced with the mystery of a very small number of plants that had strange powers over his mind and body, whereas the great majority had no effects, primitive man had to resort to the only plausible explanation: these psychoactive plants were the residence of divinities or supernatural forces and, therefore, sacred. Civilized man now knows that these "divinities" are chemical compounds, sometimes structurally novel and often of extraordinary phytochemical and physiological interest. Scientific investigation of these plants, thanks to interdisciplinary studies, have led to most unusual, startlingly unexpected discoveries in sundry fields. The impact of these discoveries has demonstrated how vital it is to be ever mindful of the native's beliefs in and reverences for the supernatural origin of these amazing psychoactive properties, that to pass over these beliefs and reverences might easily frustrate and doom to failure the most meticulously prepared scientific search (Schultes, 1960, 1962). And, above all, reports of aboriginal uses of plants must no longer be prejudged.

More than a century ago, in 1855, von Bibra published his *Die narkotischen Genussmittel und der Mensch*. This book, the first of its kind, considered 17 plant stimulants and narcotics and urged that chemists undertake assiduous study of a field so promising for research and so fraught with enigmas.

Half a century later, in 1911, Hartwich, in his *Die menschlichen Genussmittel,* discussed at length about 30 vegetal narcotics and stimulants and mentioned many others in passing. He pointed out that von Bibra's pioneer work was out of date, that research on the botanical aspects and on the chemical contituents of these plants had, in 1855, scarcely begun but that, by 1911, these studies were either progressing well or had already been completed.

Thirteen years later, in 1924, Lewin's *Phantastica — die betäubenden und erregenden Genussmittel* appeared, later to be translated into other languages. A novel kind of book, basic to what is now called *psychopharmacology,* it presented the total picture of some 28 plants that were employed for their stimulating or narcotic properties in many parts of the world. Lewin emphasized the importance of these plants to research in botany, ethnobotany, chemistry, pharmacology, medicine, psychology, psychiatry as well as to ethnology, history, and sociology. "The contents of this book," he humbly understated in the preface, "will provide a starting point from which original research in the above-mentioned departments of science may be pursued." This is exactly what the book has done — and admirably so. Without exaggeration, it may be said that it was Lewin's *Phantastica* that led directly to today's intensive and extensive interdisciplinary interest in narcotics, especially in those called the *hallucinogens.*

If a date were chosen to mark the beginning of the present phase of ethnobotanical interest in New World narcotics, however, it would have to be 1915, the year of publication of Safford's paper entitled "An Aztec narcotic." Even though in this and other papers that appeared some half century ago, Safford fell into several grievous errors that, in some ways, retarded progress, he did succeed in calling attention to the wealth of New World ethnobotanical material still awaiting exploration.

The "prototype," perhaps, of the New World hallucinogens is the peyote cactus, *Lophophora Williamsii* (LaBarre, 1938; Rouhier, 1927; Schultes, 1937a,b,c). Known by many natives of central and northern Mexico, this sacred plant was the center of a significant religious cult in the Aztec world. The rites surrounding its use were driven into hiding for several centuries by the ignorance and bigotry of the Spanish conquerors, but it persisted among the desert peoples of northern Mexico. Furthermore, the plant was discovered during the last half of the past century by marauding Plains Indians from the United States, was brought back, and, with alterations of form and emphasis, a religious cult peculiar to the Indians of the United States developed and spread, until at present this cult, fully organized into the Native American Church, counts some 200,000 adherents and is practiced as far north as Saskatchewan and as far west as California (LaBarre, 1960). Such is the importance today of a rather insignificant-looking cactus. But the importance of *Lophophora Williamsii* does not end there.

Identified botanically at Harvard University from dried tops brought out from Tarahumare country in the late 1800s by the explorer Lumholtz (1902), peyote immediately attracted chemical and pharmacological attention. There has grown up an astounding body of literature from interdisciplinary research into this cactus. The botanical literature alone is bewildering, and present knowledge of the chemistry of the plant now indicates a total of 13 alkaloids, 1 of which—mescaline, the causative agent of the visual hallucinations—remains perhaps the most interesting (McLaughlin and Paul, 1966). Anthropological awareness of peyote has been and continues to be extraordinarily extensive, while newer fields— art, religion, philosophy, psychiatry—have become active in evaluating the plant and its use (LaBarre, 1960).

It might justifiably be assumed that, given so much interest, the understanding of peyote and unrelated narcotic species of cactus, would be clear and extensive. On the contrary, much remains to be done about the relationship between the Cactaceae and the medico-religious practices of New World aborigines. Lumholtz himself enumerated several species of *Mammillaria (M. micromeris, M. fissurata)* and *Echinocactus* that the Tarahumare Indians prize and even worship, considering them "demigods who have to be treated with great reverence," since eating them "causes a state of ecstasy" and brings about other physiological changes. It is clear from Lumholtz's notes that the field for narcotic cactuses is rich in northern Mexico. Furthermore, there are numerous species of cactus which, in other parts of Mexico, are classed as "peyote," either because they resemble *Lophophora* or because they produce similar effects. Belonging to the genera *Ariocarpus, Astrophytum, Aztekium, Dolichothele, Obregonia, Pelecyphora,* and *Solisia,* several of them are known to be alkaloidal (Willaman and Schubert, 1961). And even more astounding is the recent discovery of the use as a narcotic by medicine men in Peru of the gigantic columnar cactus, *Trichocereus Pachanoi* (Friedberg, 1959; Gutiérrez-Noriega, 1950), and the report of mescaline in several species of this South American genus (Willaman and Schubert, 1961).

Outstanding as narcotics among the Solanaceae is *Datura,* species of which have an ancient history of magical and religious use in both hemispheres. In the New World there are two main centers for use of *Datura:* the American Southwest and Mexico, where several herbaceous species, the *toloache* of Mexico, have been and still are employed; and the Andean areas of South America from Colombia to Chile, where sundry species of tree *Datura* have been valued as intoxicants from earliest times.

In Mexico and the American Southwest, several species of this toxic solanaceous genus are, and for centuries have been, employed as divinatory and prophetic intoxicants (Safford, 1920, 1921). The custom persists in the drier parts of this area and seems to be centered mainly around the use of *Datura inoxia,* a plant with strong psychotropic properties attributable to its relatively high content of tropane alkaloids.

It is in the Andes of South America, however, that the genus *Datura* really comes into its own as a narcotic (Schultes, 1965). *Datura* in the Andes is represented by members of the subgenus *Brugmannsia,* all trees and all cultigens unknown in the truly wild state (Bristol, 1966b). Possessing the same tropane alkaloids (atropine, hyoscyamine, scopolamine, etc.) as the herbaceous species of North American *Datura,* albeit in different proportions, the tree Daturas of South America apparently enjoyed a more significant role in pre-Spanish cultures than at the present time, when their use is either criminal (in urban civilization) or superstitious (in marginal tribes of the Andes).

The use of tree Daturas is at present concentrated along the eastern slopes of the Ecuadorean Andes. No species of tree *Datura* has been found in a truly wild state, that is, far from the possible influence of agricultural man. There are areas (such as the 10,000-ft, mountain-girt Valley of Sibundoy in southernmost Andean Colombia) where the aborigines recognize and vegetatively propagate certain "races" of *Datura,* assigning to them specific native names and distinctive physiological effects. These "varieties" or "races" are morphologically distinguishable, even though there are numerous intergradations which may be due to mutations.

The tree *Datura* species are referred to usually as *D. arborea, D. aurea, D. candida, D. dolichocarpa, D. sanguinea, D. suaveolens,* and *D. vulcanicola* (Schultes, 1963a,b). Their classification has been confused. A recent treatment (Bristol, 1966b) suggests that there may be, in reality, only several species and numerous cultivars.

The preparation and use of *Datura* narcotics differ widely in the New World. The intoxicant is usually taken in the form of pulverized seeds, often in fermented fruit drinks. The intoxication is fraught with grave dangers because of the extreme toxicity of the alkaloids and their variable concentration of these toxic constituents. The principal alkaloids of

Datura are hyoscyamine, scopolamine, and atropine. The effects usually comprise an initial state of violence, so furious that the partaker must be restrained until a deep, disturbed sleep overtakes him. Visual hallucinations are experienced.

Although their employement as narcotics dates from early times, this genus still offers a fertile field for botanical, chemical, and ethnobotanical research.

One of the physiologically most effective and academically most interesting of the solanaceous narcotics of Sibundoy has been described as a new genus, *Methysticodendron Amesianum* (Schultes, 1955). Known among the aborigines as *culebra borrachera,* this distinctive tree probably has resulted, as suggested in the literature, from one or a series of mutations from *Datura.* Its acceptance by the natives as distinct and its employment by them for specific purposes, in addition to its chemical constitution, indicate the presence of a fundamental problem in which man and his ethnobotanical manipulations are playing a major part in the evolution of a new form of plant life.

Recent studies seem to indicate that it may be a cultivar "derived from one of the white-flowered tree-*Daturas,*" possibly *D. candida* (Bristol, 1966b). The natives of the Valley of Sibundoy further recognize and propagate for specific medicinal purposes a number of clones of *Datura* which are variously "atrophied" (Bristol, 1966b; Schultes, 1961b). It has been suggested that these clones or "races," all known by distinctive native names, have arisen through virus infection, for similar monstrosities are known in the Solanaceae and elsewhere to be responses to viral attack. Long field study indicates (Bristol, 1966b), however, that they may "represent" several, or possibly many, genetic lines "and that each cultivar is genetically distinct, quite apart from the possible influence of viruses on the leaves." It is obvious that the tree Daturas constitute a genetically highly plastic group and, in the light of this plasticity, it is possible that *Methysticodendron,* like the numerous Sibundoy "races" of *Datura,* may eventually be shown to represent a most extreme variation along these lines of evolutionary development.

A fascinating possibility of adding to our list of solanaceous narcotics lies in further study of *Brunfelsia,* a toxic tropical New World genus of about 25 species, several of which are either known as poisons or employed in folk medicine (Schultes, 1966, 1967a). Evidence for the possible narcotic use of *Brunfelsia* in the Amazonian areas of Colombia, Ecuador, and Peru is quite real but is not yet corroborated by a good body of field observation. Intensive ethnobotanical work may still uncover indications of a former use of *Brunfelsia* as an hallucinogenic agent (there seems to be an appropriate chemical constitution), since such a use may once have been common and have disappeared.

There is a poorly understood solanaceous plant, *Latua pubiflora,* called *árbol de los brujos* in Chile, where it grows as a spiny shrub on the coastal slopes from Valdivia to Chiloe (Murillo, 1889). The plant contains tropane alkaloids and is extremely toxic, and especially toxic is the fruit which, if ingested, causes delirium, hallucinations, and insanity. It is said to be employed by the medicine men of the Araucarian Indians, but little reliable ethnobotanical knowledge is available.

The Leguminosae have given American ethnopharmacology various interesting psychotomimetics. *Sophora secundiflora,* a characteristic shrub of the drier parts of the American Southwest and northern Mexico, bears dark red seeds known as *red beans* or *mescal beans* (LaBarre, 1938; Schultes, 1963a,b). The seeds contain (Willaman and Schubert, 1961) a highly toxic pyridine alkaloid, cytisine, the effects of which are nausea, convulsions, hallucinations, and occasional death from respiratory failure. An early report by the Spanish explorer Cabeza de Vaca mentioned mescal beans as an article of trade among the Indians of the Texas area in 1539, and the Stephen Long Expedition in 1820 reported the Arapaho and Iowa tribes using large red beans as a medicine and narcotic. Mescal beans have been found in a number of archaeological sites in Texas and northern Mexico, all dated before 1000 A.D., and in some instances there appears to be evidence of ritualistic use of the beans.

Indian groups in Texas and northern Mexico formerly ingested these seeds in the ceremonial Red Bean Dance. Various Plains Indians likewise employed mescal beans in distinct patterns of use: as an oracular or divinatory medium, to induce visions in initiation rites, and as a ceremonial emetic and stimulant. The Kiowas and Comanches employ it today only as part of the ornamental dress of the leader of the peyote ritual, pointing perhaps to its earlier use as a narcotic, a role which it lost with the arrival of the much safer and much more spectacularly hallucinogenic peyote.

Several species of the leguminous genus *Rhynchosia* may also have been employed as narcotics in ancient Mexico (Schultes, 1965). In Oaxaca, the red and black beans of *Rhynchosia phaseoloides* and *R. pyramidalis* are known as *piule,* a name employed likewise for the convolvulaceous narcotic *Rivea corymbosa;* and the Chinantec and Mazatec of Oaxaca recognize *Rhynchosia* seeds as toxic (Schultes, 1941b). An as yet uncharacterized alkaloid has been isolated from beans of *Rhynchosia pyramidalis. Rhynchosia* seeds have been identified from ancient Aztec paintings together with mushrooms (Heim and Wasson, 1958); this is another indirect suggestion that they may have been valued as narcotics.

The other known leguminous narcotics are South American and belong to the *Mimosa* group of the family. The Kararí and Pankarurú Indians of eastern Brazil practice the ancient yurema cult, during which a gourd of the yurema-root infusion is given to warriors who experience visual hallucinations (Gonçalves de Lima, 1946). The rite was once much more widespread. It has been learned about from at least three other tribes of the region. The source of this potent beverage is probably the same as that reported under the Portuguese name *vinho de Jurema* and prepared from the roots of *Mimosa hostilis*. An alkaloid was isolated from this plant in 1946 and named nigerine, but this compound has since been shown to be identical with *N,N*-dimethyltryptamine, a constituent found in seeds of several related legumes (Pachter *et al.,* 1959).

One of the most interesting and enigmatic South American narcotics is *Anadenanthera peregrina,* more widely known as *Piptadenia peregrina.* A powder prepared from the beans of this tree is snuffed in northern South America and was formerly snuffed in the Antilles as well (Altschul, 1964). Tobacco, commonly taken as a snuff in the West Indies and South America, has constantly been confused with other snuffs, as in the case of the ceremonial *cohoba* snuff of Hispaniola, mentioned in the very first work (1496) that reported on the ethnology of the Western Hemisphere. It was not until 1916 that *cohoba* was identified as probably the same as the *ñopo* or *yopo* employed as a snuff by the Indians of the upper Orinoco in Venezuela (Safford, 1916).

A number of reports in the literature ascribed the source of Amazonian snuffs to various leguminous trees, and that may have led Bentham to conclude "that all South American trees . . . referred to as the source of narcotic snuff were probably one species and were identical with Linnaeus' *Mimosa peregrina* . . .," a statement that has led to one of the most extraordinarily erroneous generalizations in ethnobotany: that all the narcotic snuffs of South America that were not obviously tobacco must have been prepared from *Anadenanthera peregrina.* In many of the ancient reports of snuffing, it is impossible to distinguish between the use of tobacco and the snuffing of a powder prepared from *Anadenanthera* or of some other plant (Schultes, 1967b). There should, nonetheless, be no uncertainty in modern anthropological and ethnobotanical reports, but there is confusion more often than not.

A map (Cooper, 1949) purporting to show the distribution of the use of *Anadenanthera* snuffs includes the entire Orinoco basin and adjacent areas of southern Venezuela to the east; westward across the northern

Colombian Andes and much of the Magdalena Valley; down the Andes through Colombia, Ecuador, Peru, and Bolivia; the coastal region of Peru; scattered isolated localities in northern Argentina; and the central and western part of the Amazon Valley. Even though this map is meant to outline the range of the use of several species in this genus—and there have been suggestions that other species have been the source of narcotic snuffs in the southernmost parts of the indicated range—the area for the employment of *Anadenanthera peregrina* is extraordinarily exaggerated. It extends far beyond the known botanical distribution of this tree, even though the range may have been extended by human agency.

The seeds and pods contain bufotenine and *N,N*-dimethyltryptamine and the oxides of both (Holmstedt and Lindgren, 1967). Thanks to several excellent monographic studies (Altschul, 1964; Ducke, 1949), *Anadenanthera peregrina,* in Venezuela, is known to belong to secondary forests, "savannahs, light forests and riversides"; in British Guiana, to be confined to "savannahs and riverside forests"; while in Brazil it is restricted to "savannah-like areas, usually in or near the Rio Madeira and Rio Branco basins." It is, at least in the present century, far from common in the Amazon basin.

The main area of modern use of *yopo* or *ñopo,* the snuff prepared, usually with an alkaline admixture, from the beans of *Anadenanthera peregrina,* comprises principally the "llanos" of eastern Colombia, the Orinoco basin of Venezuela, and the region eastward across southern Venezuela (Schultes, 1967b). Whether or not some of the intoxicating snuffs reported from the Madeira and other southern tributaries of the Amazon may be attributable to *Anadenanthera peregrina* is doubtful and must await identifiable voucher specimens, but it is highly unlikely, in my opinion, that this species supplies the snuffs of these regions. It is unfortunate that the erroneous distribution of *Anadenanthera* snuffs persists in the literature despite efforts to point out reasons for its abandonment.

It was apparently Safford who first suggested that species of *Anadenanthera* other than *A. peregrina* might represent sources of other snuffs in South America. He identified the *vilca* or *huilca* of southern Peru and Bolivia and the *cébil* of northern Argentina (Altschul, 1964) with seeds of *Piptadenia macrocarpa,* now correctly called *Anadenanthera colubrina* var. *Cebil,* known to contain the same four indole bases that have been isolated from the pods and seeds of *A. peregrina,* and therefore obviously effective as a narcotic snuff.

Safford's identification of vilca has been widely accepted, but the evidence, in my opinion, is rather weak, and "there is evidence in the literature and in unpublished materials that vilca may involve other plants as well as *Anadenanthera colubrina* var. *Cebil,* and that it may have been used in forms different from snuff" (Altschul, 1967). An example of the use of vilca other than snuff is the very earliest report of the drug that described the Inca witch doctors' taking the juice of vilca in chicha to induce an intoxication to foretell the future through communion with the devil. Reports of early use of cébil are usually equally vague. Cébil snuffs used at the time of the contact in "the Mataco and Vilela cultures of northern Argentina appear to have been *Anadenanthera*-derived," although the employment of this drug "further south, beyond its natural distribution is less likely."

Whether or not the true identity of the vilca and cébil snuffs, used mostly in cultures now nonexistent and known either from ancient and fragmentary reports or by inference from artifacts in archaeological sites, will ever be known is problematical. It is certain, nevertheless, that *Anadenanthera colubrina* var. *Cebil* is chemically appropriate for the elaboration of an hallucinogenic snuff.

A most mysterious snuff of which almost nothing is known botanically and chemically is said to be prepared from the fruits of the enormous moraceous jungle tree *Olmedioperebea sclerophylla* (Schultes, 1965). It is reputedly employed in the central part of Amazonian Brazil, but it is known only by the general Portuguese term *rapé dos indios* ("Indian snuff"). Voucher specimens for exact botanical determination seem to be lacking in herbarium collections, and phytochemical examination of the fruits apparently has not yielded any psychotomimetic substances.

In 1954, a strange hallucinogenic snuff prepared from the myristicaceous genus *Virola* was reported from Amazonian Colombia (Schultes, 1954b). Tobacco and a mixture of tobacco and powdered coca *(Erythroxylon Coca)* were known to be employed as snuffs in that region (Schultes, 1967b), but both of these preparations were available to the whole male population of certain tribes. Only the witch doctors took *paricá* or *yakee,* a powerful snuff prepared from the red bark resin of *Virola calophylla* and *V. calophylloidea* plus ashes of the bark of a wild species of *Theobroma.*

Virola snuff is known among a number of tribes in eastern Colombia, especially in the basins of the Inírida, Guainía, Vaupés, and Apaporis, where the inhabitants strip bark from the trunks before the sun has risen high enough to heat up the forest. A blood-red resin oozes from the inner surface of the bark. It is scraped off with a knife after congealing, is boiled in an earthen pot for hours until a thick paste is left. This paste is sun-dried, pulverized, sifted through a fine cloth, and finally added to an equal amount of ashes.

It was very probably this *Virola* snuff that the German ethnologist Koch-Grünberg (1909) found early in the century among the Yekwana Indians of the headwaters of the Orinoco. He reported that they prepared their narcotic snuff from the bark of an unidentified tree. It is curious and perhaps significant that the related Waiká living on the Rio Tototobí at present call their *Virola* snuff *ñekwána.*

The manufacture of snuff from *Virola* bark has recently been reported from a number of related groups of Waiká Indians from the uppermost tributaries of the Orinoco eastward across the Brazilian-Venezuelan frontier region, where the narcotic is often called *epéna* (Wassén, 1968). Recently contacted groups of these Indians living on northern affluents of the Rio Negro of Brazil usually prepare the snuff with the ashes of the bark of an as yet unidentified leguminous tree, and sometimes with powdered leaves of a fragrant herb of the acanthaceous genus *Justicia.*

Among some of these natives, however, the snuff has no admixture. The Waiká of the Tototobí, for example, dry the resin, pulverize it finely, and blow it into the nostrils in this form. They may occasionally add powder from *Justicia* leaves but assert that this is not essential and merely adds a pleasant fragrance to the snuff. Neither it is considered important by these people to add ashes to the snuff. Most significant is the use of *Virola* resin, without any other ingredients, as an arrow poison by the Tototobí Waiká.

Although the source of *epéna* of the upper Rio Negro tributaries has been reported to be *Virola calophylloidea,* recent ethnobotanical work among the same inhabitants and collections indicate that it is *V. theiodora* that is employed.

Though it has been known that these *Virola* snuffs, like those made from *Anadenanthera,* possess tryptamines, there has not always been certainty about the botanical components of the powder. Examination of Waiká *Virola* snuff prepared from the resin of *V. theiodora* with no admixture has recently shown a content of 8% of 5-methoxy-N,N-dimethyltryptamine with traces of other tryptamines.

One of the most curious of the New World hallucinogens is the drink known in the western Amazon as *ayahuasca, caapi,* or *yajé* and prepared from sundry malpighiaceous plants (Schultes, 1957). Although not so commonly known as peyote or the Mexican mushrooms, this psychotomimetic drink has nonetheless inspired an undue share of sensational articles that have played fancifully with unfounded claims, especially concerning its presumed telepathic powers.

Despite its obvious great age, this narcotic drink became known to Europeans only about a century ago, and it remains one of the American hallucinogens most in need of clarification and study.

The first mention of *ayahuasca* appeared in 1858 in a book on the geography of Ecuador (Villavicencio, 1858). The drug, attributed to a vine, was taken "to foresee and to answer accurately in difficult cases, be it to reply opportunely to ambassadors from other tribes in a question of war; to decipher plans of the enemy through the medium of this magic drink and take proper steps for attack and defense; to ascertain, when a relative is sick, what sorcerer has put on the hex; to carry out a friendly visit to other tribes; to welcome foreign travellers or, at last, to make sure of the love of their womenfolk." A few years earlier, in 1852, the British plant explorer, Spruce (1908), encountered a liana known as *caapi* in the upper Rio Negro basin of Brazil and precisely identified the drug plant as a new species of the Malpighiaceae, now known as *Banisteriopsis caapi*. The natives of the Rio Negro basin of Brazil and Colombia use it for prophetic and divinatory purposes and to fortify the bravery of male adolescents about to undergo the initiation ceremony into manhood, and it was similarly employed for these purposes a century ago. In 1854, Spruce found the intoxicant being used by the indians along the upper Orinoco; and, in 1857, he identified the *ayahuasca* of the Peruvian Andes as the same narcotic as *caapi*.

Many subsequent explorers of the Amazon have referred to *ayahuasca, caapi,* or *yajé.* The range of use of this narcotic now comprises the western Amazon (including Bolivia, Brazil, Colombia, Ecuador, and Peru; the upper Orinoco of Colombia and Venezuela; and the Pacific coast of Colombia). It contains harmala-type alkaloids (Willaman and Schubert, 1961).

Later investigators have shown that other species of *Banisteriopsis (B. inebrians, B. Rusbyana)* are, especially in the westernmost Amazon at the foothills of the Andes, either the source of the narcotic drink or an additional ingredient in preparing the brew. *Banisteriopsis quitensis* and *B. longialata* have likewise been reported as sources of yajé. It has further been suggested that *Mascagnia psilophylla* var. *antifebrilis* might be so employed. Recently, the use of a new species of the allied malpighiaceous genus *Tetrapteris (T. methystica)* was authentically shown to be the source of a kind of caapi along the Rio Tikié in northwestern Brazil.

Although much more careful field work needs to be done before the whole picture is clearly in focus, there is every probability that the active ingredients of the ayahuasca-caapi-yajé narcotics are malpighiaceous plants.

A number of other plants are occasionally added to the beverage, but rarely do they appear to be essential to the intoxication that is being sought. In the westernmost Amazon of Colombia, Ecuador, and Peru, the leaves of *Alternanthera lehmannii* or of the toxic *Malouetia tamaquarina* are sometimes added. The addition of material of the rubiaceous genus *Psychotria* is not uncommon, especially in Peru. In all of these cases, however, the admixture seems to be nearly or wholly without intoxicating effect.

In 1921, through a misinterpretation of one of Spruce's field notes, it was suggested that the narcotic drink called yají in Colombia and Ecuador was derived from *Prestonia (Haemadictyon) amazonica* (Schultes and Raffauf, 1960). This suggestion has, unfortunately, been so widely accepted and disseminated that it has clouded with confusion the study of these malpighiaceous narcotics of South America. It has now been conclusively shown that *Prestonia* does not enter into the preparation of any known South American narcotic; the genus is, however, an interesting one and, belonging to the Apocynaceae, a family rich in active principles, merits serious phytochemical examination.

There remain to discuss several hallucinogens of the ancient Aztecs that are still employed in modern Mexico.

The utilization in the Mazatec country of Oaxaca of leaves of several members of the Labiatae has opened up new vistas in our search for psychotomimetic plants. One of these, *Salvia divinorum,* known as *yerba de la pastora,* is a native species (Wasson, 1962). Its narcotic effects have been proved, although as yet no psychoactive constituent has been isolated from it. Employed by the inhabitants when other local intoxicants are scarce or out of season, this *Salvia* has been suggested as representing the *pipiltzintzintli* of the Aztecs. Two species of the allied genus *Coleus (C. blumei* and *C. pumila),* both introductions from the Old World, have been reported (Wasson, 1962) to be similarly used in Oaxaca. This narcotic employment of members of the mint family assumes more than ethnobotanical interest in view of the existence in Turkestan of another reputedly intoxicating mint, *Lagochilus inebrians,* from which an active crystalline principle, lagochiline (a polyhydric alcohol), has been isolated (Tyler, 1966).

The early chroniclers of Mexico occasionally mentioned *ololiuqui,* the sacred, vision-inducing, lentil-like seed of a vine with cordate leaves. Its illustrations by several writers, most precisely by the Spanish physician, Hernández (1790), leave no question that they represented a morning glory. Most of the chroniclers were ecclesiastics who railed violently against this "diabolic seed" that the people esteemed as a divine messenger capable of taking man's mind to spirit realms. But the identity of ololiuqui was in doubt for four centuries. No morning glory has ever been found in use as a sacred hallucinogen. Furthermore, intoxicating constituents were unknown in the morning glory family. Then, in 1916, a categorical denial (Safford, 1916) that *ololiuqui* could be convolvulaceous was published, and, on the basis that the Aztecs were misleading the Spaniards to protect a sacred plant, an identification of ololiuqui as a species of *Datura* was offered. With no tangible evidence beyond the known toxicity of *Datura,* such an opinion was unfounded, yet it was immediately and widely accepted.

In spite of several objections to this "identification," it was not until the 1930s that actual botanical voucher specimens of *Rivea corymbosa* were made. They allowed ololiuqui to be referred to the Convolvulaceae and the statements in the early reports to be substantiated (Schultes, 1941a). Even though psychiatric experiments indicated the hallucinogenic effects of the seeds of *Rivea corymbosa* (Osmund, 1955), chemists were unable to isolate active principles until 1960, when the presence of amides of lysergic acids and of *d*-lysergic acid, chanoclavine and elymoclavine, substances hitherto known only from the fungus ergot *(Claviceps purpurea),* were isolated from this morning glory (Hofmann, 1961, 1963).

More recently, seeds of a second morning glory, *Ipomoea violacea,* have been identified as an hallucinogen in relatively wide use in Oaxaca (Wasson, 1963), and the same active principles have been isolated from them as from the seeds of *Rivea corymbosa* (Hofmann, 1963). During the last few years, in fact, chemical studies have shown that psychoactive indoles are comparatively widespread in the Convolvulaceae.

The early Mexican chroniclers likewise reported, and on a number of occasions, the religious use among the conquered peoples of intoxicating mushrooms called *teonanacatl* or "flesh of the gods" in Nahuatl. As in the case of ololiuqui, most of the chroniclers violently attacked such a loathsome pagan custom, and church persecution drove this interesting native cult into hiding for four centuries.

One of the old chroniclers referred to mushrooms that "are harmful and intoxicate like wine" so that those who eat of them "see visions, feel a faintness of heart and are provoked to lust"; and, in another reference to the fungi, he described the intoxication minutely. None of the references to the sacred mushrooms, however, is more thorough than that of Hernández (1790), who spoke of three kinds of hallucinogenic mushrooms worshipped by the natives. Some, he wrote, "cause not death but madness that on occasion is lasting, of which one symptom is a kind of uncontrolled laughter . . . these are deep yellow, acrid and of a not displeasing freshness. There are others again which, without inducing laughter, bring before the eyes all kinds of things, such as wars and the likeness of demons. Yet others there are not less desired by princes for their festivals and banquets, and these fetch a high price. With night-long vigils are they sought, awesome and terrifying. This kind is tawny and somewhat acrid."

Notwithstanding these and other such specific reports, nothing was actually known about these mushrooms until recently. Even more inexplicable is the wide acceptance of a patently erroneous assertion (Safford, 1916), made in 1916, that, as in the case of ololiuqui, the early Spanish chroniclers had been misled and beguiled by the Indians who, in order to protect the true teonanacatl, indicated that mushrooms represented this narcotic.

It was suggested that teonanacatl and the dried head of the peyote cactus were one and the same narcotic, notwithstanding the fact that the cactus grows only in the deserts of central and northern Mexico, hardly a propitious environment for mushrooms.

In spite of its wide acceptance, there were protests, but it was not until the 1930s that actual specimens of mushrooms employed in religious rites in the Mazatec Indian country of Oaxaca were collected and reported. The first to be identified was *Panaeolus campanulatus* var. *sphinctrinus* (Schultes, 1939). Later, intensive field research in Mexico, especially during the 1950s, has disclosed the narcotic use of some 20 other species in four genera among nine Indian groups (Heim and Wasson, 1958). The most important of them are *Psilocybe mexicana,* a small, tawny inhabitant of wet pastures, apparently the most highly prized of the hallucinogenic mushrooms; *P. aztecorum,* called "child of the waters" by the Aztecs; *P. zapotecorum* of marshy ground and known by the Zapotecs as "crown of thorns mushroom"; *P. caerulescens* var. *mazatecorum,* the so-called "landslide mushrooms" that grow on decaying sugar cane bagasse; *P. caerulescens* var. *nigripes,* the native name of which means "mushrooms of superior reasoning"; and *Stropharia cubensis.*

The religious use of mushrooms goes back apparently beyond 1000 B.C. among the highland Maya of Guatemala, even though they are not so employed there at present (Heim and Wasson, 1958). The existence of the mushroom cult in such remote times has been inferred from the abundant presence of archaeological artifacts now called "mushroom stones" and consisting of an upright stem with a manlike figure crowned with an umbrella-shaped top. Their meaning has long been an archaeological mystery; they are now thought to represent a kind of icon connected with mushroom worship.

A psychoactive constituent of most unusual structure for plant tissue has been found in a number of the sacred Mexican mushrooms: psilocybine, an indole derivative with a phosphorylated side chain, actually an acidic phosphoric acid ester of 4-hydroxydimethyltryptamine (Hofmann,

1958), a substance allied to such naturally occurring compounds as *bufotenine* and *serotonine*. Psilocybine has been isolated from *Panaeolus, Psilocybe,* and *Stropharia.* Another constituent sometimes found with psilocybine is psilocine, an unstable indolic compound occurring in minute amounts (Hoffer and Osmund, 1967; Hofmann, 1958).

The curious intoxication—marked by a kaleidoscopic play of visual hallucinations in color, muscular relaxation, flaccidity, mydriasis, followed by a period of emotional disturbance such as extreme hilarity and difficulty in concentrating—is due primarily, perhaps exclusively, to psilocybine.

Even such a superficial treatment of the American plant hallucinogens illustrates how much of a basis modern ethnobotanical and ethnopharmacological research has for the fast-unfolding panorama of the search for new psychoactive species of possible promise in modern medicine (Schultes, 1963c). Sundry lines of investigation which are suggested by what is now known should most certainly be followed, but, in view of the rapid disintegration of primitive New World cultures, it behooves all researchers to pursue every line open to them. A random sampling of the Plant Kingdom for psychoactive substances presents one approach. Another consists of more intensive examination of early records, fantastic though many may be; reports of any aboriginal use of a plant cannot be ignored merely because they seem to fall beyond the limit of credibility. A third and very promising approach, and one that has only recently attracted attention, is a search through the larger herbaria of the world for collectors' reports of such uses of plants. Still the most promising and certain approach, however, would appear to be intensive ethnobotanical investigation in the field of those primitive cultures that are as yet wholly or partly intact, before the beliefs and practices peculiar to these cultures pass forever from the mind and memory of man.

REFERENCES

Altschul, S. von R. (1964). A taxonomic study of the genus *Anadenanthera. Contrib. Gray Herbarium Harvard Univ.* **193.**

Altschul, S. von R. (1967). Vilca and its use. "Ethnopharmacologic Search for Psychoactive Drugs," *U.S. Pub. Health Serv. Publ.* **1645,** 307–314.

Bristol, M. L. (1966a). Notes on the species of tree *Daturas. Botan. Mus. Leaflet, Harvard Univ.* **21,** 229–248.

Bristol, M. L. (1966b). Tree *Datura* drugs of the Colombian Sibundoy. *Botan. Mus. Leaflet, Harvard Univ.,* ined.

Cooper, J. M. (1949). Stimulants and narcotics." *In* "Handbook of South American Indians," *Bur. Am. Ethnol. Bull.* **143** (5), 525–558.

Ducke, A. (1949). As leguminosas da Amazônia brasileira. *Bol. Tec. Inst. Agron. Norte (Belem, Brazil)* **18.**

Friedberg, C. (1959). Rapport sommaire sur une mission au Perou. *J. Agr. Trop. Botan. Appl.* **6,** 439–450.

Gonçalves de Lima, O. (1946). Observacões sôbre o 'vinho de Jurema' utilizado pelos ïndios Pancarú de Tacaratú (Pernambuco). Arquiv. Inst. Pesquises Agron. *(Pernambuco)* **4,** 45–80.

Gutiérrez-Noriega, C. (1950). Area de mescalismo en el Perú. *Am. Ind.* **10,** 215.

Hartwich, C. (1911). "Die menschlichen Genussmittel."

Heim, R. (1963). "Les champignons toxiques et hallucinogènes."

Heim, R., and Wasson, R. G. (1958). "Les champignons hallucinogènes du Mexique."

Hernández, F. (1790). "Opera: Historia plantarum Novae Hispaniae." Vol. 2, Bk. 9, Chap. 95.

Hoffer, A., and Osmund, H. (1967). "The Hallucinogens."

Hofmann, A. (1958). Psilocybin, ein psychotroper Wirkstoff aus dem mexikanischen Rauschpilz *Psilocybe mexicana* Heim. *Experientia* **14,** 107–112.

Hofmann, A. (1960). Die psychotropen Wirkstoffe der mexikanischen Zauberpilze. *Chimia* **14,** 309–318.

Hofmann, A. (1961). Die Wirkstoffe der mexikanischen Zauberdroge "Ololiuqui." *Planta Med.* **9,** 354–367.

Hofmann, A. (1963). The active principles of the seeds of *Rivea corymbosa* and *Ipomoea violacea. Botan. Mus. Leaflet, Harvard Univ.* **20,** 194–212.

Holmstedt, B., and Lindgren, J. E. (1967). Chemical constituents and pharamacology of South American snuffs. *In* "Ethnopharmacologic Search for Psychoactive Drugs," *U.S. Pub. Health Serv. Publ.* **1645,** 339–373.

Johnson, J. B. (1939a). Elements of Mazatec witchcraft. *Ethnol. Studies* **9,** 119–150.

Johnson, J. B. (1939b). Some notes on the Mazatec, pp. 142–156.

Koch-Grünberg, T. (1909). Zwei Jahre unter den Indianern, p. 298.

LaBarre, W. (1938). The peyote cult. *Yale Univ. Publ. Anthropol.* **19.**

LaBarre, W. (1960). Twenty years of peyote studies. *Current Anthropol.* **1,** 45–60.

LaBarre, W. (1964). The narcotic complex of the New World. *Diógenes* **48,** 125–138.

Lewin, L. (1924). Phantastica – die betäubenden und erregenden Genussmittel.

Lumholtz, C. (1902). "Unknown Mexico." Vol. 1, pp. 356–379.

McLaughlin, J. J., and Paul, A. G. (1966). The cactus alkaloids I. Identification of N-methylated tryamine derivatives in *Lophophora Williamsii. Lloydia* **29,** 315–327.

Murillo, A. (1889). "Plantas médicinales du Chili," 152–153.

Osmund, H. (1955). Ololiuqui: the ancient Aztec narcotic. *J. Mental Sci.* **101,** 526–537.

Pachter, I. J., Zacharias, D. E., and Ribeiro, O. (1959). Indole alkaloids of *Acer saccharinum* . . . and *Mimosa hostilis. J. Org. Chem.* **24,** 1285–1287.

Reko, B. P. (1934). Das mexikanische Rauschgifte Ololiuqui. *El Mexico Ant.* **3,** 1–7.

Rouhier, A. (1927). La plante qui fait les yeux émerveillés – le peyotl.

Safford, W. E. (1915). An Aztec narcotic. *J. Heredity* **6,** 291–311.

Safford, W. E. (1916). Narcotic plants and stimulants of the ancient Americans. *Smithsonian Inst. Ann. Rept.* 387–424.

Safford, W. E. (1920). Daturas of the Old World and New: an account of their narcotic properties and their use in oracular and initiatory ceremonies. *Smithsonian Inst. Ann. Rept.* 537–568.

Safford, W. E. (1921). *Datura,* an inviting genus for the study of heredity. *J. Heredity* **12,** 178–190.

Schultes, R. E. (1937a). Peyote and plants used in the peyote ceremony. *Botan. Mus. Leaflet, Ha, vard Univ.* **4**, 129–152.

Schultes, R. E. (1937b). Peyote *(Lophophora Williamsii)* and plants confused with it. *Botan. Mus. Leaflet, Harvard Univ.* **5**, 61–88.

Schultes, R. E. (1936c). Peyote *(Lophophora Williamsii)* (Lem. Coulter) and its uses. Unpub. thesis, Harvard Univ.

Schultes, R. E. (1939). Plantae Mexicanae II. The identification of teonanacatl, a narcotic Basidiomycete of the Aztecs. *Botan. Mus. Leaflet, Harvard Univ.* **7**, 37–54.

Schultes, R. E. (1940). Teonanacatl – the narcotic mushroom of the Aztecs. *Am. Anthropol.* **42**, 429–443.

Schultes, R. E. (1941a). A contribution to our knowledge of *Rivea corymbosa,* the narcotic ololiuqui of the Aztecs.

Schultes, R. E. (1941b). Economic aspects of the flora of northeastern Oaxaca, Mexico. Unpub. thesis, Harvard Univ.

Schultes, R. E. (1954a). Plantae Austro-Americanae IX. Plantarum novarum vel notabilium notae diversae. *Botan. Mus. Leaflet, Harvard Univ.* **16**, 202–205.

Schultes, R. E. (1954b). A new narcotic snuff from the northwest Amazon. *Botan. Mus. Leaflet, Harvard Univ.* **16**, 241–260.

Schultes, R. E. (1955). "A new narcotic genus from the Amazon slope of the Colombian Andes." *Botan. Mus. Leaflet, Harvard Univ.* **17**, 1–11.

Schultes, R. E. (1957). The identity of the malpighiaceous narcotics of South America. *Botan. Mus. Leaflet, Harvard Univ.* **18**, 1–56.

Schultes, R. E. (1960). Tapping our heritage of ethnobotanical lore. *Econ. Botany.* **14**, 257–262.

Schultes, R. E. (1961a). Botany attacks the hallucinogens. *Texas J. Pharm.* **2**, 168–185.

Schultes, R. E. (1961b). Native narcotics of the New World. *Texas J. Pharm.* **2**, 141–167.

Schultes, R. E. (1962). The role of the ethnobotanist in the search for new medicinal plants. *Lloydia* **25**, 257–266.

Schultes, R. E. (1963a). Botanical sources of the New World narcotics. *Psychol. Rev.* **1**, 145–166.

Schultes, R. E. (1963b). Hallucinogenic plants of the New World. *Harvard Rev.* **1**, 18–32.

Schultes, R. E. (1963c). The widening panorama in medical botany. *Rhodora* **65**, 97–120.

Schultes, R. E. (1965). Ein halbes Jahrhundert Ethnobotanik amerikanischer Halluzinogene. *Planta Med.* **13**, 125–157.

Schultes, R. E. (1966). The search for new natural hallucinogens. *Lloydia* **29**, 293–308.

Schultes, R. E. (1967a). The place of ethnobotany in the ethnopharmacologic search for psychotomimetic drugs. *In* "Ethnopharmacologic search for psychoactive drugs." *U.S. Pub. Health Serv. Publ.* **1645**, pp. 33–37.

Schultes, R. E. (1967b). The botanical origins of South American snuffs. *In* "Ethnopharmacologic search for psychotropic drugs." *U.S. Pub. Health Serv. Publ.* **1645**, pp. 291–306.

Schultes, R. E., and Raffauf, R. F. (1960). *Prestonia:* an Amazon narcotic or not? *Botan. Mus. Leaflet, Harvard Univ.* **19**, 109–122.

Spruce, R. (1908). Notes of a botanist on the Amazon and Andes. (A. R. Wallace, ed.). Vol. 2, pp. 414–425.

Tyler, V. E. (1966). The physiological properties and chemical constituents of some habit-forming plants. *Lloydia* **29**, 275–292.

Villavicencio, M. (1858). "Geografía de la República del Ecuador." p. 371.

Von Bibra, E. (1855). "Die narkotischen Genussmittel und der Mensch."

Wassén, S. H. (1968). The use of some specific kinds of South American Indian snuffs and related paraphernalia. *Etnolog. Studier* **28.**

Wasson, R. G. (1962). A new Mexican psychotropic drug from the Mint Family. *Botan. Mus. Leaflet, Harvard Univ.* **20,** 77–84.

Wasson, R. G. (1963). Notes on the present status of ololiuhqui and the other hallucinogens of Mexico. *Botan. Mus. Leaflet, Harvard Univ.* **20,** 161–193.

Willaman, J. J., and Schubert, B. G. (1961). Alkaloid-bearing plants and their contained alkaloids. *U.S.D.A. Tech. Bull.* **1234.**

Nutmeg and Other Psychoactive Groceries

Andrew T. Weil

The ethnobotanical search for new psychoactive drugs has led recent investigators to many faraway places: to southeast Asia, Siberia, Africa, Mexico, and, perhaps most frequently, to the densely forested river basins of South America. From these travels has come understanding of unusual kinds of intoxications witnessed by observers of the people in these areas. Botanical samples, carefully collected under the most adverse conditions and reverently transported to modern laboratories, have yielded whole families of compounds affecting human consciousness, many of which have been synthesized and are now being tested rigorously for psychopharmacological activity. The harmala alkaloids, psilocybin from the sacred mushrooms of the Aztecs, muscimol from *Amanita muscaria,* and all manner of hallucination-inducing tryptamines have now been added to that special class of drugs designated *Phantastica* by Louis Lewin in 1924.

Lewin could scarcely have imagined how extensive or how famous this group of compounds would become. They are no longer called phantastica, but a better name has not been found. "Psychotomimetic" worked for a time in the early fifties, when many enthusiastic researchers thought that LSD and its cousins produced "model psychoses" that would disclose the biochemical basis of schizophrenia. Unfortunately, this possibility has not been realized, and the term is outmoded. "Hallucinogen" was tried next, but it was not terribly euphonious and described only one aspect of the complicated intoxication. "Psychedelic" is a word of dubious etymology promulgated by partisans of expanded consciousness; it is as prejudiced in favor of these substances as psychotomimetic was against them. The most recent attempt at a neutral designation is "psychodysleptic," meaning "distorting of mental function" (Freyhan, 1961). Perhaps "phantastica" was a better term.

Whatever they are called, these drugs are important for sociological, psychiatric, and public health reasons as well as for purely pharmacological and botanical ones. Their continuing identification and isolation, particularly from New World plants, is indeed an impressive "unfolding panorama," as Schultes has written. Therefore all the visits by ethnobotanists to faraway places are quite appropriate; I hope they will not stop.

At the same time I am somewhat disappointed that so little attention has turned to the United States. On both coasts and throughout much of the midlands for the past few years, tribes of Americans have been busily sorting out psychopharmacological effects of plants and plant products in their own environments. I do not mean the Indians; I mean—and here is another nomenclature problem—the bohemians, beatniks, hippies, pot-heads, "acid-freaks," or what-have-you. Many of them have conducted valuable self-experiments with reportedly psychoactive substances and are quite happy to discuss their findings with anyone interested. The trouble is that most people in the laboratory lack reliable connections with the hippie world. This is unfortunate because an important body of data is soon going to be lost.

Until quite recently, this drug-taking population spent much effort and ingenuity in ferreting out new sources of psychoactivity. They did so because the familiar hallucinogenic drugs were expensive, illegal, and, above all, in short supply. But, within the past year, the availability of marihuana and LSD has increased enormously. I do not care to speculate about how many people have tried these drugs; I merely report my observation that in many communities in the East, marihuana and LSD can be bought with minimal difficulty and, with persistence, more esoteric drugs like hashish, dimethyl- or diethyltryptamine, STP (a mescaline derivative), or mescaline itself can be obtained. What bothers me about this change is that it has virtually wiped out experimentation with alternative drugs. Why would anyone bother with morning glory seeds, nutmeg, or untried roots and leaves that might cause nausea, vomiting, or nothing at all when he can buy an ounce of old reliable marihuana for $15 any time he feels the need to alter his consciousness? It is not surprising that hippie pharmacognosy, so active a few years back, is dying out as fast as that of the American Indian; in both cases a result of the successes of modern pharmacology. Indeed, even marihuana may become a victim of technology. In a recent statement to the New York *Times* (1967) a spokesman for the National Institute of Mental Health expressed concern that organized crime might begin producing and marketing synthetic tetrahydrocannabinol, believed to be the active principle in cannabis resin.

Here I discuss several entries salvaged from this nearly out-of-print pharmacopeia. About only one of them, nutmeg, can I give definitive information. The others are merely curiosities of ethnobotany at the moment, since little research on their effects has been done. All have been called psychoactive by persons who consider themselves drug connoisseurs, and all can be had at the nearest grocery store. In addition to nutmeg and several other spices, I mention bananas and green peppers.

Nutmeg (Weil, 1967)

Two spices, nutmeg and mace, come from the nutmeg tree, *Myristica fragrans* (family Myristicaceae), a handsome tropical tree native to the Banda Islands and other islands of the East Indian archipelago. The genus *Myristica* comprises about 100 species found throughout the torrid zone, especially in the Malayan region; but, of these, *M. Fragrans* alone contains enough of an aromatic essential oil to make it worthy of cultivation. Usually 30 or 40 ft tall, the nutmeg tree has a dark gray bark, spreading branches, and alternate, oblong-ovate leaves that are 4 in. long, leathery, and glossy green. Normally, the species is dioecious. Flowers, male and female, look like those of the lily-of-the-valley; they are pale yellow, fleshy, and have a strong scent of nutmeg. The fruit is a pendulous, fleshy drupe resembling an apricot.

When ripe, the fleshy husk, or pericarp, of this fruit splits open into two halves, revealing a shiny brown seedcoat, or testa. Inside this shell is the seed, which is the nutmeg of commerce. Outside the shell, closely enwrapping it, is a bright crimson network, or arillus, which is the mace. In preparing the spices for export, field workers first remove the pit with its mace from the husk. The aril is then carefully peeled away from the seed coat. Fresh arils are brilliant red and leathery and have a strong flavor of turpentine. The mace may be kept in one piece (called "double blade" in the trade) or separated into two halves ("single blade") before it is flattened by hand or between boards. It is then dried thoroughly in the sun or by artificial heat; during this process it gradually turns orange, then orange-yellow, and acquires its characteristic aroma.

The nutmegs, still in their shells, are also dried, frequently over a smouldering fire. When completely dry, the seed rattles in the testa. Usually the shells are then cracked by machine or with wooden mallets, and the seeds are removed for export. Sometimes shelled nutmegs are treated with lime before shipping to protect them from insects. They are then sorted by size and packed. For the spice trade, nutmegs are valued according to size, smoothness, and freedom from adulteration with wild seeds.

The essential or volatile oils of nutmeg and mace, in which resides the pharmacological activity, are obtained by steam distillation. Commercial oil of nutmeg is a mobile, pale yellow liquid with an odor and flavor of nutmeg. Chemically, it is a complex mixture of alcohols, esters, and organic acids, including about 4% myristicin, the main pharmacologically active component.

Like most aromatics, nutmeg was as important in early medicine as it was in cooking. Its therapeutic applications were first catalogued by Arab physicians as early as the 7th century A.D. Originally, it seems to have been a remedy for disorders of the digestive system, but before long it was considered beneficial in such diverse conditions as kidney disease, pain, and lymphatic ailments. The history of nutmeg in ancient medicine has been reviewed elsewhere (Weil, 1965).

By the end of the 1700s, the spice attained its greatest reputation; thereafter, with the development of modern pharmacy, its importance as a medicine gradually subsided.

Curiously, nutmeg's popularity as a folk remedy had a brief, spectacular resurgence less than one hundred years ago. Near the end of the 1800s, a rumor spread among women in England and America that nutmeg could bring on overdue menstruation and even induce abortion. The origin of this mistaken belief is unclear, but its influence is well documented in dozens of case reports of nutmeg poisoning published in British and American medical journals of the period. The idea has even persisted into our times: Green in 1959 wrote of a 28-year-old Virginia woman who ate "18.3 Gm. of finely ground nutmeg in an attempt to induce the menses, which had been delayed two days."

Reports of nutmeg poisoning date back to the late Middle Ages when several early physicians first wrote down their observations on the stupor-inducing powers of the spice. Doubtless, most of these intoxications resulted from overdoses taken as remedies. A late example comes from *A Treatise on the Materia Medica* written in 1789 by an English physician, William Cullen. He wrote:

> I have myself had an accidental occasion of observing its [nutmeg's] soporific and stupefying power. A person by mistake took two drams or a little more of powdered nutmeg; he felt it warm in his stomach, without any uneasiness; but in about an hour after he had taken it, he was seized with a drowsiness, which gradually increased to a complete stupor and insensibility; and not long after, he was found fallen from his chair, lying on the floor of his chamber in the state mentioned. Being laid abed he fell asleep; but waking a little from time to time, he was quite delirious: and he thus continued alternately sleeping and delirious for several hours. By degrees, however, both these symptoms diminished, so that in about six hours from the time of taking the nutmeg he was pretty well recovered from both. Although he still complained of headache and some drowsiness, he slept naturally and quietly through the following night, and next day was quite in his ordinary health.
>
> There is no doubt that this was entirely the effect of the nutmeg . . . .

Again, the greatest numbers of people poisoned by *Myristica* have been English and American women of the late 19th and early 20th centuries. Summarizing many of these cases in 1962, McCord and Jervey wrote:

> . . . patients have consumed from 1 to 3 nutmegs and have experienced restlessness, dizziness, fear of death, coldness of extremities, occasional nausea and vomiting, abdominal pain, and precordial pain or oppression. These patients were found to be extremely agitated, delirious, and dyspneic and have had weak, rapid pulses and decreased body temperature. On several occasions patients were found unconscious. Occasionally there was flushing of the face while at other times pallor with cyanosis of the lips and nails predominated.

They attributed these intoxications to "a central nervous system depressive effect with periods of stimulation and associated respiratory and cardiovascular difficulties."

Only one fatality has ever been ascribed to nutmeg ingestion: near the beginning of this century, an 8-year-old boy ate two whole nutmegs, became comatose, and died less than 24 hr later (Cushny, 1908).

The apparent epidemic of nutmeg intoxications around the turn of the century subsided after World War I. Cases since then have been rare. In 1963, Payne presented one of the only published reports of deliberate ingestion of *Myristica* for narcotic effects. He described two college students 19 and 20 years old, who each consumed 2 tablespoons (about 14 g or the equivalent of two whole seeds) of powdered nutmeg suspended in milk). About 5 hr later,

> . . . each had the onset of a significant pharmacologic effect, heralded by a leaden feeling in the extremities and a nonchalant, detached mental state described as "unreal" or "dreamlike." Rapid heart rates and palpitations were noted, and both complained of dry mouth and thirst. Onlookers observed that one student became quite hyperactive and agitated and talked incoherently. It was noted that the faces of both were as "red as beets." Nausea, vomiting, and abdominal cramps were absent . . . . One described a sense of impending doom, as if he were "breaking up inside."

Extreme drowsiness occurred about 7 hr after these symptoms began and continued for the next 24 hr. Recovery was complete, but "both patients stated emphatically that a sense of unreality persisted for 48 to 60 hours from the time of one oral dose of nutmeg."

A history of the use of nutmeg for the express purpose of inducing these bizarre physical and mental effects is hard to piece together simply because reliable data on *Myristica* narcosis are not available. The medical literature is of no help, for example, because nearly all the reported cases have resulted from accidental ingestions or overdoses taken as remedies. Most of the information on nutmeg as a psychoactive drug is anecdotal, and it has been most difficult to document the anecdotes.

It is relatively easy to confirm rumors of nutmeg use by prison inmates, despite denials of such reports by prison officials. One interesting reference occurs in *The Autobiography of Malcolm X* (1964), in which the late Black Muslim leader describes his incarceration in a Boston prison in 1946. He was then a user of marihuana and other drugs and found himself suddenly cut off from them. He wrote:

> I first got high in Charleston [prison] on nutmeg. My cellmate was among at least a hundred nutmeg men who, for money or cigarettes, bought from kitchen-worker inmates penny matchboxes full of stolen nutmeg. I grabbed a box as though it were a pound of heavy drugs. Stirred into a glass of cold water, a penny matchbox full of nutmeg had the kick of three or four reefers.

A more recent but less accessible reference was a short article on page 22 of the Chicago *Sun-Times* for March 3, 1961. It told of the dismissal of a Cook County Jail guard caught smuggling nutmeg and nose inhalers into the jail.

An officer of the Federal Bureau of Prisons (Alldredge, 1964) has written:

> We are aware of the narcotic reaction these spices may have when improperly used, and, therefore, it is standard practice in the Federal prisons to maintain careful control of both items [i.e., nutmeg and mace]. Due to this control and also to the fact . . . that few people are aware of their stupor-inducing powers, we have no problems with these items. I have read articles in various publications which imply that the use of nutmeg and mace is widespread in prisons. However I do not know of a single instance in the Federal Prison system where either spice was used by inmates for its narcotic effect.

There is, however, ample confirmation of this rumored use of nutmeg in a study conducted by Weiss at the New Jersey State Prison at Trenton in 1960. Weiss wrote:

> It is widely believed by inmates of correctional institutions that the drug action of nutmeg produces reactions similar to those of legally prohibited drugs which are considered habit-forming and addicting. Although its illicit application is most certainly not widely known in the extra-mural setting, personal communications by prisoners are to the effect that it is used, not only in the community [i.e., the outside], but was also used in the armed forces in Europe in World War II.

To summarize: The toxic properties of nutmeg have been recognized for hundreds of years, probably ever since the spice was first prescribed medicinally in large doses. Published reports of *Myristica* narcosis were most frequently around the turn of the last century when many women took nutmeg as an emmenagogue or abortifacient. Some evidence suggests that nutmeg may have long been used as an intoxicant in certain parts of Asia. In this century, for at least the past thirty years, prisoners, jazz musicians, sailors, and probably others have used nutmeg as a substitute for marihuana or other drugs. They either eat or snuff it in variable amounts and commonly experience symptoms much more like those of the familiar hallucinogens than those described in the old reports of nutmeg poisoning.

Because students and hippies are now the predominant drug users in the society, I have tried to determine whether they have turned to nutmeg. Only one case of this sort has appeared in the medical literature — Payne's report of 1963, mentioned earlier. His two students had gotten the idea of taking nutmeg from a "beatnik acquaintance," who told them it would provide "a mental state somewhat akin to ethanol intoxication without requiring the use of alcohol." I have been able to find only one other published account, an article titled "Nutmeg Jag" in the summer, 1964, issue of a University of Mississippi student magazine. It described a nutmeg party attended by 8 persons. One participant, a young man who consumed a whole standard-size can of ground spice (nearly 40 g or 1.5 oz), recalled afterward (Andre, 1964):

> I felt as if I were in an echo chamber . . . my voice sounded vague and distant . . . it was like being drunk without the ordinary alcoholic effects. . . . Two friends of mine had told me about the 30-cents, three-day drunk they had after taking nutmeg, so I tried it out of sheer disbelief.

Last year, I was in touch with officials of student health services at representative universities throughout the country in an attempt to collect additional reports of *Myristica* intoxications. Significantly, most of the responding physicians were unaware of nutmeg's nonculinary uses. Only two university clinics had cases on record. Dr. Henry B. Bruyn of the University of California at Berkeley student health service noted two instances of intoxication, and Dr. B. W. Murphy of the University of Maryland wrote that he knows of a male student who induces dreamy hallucinatory states by ingesting a whole can of ground nutmeg.

Does the scarcity of reported cases indicate a low frequency of nutmeg use by students? Probably not, because students are reluctant to present themselves for medical treatment of drug intoxications, even when they suffer alarming symptoms. Relying solely on health services records one would conclude that marihuana is also very little used by college students.

To get a more accurate idea of the extent of experimentation with nutmeg on college campuses, I placed advertisements requesting information about the spice in several student and underground newspapers and also interviewed students from many areas of the country. By these methods I easily collected a number of accounts of nutmeg narcosis, which I have published elsewhere (Weil, 1967). From such cases, I have drawn the following conclusions:

1. Significant numbers of students and persons living in student communities attempt to induce hallucinations with *Myristica*.

2. Unlike prisoners or musicians, who resort to nutmeg when their supplies of standard drugs are cut off, students often take nutmeg as a first experience before they try cannabis or other substances. Nutmeg and mace are cheap, legal, and available at the nearest grocery store.

3. Typically, the young nutmeg-eater first learns of the spice's psychoactivity from a friend or from a published reference.

4. Doses range from 1 teaspoon to a whole can of ground nutmeg. Almost always, the spice is drunk in a glass of juice or water.

5. Onset of action is commonly 2 to 5 or more hours after ingestion. Most neophytes are not aware of the delay. In a very common pattern of intoxication, a person takes an adequate dose of nutmeg in the evening, goes to bed after several hours of waiting in vain for effects, and wakes up the next morning with many of the physical symptoms of toxicity: malaise, headache, dry mouth, tachycardia, dizziness.

6. Some of the reported reactions to nutmeg must be purely psychological. A dose of 1 teaspoon is probably insufficient to cause true symptoms. Similarly, hallucinations or mental changes that come on within 30 min of ingestion are likely to be factitious.

7. Reactions to nutmeg vary from no mental changes at all to full-blown hallucinogenic experiences like those caused by hashish or LSD. There is no apparent correlation between dose and psychoactive effect. Might this extreme variability represent differences in pharmacological potency of different batches of nutmeg? Or do people vary greatly in their sensitivity to the active principle?

8. Visual hallucinations are rather less frequent with nutmeg than with drugs like LSD or mescaline, but distortions of time and space perception with feelings of unreality are common, as with cannabis. Sensations of floating, being transported aloft, or having one's limbs separated from the body are frequently reported.

9. Effects of a single dose of nutmeg usually subside within 12 to 48 hr. An intriguing aftereffect occasionally mentioned is persistent sensitization to the taste of the spice.

10. Most young people who try nutmeg take it once or twice but do not use it habitually. Those who regularly smoke marihuana regard nutmeg as an inferior hallucinogen, largely because of the unpleasant side effects.

Last year I wrote (Weil, 1967) that "ignorance of the psychoactive properties of nutmeg is unquestionably the most important factor limiting extent of its use as a drug." Today I would have to change my statement. At present the ready availability of marihuana is a more important limiting factor, and only in places where marihuana is hard to get, such as prisons, is use of nutmeg likely to be extensive.

There is not time here to examine the pharmacology of nutmeg, but this subject has been well reviewed by Shulgin *et al.* (1967) and Truitt (1967). I simply note that it is not certain that myristicin is solely responsible for the effects of nutmeg on consciousness, and that further work is needed to determine the effects of other components.

Other Spices

Like nutmeg, other spices have long histories of use in ancient medical practice and, like nutmeg, most spices contain complex mixtures of esters, alcohols, and organic acids with probable central nervous system effects. Some exuberant drug users claim that nearly everything on the spice shelf, taken in larger-than-usual quantities, can be used to "get high," although it is difficult to believe isolated claims that the smoking of paprika leads to a "powerful experience" or that ingested ginger can be "dangerously potent." The difficulty is that pharmacological effect that manifests itself solely as subjective psychic change is not easily separated from placebo effect. In view of the startling pharmacological power of nutmeg, it may be wise to keep an open mind about other spices until they have been tested carefully. It is certainly possible that some, like nutmeg, will produce clinical signs that can be measured objectively, such as changes in pupil size, pulse rate, and blood pressure.

Spices of highest priority for such testing are cinnamon, black pepper, and ginger because they are most frequently said to be intoxicating. I have received an unsubstantiated report on the ritual smoking of cinnamon sticks by people in remote parts of Mexico, and I have heard nutmeg eaters discuss the oral use of powdered cinnamon to induce a mild intoxication that sounds more like dreamy sedation than anything hallucinatory.

Black pepper and ginger both seem to have effects on the autonomic nervous system when ingested.

A useful first step in evaluating these substances would be a search of the older literature on them, which might be as extensive as that on nutmeg. Perhaps the animal pharmacology of pepper is waiting to be dug up in some old journal.

Bananas

The use of a preparation of banana skins to achieve alterations of consciousness came to national attention at the beginning of April of 1967. It seems to have started in San Francisco, months before, and to have spread East. The recipe, as usually given, was to scrape the inner white pulp from the skins of a number of ripe bananas, boil it with water to a paste, spread this paste on a metal pan, and dry it slowly in a 200° oven. The dried material, a fine black powder, was then smoked in pipes or cigarettes. The claim was that one to four cigarettes induced mild, short-lasting, marihuanalike intoxication.

Despite the lengthy preparation, this practice enjoyed a brief surge of popularity. In Cambridge, at least, numerous banana parties were held. Doubtless, psychopharmacologists would not have taken much notice were it not for the well-known fact that bananas, along with pineapples, plums, and some nuts, contain significant amounts of 5-hydroxytryptamine or serotonin, a possible transmitter substance in the human nervous system. This chemical is especially noteworthy because of its close structural relation to the tryptamine hallucinogens: simple changes in the serotonin molecule result in some of the most powerful psychoactive drugs known.

Yet serotonin itself is not hallucinogenic at all. Might it be converted to something else when banana skin pulp is heated slowly in the oven, or might some of its chemical relatives be present in the pulp to begin with? The answer to the second question seems to be "no" (Angrist *et al.,* 1967).

A current theory is that the great banana craze of last spring was a hippie "put on," that is, a simple hoax. Still, some users insist thay have "real" effects: just like marihuana, they say, except much weaker. Further chemical analysis of dried banana pulp and, especially, the smoke of this pulp, are warranted.

Green Peppers

A still more unusual practice that came to light in the spring of 1967 was the smoking of rotten green peppers for effects on consciousness. This use never came to the attention of the press, and it was never so widespread as banana smoking. Yet it may have a more substantial basis in pharmacological fact.

According to several hippie informants, ordinary sweet green peppers are allowed to rot in the sun or indoors until they become well decomposed. The rotted pulp is then smeared on tobacco cigarettes and smoked, or a cigarette is inserted into the hollow of the pepper and the smoke is drawn through the vapors of the decomposition products.

Early in 1967 an avant-garde newspaper in New York City printed this recipe. Shortly afterward the practice was noted among inpatients in a psychiatric department in this city. Users report that hallucinations come on within an hour of smoking.

Recent chemical work suggests that rotten peppers contain a substance having the general molecular structure of the tryptamines (Holmstedt, 1967). Whether it is really psychoactive remains to be discovered, but work on the problem is going on.

The sweet pepper, botanically, is *Capsicum frutescens* var. *grossum* in the potato family, a plant group famous for toxic alkaloids. The genus *Capsicum* has never been associated with psychoactivity except in one intriguing reference. There is an anthropological report, now 60 years old, describing the use of peppers as "stimulants and excitants" among the Makusi Indians of British Guiana. Apparently, these peppers were a *Capsicum* (Roth, 1924).

I hope that soon we will know whether any of these grocery-store items have definite activity. I hope also that we can collect other reports on suspected psychoactivity in plants and plant products of our own country. There is a wealth of data to be considered: the testimony of users, reports of observers, the medical literature on unusual types of poisoning, ancient pharmacological treatises, and laboratory analyses of common plant products. In all of this material may lie clues to new and yet more interesting psychoactive compounds

REFERENCES

Alldredge, N. L. (1964). Deputy Assistant Director, U.S. Bureau of Prisons, personal communication.

Andre, S. (1964). Nutmeg jag, *Mississippi Mag.* **4**, 18

Angrist, B. M., *et al.* (1967). *N. Y. State J. Med.*

Cushny, A. R. (1908). *Proc. Royal. Soc. Med.* **1**, 39.

Freyhan, F. A. (1961). *Comp. Psychiatry* **2**, 241–247.

Green, R. C. (1959). *J. Am. Med. Assoc.* **171**, 1342–1344.

Holmstedt, B. (1967). Personal communication.

Lewin, L. (1924). "Phantastica."

McCord, J. A., and Jervey, L. P. (1962). *J. S. Carolina Med. Assoc.* **58,** 436–438.

Malcolm X., with A. Haley, (1964). The Autobiography of Malcolm X.

New York *Times* (1967). October 27.

Payne, R. B. (1963). *New Engl. J. Med.* **269,** 36–38.

Roth, E. E. (1924). *38th Ann. Rept. Bur. Am. Ethnol. 1916–17,* 25; quoted by R. E. Schultes *In* "Ethnopharmocologic Search for Psychoactive Drugs," 1967.

Shulgin, A. T., *et al.* (1967). *In* "Ethnopharmacologic Search for Psychoactive Drugs."

Truitt, E. B. (1967). *In* "Ethnopharmacologic Search for Psychoactive Drugs."

Weil, A. T. (1965). Nutmeg as a narcotic. *Econ. Botan.* **19,** 194–217.

Weil, A. T. (1967). Nutmeg as a psychoactive drug. *In* "Ethnopharmacologic Search for Psychoactive Drugs."

Weiss, G. (1960). *Psychiat. Quart.* **34,** 346–356.

Some Hallucinogenic and Related Plants

Norman R. Farnsworth

> ... We can no longer afford to ignore reports of any aboriginal use of a plant merely because they seem to fall beyond the limit of our credence. To do so would be tantamount to the closing of a door, forever to entomb a peculiar kind of native knowledge which might lead us along paths of immeasurable progress.
>
> R. E. Schultes, 1963

In most cases, the psychotomimetic effects of the plants to be discussed can be directly attributed to the presence of known chemical constituents. In other instances, partial explanations can be given for the reported biological effects on the basis of the presence of constituents which should be expected to be the active principles. However, there may be some question as to whether or not the nature of the active constituents present in other plants to be discussed is really known. Finally, there is a group of plants, alleged to exert psychotomimetic effects, for which there is no rational explanation.

Strangely, the first source of information relating to a new psychotogen is often the lay press. However, these lay reports, even when written by so-called science reporters, are seldom accurate. A recent example bears out this point. The following article recently appeared in a national weekly news magazine (Anon., 1967).

Perils of Periwinkle—Marihuana, LSD, mushrooms, banana peels—and now periwinkle leaves. Psychedelic periwinkle? No one is sure how the word got out, but the first case of periwinkle high has been reported in Bradenton, Fla., where five teen-agers disclosed that they were smoking the dried and shredded leaves of the periwinkle, a blue-blossomed plant common throughout the U.S. The smoke, the youngsters reported, made their skin tingle as though ants were crawling over it and they seem to see the world through the wrong end of a telescope. When Dr. George Dame, the health official in Manatee County, where Bradenton is situated, heard about the episode he did some investigating.

Periwinkle leaves, Dame recalled, are the source of vincristine and vinblastine, two potent drugs used in the treatment of acute leukemia and Hodgkin's disease. The drugs work by reducing the production of white blood cells. As the number of white cells decreases, patients taking the drugs may become unusually vulnerable to infections; other vincristine and vinblastine side effects include loss of hair and muscle weakness. Assuming that continued smoking of periwinkle could lead to similar effects, Dame issued a warning against periwinkle highs.

A chemist at Eli Lilly and Company, Indianapolis, where the drugs vincristine and vinblastine were developed, said last week that the perils may not be as great as Dame suspects. Both vincristine and vinblastine, he pointed out, are highly unstable and probably do not get into the smoke of burning periwinkle leaves in an active form. Nonetheless, the chemist was quick to put down the periwinkle cult. "Periwinkle," he said, "like most inedible plants, is toxic. You might get pretty sick to your stomach."

There are a number of inaccuracies in this article.

1. If the observation of the blue-flowering periwinkle used by these school children is correct, the reference must be to *Vinca minor*. However, there is some confusion since the Madagascan periwinkle, *Catharanthus roseus (Vinca rosea)*, also grows throughout Florida almost as a weed, but this plant has either pink or white flowers, or flowers with a white corolla and a red center. The writer of this news article was quick to place the blame on the latter of these plants, when reference most surely was to the former.

2. Even if the plant in question was *Catharanthus roseus,* the following inaccuracies can also be cited.

(a) Vincristine and vinblastine do not exert their anticancer action in the same manner. Vincristine does not cause a marked decrease in the number of white blood cells, as this article points out so strongly.

(b) Periwinkle plants, both *Vinca minor* and *Catharanthus roseus,* have been used extensively as folkloric remedies for centuries (Farnsworth, 1961). No toxicities have been reported in the literature as due to the ingestion of either of these plants, in moderate amounts, which is how they are used in the folklore.

This example is cited because it exemplifies most reports of the use of plants as psychedelics in the lay press. Such reports prompt others to experiment dangerously with the plant, and they disseminate inaccurate and possibly harmful information to the general public.

The active principles of plants that have been used for psychotomimetic effects can be broadly classified into the following groups.

I. Plants containing non-nitrogenous active principles.

    A. Phenylpropene-containing plants.

        1. *Myristica fragrans* (Myristicaceae).

Nutmeg of commerce is the dried seed of *Myristica fragrans* (Myristicaceae), produced from trees grown either in the East or the West Indies. A good tree produces 1500 to 2000 nuts annually, which weigh about 10 lbs. In 1965 the United States imported some 5,300,000 lbs

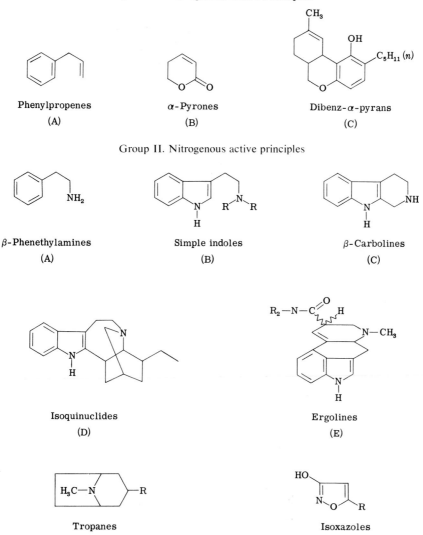

Group I. Non-nitrogenous Active Principles

Phenylpropenes
(A)

α-Pyrones
(B)

Dibenz-α-pyrans
(C)

Group II. Nitrogenous active principles

β-Phenethylamines
(A)

Simple indoles
(B)

β-Carbolines
(C)

Isoquinuclides
(D)

Ergolines
(E)

Tropanes
(F)

Isoxazoles
(G)

of nutmeg, the majority of which was undoubtedly used as a condiment. Weil (1965, 1967), who has studied the nutmeg problem extensively has listed, in this volume, a number of conclusions with regard to its use as a psychotomimetic drug.

It seems clear that the active psychotomimetic substances are present in the volatile oil derived from nutmeg, which represents some 8 to 15% of the weight of the seeds when obtained by steam distillation (Weil, 1967). This volatile oil contains fatty acids, terpenes, and aromatics (Shulgin *et al.*, 1967). The remainder of the seed is made up of 25 to 40% of a fixed oil (nutmeg butter), comprising trimyristicin, glycerides, and unknown constituents, in addition to 45 to 60% "inert" pulp (Shulgin *et al.*, 1967). Analyses reported by several investigators offer real evidence as to the chemical variability of nutmeg oil samples, both qualitatively and quantitatively. Table 1 gives a recent analysis of a sample of West Indian volatile oil of nutmeg.

Although there is no evidence in the literature to the effect that con-

TABLE 1

ANALYSIS OF WEST INDIAN SAMPLE OF NUTMEG OIL [a]

		Percent
I.	Terpene fraction	
	α-Pinene	36.16
	1,8-*p*-Menthadiene	12.78
	Sabinene	12.75
	β-Pinene	6.16
	1,4-*p*-Menthadiene	3.47
	Camphene	2.97
	1-Menthene-4-ol	2.93
	p-Cymene	1.82
	1,4(8)-*p*-Menthadiene	1.12
	1-Menthene-8-ol	0.41
	Geranyl acetate	0.20
	Linalool	0.15
	Toluene	0.10
II.	Aromatic fraction	
	Myristicin	7.04
	Elemicin	2.36
	Safrole	1.29
	Methyleugenol	0.62
	Methylisoeugenol	0.36
	Methoxyeugenol	0.25
	Isoeugenol	0.19
	Eugenol	0.17
	Isoelemicin	0.11
III.	Others	
	Unidentified	3.72
	Myristic acid	2.87

[a] Shulgin *et al.* (1967).

stituents of the terpene fraction are inactive as psychotomimetic agents, this is universally presumed. Therefore, attention is focused on the aromatic fraction. Safrole, myristicin, and elemicin are most frequently judged to be the active agents in nutmeg. If this is true, there is reason to believe that differences in the psychotomimetic effect of various lots of nutmeg are due to variations in the content of one or more of these three substances. A recent comparison involving the analysis of eight lots of nutmeg oil from various sources has shown that the safrole content varied from 0.53 to 3.42%, the myristicin content from 3.86 to 12.78%, and the elemicin content from 0.02 to 2.36% (Shulgin *et al.,* 1967). However, in all samples analyzed, these three compounds always accounted for 84 to 95% of the total aromatic fractions of the oil. The structure of known components of the aromatic fractions of nutmeg oil are given in Fig. 1.

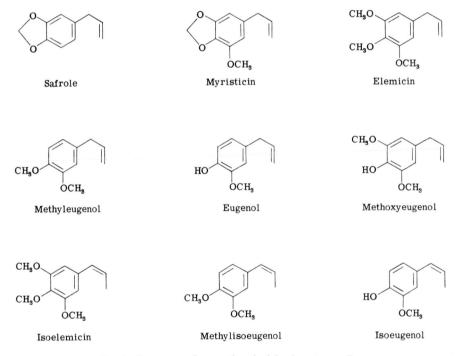

Safrole   Myristicin   Elemicin

Methyleugenol   Eugenol   Methoxyeugenol

Isoelemicin   Methylisoeugenol   Isoeugenol

FIG. 1. Structures of aromatic principles in nutmeg oil.

To date, psychopharmacologic investigations on pure safrole or elemicin have not been reported. The early reports available on myristicin concerned a product that was obtained by distillation from oil of nutmeg, and it is known that elemicin-free myristicin cannot be obtained in this manner. Thus, unless the myristicin-source oil was relatively free of elemicin, the latter compound may have been responsible for at least some of the psychotomimetic responses observed in these tests. In any event, elemicin may be a major contributor of activity, but it has not been made available in pure form for testing.

Safrole is probably not an active psychotropic substance, judged indirectly by the fact that sassafras oil contains some 80% of safrole, and this oil has never had a reputation of being used as a psychotomimetic substance.

Myristicin has been tested in man at twice the dose which would be obtained if 20 g of typical nutmeg were administered. The symptoms were only suggestive of psychotropic effects in 6 to 10 subjects (Shulgin et al., 1967). Thus, owing to an absence of marked effects, it appears that myristicin also is not the major contributor of psychotomimetic activity.

In conclusion, the following facts are fairly well established with regard to the identity of the active constituents in nutmeg.

1. The active psychotomimetic principles probably reside in the aromatic fraction of the volatile oil derived from *Myristica fragrans* seed.

2. These principles probably vary according to the source and lot.

3. Either the activity is due to elemicin, a synergism between combinations of safrole, myristicin, and elemicin, or the active principle is either a known or unknown trace component of the aromatic fraction which has not yet been evaluated.

4. There is a distinct possibility that safrole, myristicin and/or elemicin are converted by some unknown mechanism into nitrogenous compounds (Fig. 2), which would be amphetamine-like derivatives. Various schemes

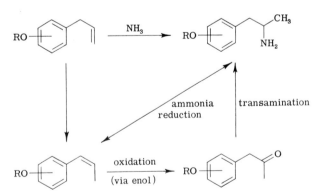

Fig. 2. Postulated mechanisms for conversion of phenylpropenes into corresponding nitrogen derivatives (Shulgin *et al.*, 1967).

for this conversion have been postulated by Shulgin *et al.* (1967). The psychotropic activities of these nitrogen-containing phenylpropenes could be explained more easily than the activities of the nitrogen-free and naturally occurring phenylpropenes of nutmeg.

    B. α-Pyrone-containing plants.

        1. *Piper methysticum* Forst. (Piperaceae).

This plant is a perennial shrub indigenous to many islands of the South Pacific. A beverage is prepared from the roots of this plant which is popularly known as Kava, Kawa, or Awa. Although the first major scientific examination of Kawa was published by Lewin in 1886, the biological effects of this beverage were described by Captain James Cook in 1768. Many scientific investigators have reported that Kawa can induce a form of euphoria, described as a happy state of complete comfort and peace, with ease of conversation and increased perceptivity, followed by restful sleep. The descriptions have indicated that the Kawa experience is apparently pleasant and free of hangover or other side or after effects. In recent years, several people have indicated that the beverage now available in the South Sea Islands and known as Kawa is a refreshing drink, but it does not offer the euphoric effects described by earlier workers. This controversy continues today (Holmes, 1967; Gajdusek, 1967; Ford, 1967; Steinmetz, 1960).

To understand part of the problem, it must be realized that in former times the Kawa beverage was prepared in a ceremonial rite in which selected people from a tribe were responsible for masticating the roots of the Kawa plant. The saliva so obtained was then transferred to a suitable vessel, mixed with coconut milk or water, and then taken by the members of the tribe. Today, the ritual has not changed much except that the mastication process has been substituted by grinding in a stone mortar.

Various investigators have attempted to prove that the mastication process was necessary because it "emulsified" the active constituents and presented them to the body in a more satisfactory form than a simple grinding process. Enzymatic conversion of Kawa principles during the mastication process has also been advanced as a theory for formation of active principles from inactive precursors, but evidence for this possibility is lacking.

A great deal of chemical work has been reported in an attempt to isolate the euphoric principle(s) from *Piper methysticum* (Klohs, 1967; Keller and Klohs, 1963). Most of this work has been concerned with the isolation of a series of related water-insoluble α-pyrones. Some of the major reasons for this emphasis on water-insoluble constituents (and we have had some experience with this plant in our own laboratories) are that the

α-pyrones are isolated in relatively high yield, they are amenable to crystallization, and they are not particularly difficult to separate. A summary of the substances isolated to date from *Piper methysticum* is found in Fig. 3. Eight of these isolated principles are α-pyrones: methysticin (I), dihydromethysticin (II), kawain (III), dihydrokawain (IV), yangonin (V), desmethoxyyangonin (VI), 11-methoxyyangonin (VII), 11-methoxy-*nor*-yangonin (VIII), and 5,6-dehydromethysticin (IX). In addition, two chalcones, flavokawin A (X) and flavokawin B (XI), have been isolated from this plant. It is interesting to note that the corresponding dihydro derivatives of yangonin, desmethoxyyangonin, 11-methoxy-yangonin, 11-methoxy-*nor*-yangonin, and 5,6-dehydromethysticin, have never been isolated from this plant, whereas the presence of dihydro derivatives of methysticin and kawain is well established. Compounds I to VI have each been evaluated for their effects on the central nervous system in animals (Klohs, 1967). However, although methysticin and dihydromethysticin proved effective as sedative agents, a chloroform extract of the root, and the ground root by itself, each gave better results than the crystalline compounds tested. Hence, since this work was done under the same conditions and in the same laboratory, it would appear that the most potent sedative and/or psychotomimetic constituent(s) remain to be discovered.

No pharmacologic studies have been reported to date on 11-methoxy-yangonin (VII), 11-methoxy-*nor*-yangonin (VIII), or 5,6-dehydro-methysticin (IX); however, structure-activity studies with a series of synthetic compounds have shown that saturation of the 5,6 positions in the α-pyrone ring is necessary for activity. Since these compounds are all 5,6-dehydro-α-pyrones, they undoubtedly would be devoid of activity, or would have greatly reduced activity, on the central nervous system. Flavokawin A (X) and flavokawin B (XI) also remain uninvestigated.

A most amazing fact about the whole Kawa problem has been that, until recently, the water-soluble constituents of *Piper methysticum* roots have remained uninvestigated. It would appear from all reasonable assumptions that, if the active Kawa beverage was prepared by mastication, followed by mixing with coconut milk or water, the true psychotomimetic principle(s) should be in a water-soluble, rather than an organic solvent-soluble, fraction.

Indeed, Buckley and his co-workers have found that, by steam distilling an aqueous mixture of *Piper methysticum* roots, a material could be obtained that appears to have true tranquilizing properties, at least from a vast amount of pharmacological data obtained to date. This active fraction has been shown to be completely devoid of α-pyrones, has no nitrogen, and is water-soluble (1967).

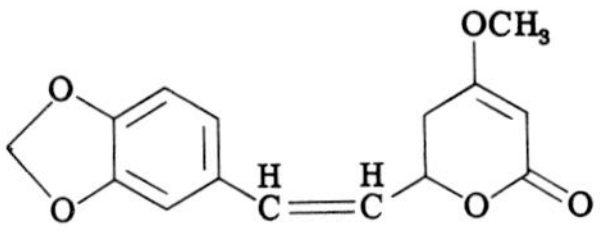

Methysticin
(I)

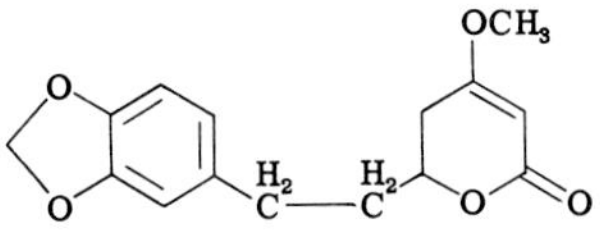

Dihydromethysticin
(II)

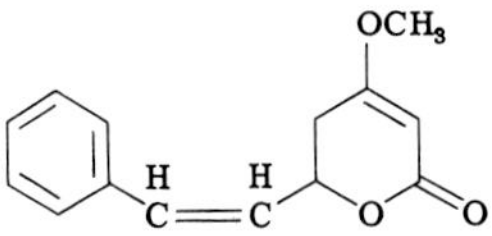

Kawain
(III)

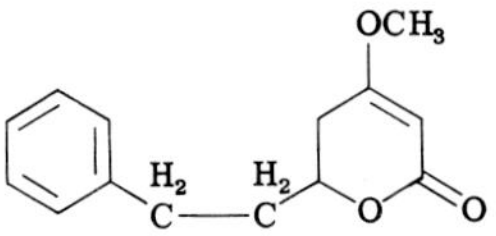

Dihydrokawain
(IV)

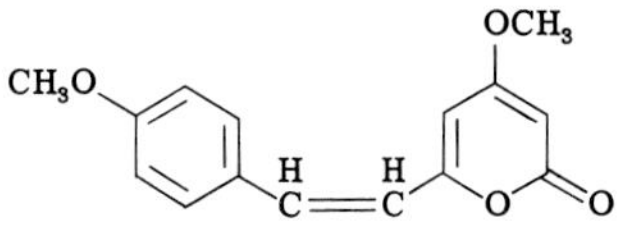

Yangonin
(V)

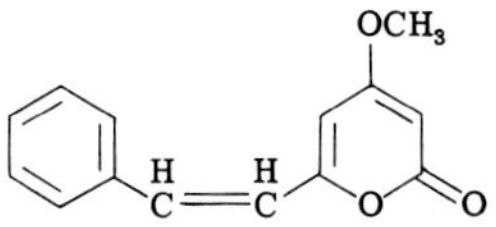

Desmethoxyyangonin
(VI)

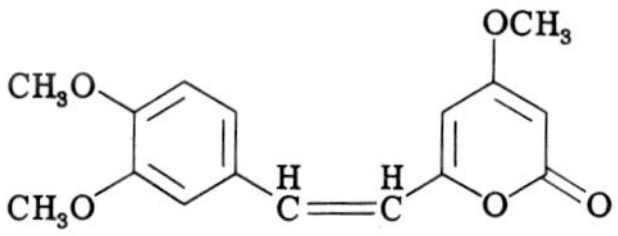

11-Methoxyyangonin
(VII)

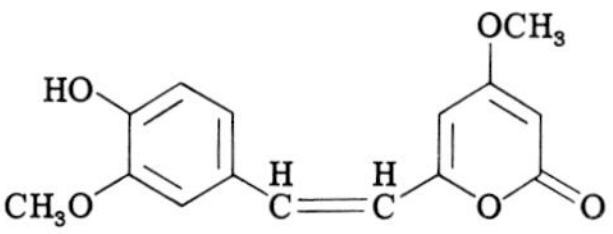

11-Methoxy-*nor*-yangonin
(VIII)

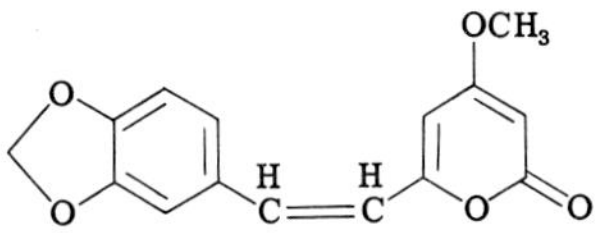

5,6-Dehydromethysticin
(IX)

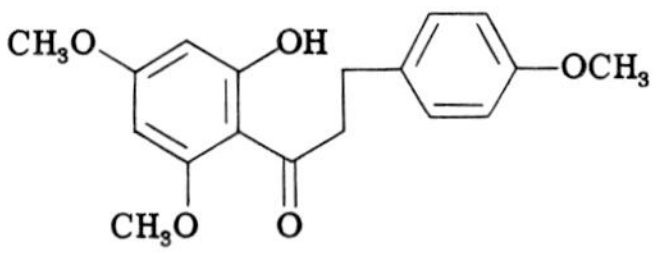

Flavokawin A
(X)

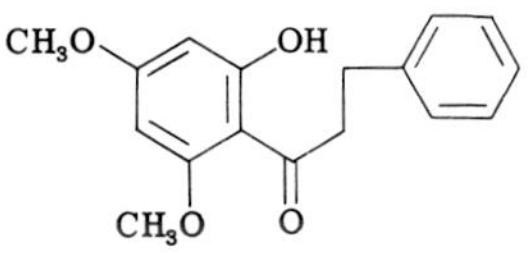

Flavokawin B
(XI)

Fig. 3. Crystalline principles from *Piper methysticum.*

In summary, and to date, the riddle of Kawa that has remained unsolved since Cook's reports in 1768 stands as follows:

1. None of the α-pyrones known to occur in *P. methysticum,* and which have been available for testing, have shown the biological activity ascribed to the Kawa beverage.

2. There is evidence that activity resides in chloroform, as well as in aqueous extracts from the roots of this plant, that cannot be explained on the basis of constituents isolated from this plant.

3. Five crystalline compounds isolated from *P. methysticum* have never been evaluated for psychotropic effects.

    C. Dibenz-α-pyrans.

        1. *Cannabis sativa* L. (Cannabinaceae).

Marihuana has presented a perplexing problem to various cultures and societies of the world since before the year 2737 B.C. The conflict arising in recent times over whether the use of marihuana is "good" or "bad" can be brought out by recalling some of the adjectives used to describe the plant (and its effects) by several different generations. In the B.C. era, the Chinese often referred to it as the "Liberator of Sin," whereas at a later period the same people gave it the name "Delight Giver." Hindus have long termed it "The Heavenly Guide" and the "Soother of Grief." The extent to which adjectives are affixed to the name of this plant is, undoubtedly, dependent on whether the interest lies in using it as a psychotomimetic, or whether the interest is in the prevention of its use. To give valid scientific evidence against its use has been difficult for a number of reasons. An understanding of the plant itself, its growth characteristics and its chemical constituents, might well lead to a better understanding of the problem involved.

Botanically speaking, marihuana is derived from the plant *Cannabis sativa* L. (Cannabinaceae). It is a tall, annual weed, sometimes attaining a height of 15 or more feet, and it grows in almost any waste or fertile area. It is important to emphasize that this plant is dioecious. The staminate plant usually grows taller than the pistillate plant. The staminate flowers are axillary and borne in panicles, whereas the axillary pistillate flowers are long catkins. Differentiation of the male and female plants is important because the chemical compounds which are responsible for the euphoric effect of marihuana are found primarily in a sticky resin that covers the female flowers and adjacent leaves. Of characteristic importance in identifying both the male and female plants are the leaves, which are large and palmately compound, each having 5 to 7 linear-lanceolate leaflets, with serrate leaf margins. Although the literature invariably refers to the resin covering the female flower parts as the only part of the plant containing the euphoric principles, very few exacting data are available to substantiate this assumption and, indeed, the male plant also may contain active substances. Detailed phytochemical studies of all parts of both male and female plants seem to be in order.

Federal control of marihuana is currently a responsibility of the Bureau of Narcotics of the U.S. Treasury Department. However, since it is fairly well established that this drug is distinctly different in its biological effects from the truly addicting opiates, it is felt that marihuana control may soon be shifted to the Department of Health, Education and Welfare, and this may pave the way for more liberal marihuana laws.

Although the layman may not always use the proper terminology when he speaks of marihuana or its derivatives, certain terms associated with this drug are quite clear in their meaning. *Hashish, charas, churrus,* and *churus* are all terms referring to the unadulterated resin from the flowering tops of cultivated female *Cannabis sativa* plants. *Bhang* is prepared from uncultivated plants from which the tops of female plants are cut and a decoction in water or milk is made. The decoction is also sometimes dried and smoked. *Ganja* is prepared by harvesting the female tops from very carefully selected cultivated plants. These tops are made into an infusion, or dried and smoked, giving a preparation superior to bhang but inferior to hashish. *Majun* is ganja that has been incorporated into sweetmeats.

Most of these terms are seldom encountered in the United States, with the exception of hashish, which on most occasions is incorrectly used, since most of the *Cannabis sativa* used in this country is composed of the dried, cut, flowering tops of *Cannabis sativa* plants (probably a mixture of both male and female plants in most cases). This is admixed with considerable leaf material, and generally passed more correctly under the names of *marihuana, pot,* or *grass.* Cigarettes containing marihuana are referred to as *reefers, mooters, muggles, greeters, gates,* and so on. The majority of marihuana which finds its way into the United States is smuggled across the border from Mexico, and is often referred to as *Acapulco gold* by its users.

A number of chemical compounds have been isolated from the resin of *Cannabis sativa* (hashish) (Wolstenholme and Knight, 1965; Gaoni and Mechoulam, 1966; Korte *et al.,* 1965). Among these are cannabinol (CBN), cannabidiol (CBD), cannabidiolic acid (CBDA), tetrahydrocannabinol carboxylic acid, cannabigerol (CBG), cannabichromene (CBC), and a mixture of stereoisomers known collectively as tetrahydrocannabinols (THC). Some of the tetrahydrocannabinols (mixtures) examined show considerable variation in their pharmacological activity, but most give marihuana-like activity in varying degrees. Recently it was established that Δ^1-tetrahydrocannabinol is, in fact, the major active euphoric principle in *Cannabis sativa* resin. These compounds and their close relationships, are shown in Fig. 4.

In addition to the euphoric activity of the tetrahydrocannabinols, and particularly the major active principle Δ^1-tetrahydrocannabinol, cannabichromene is said to have similar activity (Gaoni and Mechoulam, 1966). Cannabinol and cannabidiol are inactive. Cannabigerol and cannabidiolic acid are sedative principles which do not exert euphoria, and cannabidiolic acid is a potent antimicrobial agent (Wolstenholme and Knight, 1965).

One of the major reasons for variation in the chemical composition and biological activity of *Cannabis sativa* is that some of the constituents are unstable and change form. It has been explained that on aging, cannabidiolic acid (inactive) is gradually converted into cannabidiol (inactive), then into tetrahydrocannabinols (active), and finally into cannabinol (inactive) (Grlic, 1964). These biological conversions proceed at a more rapid rate in tropical areas than in more temperature zones. Therefore samples of varying age give rise to differences in biological effects in man. Of course, other factors, such as ecological and geographical ones, are also important, since it is presumed that the active constituents are mainly present in the resin, and a great deal more of the resin is produced when the plant grows in hot climates than in the temperate zones of the world (Grlic, 1964).

A great problem facing lawmakers with regard to marihuana has been a conflict of opinion about the exact physical and mental effects of the active principles from this plant. This has been due to a lack of valid, controlled, scientific experiments. Many available biological data have been obtained through experiments involving crude plant preparations, in which the chemical constituents were unknown, both qualitatively and quantitatively. Even experiments with "tetrahydrocannabinol" were probably actually conducted using a mixture of stereoisomers, each component of the mixture having different degrees of biological activity. Thus it has been almost an impossibility to correlate published data on the effects of marihuana.

Recently Drs. Rafael Mechoulam and Yehiel Gaoni, of the Hebrew University in Israel, announced that they had succeeded in producing pure Δ^1-tetrahydrocannabinol, believed to be identical with the active euphoric principle of marihuana, in large-scale laboratory experiments. If this compound is indeed the major active principle in *Cannabis sativa,* a major breakthrough in our understanding of marihuana and its biological

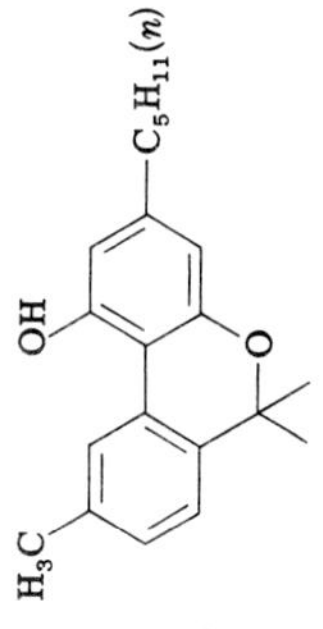
Cannabinol (CBN)

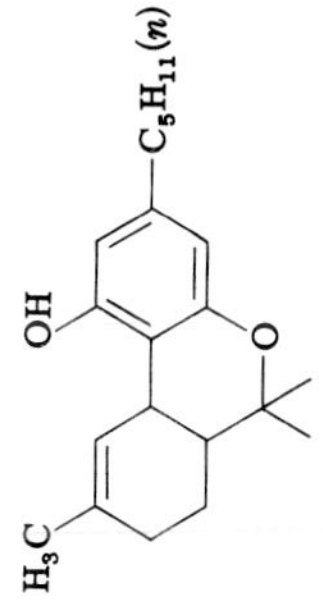
Δ^1-Tetrahydrocannabinol (THC)

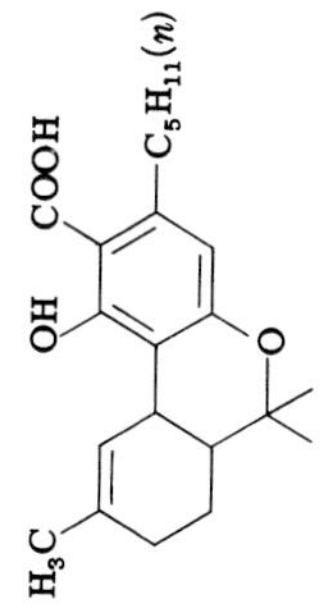
Δ^1-Tetrahydrocannabinol carboxylic acid

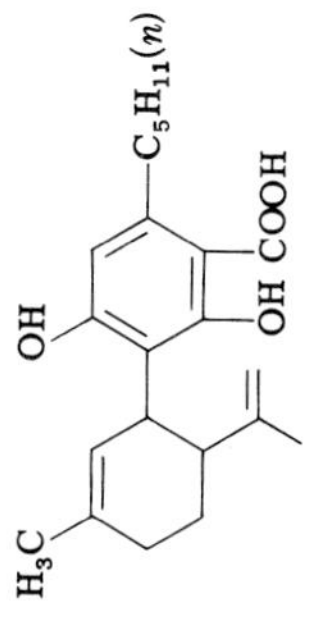
Cannabidiolic acid (CBDA)

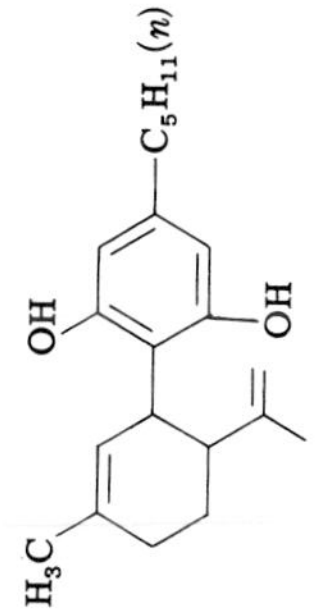
Cannabidiol (CBD)

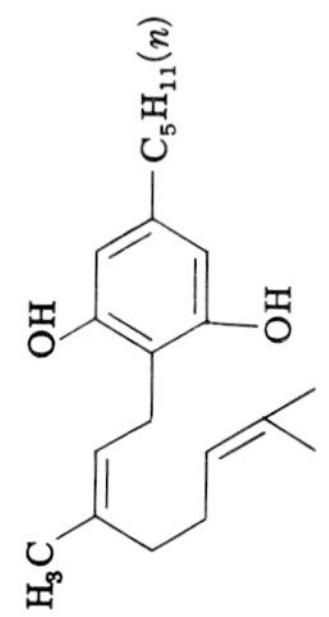
Cannabigerol

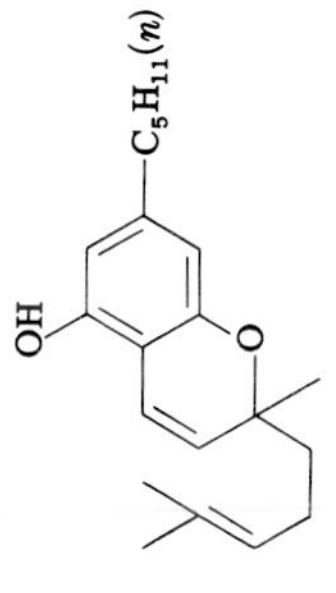
Cannabichromene

FIG. 4. Constituents of *Cannabis sativa* L. (Hashish).

effects is now imminent. This will now allow pharmacologists to pursue the long- and short-term effects of the pure active principle of marihuana in laboratory animals, and then in man. This should logically lead to information on the exact mechanism of action of Δ^1-tetrahydrocannabinol.

This finding, then, should place science at the threshold of a new understanding of marihuana and its effects, and should give information that can reinforce decisions regarding the legal control of this plant on the basis of scientific evidence rather than on emotions. The question will then arise: Will society accept the basic scientific facts about this plant and its active principles, and its effects on the body, and govern itself accordingly?

II. Plants Containing Nitrogenous Active Principles.
     A. β-Phenethylamine-containing plants.
          1. *Lophophora williamsii* (Lem.) Coulter (Cactaceae).

Peyote, or mescal button, is derived from the cactus *Lophophora williamsii (Anhalonium lewinii)* and has been used for hallucinatory purposes for centuries (LaBarre, 1959). It is most commonly employed in the southwestern part of the United States, but in recent years its use has spread throughout the country. In 1918 the Native American Church was formed, and a part of the ceremonial rites of this church involved the use of peyote. This church now has an estimated membership of some 225,000. The Native American Church preaches family responsibility, brotherly love, and abstinence from alcohol. Recently the courts ruled that peyote could be legally used as part of the ritual of this church.

Although some fifteen β-phenethylamine and simple isoquinoline alkaloids (Figs. 5, 6) have been isolated from *Lophophora williamsii*

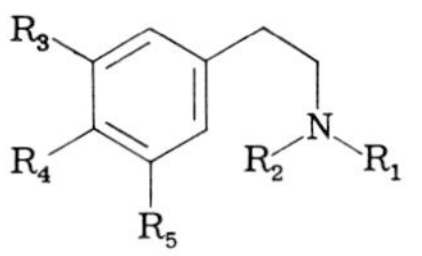

R_{-1}	R_{-2}	R_{-3}	R_{-4}	R_{-5}	Alkaloid
H	H	H	OH	H	Tyramine
H	CH_3	H	OH	H	N-Methyltyramine
CH_3	CH_3	H	OH	H	Hordenine
H	H	OCH_3	OCH_3	OCH_3	Mescaline
H	CH_3	OCH_3	OCH_3	OCH_3	N-Methylmescaline
H	Ac	OCH_3	OCH_3	OCH_3	N-Acetylmescaline
$(CH_3)_3^+$		H	OH	H	Candicine

FIG. 5. β-Phenethylamine alkaloids of *Lophophora williamsii*.

(Der Marderosian, 1966), the major hallucinogenic principle is well established as mescaline.

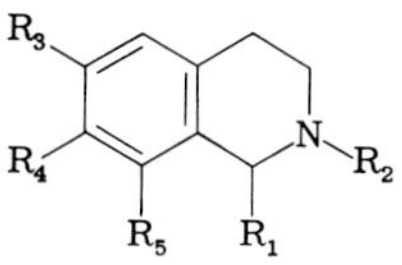

R_1	R_2	R_3	R_4	R_5	Alkaloid
H	H	OCH_3	OCH_3	OH	Anhalamine
H	H	OCH_3	OCH_3	OCH_3	Anhalinine
CH_3	H	OCH_3	$-O-CH_2-O-$		Anhalonine
CH_3	H	OCH_3	OCH_3	OH	Anhalonidine
CH_3	H	OCH_3	OCH_3	OCH_3	O-Methylanhalonidine
H	CH_3	OCH_3	OCH_3	OH	Anhalidine
CH_3	CH_3	OCH_3	OCH_3	OH	Pellotine
CH_3	CH_3	OCH_3	$-O-CH_2-O-$		Lophophorine

FIG. 6. Isoquinoline alkaloids of *Lophophora williamsii.*

The psychotomimetic effects of mescaline are elicited with doses of 0.3 to 0.5 g. After ingestion, mescaline first induces nausea, tremor, and perspiration. After 1 to 2 hr, these unpleasant effects subside and a dream-like intoxicating phase follows in which vivid kaleidoscopic visions are induced before the user falls into a deep sleep (Der Marderosian, 1966; Kluver, 1966).

It is thought by some groups that mescaline is transformed into a compound resembling LSD in the body, but factual confirmation of this hypothesis is lacking (Fischer, 1965; Hofmann, 1961).

B. Simple indole-containing plants.
1. *Piptadenia* species (Leguminosae).

A number of *Piptadenia* species have been used in South America by Indians to induce psychotomimetic effects (Schultes, 1963b, 1967; Altschul, 1967; Seitz, 1967). The plant material is prepared into a snuff and is blown into the nasal cavity in any one of several ways. Although some chemical work has been done on these snuffs, much of it has utilized plant material that was not properly identified, or which was misidentified. Only recently have several studies on botanically authenticated materials been made; the major chemical compounds responsible for the psycho-tomimetic effects of these snuffs have been identified as a series of substituted β-phenethylamines: *N,N*-dimethyltryptamine (DMT), *N*-monomethyltryptamine (MMT), 5-methoxy-*N,N*-dimethyltryptamine (5-MeO-DMT), 5-methoxy-*N*-monomethyltryptamine (5-MeO-MMT), 5-hydroxy-*N,N*-dimethyltryptamine (bufotenin) (5-OH-DMT), *N,N*-dimethyltryptamine-*N*-oxide (DMT-*N*-oxide) and 5-hydroxy-*N,N*-dimethyltryptamine-*N*-oxide (5-OH-DMT-*N*-oxide) (Fig. 7). For a comparison of the different substituted tryptamines in certain South American snuffs, see Table 2 (Holmstedt and Lindgren, 1967).

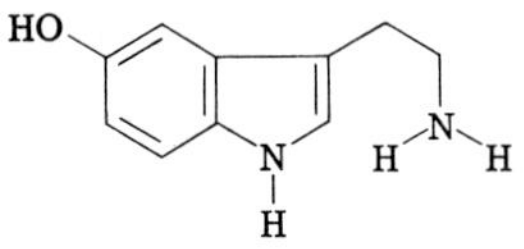

5-Hydroxytryptamine
(5-HT) (serotonin)

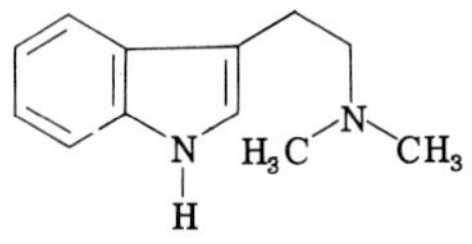

Dimethoxytryptamine
(DMT)

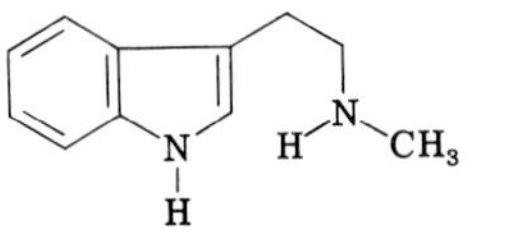

Monomethoxytryptamine
(MMT)

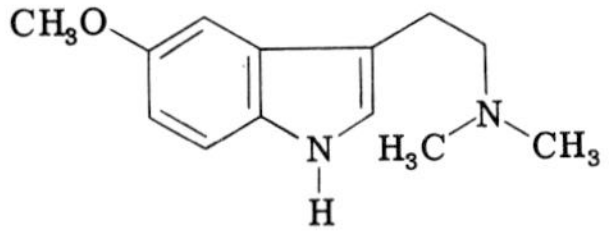

5-Methoxydimethyltryptamine
(5-MeO-DMT)

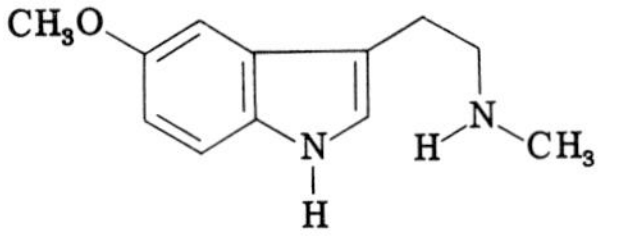

5-Methoxymono-
methyltryptamine
(5-MeO-MMT)

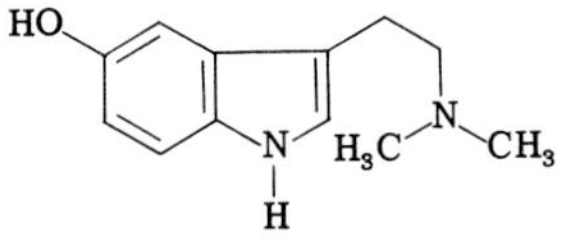

5-Hydroxydimethyl-
tryptamine
(5-OH-DMT, bufotenine)

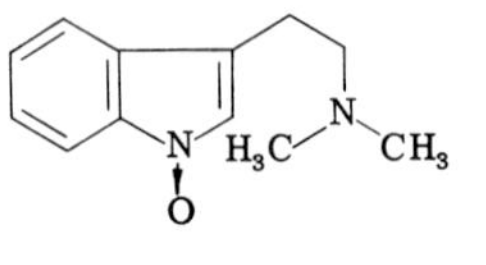

Dimethyltryptamine-
N-oxide (DMT-*N*-oxide)

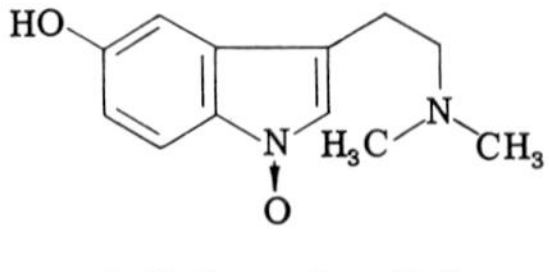

5-Hydroxydimethyl-
tryptamine-*N*-oxide
(5-OH-DMT-*N*-oxide)

FIG. 7. Structures of alkaloids in South American snuffs and their relationship to 5-hydroxytryptamine (serotonin).

TABLE 2

β-PHENETHYLAMINES IN CERTAIN SOUTH AMERICAN HALLUCINATORY SNUFFS[a]

Species	Plant part	β-Phenethylamine content[b]						
		1	2	3	4	5	6	7
Piptadenia peregrina Benth.	Seed	−	−	+	+	+	+	+
Piptadenia peregrina Benth.	Bark	+	+	+	−	+	−	−
Piptadenia macrocarpa Benth.	Seed	−	+	+	+	−	+	+
Piptadenia excelsa (Gris.) Lillo	Seed	−	−	+	−	−	+	+
Piptadenia colubrina Benth.	Seed	−	−	−	−	−	+	−
Mimosa hostilis Benth.	Root	−	−	+	−	−	−	−
Virola calophylla Warburg	Bark	+	−	+	−	+	−	−

[a] Holmstedt and Lindgren (1967).

[b] (1) MMT, (2) 5-MeO-MMT, (3) DMT, (4) DMT-*N*-oxide, (5) 5-MeO-DMT, (6) 5-OH-DMT, and (7) 5-OH-DMT-*N*-oxide.

It is assumed that the active tryptamines reach the brain via absorption from the vascular nasal mucosa into the bloodstream, or that they act directly on the brain without having been transported through the general circulation. Although all the tryptamines known to be present in these snuffs have not been pharmacologically investigated, it is reasonably certain that 5-OH-DMT (bufotenin) does not account for the psychotomimetic action. DMT and 5-MeO-DMT, on the other hand, have been shown to be potent psychotomimetic agents. This has been explained on the basis of a low lipid solubility of 5-OH-DMT, as compared with a high lipid solubility for DMT and 5-MeO-DMT. Thus the latter compounds are more effectively able to penetrate the nervous system and exert their effects (Holmstedt and Lindgren, 1967).

It is truly amazing that the South American Indians found it necessary to utilize these hallucinogens in the form of a snuff, whereby the activity of the tryptamines became evident. Oral use of these snuffs would have been ineffective, since the tryptamines are not active by this route of administration.

2. Fungi.

The mushroom-worshipping indians of Mexico have long utilized *Teonanacatl* ("Flesh of the Gods") as a sacrament or communion in Aztec religious rites, and the fungi have indeed been shown to elicit psychotomimetic effects (Schultes, 1939, 1963a,b). Several different genera of mushrooms have been employed as sacred psychotomimetic drugs, and the genera *Psilocybe, Conocybe* and *Stropharia* have been identified as comprising these mushrooms (Schultes, 1963a,b).

The most important of the psychotropic mushrooms is *Psilocybe mexicana,* which was chemically examined by Hofmann and co-workers, and found to contain the 4-hydroxydimethyltryptamines psilocybine and psilocine, which are the active principles (Schultes, 1963b). Psilocybine is the first example of a phosphorus-containing indole found in nature and, unlike most other substituted tryptamines, is an active psychotomimetic substance when taken orally.

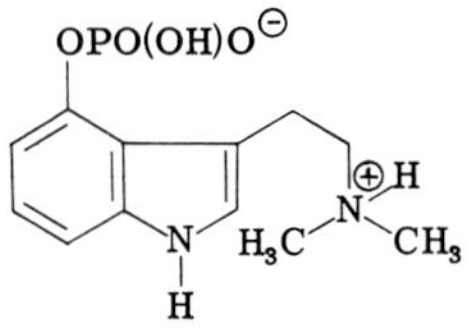

OPO(OH)O$^{\ominus}$

Psilocybine

OH

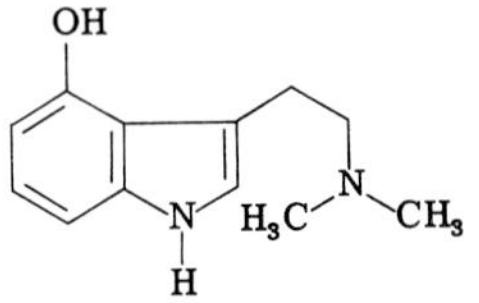

Psilocine

3. Miscellaneous plants.

Widespread knowledge of the distribution of 5-hydroxytryptamine (5-HT) (serotonin) in the plant kingdom has prompted thrill seekers to experiment with certain of these plants in an attempt to induce psychotomimetic effects. A recent report in the lay press to the effect that smoking dried banana peels would induce hallucinations is a typical example.

With regard to this problem, it has been shown that the peel of unripe bananas contains ca. 0.3 μg/g (fresh weight) of 5-HT, while the pulp of unripe bananas contains ca. 25 μg/g of 5-HT (fresh weight); the peel and pulp of ripe bananas, on the other hand, contain considerably more 5-HT,

5-Hydroxytryptamine
(5-HT)

measuring 92 μg/g and 19 μg/g (fresh weight), respectively, for peel and pulp (West, 1958). These concentrations decrease in overripe fruits, concorrently with a darkening in color of the peel. It is thought that, on ripening, the 5-HT oxidizes to melanin precursor, that is, a 5,6-dihydroxy-indole compound (Waalkes *et al.,* 1958).

Ingestion of bananas or banana peels would not give rise to biological effects due to the 5-HT content, since this compound is not active when administered orally. Up to 600 mg of 5-HT can be taken orally without any apparent physiologic effect (Waalkes *et al.,* 1958). Even though serotonin (5-HT) is a neurohormone and, as such, has a variety of definite biological activities, including involvement of the central nervous system (Garattini and Valzelli, 1965), it does not cross the blood-brain barrier after injection or by oral administration. It is therefore difficult to explain any psychotomimetic effects that are alleged to be produced by smoking 5-HT containing banana peels, at least on the basis of 5-HT content.

On the other hand, slight modifications in the structure of 5-HT can give rise to extremely active psychotomimetic substances, such as the dimethyl-substituted tryptamines, which are known to be the active hallucinogenic principles of the South American snuffs previously discussed (Holmstedt and Lindgren, 1967). These methylated tryptamine derivatives, however, have not been demonstrated in banana peels.

Therefore there is no scientific evidence that smoking dried banana peels will deliver 5-HT in an active form to the body. There is also the distinct possibility that a large percentage of the 5-HT in banana peels is oxidized to the inactive 5,6-dihydroxyindole form during the drying process.

In addition to banana peels and pulp (*Musa sapientum* — Musaceae) (West, 1958; Waalkes *et al.,* 1958; Sinha *et al.,* 1961; Undenfriend *et al.,* 1959), 5-HT has been reported in many common vegetables, fruits, and other plant materials throughout the world; however, none of them has as yet been implicated as being used as hallucinogens. Examples are plantain (*Musa sapientum* var. *paradisiaca* — Musaceae) (Foy and Parratt, 1960;

Marshall, 1959), tomatoes (*Lycopersicum esculentum*—Solanaceae) (West, 1959a,b), nettle (*Urtica dioica*—Urticaceae) (Chesher and Collier, 1955; Collier and Chesher, 1956), cowhage (*Mucuna pruriens*—Leguminosae) (Bowden *et al.*, 1954), pineapple (*Ananas comosus*—Bromeliaceae) (Bruce, 1960), egg plant (*Solanum melongana*—Solanaceae) (Sinha *et al.*, 1961; Udenfriend *et al.*, 1959), ladies finger (*Hibiscus esculentus*—Malvaceae) (Sinha *et al.*, 1961), palwal (*Trichosanthes dioica*—Cucurbitaceae) (Sinha *et al.*, 1961), kerela (*Momordica charantia*—Cucurbitaceae) (Sinha *et al.*, 1961), cotton plant (*Gossypium hirsutum*—Malvaceae) (Bulard and Leopold, 1958), skunk cabbage (*Symplocarpus foetidus*—Araceae) (Bulard and Leopold, 1958), red plum (*Prunus* sp.—Rosaceae) (Udenfriend *et al.*, 1959), passion fruit (*Passiflora foetida*—Passifloraceae) (Foy and Parratt, 1960), papaw (*Carica papaya*—Caricaceae) (Foy and Parratt, 1960), and walnut (*Juglans* sp.—Juglandaceae) (Garattini and Valzelli, 1965). In addition, 5-HT has been found in such fungi as *Panaeolus campanulatus* (Tyler, 1958) and *P. foenescii* (Agaricaceae) (Tyler, 1965).

  C. *β*-Carboline-containing plants.
   1. *Peganum harmala* L. (Zygophyllaceae).
  The seeds of *Peganum harmala* have been used as a spice and as an intoxicant, and psychotropic effects have been attributed to them in India (Naranjo, 1967).

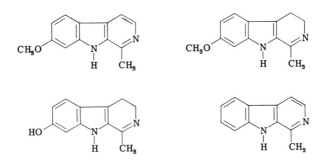

FIG. 8. Structures of *β*-carboline alkaloids from *Peganum harmala* seeds.

  In addition to the major *β*-carboline base harmine, the seeds of this plant also contain harmaline, harmalol, and harman (Fig. 8).
  Harmine and harmaline have both been shown to elicit hallucinogenic effects in man when administered orally at doses above 4 mg/g (Naranjo, 1967). Of interest is the recent discovery that 6-methoxytetrahydrohar-

man is a natural hormone of the pineal body (Naranjo, 1967), and that it is closely related to the harmala bases (Fig. 8).

It has been shown that harmaline is more of a pure hallucinogen than

6-Methoxy-
tetrahydroharman

is mescaline (Naranjo, 1967) and that tetrahydroharmine is three times less active than harmaline. Synthetic 6-methoxyharmalan is active at oral doses of 1.5 mg/g, whereas 6-methoxytetrahydroharman from the pineal body is also a hallucinogen at the same dosage (Naranjo, 1967).

2. *Banisteriopsis* sp. (Malpighiaceae).

Natives of the upper Rio Negro of Brazil and adjacent parts of Colombia, as well as Indians in Amazonian Peru and Boliva, employ narcotic beverages known as "Ayahuasca," "Caapi," and "Yaje" for prophetic and divinatory purposes and to prepare the male adolescent for the painful manhood initiation rites. It is generally recognized that these three beverages are prepared from any one of several species of *Banisteriopsis (B. caapi, B. inebrians, B. rusbyana),* either alone, together, or admixed with other plants (Schultes, 1963b; 1957).

There is general agreement that the psychotomimetic principles in these *Banisteriopsis* species are β-carboline alkaloids, represented by harmine, harmaline, and (+)-tetrahydroharmine (Fig. 8) (Deulofeu, 1967), although it is clear that exhaustive chemical studies on *Banisteriopsis* species are lacking, and a closer look at them might well yield additional hallucinogens.

3. *Mitragyna speciosa* Korthals (Rubiaceae).

Although this plant has not been directly implicated with psychotomimetic usage, it has yielded the alkaloid mitragynine, which is similar in structure to the 4-substituted indole derivatives psilocybine, psilocine, and lysergic acid amide.

The leaves of this species are used in Malaya as a substitute for opium and, indeed, mitragynine itself exerts biological activities which are quite similar to those induced by cocaine (Tyler, 1966). Other alkaloids from *M. speciosa* are ajmalicine, corynantheidine, isomitraphylline, mitra-

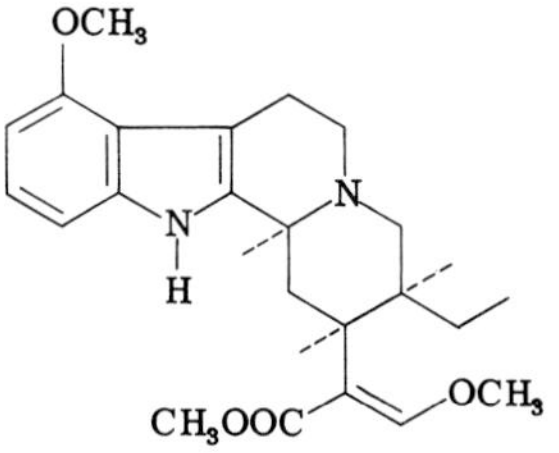

Mitragynine

phylline, paynantheine, speciogynine, speciofoline, and speciophylline (Tyler, 1966; Beckett *et al.*, 1965a,b). The latter alkaloids do not appear to have been evaluated for their effects on the central nervous system.

D. Isoquinuclide-containing plants.
 1. *Tabernanthe iboga* Baillon (Apocynaceae).

It is known that natives of certain sections of Africa chew the root of *Tabernanthe iboga* (Iboga), and an intoxication follows that is characterized by excitement, mental confusion, and possibly hallucinations (Tyler, 1966). The major alkaloid responsible for these activities is the 5-methoxyindole, ibogaine (Tyler, 1966).

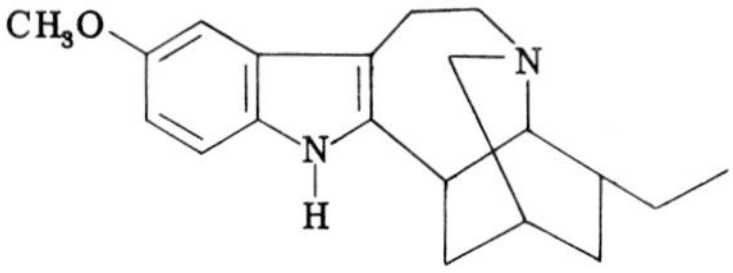

Ibogaine

Ibogaine has recently been placed in the same category as LSD by the Federal Food and Drug Administration since it has been shown to be a true hallucinogen (Naranjo, 1967).

E. Ergoline-containing plants.
 1. Convolvulaceous plants.

The seeds of the morning glory *Ipomoea violacea* L. (*Ipomoea tricolor* Cav., *Ipomoea rubrocaerulea* Hook.), known as "badoh negra," and *Rivea corymbosa* (L.) Hallier filius [*Turbina corymbosa* (L.) Raf. or *Ipomoea corymbosa* (L.) Roth.], known as "ololiuqui," have been used since Aztec times in the uplands of southern Oaxaca in Mexico for divinatory and hallucinogenic purposes (Wasson, 1963; Schultes, 1941; Der Marderosian, 1967). It has been firmly established that the active psychotomimetic agents in these seeds are ergoline (lysergic acid) derivatives, closely related to lysergic acid diethylamine (LSD) (Wasson, 1963; Schultes, 1941; Der Marderosian, 1967). The natives of Mexico are known to have used smaller quantities of *Ipomoea violacea* than of *Rivea corymbosa* for hallucinogenic effects (Schultes, 1941; Der Marderosian, 1967). Hofmann (1968) has pointed out that seeds from the former plant contain larger quantities of the active ergoline principles than do seeds of the latter species; thus he confirmed the wisdom of the natives with respect to this practice. He subsequently was able to isolate, in pure form, several indole alkaloids from the seeds of these two plants (Hofmann, 1963). Interestingly enough, the major active constituent of each proved to be *d*-lysergic acid amide (ergine), whereas a second important alkaloid was *d*-isolysergic acid amide (isoergine). In addition, the alkaloids chanoclavine and elymoclavine were also isolated from each species, but they were devoid of psychotomimetic effects. Ergometrine (ergonovine), a well-known active uterotonic and hemostatic alkaloid found in ergot, was isolated from *Ipomoea violacea* but not from *Rivea corymbosa*. On the other hand, lysergol was found in *Rivea corymbosa,* but not in the closely related *Ipomoea violacea*. The structural relationships and similarities of these active compounds from *Ipomoea* and *Rivea* to the synthetic and highly active *d*-lysergic acid diethylamide (LSD), can be seen in Fig. 9. A comparison of the alkaloids, as determined in these seeds, is presented in Table 3.

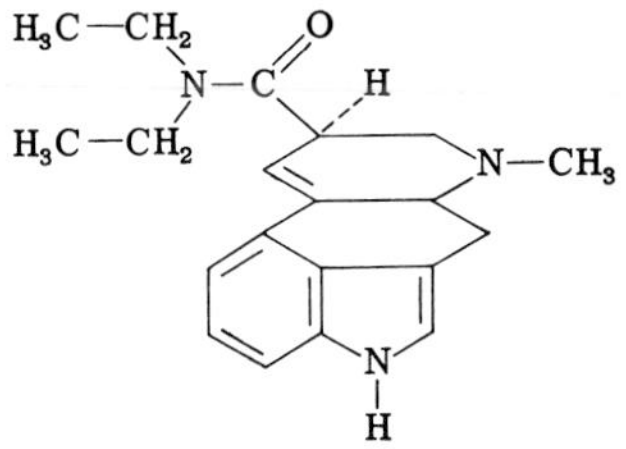

d-Lysergic acid
diethylamide (LSD)

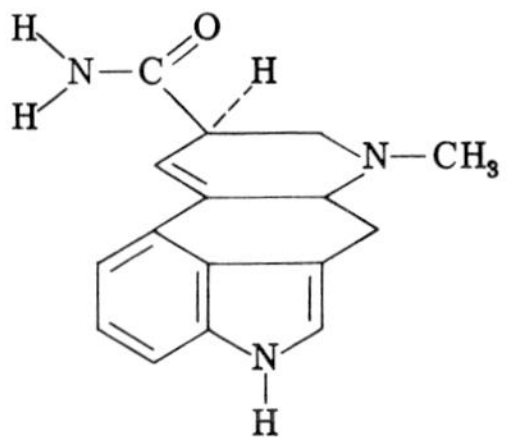

d-Lysergic acid amide

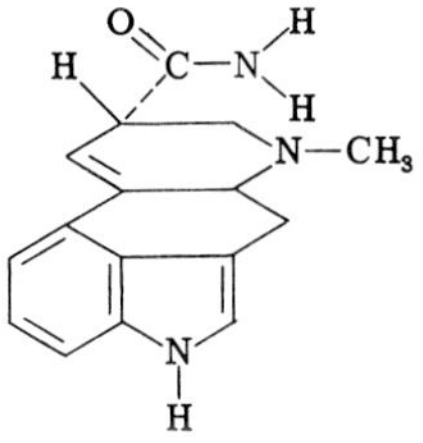

d-Isolysergic acid amide

FIG. 9. Relationship of active *Rivea* and *Ipomoea* alkaloids to *d*-lysergic acid diethylamide (LSD).

TABLE 3

ALKALOIDS OF *Rivea corymbosa* AND *Ipomoea violacea* SEEDS[a]

Alkaloid	*Rivea corymbosa* (ololiuqui)	*Ipomoea violacea* (badoh negra)
d-Lysergic acid amide (ergine)	0.0065%	0.035%
d-Isolysergic acid amide (isoergine)	0.0020%	0.005%
Chanoclavine	0.0005%	0.005%
Elymoclavine	0.0005%	0.005%
Lysergol	0.0005%	—
Ergometrine (ergonovine)	—	0.005%

[a] Hofmann (1967).

Other convolvulaceous seeds have been shown to contain ergoline derivatives, and to date the following have been detected: ergine (lysergic acid amide), isoergine (isolysergic acid amide), ergosine, ergosinine, chanoclavine, elymoclavine, lysergol, ergometrine (ergonovine), ergo-metrinine, agroclavine, penniclavine, and lysergic acid-α-hydroxy-ethylamide (Der Marderosian, 1967; Hofmann, 1963; Stauffacher *et al.*, 1965).

With regard to the use of "morning glory" seeds as hallucinatory agents by the general public, it should be pointed out that certain commonly available horticultural varieties of *Ipomoea violacea* all contain active indole derivatives. These varieties include those sold under the names "Heavenly Blue," "Pearly Gates," "Wedding Bells," "Summer Skies," "Blue Star," and others (Der Marderosian, 1967). Common horticultural morning glories that have been identified as *Ipomoea purpurea,* and which are devoid of ergoline derivatives, are "Crimson Rambler," "Con-volvulus Major," "Sunrise Serenade," "Rose Marie," and "Tinkerbell's Petticoat," whereas "Scarlet O'Hara," "Candy Pink," "Cornell," "Royal Crown," and "Darling," which are also devoid of ergolone derivatives, represents the species *Ipomoea nil* (Der Marderosian, 1967).

When it was first announced that morning glory seeds contained these active alkaloids, seed suppliers soon reported a depletion of their stocks, and a serious public health problem arose out of their misuse. In addition to the expected psychic phenomena due to the lysergic acid-like alkaloids, serious physical effects and deaths were induced (Der Marderosian, 1967; Ingram, 1964; Rice and Genest, 1965). In the same vein, it should be pointed out that some reports have indicated that ingestion of *Ipomoea violacea* seeds produced no effects. In most of these cases the reason was that the seeds were not pulverized before ingestion. If this is not done, the hard impervious seed coats will allow them to pass through the alimentary tract intact and the active alkaloids will not be absorbed (Der Marderosian, 1967).

At present there is no specific legislation prohibiting the sale of morning glory seeds, and they continue to be used for psychotomimetic purposes. It has been stated that in England there is a proposal under consideration to ban the sale of these seeds because they have been subject to such misuse (Wellendorff, 1966). In a practical sense, this appears to be impossible.

F. Tropane-containing plants.
1. *Datura* species (Solanaceae).

The seeds of the common Jimson weed *(Datura stramonium)* as well as other *Datura* species have been used to produce psychotomimetic effects (Schultes, 1963b; Johnson, 1967). My first knowledge of the use of these seeds in the United States for this purpose came several years ago when I was driving from Boston to Pittsburgh. A young man was hitchhiking and I offered him a ride. It turned out that he was an anthropology college senior, just finishing his studies at Yale, and he was making plans to continue his work in South America. He indicated to me, in some detail, how he and his friends prepared extracts of *Datura* seeds and consumed them for their psychotomimetic effects.

Practically all *Datura* species contain tropane alkaloids, the total alkaloid content usually being made up of atropine, hyoscyamine, and scopolamine. The hallucinogenic effects of scopolamine are well known (Goodman and Gilman, 1955).

l-Scopolamine

2. *Methysticodendron amesianum* R. E. Schultes (Solanaceae)

The leaves and stems of this South American plant have been used by Indians in their witchcraft rites (Schultes, 1963b). It has been found that *l*-scopolamine constitutes over 80% of the alkaloid content of this plant (Pachter and Hopkinson, 1960).

Interestingly enough, the natives consider this plant to be more potent than the related *Datura* species which are also used to produce a frenzy and narcosis in their ceremonies. This is undoubtedly true, since the scopolamine-atropine ratio is higher in *Methysticodendron* than in *Datura* (Pachter and Hopkinson, 1960). Scopolamine may produce excitement, hallucinations, and delirium, even at therapeutic doses, whereas, with atropine, doses bordering on the toxic are generally required before hallucinations and central excitement are observed (Goodman and Gilman, 1955).

G. Isoxazole-containing plants
1. *Amanita muscaria* Fr. (Agaricaceae)

Amanita muscaria Fr. (Agaricaceae) (fly agaric) has an interesting history in Eurasian culture, where it has been employed as a psychotomimetic agent (Wasson, 1967). Ingestion of the mushroom brings about effects after about 15 to 20 min. Initially, sleep, which is of about 2 hr duration, is induced. At times, colored visions are also experienced. Some subjects have enjoyed a feeling of elation that lasted for 3 to 4 hr after waking from a sound sleep. Such individuals are said to often perform extraordinary feats of physical effort, while also enjoying these feats (Wasson, 1967).

The hallucinogenic properties of fly agaric pass into the urine, and for this reason it has been recorded that, during times when the mushroom was not readily available in abundance, the urine from one consuming the mushrooms was drunk to produce the same effects (Wasson, 1967).

To date, the following substances have been reported as isolated or detected in *Amanita muscaria:* muscarine, acetylcholine, choline, ibotenic acid (prämuscimol), pantherine (muscimol), muscazone, muscaridine, bufotenin, atropine, scopolamine, and hyoscyamine (Eugster, 1967; Waser, 1967) (Fig. 10). Recent studies, however, have revealed that perhaps earlier reports concerned with the presence of tropane alkaloids (atropine, scopolamine, hyoscyamine) in this fungus were due to misinterpretations of chromatographic data (Tyler, 1965). Furthermore, the report of bufotenin from *A. muscaria* has been shown to be incorrect. In all probability, the report was due to the examination of *A. muscaria* which was contaminated with *A. citrina* or *A. porphyria* (Tyler, 1965), both of which contain bufotenin.

Ibotenic acid is the zwitterion of α-amino-α-[3-hydroxyisoxazolyl-(5)]-acetic acid monohydrate (Fig. 10) and is considered to be the major psychotropic constituent of *Amanita muscaria* (Eugster, 1967). Pantherine, also an active principle, is the enolbetaine of 5-aminomethyl-3-hydroxy-isoxazole (Fig. 10) and is easily formed by decarboxylation and loss of

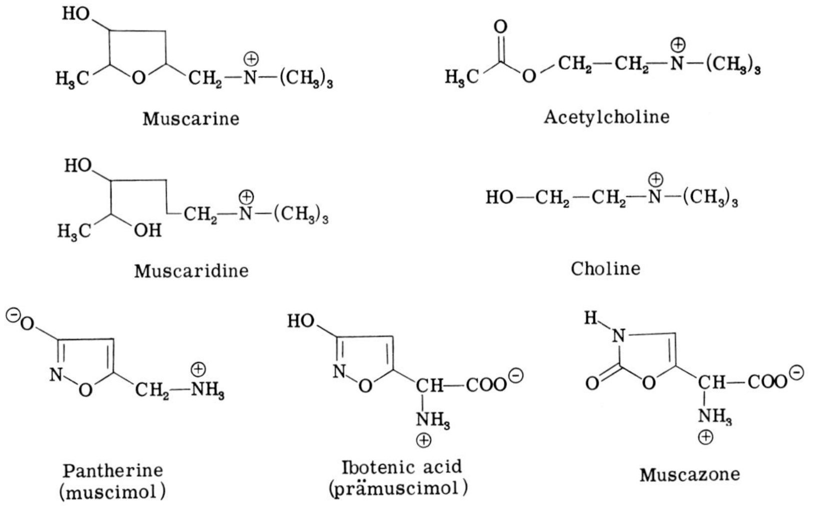

FIG. 10. Constituents of *Amanita muscaria* (fly agaric).

water from ibotenic acid (Eugster, 1967) (Fig. 10). The pharmacologically less active muscazone (Fig. 10) is thought to be formed from ibotenic acid (Eugster, 1967). Thus, varying ratios of ibotenic acid and muscazone would be expected to be found in *Amanita muscaria;* this could well account for variations in the biological effects induced by ingesting this fungus that have been reported in the literature (Eugster, 1967).

The antibiotic oxamycin (D-4-amino-3-isoxazolidone) is structurally related to the active isoxazoles present in *Amanita muscaria,* and side effects of this useful drug in man involve the central nervous system and include mental confusion, acute psychotic episodes, convulsions, and other abnormal behavioral states (Goodman and Gilman, 1965). Therefore it is to be expected that the isoxazoles of *Amanita muscaria* will exert similar effects when ingested.

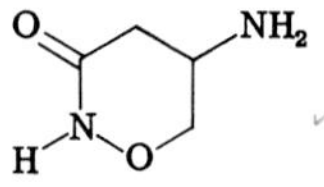

Oxamycin

III. Plants Having Unknown or Unconfirmed Active Principles.

A. *Salvia divinorum* Epling and Javito (Labiatae)

In the southern Mexican state of Oaxaca, Mazatec Indians utilize the leaves of *Salvia divinorum,* known as "Pipilzintzintli," as a divinatory and hallucinogen (Wasson, 1962, 1963; Epling and Javita-M, 1962). Dancing colors in elaborate three-dimensional designs were experienced by Wasson (1962) after drinking the juice expressed by hand from 68 leaves of this plant.

No chemical substances have been reported isolated from *Salvia divinorum* that would explain these effects, and preliminary attempts to isolate the active principle(s) by Hofmann have been unsuccessful because of their apparent instability (Tyler, 1966).

B. *Olmedioperebea sclerophylla* Ducke (Moraceae).

Natives living in the central part of the Brazilian Amazon prepare a psychotomimetic snuff from the fruit of *O. sclerophylla* (Schultes, 1965). Nothing is known of the active principles of this plant.

C. Soma.

More than 144 hymns of the Rigveda, oldest holy scripture of the Aryan settlers of the Indus basin, glorify a divine plant and an intoxicating beverage prepared from it, both of which are known as "Soma." Scientists have not been able to trace the identity of this plant with any degree of certainty. The plants which have been suggested, but which are discounted on specific points, are *Sarcostemma viminale, Periploca aphylla, Rheum* sp., *Ephedra* sp., *Peganum harmala,* and *Amanita muscaria* (Tyler, 1966; Holmstedt and Kline, 1967).

Wasson has been investigating this problem for several years and still has not reached a definite conclusion as to the identity of the elusive and mysterious "Soma."

Summary

The chemical principles responsible for the effects elicited by the major hallucinogenic plants are summarized in Table 4. It is interesting to note that the twelve genera are distributed in nine different plant families, and the chemical substances responsible for the hallucinogenic effects are distinctly different for eight of the ten families. Or, put another way, when different genera or species of a particular plant family are found to contain true psychotogens, these substances are always chemically similar, if not identical. This is a remarkable coincidence indeed, since chemotaxonomic relationships are not always so clear-cut.

TABLE 4

MAJOR HALLUCINOGENIC PLANTS AND THEIR ACTIVE PRINCIPLES

Cannabis sativa	Moraceae	Δ^1-Tetrahydrocannabinol
Lophophora williamsii	Cactaceae	Mescaline
Piptadenia species	Leguminosae	Substituted tryptamines
Psilocybe mexicana	Agaricaceae	Psilocybine
Peganum harmala	Zygophyllaceae	Harmaline, harmine
Banisteriopsis species	Malpighiaceae	Harmaline, harmine
Tabernanthe iboga	Apocynaceae	Ibogaine
Ipomoea violacea	Convolvulaceae	*d*-Lysergic acid amide, *d*-Isolysergic acid amide
Rivea corymbosa	Convolvulaceae	*d*-Lysergic acid amide, *d*-Isolysergic acid amide
Datura species	Solanaceae	*l*-Scopolamine
Methysticodendron amesianum	Solanaceae	*l*-Scopolamine
Amanita muscaria	Agaricaceae	Pantherine, ibotenic acid

Although the active principle is well established for *Mitragyna speciosa,* (that is, mitragynine), this plant does not appear to be a true hallucinogen, and perhaps it should not have been included in this discussion.

The active principle of *Piper methysticum* appears to be unknown, but again, this plant probably should not be classified as a hallucinogen, but rather as a sedative.

The active psychotomimetic principle of *Myristica fragrans* is not known for certain at present, but it appears to be either elemicin or myristicin. Undoubtedly this problem is now being investigated and the answer should be forthcoming.

Several other minor psychotomimetic plants remain a mystery, for example, *Salvia divinorum* and *Olmedioperebea sclerophylla,* but we do not even know the botanical identity of Soma. A number of additional hallucinogenic plants are alleged to exist, but there is a need for verifying their effects, whereas others are not botanically authenticated.

Most of our definitive chemical knowledge of hallucinogenic plants has evolved only during the past decade or so. Three important factors have been responsible for this. First, valid botanical authentication of many hallucinogenic plants has only been accomplished during this period of time. Before this, chemical reports on these plants were, to say the least, chaotic. Second, the isolation and identification of active principles have been enhanced by the introduction of modern research techniques which require only small amounts of plant material. Finally, there has been an acute need for the active principles present in hallucinogenic plants, either as potentially useful drugs in the treatment of mental disease, or as new tools for the pharmacologist in his attempts to shed some light on the biochemical causes of mental illness. These needs have accelerated much of the research.

It can be said that the entire scientific community has benefited from all this work. Success has been attained perhaps only because of a strained cooperative effort among botanists, ethnobotanists, ethnologists, chemists, pharmacognosists, pharmacologists, psychologists, and other groups of scientists. On the other hand, it has been of interest to note that certain scientists in each of these groups have felt that scientists outside of their own field of specialization were intruding in an area of research that was not of their concern.

Research support, especially that from the federal government, has been noticeable by its absence in most of the successful studies on hallucinogenic plants. Perhaps this has been true because those holding the purse strings for research funds have read the book entitled "Hallucinogenic Plants" and have been convinced of its purely fictional nature. Indeed, though the book has not been completed, the final chapter is not yet near because research successes by a few have changed this "book" into fact.

A major drawback in the scientific evaluation of hallucinogenic substances has been in the area of biological evaluation. Even today there is not an acceptable and reliable indicator for hallucinogenic activity in laboratory animal systems. In addition, the role of the atmosphere, or conditions under which hallucinogens are taken, in causing or altering the hallucinogenic response has yet to be learned. Do other substances frequently used by individuals partaking of hallucinatory substances, such as amphetamines or alcohol, enhance these effects?

REFERENCES

Altschul, S., Reis von (1967). *Vilca* and its use. *In* "Ethnopharmacologic Search for Psychoactive Drugs." (B. Holmstedt and N. S. Kline, Eds.). N.I.M.H., No. 2, U.S. Dept. of Health, Education and Welfare, pp. 307–314.

Anon. (1967). Perils of periwinkle. *Newsweek,* June 26, p. 68.

Beckett, A. H., Shellard, E. J., Phillipson, J. D., and Lee, C. M. (1965b). Alkaloids from *Mitragyna speciosa* (Korth.). *J. Pharm. Pharmacol.* **17,** 753–755.

Beckett, A. H., Shellard, E. J., and Takie, A. N. (1965a). The *Mitragyna* species of Asia. Part IV. The alkaloids of the leaves of *Mitragyna speciosa* Korth. Isolation of mitragynine and speciofoline. *Planta Med.* **13,** 241–246.

Bowden, K., Brown, B. G., and Batty, J. E. (1954). 5-Hydroxytryptamine: its occurrence in cowhage. *Nature* **174,** 925–926.

Bruce, D. W. (1960). Serotonin in pineapple. *Nature* **188,** 147.

Buckley, J. P., Furgiuele, A. R., and O'Hara, M. J. (1967). Pharmacology of Kava, pp. 141–151. *In* "Ethnopharmacologic Search for Psychoative Drugs." (B. Holmstedt and N. S.

Kline, eds.) Workshop Series of Pharmacology Section, N.I.M.H., No. 2, U.S. Dept. Health, Education and Welfare.

Bulard, C., and Leopold, A. C. (1958). 5-Hydroxytryptamine chez les plantes supérieures. *Compt. rend.* **247,** 1382–1384.

Chesher, G. B., and Collier, H. O. J. (1955). Identification of 5-hydroxytryptamine in nettle sting. *J. Physiol. Soc. (London)* **130,** 41P–42P.

Collier, H. O. J., and Chesher, G. B. (1956). Identification of 5-hydroxytryptamine in the sting of the nettle *(Urtica dioica)*. *Brit. J. Pharmacol.* **11,** 186–189.

Der Marderosian, A. (1966). Current status of hallucinogens in the Cactaceae. *Am. J. Pharm.* **138,** 204–212.

Der Marderosian, A. (1967). Psychotomimetic indoles in the Convolvulaceae. *Am. J. Pharm.* **139,** 19–26.

Deulofeu, V. (1967). Chemical compounds isolated from *Banisteriopsis* and related species, p. 393–402. *In* "Enthnopharmacologic Search for Psychotropic Drugs" (B. Holmstedt and N. S. Kline, eds.). Workshop series in pharmacology section, N.I.M.H., No. 2, U.S. Dept. Health, Education and Welfare.

Epling, C., Jativa-M., C. D. (1962). A new species of *Salvia* from Mexico. *Botan. Mus. Leaflets Harvard Univ.,* **20,** 75–76.

Eugster, C. H. (1967). Isolation, structure and synthesis of central-active compounds from *Amanita muscaria* (l. ex Fr.) Hooker. pp. 416–418. *In* "Ethnopharmacologic Search for Psychoactive Drugs" (B. Holmstedt and N. S. Kline, eds). Workshop series of pharmacologic section, N.I.M.H., No. 2, U.S. Dept. Health, Education and Welfare.

Farnsworth, N. R. (1961). The pharmacognosy of the periwinkles: *Vinca* and *Catharanthus. Lloydia* **24,** 105–138.

Fischer, R. (1965). Possible biosynthesis of D-lysergic acid diethylamine-like compounds from mescaline. *Experientia* **11,** 162–163.

Ford, C. S. (1967). Ethnographical aspects of Kava, pp. 162–173. *In* "Ethnopharmacologic Search for Psychoactive Drugs," (B. Holmstedt and N. S. Kline, eds). N.I.M.H., No. 2. U.S. Dept. of Health, Education and Welfare.

Foy, J. M., and Parratt, J. R. (1960). A note on the presence of noradrenaline and 5-hydroxytryptamine in plantain *(Musa sapientum* var. *paradisiaca)*. *J. Pharm. Pharmacol.* **12,** 360–364.

Gajdusek, D. C. (1967). Recent observations on the use of Kava in the New Hebrides, pp. 119–125. *In* "Ethnopharmacologic Search for Psychoactive Drugs" (B. Holmstedt and N. S. Kline, eds). N.I.M.H., No. 2. U.S. Dept. Health, Education and Welfare.

Gaoni, Y., and Mechoulam, R. (1966). Cannabichromene, a new active principle in hashish. *Chem. Commun.,* p. 20.

Garattini, S., and Valzelli, L. (1965). "Serotonin." Elsevier, New York.

Goodman, L. S., and Gilman, A. (1955). "The Pharmacological Basis of Therapeutics, 2nd edition, p. 544. Macmillian, New York.

Goodman, L. S., and Gilman, A. (1965). "The Pharmacological Basis of Therapeutics, 3rd edition, pp. 1326–1327. Macmillian, New York.

Grlic, L. (1964). Recent advances in the chemical research of *Cannabis. Bull. Narcotics* **16**(4), 29–38.

Hofmann, A. (1961). Chemical, pharmacological and medical aspects of psychotomimetics. *J. Exptl. Med. Sci.* **5,** 31–51.

Hofmann, A. (1963). The active principles of the seeds of *Rivea corymbosa* and *Ipomoea violacea. Botan. Mus. Leaflet Harvard Univ.,* **20,** 194–212.

Holmes, L. D. (1967). The function of Kava in modern Samoan culture. pp. 107–117. *In* "Ethnopharmacologic Search for Psychoactive Drugs" (B. Holmstedt and N. S. Kline, eds.). Workshop Series in Pharmacology Section, N.I.M.H., No. 2. U.S. Dept. Health, Education and Welfare.

Holmstedt, B., and Kline, N. S. (eds.) (1967). "Ethnopharmacologic Search for Psychoactive Drugs," pp. 441–451. Workshop Series of Pharmacology Section, N.I.M.H., No. 2. U.S. Department of Health, Education and Welfare.

Holmstedt, B., Lindgren, J. E. (1967). Chemical constituents and pharmacology of South American snuffs, pp. 339–373. In "Ethnopharmacologic Search for Psychoactive Drugs" (B. Holmstedt and N. S. Kline, eds.). Workshop Series in Pharmacology Section, N.I.M.H., No. 2. U.S. Dept. Health, Education and Welfare.

Ingram, A. L., Jr. (1964). Morning glory seed reaction. J. Am. Med. Assoc. 190, 1133–1134.

Johnson, C. E. (1967). Mystical force of the nightshade. Intern. J. Neuropsychiatry 3, 268–275.

Keller, F., and Klohs, M. W. (1963). A review of the chemistry and pharmacology of the constituents of Piper methysticum. Lloydia 26, 1–15.

Klohs, M. W. (1967). Chemistry of Kava, pp. 126–132. In "Ethnopharmacologic Search for Psychoactive Drugs" (B. Holmstedt and N. S. Kline, eds). Workshop Series of Pharmacology Section, N.I.M.H., No. 2. U.S. Department of Health, Education and Welfare.

Kluver, H. (1966). "Mescal and Mechanisms of Hallucinations." Univ. of Chicago Press, Chicago.

Korte, F., Haag, H., and Claussen, U. (1965). Tetrahydrocannabinol carboxylic acid, a component of hashish. Angew. Chem. 77, 862.

LaBarre, W. (1959). "The Peyote Cult." The Shoe String Press, Hamden, Conn.

Marshall, P. B. (1959). Catechols and tryptamines in the "matoke" banana (Musa paradisiaca). J. Pharm. Pharmacol. 11, 639.

Naranjo, C. (1967). Psychotropic properties of the Harmala alkaloids, pp. 385–391. In "Ethnopharmacologic Search for Psychoactive Drugs." (B. Holmstedt and N. S. Kline, eds.). Workshop Series in Pharmacology Section, N.I.M.H., No. 2. U.S. Dept. Health, Education and Welfare.

Pachter, I. J., Hopkinson, A. F., (1960). Note on alkaloids of Methysticodendron amesianum. J. Am. Pharm. Assoc. Sci. Ed. 49, 621–622.

Rice, W. B., and Gnest, K. (1965). Acute toxicity of extracts of morning glory seeds in mice. Nature 207, 302–303.

Schultes, R. E. (1939). Plantae Mexicanae II. The identification of Teonanacatl, a narcotic basidiomycete of the Aztecs. Botan. Mus. Leaflet Harvard Univ. 7, (3) 37–56.

Schultes, R. E. (1941). "A Contribution to Our Knowledge of Rivea corymbosa, the Narcotic Cololiuqui of the Aztecs" p. 45. Botanical Museum, Harvard Univ., Cambridge, Mass.

Schultes, R. E. (1957). The identity of the malpighiaceous narcotics of South America. Botan. Mus. Leaflet Harvard Univ. 18, (1) 1–56.

Schultes, R. E. (1963a). Botanical sources of new world narcotics. Psychedelic Rev. 1, (2), 145–166.

Schultes, R. E. (1963b). Hallucinogenic plants of the new world. Harvard Rev. 1(4), 18–32.

Schultes, R. E. (1965). Ein halbes Jahrhundert Ethnobotanik amerikanischer Halluzinogene. Planta Med. 13, 125–157.

Schultes, R. E. (1967). The botanical origins of South American snuffs, pp. 291–306. In "Ethnopharmacologic Search for Psychoactive Drugs" (B. Holmstedt and N. S. Kline, eds.). Workshop Series of Pharmacology Section, N.I.M.H., No. 2. U.S. Department of Health, Education and Welfare.

Seitz, G. J. (1967). Epena, the intoxicating snuff powder of the Waika indians and the

Tucano medicine man, Agostino, pp. 316–338. *In* "Ethnopharmacologic Search for Psychoactive Drugs" (B. Holmstedt and N. S. Kline, eds.). Workshop Series in Pharmacology Section, N.I.M.H., No. 2. U.S. Department of Health, Education and Welfare.

Shulgin, A. T., Sargent, T., and Naranjo, C. (1967). The chemistry and psychopharmacology of nutmeg and of several related phenylisopropylamines, pp. 202–214. *In* "Ethnopharmacologic Search for Psychoactive Drugs" (B. Holmstedt and N. S. Kline, eds). Workshop Series in Pharmacology Section, N.I.M.H., No. 2. U.S. Department Health, Education and Welfare.

Sinha, S. N., Sanyal, R. K., and Sinha, Y. K. (1961). Some observations on 5-hydroxytryptamine content of edible fruits and vegetables and its effects on gastric acidity. *Indian J. Med. Res.* **49,** 681–687.

Stauffacher, D., Tscherter, H., and Hofmann, A. (1965). Isolierung von Ergosin und Ergosinin neben Agroclavin aus den Samen von *Ipomoea argyrophylla* Vatke (Convolvulaceae). *Helv. Chim. Acta* **48,** 1379–1380.

Steinmetz, E. F. (1960). *"Piper methysticum* (Kava)" 46 pp. E. F. Steinmetz, Amsterdam.

Tyler, V. E., Jr. (1958). Occurrence of serotonin in a hallucinogenic mushroom. *Science* **128,** 718.

Tyler, V. E., Jr. (1965). Recent studies of the chemical constituents of the Agaricales, pp. 501–507. *In* "Beitrage zur Biochemie und Physiologie von Naturstoffen." Gustav Fischer Verlag, Jena.

Tyler, V. E., Jr. (1966). The physiological properties and chemical constituents of some habit-forming plants. *Lloydia* **29,** 275–292.

Udenfriend, S., Lovenberg, W., and Sjoerdsma, A. (1959). Physiologically active amines in common fruits and vegetables. *Arch. Biochem. Biophys.* **85,** 487–490.

Waalkes, T. P., Sjoerdsma, A., Creveling, C. R., Weissbach, H., and Undenfriend, S. (1958). Serotonin, norepinephrine and related compounds in bananas. *Science* **127,** 648–650.

Waser, P. G. (1967). The pharmacology of *Amanita muscaria,* pp. 419–439. *In* "Ethnopharmacologic Search for Psychoactive Drugs" (B. Holmstedt and N. S. Kline, eds.). Workshop Series of Pharmacology Section, N.I.M.H., No. 2. U.S. Department of Health, Education and Welfare.

Wasson, R. G. (1962). A new Mexican psychotropic drug from the mint family. *Botan. Mus. Leaflet Harvard Univ.* **20,** 77–84.

Wasson, R. G. (1963). Notes on the present status of Ololiuhqui and the other hallucinogens of Mexico. *Botan. Mus. Leaflet Harvard Univ.* **20**(6), 161–212.

Wasson, R. G. (1967). Fly agaric and man, pp. 405–414. *In* "Ethanopharmacologic Search for Psychoactive Drugs" (B. Holmstedt and N. S. Kline, eds). Workshop Series of Pharmacology Section, N.I.M.H., No. 2. U.S. Dept. Health, Education and Welfare.

Weil, A. T. (1965). Nutmeg as a narcotic. *Econ. Botany* **19,** 194–217.

Weil, A. T. (1967). Nutmeg as a psychoactive drug, pp. 188–201. *In* "Ethnopharmacologic Search for Psychoactive Drugs" (B. Holmstedt and N. S. Kline, eds.). Workshop Series of Pharmacology Section, N.I.M.H., No. 2. U.S. Department of Health, Education and Welfare.

Wellendorff, M. (1966). *Ipomoea* banning. *A.S.P. Newsletter* **3,** 3.

West, G. B. (1958). Tryptamines in edible fruits. *J. Pharm. Pharmacol.* **10,** 589–590.

West, G. B. (1959a). Indole derivatives in tomatoes. *J. Pharm. Pharmacol.* **11,** 275T–277T.

West, G. B. (1959b). Tryptamines in tomatoes. *J. Pharm. Pharmacol.* **11,** 319–320.

Wolstenholme, G. E. W., and Knight, J. (1965). "Hashish: Its Chemistry and Pharmacology." Little, Brown, Boston.

VII

An Attack on Some Unresolved Problems of Plant Life in the Environment of a Major City

Pesticides in Suburbia

William A. Niering

Man's impact on his environment brings to mind the recent comments of René Dubos: "Man is rapidly losing control over his environment. He introduces new forces at such a rapid rate that . . . the effects are upon him before he has a chance to evaluate their consequences. One can almost take for granted that unless social attitudes change society will become adjusted to levels of pollution that do not have gross immediate nuisance value . . . even though this apparent adaptation will eventually result in much pathological damage and social burden . . ." What are the problems, the hazards, the unknowns, the possible alternatives and solutions as man strive to improve the quality of his environment? Corrective action in arresting existing pollution is obviously the initial step, but there must also be efforts toward preventive action which involve man's harmonious ecological integration with the environment. In the past, as technology was used to exploit the land, basic ecological principles were ignored. This must no longer occur. The major pollution problems have resulted from man's activities, and many have accelerated in recent years with the increase in population. Therefore efforts toward environmental improvement without population limitation are unthinkable. Both must work hand in hand. The goal may best be summarized as by Sir Julian Huxley: "We want more varied and fuller achievement in human societies, as against drabness and shrinkage. We want more enjoyment and less suffering. We want more beauty and less ugliness. We want more adventure and disciplined freedom, as against routine and slavishness. We want more knowledge, more interest, more wonder, as against ignorance and apathy."

During the past decade those living in both rural and urban environments have become acutely aware of pesticide pollution. In 1962 Rachel Carson's *Silent Spring* awakened a nation in a way that her fellow scientists had not with their hundreds of scientific papers. It took the shock treatment, which seems to work well in this age of technology, when man has become lulled into an illusion that he can do no wrong in the name of "progress" and that science and technology will always save him in the end. Egler (1966) in his fourth and most recent review of the biocide problem eloquently summarizes the situation: "Pesticides are the greatest single tool for simplifying the habitat ever conceived by the simple mind of man, who may yet prove too simple to grasp the fact that he is but a blind strand of an ecosystem web, dependent not upon himself, but upon the total web, which web nevertheless he has the power to destroy."

Although emphasis here is on some of the pesticide problems within the sprawling megalopolis along the northeastern seaboard, these problems are worldwide in scope, for pesticide contamination has now reached all major aquatic and terrestrial ecosystems known to man. How do they affect the total environment: plant and animal life including man, along with the soil, water, and air which holistically comprise the biosphere or, possible more correctly, the noosphere, since so much of the environment is currently being manipulated and controlled by the mind of man? What are some of the problems which must be overcome as he strives toward a sound ecological approach in the use of biocides?

Impact of Insecticides on the Total Environment

Throughout the present decade the production of insecticides, herbicides, fungicides, and rodenticides has continued to increase, reaching over 1 billion pounds in 1966. It is estimated that pesticide application on the nation's landscape has now reached 1 of every 10 acres, each being sprayed with an average of 4 lb/acre (Anon., 1966). Although most of the insecticides are used in agriculture, where the monocultures especially favor insect pests, large quantities are also used in forestry and by the homeowner. Current agricultural data seem to indicate that the persistent use of insecticides markedly increases short-term yields and quality of produce. However, there is no evidence that the potential long-range deleterious effects are considered in the cost-benefit equation. In fact, there is considerable evidence that many treatments are merely insurance applications, and not infrequently the potential insect damage is greatly exaggerated (Rudd, 1964). Increased use of pesticides is also related to the fastidious demands of the average consumer, who will not tolerate an insect-marred piece of produce or even the mere presence of a harmless insect. Intensified by advertising, this situation has now placed unrealistic demands on agriculture.

Although the inhabitants of suburbia may not be directly concerned with agricultural spraying, they are the recipients of farm produce in which permitted pesticide residues such as that of DDT should not exceed 7 ppm. They may also be directly exposed through Dutch elm, gypsy moth, or other spray programs, in addition to the use of pesticides around the home. Although data on the deleterious chronic effects of pesticides on man are still in the stage of uncertainty, effects on other nontarget organisms may result in reduced reproductive capacity, disruption of species balance, subtle behavioral changes, or death. An examination of some of the problems and sources of insecticide contamination follows.

THE GYPSY MOTH, A NUISANCE INSECT

Introduced into Massachusetts about 1869, the gypsy moth has now become a naturalized insect capable of defoliating native trees within the suburban forest. Although a single defoliation of evergreens such as hemlock can kill the trees, preferred species, including the various oaks, are much more resistant and usually leaf out again later in the summer. Even though considerable numbers of large timber trees on more mesic sites have been reported killed, in correlation with factors in addition to the gypsy moth (Crossman, 1948), the most serious losses typically occur on dry, rocky ridges where the trees are of marginal commercial value and where periodic droughts are a contributing factor in natural mortality. Seldom do timber losses exceed 5 to 6% in the Northeast as compared to a 2% mortality under natural undisturbed conditions. To combat the moth, parasites and predators, among them the Calosoma beetle, were introduced during the early 1900s. Bess (1961) reports that up to 13% of the gypsy moth larvae and pupae not parasitized have been destroyed by this beneficial insect.

After World War II there was a highly organized effort to "eradicate" the gypsy moth with DDT (1,1,1-trichloro-2,2-bis-(*p*-chlorophenyl)-ethane). This costly endeavor understandably failed. In recent years, owing to DDT's toxicity to birds, amphibians, and fish, there has been a shift to Sevin, a compound less toxic than DDT but still lethal to bees and aquatic insect life. Although spraying may reduce the immediate population outburst, it frequently tends to delay the natural collapse of the moth population that normally occurs after 3 or 4 years without spraying. Such delays have been reported in New York and Connecticut (Smiley, 1964).

Where local infestations occur within suburbia, homeowners can themselves assume the responsibility for control measures. Egg masses on the bark of trees can be killed by painting them with creosote during the winter. If the infestation is light, Tanglefoot, a sticky compound, can be placed around the trees to engulf the caterpillars once they emerge.

Where heavy infestations occur, local spraying from the ground mini-mizes the caterpillar nuisance. Along certain heavily infested roadsides a community may find it desirable to undertake a limited ground-spraying program to preserve the aesthetic qualities of the roadside for local residents during a few critical weeks in early summer. Broadcast aerial treatment is ecologically unsound and therefore never recommended.

Dutch Elm Spraying and Loss of Songbirds

Loss of bird populations as a result of Dutch elm spray programs has been documented on several college campuses (Wallace, 1960; Hickey and Hunt, 1960; Wurster et al., 1965). One of the most dramatic incidents was reported from Hanover, New Hampshire (Wurster et al., 1965) where, following the application of 1.9 lb of DDT/acre, the robin population dropped 70%; 300 to 400 died, including individuals of the reentering population. Trembling and dead birds have been observed on the Wes-leyan University campus after elm spraying. In this ecological relation-ship the earthworm, which is relatively resistant to the pesticide, may accumulate up to 8 times that present in the soil (Hunt, 1965), only to be consumed later by the DDT-sensitive robins. If a good tree-care program fails to reduce elm mortality and spraying is deemed necessary, the less toxic methoxychlor should be substituted for DDT. On the 61-acre University of Wisconsin campus where this substitution was made, the robin population rose from 3 to 29 pairs (Hickey and Hunt, 1960).

In the near future systemic or biological controls may eventually obviate the use of compounds which are toxic to nontarget organisms and to the ecosystem. The recent introduction of a tiny wasp (Dendroso-ter protuberans), which attacks the European elm bark beetle, has proved promising in parasitizing the Dutch elm beetle larvae in Ohio and Mis-souri. These wasps are now being reared by the millions for further mass release in infested areas (Anon., 1967). In Europe, where disease is not a problem, the wasp kills 70% of the beetle larvae. Research is also in progress on creation of a disease-resistant elm. At the U.S.D.A. Plant Industry Station, Beltsville, Maryland, geneticist Haig Dermen and plant pathologist Curtis May are attempting to create a genetically compatible elm using the Siberian elm, which is highly resistant to the disease. Since the Siberian elm has only one-half the chromosome number of that of the American elm, they have subjected buds of the former to colchicine treatment. This tends to prevent the normal division of a typical cell and thereby results in a doubling of the chromosome number. They have successfully created rooted Siberian cuttings with 56 chromosomes which they hope to cross with the American elm to produce an ornamentally desirable elm which will be resistant to the disease. Until more satisfactory control measures are available for the Dutch elm disease, emphasis should be on sound cultural practices.

THE OSPREY DECLINE; REPRODUCTIVE FAILURE

Along the northeastern coastline, now being engulfed by a sprawling megalopolis, the osprey, a fish-eating bird, has been on the decline since the early 1900s. Decreasing at about 2 to 3% during the first half of the century, it is currently disappearing at the rate of 30% annually. Suggested causal factors have included harassment by man, increasing urbanization, and pesticides. It is significant that reproductive failure is not restricted to areas near civilization. In a relatively inaccessible Rhode Island swamp, eight nests yielded only 3 instead of the expected 20 young birds. Studies by Ames (1966) have recently added considerably to our knowledge concerning the possible role of pesticides. Comparative studies of DDT content in osprey eggs and their hatchability at the mouth of the Connecticut River now reveal that few osprey (only 0.5 young per nest) are being reared in Connecticut where eggs contain 5.1 ppm DDT and its congeners. Along the coast of Maryland, hatchability is slightly higher (1.3 to 1.6 young per nest), and DDT levels in the eggs are lower (only 3.0 ppm). These data indicate a direct relationship between the amount of DDT and hatchability; the greater the quantity of DDT present, the fewer young hatched. Normally about 2.5 young per nest can be expected from healthy osprey colonies.

The mechanism whereby reproductive processes may be affected has been elucidated by Hart and Fouts (1963) and by Hart (1965). Laboratory studies on small mammals have revealed that chlordane and DDT induced the production of certain enzymes in the liver which inactivated the naturally occurring sex hormones such as progesterone, estradiol, and testosterone. Other investigators have found that mice showed a decrease in fertility after being subjected to small quantities of chlordane. Could the 12 ppm DDT in our body fat in itself, or in combination with other pesticide residues, also eventually cause decreased fertility in man? This may be a subtle solution to man's overpopulation problem, but at best it would be a dangerously haphazard approach. Sufficient evidence is already at hand to ban the broadcast use of DDT and other persistent pesticides.

EFFECTS OF MOSQUITO SPRAYING

During the last two decades many of the tidal marshes around major cities along the Atlantic seaboard have been the target of intensive mosquito-control spraying programs. The effects of such spraying on the nontarget organisms have been especially striking. In Florida, applications of as little as 0.2 lb/acre of DDT resulted in the loss of thousands of fish, along with a drastic reduction in the shrimp population (Croker and Wilson, 1965). Using similar applications, Butler and Springer (1963) report almost complete elimination of lower food chain organisms including various crustaceans. Shrimp are among the most sensitive of marine animals. Concentrations in the range of as little as 0.6 to 6 *parts per billion* kill or immobilize a shrimp population within 2 days (Butler and Springer, 1963). One of the most dramatic effects of the continuous application of DDT has been the accumulation of up to 32 lb/acre of this persistent insecticide in the marsh muds of Long Island Sound, where mosquito-control spraying has been under way for some twenty years (Woodwell *et al.,* 1967). This pesticide has not only persisted, but it is now found also in increasing amounts as one goes from one trophic level to the next. Plankton contains .04 ppm; shrimp, .16 ppm; minnows, 1 to 2 ppm; and ring-billed gulls, 75.5 ppm. Avian populations near the top of the food chain have DDT residues about a million times greater than the concentration of the chemical in the water. DDT levels are now considered sufficiently high that it can be assumed that certain populations of nontarget organisms are being eliminated as food chain accumulations reach toxic levels. As a result of this mosquito-control spraying, residues are now constantly available to be recirculated and concentrated by marine organisms with subtle but continuous losses.

A recent court case on Long Island has highlighted this environmental contamination of DDT and has led to a temporary injunction against the Suffolk County Mosquito Control Commission. In this case the private citizen with the help of expert scientific witnesses was successful in at least temporarily arresting further spraying. Stickel (1967) in a recent review of the mosquito-control problem recommends Abate, a new organic phosphate closely related to melathion and parathion, as a safer substitute for DDT and other persistent chlorinated hydrocarbons.

INDISCRIMINATE USE OF INSECTICIDES BY THE HOMEOWNER

Fifteen percent of the pesticides produced are used by the home gardener. Through commercial advertising and various other publications the use of persistent pesticides is still being promoted. One such publication (Favretti and Savos, 1965) available from a university extension service tends to give the public what it wants rather than what is most desirable ecologically. Among the 93 entries or activities listed from April through September, half recommend spraying some 20 groups of ornamentals including rhododendrons, laurel, privets, maples, hollies, birches, dogwoods, and lilacs. These are routine preventive spray applications that are recommended regardless of whether or not insects are present. Among the compounds prescribed are lindane, chlordane and DDT—all persistent hydrocarbons which should be avoided whenever possible (Briggs, 1967). Nowhere in the publication is the importance of proper cultural conditions in minimizing insect pests stressed. The importance of proper site conditions in the care of ornamental plants is emphasized in an Arnold Arboretum publication: "The ability of plants in good health and vigor to resist insects and disease attacks in many cases is well known; consequently we keep our plants growing vigorously, thus helping in the battle against insects and diseases . . . ." As a specific example, Wyman (1953) writes concerning rhododendrons: "Plants growing in the right soil and in the right location seldom are attacked by serious pests, except possibly the lace bug." Yet in the aforementioned extension guide six sprayings are recommended for the rhododendrons during the growing season! When the now-retired Director of the extension service was written to concerning this publication, he replied that it "is a most popular publication. It has received not only local but regional and national attention. Thanks to the excellent job done by the authors." This type of publication, although highly appealing, provides only temporary solutions to the homeowner's pest problems. The use of DDT, chlordane, aldrin, dieldrin, endrin, heptachlor, and toxaphene, all of which act as nerve poisons, should be avoided. In their place non-persistent compounds such as Bordeaux mixture, copper-lime mixtures, rotenones, and lime sulfurs are recommended (Briggs, 1967).

BOTANICAL GARDENS AT CONNECTICUT COLLEGE — PESTICIDE-FREE FOR TWO DECADES

For over two decades the woody plant collections in the Connecticut Arboretum and the Caroline Black Botanic Garden (Fig. 1) have been maintained by the Botany Department without the use of insecticides. The Arboretum plantings, covering some 20 acres and comprising over 300 native species, are surrounded by a mosaic of natural communities which brings the Arboretum holdings to over 300 acres. The landscaped Botanic Garden occupies approximately 2 acres on a slope facing east and surrounded by woodlands and college housing. Here over 200 introduced species and varieties of woody ornamentals, such as fringe tree, sourwood, silverbell, enkianthus, azaleas, and rhododendrons, are massed in an aesthetically attractive setting. In the last twenty years, pest problems have been minimal: one flowering dogwood was lost to the

FIG. 1. Caroline Black Botanic Garden at Connecticut College where ornamental plant collections have been maintained without insecticides for over two decades.

borer; an euonymus with insect scale was removed; pruning abated scale spreading to lilac in another case, and an enkianthus disease problem was remedied by hosing with water. A sizable 15-year-old collection of hybrid rhododendrons situated on a protected exposure facing north — an ecologically favorable site — has never been sprayed, yet foliage is always vigorous and the annual floral display is spectacular. Similarly the azaleas, lilacs, maples, privets, and hollies are particularly handsome and require no spraying. The extensive mountain laurel plantings along the Laurel Walk form an unusually attractive entrance to the Connecticut Arboretum in both foliage and flowering aspects. Here, and within the more than 300 native plant collections, insect pests are not sufficiently destructive to require spraying.

Other arboreta or botanic gardens surveyed* in the Northeast have no

---

*Morris Arboretum, Longwood Gardens, Swarthmore, Brooklyn Botanic Garden, New York Botanical Garden, Arnold Arboretum, and Hunnewell Arboretum. Data obtained by Miss Marcia Robbins, a botany major, in conjunction with an undergraduate study concerning maintenance of plant collections in arboreta and botanic gardens of the Northeast.

such pesticide-free record. All use insecticides, some very extensively. Gallonage data were not obtained from all areas, but two examples give some idea of the quantities applied. In 1966 over 7750 gallons were applied in a 50-acre garden, averaging 155 gallons per acre; and, in another 200-acre area 15,000 gallons, averaging 75 gallons per acre.

The specific factors involved in minimal insect damage in the Connecticut College Botanic Station and Arboretum defy precise scientific analysis. However, it is pertinent to point out the conditions which characterize these areas. The Botanic Garden, limited in size, is dominated by a great diversity of species massed in a seminaturalistic setting and surrounded primarily by natural woodland. Although covering a somewhat larger area, the Arboretum collections are highly diverse and set in a mosaic of relatively undisturbed natural communities. It should be emphasized, however, that the plant collections are not insect-*free* but that insect damage fails to reach levels that detract from the vigor and beauty of the plantings. It would appear that the significant factors involve proper cultural conditions and a diversity of habitats that includes adequate numbers of predator organisms among the insects themselves. In other words, natural biological control has been sufficient and adequate.

The Abuse and Sound Use of Herbicides

Adverse Effects of Indiscriminate Spraying

During the past two decades herbicides or weed killers have been used widely and indiscriminately in the control of unwanted vegetation on roadsides and cross-country utility rights-of-way. It is estimated that over 60,000,000 acres are involved across our nation. During the early sixties a survey of Connecticut roadsides revealed that nonselective application of sprays, rather than more selective and effective techniques, was among those most widely employed (Egler, 1954; Goodwin and Niering, 1959, 1962). Further research revealed that this unsound ecological approach was not restricted to roadsides but was being used on all types of rights-of-way. Such indiscriminate broadcast spraying not only results in unsightly brown-outs, but also damages or kills associated desirable vegetation and frequently fails to root-kill unwanted woody growth. Dill (1962–63) describes certain New Jersey roadsides that have been sprayed 19 times in a 6-year period. Such treatment selectively eliminated the colorful roadside wild flowers, leaving a rather monotonous grassy swath along the roadsides. If such sprays are applied in the spring, especially when leaf and twig growth is still occurring, drift of spray particles or volatility effects can adversely damage surrounding unsprayed

FIG. 2. Herbicide or herbicidelike effects. *Top:* Two white oak branches, one showing "cupping" of leaves resulting from drift or volatility following indiscriminate foliar spraying alone Connecticut roadside; normal specimen to the right, 1957.

woody vegetation (Fig. 2). Such an incident has been reported along a wooded town roadside through the Connecticut Arboretum (Niering, 1959). The town indiscriminately sprayed the immediate roadside vegetation with a mixture of 2,4-D-2,4,5-T (2,4-dichlorophenoxyacetic acid-2,4,5-trichlorophenoxyacetic acid) which resulted in abnormal leaf curling on large oaks up to 300 ft from the road. On certain overhanging white oaks subsequent growth resulted in elongated weeping twigs. Evidence of this abnormal growth pattern can still be detected more than a decade after the incident (Fig. 2).

Broadcast applications can also destroy valuable aspects of native flora. Even the lichens can be eliminated. Wildlife and game can be adversely affected by loss of desirable plant cover. Fortunately, owing to the ineffectiveness of indiscriminate spraying, along with adverse publicity, more selective techniques are now being employed in Connecticut and certain other states. Although considerable progress has been made, indiscriminate broadcast spraying still occurs.

HERBICIDELIKE EFFECTS

At least two incidents are known to the writer in which vegetation within or near cities has been adversely affected by unknown pollutants with weed killer-like effects.

In Naugatuck, Connecticut, more than twenty species of garden crops and native plants were damaged or destroyed throughout the town in June, 1961 (Collins, 1961). Leaf curl and stem distortion were the typical symptoms (Fig. 2); tomatoes, which are known to be especially sensitive to 2,4-D, suffered the greatest damage. Among the other plants affected were beans, potatoes, radishes, beets, chard, peppers, peaches, ash, great laurel, giant ragweed, boneset, sugar maple, hemlock, and spruce. Tomatoes and seedling beets did not recover in the areas of most severe injury. In assessing the source of the pollutant it was found that the effect approximated a gradient with the most severe effects nearest the area of the Naugatuck Chemical Company, where maleic hydrazide, a growth inhibitor, is manufactured. One to three miles in every direction from this point the effects became less and less severe. On June 23 the local Weather Bureau reported a temperature inversion which may have

---

Center: White oak foliage exhibiting herbicidelike effects (extreme leaf "cupping") near Dow Chemical Co., Ledyard, Connecticut, 1966. *Lower left:* White oak twigs showing abnormal bending due to drift or volatility several months after indiscriminate spraying along Connecticut roadside, 1957. *Lower right:* Herbicidelike effects on chard showing extreme leaf distortion, near Naugatuck Chemical Co., Naugatuck, Connecticut, 1961.

concentrated the contaminant, thus resulting in the widespread damage. However, similar effects were also noted by some residents as early as mid-May. Experimental tomato plants grown near the source of the contamination also exhibited leaf curl several weeks after the major damage was reported. Test plants grown in New Haven, more than 10 miles to the south, in soil taken from the contaminated area also showed effects in July which suggest that the soil had accumulated the pollutant. Although numerous scientists investigated and worked on this problem, the causal agent was never identified even though the source of the contaminant appears to have been well established.

Another incident has been observed by the writer in the Town of Ledyard in southeastern Connecticut. During the abnormally dry summer of 1966 the foliage of trees around the Dow Chemical Plant at Allyns Point (where latex, used in latex paint, and styrofoam are manufactured) exhibited a pronounced leaf curling or cupping (Fig. 2) not unlike that affecting certain plants in the Naugatuck area. These symptoms also decreased in a gradient in all directions a thousand feet or more from the plant. White and black oaks were among the most sensitive trees. However, nearer the apparent source of contamination, black cherry, greenbrier, and box elder showed leaf cupping, as did practically all plant cover in the forest understory and shrub stratum. Twig elongation, which was markedly stimulated on white oak, resulted in young branches with a pronounced weeping form. Leaf and twig symptoms were remarkably similar to those produced on white oaks as a result of the indiscriminate spraying incident along the wooded roadside through the Connecticut Arboretum. White ash, especially resistant to the phenoxy herbicides, appeared to be unaffected.

During the extremely wet growing season of 1967 oak foliage appeared nearly normal. Only the trees most severely affected the previous year still showed curling and extreme aphid infestation. Officials of the Dow Chemical Company have reported that they isolated the compound responsible for the penetrating odor emanating from their latex-processing plant. During their laboratory studies, test plants exposed to this compound appeared to reveal no adverse effects (Bosscher, 1967).

According to local plant officials, weed killers have not been used around the plant for more than a decade. No railroad right-of-way spraying has been done for several years near the plant. Although roadside spraying has occurred nearby, effects similar to those described here were not detectable elsewhere along the sprayed roadsides. Company officials still consider the problem unsolved. Probably the most significant aspect of this and the Naugatuck incident is the absence of identity at this time of the causal agents. While such data are lacking, there is always the possibility of similar recurrences.

Sound Use of Herbicides
by the Homeowner and Commercial Applicator

To the homeowner, herbicides have become a most useful tool for the removal of lawn weeds and the killing of unwanted woody growth around the home. Although overall applications may be used locally on poison ivy, the more selective basal and stump treatments are recommended for woody growth. Basal applications involve wetting thoroughly the lower 12 to 18 in. of the basal bark to the grown line. On thick-barked trees several inches in diameter the bark near the ground may be notched or frilled with an axe to facilitate penetration of chemical. If standing dead trees are objectionable, they may be cut down and the stumps soaked with the herbicide. In both these techniques 2,4,5-T or 2,4-D-2,4,5-T, 1 part of chemical to 20 parts of fuel oil is an effective formulation. Spraying is effective on most woody species at any season of the year except for root-suckering species, which should be sprayed in late summer. As previously mentioned, there is always need to be cautious of drift and volatility effects, especially when using overall sprays.

Fig. 3. Right-of-way demonstration area in Connecticut Arboretum. Relatively stable mixed shrub cover has been created by selective removal of unwanted trees using basal spray techniques. Originally covered with mixed tree and shrub growth as shown in control plot (left foreground).

These basic principles and techniques are also applicable in commercial roadside, transmission, telephone, gas pipeline, and railroad right-of-way vegetation management (Egler, 1954; Niering, 1958; Goodwin and Niering, 1959). In the Connecticut Aboretum, demonstration areas established on transmission, telephone, and roadside rights-of-way more than a decade ago now exhibit a relatively stable mosaic of shrub communities (Fig. 3) created by selective herbicide techniques (Niering, 1955, 1957, 1961). Undesirable tree growth has been removed, existing shrub and herbaceous cover has been preserved. This program has resulted in an aesthetically desirable pattern of shrub communities with high wildlife values and a high degree of resistance to tree invasion. The policy means that the ecological cover types created are now helping to reduce the cost of future maintenance.

Among the utilities, the Hartford Electric Light Company adopted in 1965 a system-wide policy of selective application. The work of the Wisconsin Natural Resource Committee of State Agencies (1965) will eventually convert the entire state of Wisconsin to the selective approach along its roadsides. After a U.S. Forest Service training conference in 1965, a sound right-of-way management program became established practice from the Ozarks and Minnesota to New England (Svensen, 1966). The U.S. Forest Service has been a leader in the sound use of herbicides along the wooded roadsides within the national forests (McQuilkin and Strickenberg, 1961).

In suburbia, rights-of-way represent an invaluable open-space resource (Niering, 1967). Every effort should be made to preserve their existing native flora and to maintain the greatest habitat diversity possible. As a consequence, maximum faunistic diversity will also be maintained. Repeated broadcast sprays reduce floristic diversity and result in grassland continua that are especially vulnerable to tree invasion. Connecticut utilities that have eventually adopted the selective approach are beginning to profit not only from good public relations but also economically, since maintenance costs are being reduced on a long-range basis. As open-space resources dwindle within the cities, these nonagricultural rights-of-way will provide a new dimension in multiland use. In New England and California they are being used for Christmas tree plantations. On Long Island, where open space is at a premium, utility rights-of-way are providing a network of trails for hiking and horseback riding. Ecologically, rights-of-way are really permanent strip transects representing a broad spectrum of sites and vegetation types ideally suited to display the region's diverse natural history. There is little doubt that they will add a new dimension to outdoor recreation, especially in urban areas.

And, for the wild gardener in the suburbs who is fortunate enough to have an abandoned field growing up to "brush," there remains the fascinating challenge of naturalistic landscaping with herbicides (Niering and Goodwin, 1963; Kenfield, 1966). This involves selectively removing the less desirable trees and shrubs while accentuating the most aesthetically ornamental forms. Such naturalistically landscaped areas have been created in the Connecticut Arboretum and at Aton Forest, Norfolk, Connecticut. Herbicides provide man with a unique vegetation management tool. When properly used, they can enhance the remaining semi-natural landscapes within and around major centers of population.

Conclusion

Although some progress has been made in curtailing the use of persistent pesticides in recent years, as recommended by the President's Science Advisory Committee in 1963, their commercial production in the United States continues to increase annually. With all major biotic and abiotic environments throughout the world now contaminated, pesticidal pollution becomes an international problem. The mere restriction of their use in the United States will not prevent continued contamination of major ecosystems. It is believed that, in certain environments, populations of organisms are now being subtly eliminated as a result of recycling and subsequent accumulations through the food chain. Since biological magnification occurs, even very low residues cannot be considered safe. From a holistic point of view, it must be realized that biocides represent but one of a whole spectrum of contaminants now plaguing man's environment. In this context, every effort should be made to replace persistent pesticides not only in suburbia but also wherever they are being used throughout the world.

REFERENCES

Ames, P. L. (1966). DDT residues in the eggs of the osprey in the north eastern United States and their relation to nesting success. *J. Appl. Ecology* 3 (Suppl.), 87–97.

Anon. (1966). Fish, wildlife and pesticides. U.S. Dept. of Interior, Supt. of Doc., Washington, D. C.

Anon. (1967). Tiny wasp may curtail Dutch elm disease. Agri. Res. **16,** 14.

Bess, H. A. (1961). Population ecology of the gypsy moth. *Conn. Agri. Expt. Sta. Bull.,* p. 146.

Briggs, Shirley A. (1967). Safer pesticides for home and garden. *Atlantic Naturalist* **22,** 99–108.

Boscher, Harold (1967). Personal communication.

Butler, P. A., and Springer, P. F. (1963). Pesticides—a new factor in coastal environments. *Trans. 28th No. Am. Wildlife and Nat. Res. Conf.,* pp. 378–390.

Collins, Stephen (1961). Unpublished report.

Croker, R. A., and Wilson, A. J. (1965). Kinetics and effects of DDT in a tidal marsh ditch. *Trans. Am. Fisheries Soc.* **94,** 152–159.

Crossman, S. S. (1948). Dead and dying trees in the gypsy moth defoliated areas. Progr. Rept., Bur. Entomol. Plant Quarantine, U.S.D.A.

Dill, N. H. (1962–63). Vegetation management. *N. J. Nature News* **17,** 123–130; **18,** 151–157.

Egler, F. E. (1954). Vegetation management for rights-of-way and roadsides. *Smithsonian Inst. Rept. for 1953,* pp. 299–322.

Egler, F. E. (1966). Pointed perspectives. Pesticides in our ecosystem. *Ecology* **47,** 1077–1084.

Favretti, R. J., and Savos, M. G. (1965). Home grounds activities month by month. Cooperative Ext. Service, Univ. of Conn.

Goodwin, R. H., and Niering, W. A. (1959). The management of roadside vegetation by selective herbicide technique. *Conn. Arboretum Bull.* **11,** 4–10.

Goodwin, R. H., and Niering, W. A. (1962). What is happening along Connecticut's roadsides. *Conn. Arboretum Bull.* **13,** 13–24.

Hart, L. G., and Fouts, J. R. (1963). Effects of acute and chronic DDT administration on hepatic microsomal drug metabolism in the rat. *Proc. Soc. Exptl. Biol. Med.* **114,** 388–392.

Hart, L. G., and Fouts, J. R. (1965). Further studies on the stimulation of hepatic microsomal drug metabolising enzymes by DDT and its analogs. *Arch. Pharmakol. Exptl. Pathol.* **249,** 486–500 (in English).

Hickey, J. J., and Hunt, L. B. (1960). Initial songbird mortality following a Dutch elm disease control program. *J. Wild Mgmt.* **24,** 259–265.

Hunt, L. B. (1965). Kinetics of pesticide poisoning in Dutch elm disease control. *In* Effects of Pesticides on Fish and Wildlife. U.S. Fish Wildlife Serv. Circ. **226,** 12–13.

Kenfield, W. G. (1966). "The Wild Gardener in the Wild Landscape." 232 pp, Hafner, New York.

McQuilkin, W. E., and Strickenberg, L. R. (1961). Brush control in practice on the National Forests. *Northeastern Forest Expt. Sta., U.S. Forest Serv., Region 7. Sta. Paper* 148. Reprinted in *Conn. Arboretum Bull.* **13,** 3–9, 1962.

Niering, W. A. (1955). Herbicide research at the Connecticut Arboretum. *Proc. Northeastern Weed Control Conf.* **9,** 459–462.

Niering, W. A. (1957). The Connecticut Arboretum right-of-way demonstration area progress report. *Proc. Northeastern Weed Control Conf.* **11,** 203–208.

Niering, W. A. (1958). Principles of sound right-of-way vegetation management. *Econ. Botany* **12,** 140–144.

Niering, W. A. (1959). A potential danger of broadcast sprays. *Conn. Arboretum Bull.* **11,** 11–13.

Niering, W. A. (1961). The Connecticut Arboretum right-of-way demonstration area – its role in commercial application. *Proc. Northeastern Weed Control Conf.* **15,** 424–433.

Niering, W. A. (1967). Connecticut rights-of-way – their conservation values. *Conn. Woodlands* **32,** 6–9.

Niering, W. A., and Goodwin, R. H. (1963). Creating new landscapes with herbicides. *Conn. Arboretum Bull.* **14.**

Rudd, R. L. (1964). "Pesticides and the Living Landscape." 320 pp. Univ. of Wisc. Press, Madison.

Smiley, D. (1964). The gypsy moth in Ulster County. *John Burroughs Natural History Soc., Natural Sci. Ser.* **4,** 1–11.

Stickel, W. H. (1967). Wildlife, pesticides and mosquito control. *Mass. Audubon* **51,** 110–122.

Svensen, H. A. (1966). Vegetation management for rights-of-way. *Eastern Region Forest Serv. U.S.D.A.*

Wallace, G. J. (1960). Another year of robin losses on a university campus. *Audubon Mag.* **62,** 66–69.

Wisconsin Natural Resource Committee of State Agencies (1965). "Selective Brush Management Program on Wisconsin Roadsides." 16 p.

Woodwell, G. M., Wurster, C. F., Jr., and Isaacson, P. A. (1967). DDT residues in an east coast estuary: a case of biological concentration of a persistent insecticide. *Science* **156,** 821–824.

Wurster, Doris H., Wurster, C. F., Jr., and Strickland, W. N. (1965). Bird mortality following DDT spray for Dutch elm disease. *Ecology* **46,** 488–499.

Wyman, D. (1953). "Shrubs and Vines for American Gardens." 433 p. Macmillan, New York.

The Urban Outdoor Natural Area Museum:
A Unique Opportunity for
Education, Research, and Cultural Recreation

Frank E. Egler

There is nothing new about ecological crises in the history of the Earth; they have occurred repeatedly. Either a species adapted to environmental changes, which may or may not have been caused by the species itself, or the species became extinct. What distinguishes the present particular ecological crisis from all others is that (a) man as a species is responsible for worldwide environmental change ("pollution" and "destruction of natural resources"), and (b) man is overpopulating the ecosystem. The fears of the ecosystem ecologist are based on the axiom that an excessive human population can be maintained only by an ever more simplified ecosystem web (food chain), and simplified ecosystem webs, by their nature, are unstable. If the web collapses, so also do the culture, the civilization, the species itself. Another fear is that the environment created by technology is already, or will be, so far removed from the environment in which man evolved that the psychological and sociological strains and pressures will cause an internal collapse even before the external environment destroys him. This is a challenge to human intelligence! This is the field of the research scientist in human ecosystem ecology. There is much research to be done, on man as an anthropoid animal as well as on the external environment, and on the extremely complex ramifications between the two. The United States has yet to see arise an adequate center for the study of the unity that is man and his total environment.

In addition to research, there is the problem of formal education in the field of human ecosystem ecology — in primary schools, secondary schools, colleges, and universities. The high schools are leaders in this respect, largely through the Green Version BSCS biology textbook which bears the stamp of Marston Bates. Furthermore, high school teachers, by nature and personality, by their contacts, not only with students but also with parents, politicians, and citizens, readily grasp the unity of the human ecosystem. Universities are far slower in this respect. Although Centers and Institutes of "environmental biology" are appearing on almost every campus, they are often no more than fronts for obtaining grants for still more detailed research projects. Research biologists, by personality and by training, often are highly specialized, retired from the main currents of community activity, often uninterested in the education of any except more professionals like themselves.

In addition to research and formal education, there is the problem of communication in the field of human ecosystem ecology, that is, communication with the citizen. Most universities deliberately evade this phase as unacademic and too controversial, especially in view of their own fund-raising strategies involving private donors, industry, foundations, and government.

These three possible approaches to the problem — research, education, and communication — are most strikingly delineated in the operation of our land grant colleges of agriculture and their adjuncts. The agricultural experiment stations are the research arm. The colleges of agriculture handle the education itself. The cooperative extension services deal with communication to the farmer. Unfortunately, agriculture, as a short-term, profit-oriented, geographically restricted, monocultural system, is one of the most ecosystem-illiterate of all human endeavors. The tendency of land grant colleges of agriculture to call themselves colleges of "agriculture and natural resources" is a ploy to maintain their status in the face of diminishing manpower and acreage requirements for farm resources, and it should be viewed with alarm. (A recent example of ecosystem-illiteracy occurs in an article entitled "Food Production with Pesticides," by Walter E. Fleming, Honorary Professor of Entomology and Economic Zoology, and published in the June 1968 issue of *News and Views,* Bureau of Conservation and Environmental Science, Rutgers University, College of Agriculture.) The extension services are magnificent examples of a self-perpetuating, enlarging feedback mechanism, whereby more and more tax money is obtained to convince more and more citizens to appropriate more and more money for the continued growth of the extension service. That the U. S. Department of Agriculture continues to enlarge while the farm population continues to decrease is ample proof of the "success" of this kind of sociological "organism."

As an alternative to the colleges of agriculture and environmental sciences as interpreters of ecosystem ecology, I propose the *urban outdoor natural area museum,* particularly as a radical and innovative con-

cept for heavily urbanized areas. It will serve in all three of the categories named above — research, education, and communication. Inevitably, in a proposal of this kind, there will be semantic problems,
confusions about meanings and traditions of words, as well as about
how to get across a new concept definable only in terms of old ideas
which are to be avoided. At the material level the proposal envisages
neither a museum building nor an unprotected unmanaged wilderness
area (although it has some characteristics of both). It might be compared
to the grassland of a football field, surrounded by the stadium. It might
be compared to the "closed system" of a spaceship in which a few astro-
nauts are breathing, feeding, and eliminating in a balanced ecosystem,
albeit far, far simpler than the one under discussion here. It can best be
described as an island ecosystem dropped into the middle of a great
unstable urban area, to be enjoyed for its open space, its solitude, renewal
of the roots binding man to his nature heritage, but above all as exemplary of the close, interlocking, ecosystem web.

The Natural Area

Natural area, as the term is used here, refers to *a geographically
delimited tract, kept as free as possible from all human interference.*
At the ecosystem level, a natural area itself may unidirectionally change,
as a white pine stand in the Northeast naturally changes to mixed hemlock
and hardwoods. If a white pine stand is to be perpetuated, management
activities must be carried out. Furthermore, even a mature ecosystem
may naturally fluctuate, often violently, as in the lemming explosions of
Scandinavia, or in times of floods, hurricanes, and volcanic activity.
Whether or not man chooses to "manage" such ecosystems by flattening
the "peaks" and the "troughs" is purely an arbitrary decision. Should
he, for example, or should he not interfere with his own "natural"
famines and epidemics and internecine warfare? They were most important factors in the past in the maintenance of a balanced total ecosystem by controlling human population.

In basic and applied scientific work, the natural area is absolutely
indispensable. It is the check, the standard, the control, by which to com-
pare and to contrast the experimental work done on comparable areas, or
the management, or mismanagement, practices applied elsewhere.
Foresters have been slow to realize the role of natural areas in basic
silvics and in practical silviculture. Nevertheless, more and more experimental forests possess reserved tracts, even though they are rarely
studied (Woods, 1964). Range management professionals have obtained

a good understanding of the total plant-animal interrelationships, yet they rarely consider long-term ungrazed areas.

Contemporary naturalists talk endlessly of "the balance of nature"; there is even a recent book by that title (Milne, 1960). Although there is reason for scientists to use the phrase, within special contexts, it is a phrase which is too easily misunderstood and glamorized by the starry-eyed nature lover, and too easily hole-poked by the realist who sees the natural catastrophes of earthquakes, droughts, and fire. Climaxes are *so* satisfying; they must occur.

Urbanization, the other side of the coin from natural areas, is merely a name for whole clusters of processes, for scores of social and economic variables that are resulting in the United States becoming a nation of "metropolitan areas" (Anon., 1967a; Ewald, 1967; Mumford, 1968). The nation's metropolitan areas house 140 million Americans in less than a tenth of the country's acreage. In 1966, 224 metropolitan areas (each with a population of at least 50,000) contained 70% of the total population. It is not to be thought that small towns and farm-oriented cultures have been idyllic; per capita they may even exceed cities in characteristics considered undesirable. The more urbanization proceeds, the more incumbent it is on the ecologically knowledgeable to communicate the dependence of the city on the total environment; it includes the 90% of the country's acreage which to the urbanite may be simply "undeveloped land, waiting to be urbanized."

The stated aims and the actions of pertinent social organizations may aid in the formulation of the natural area concept. Two specialized citizen groups stand out among all the others. *The Wilderness Society* (729 15th Street, N.W., Washington, D.C. 20005) publishes *The Living Wilderness.* This society takes a major interest in such large wilderness areas as those of National Wildlife Refuges (U.S. Department of the Interior), National Parks (U.S. Department of the Interior), and National Forests (U.S. Department of Agriculture), and tracts which are considered by the Wilderness Act of 1964.

The Nature Conservancy (1522 K Street, N.W., Washington, D.C. 20005) is the leading American organization dealing with relatively small natural areas, actually for preservation, and purportedly for scientific study, education, and cultural recreation, certainly not for mass recreation. They are publishers of *Nature Conservancy News,* which consists mainly of reports on their own areas. State chapters supplement activities at the local level.

National Audubon Society (1130 Fifth Ave., New York, N.Y. 10028) should be mentioned as owning and administering a growing amount of wild lands. The *Sierra Club* (Mills Tower, San Francisco) is known to the public through its lavishly illustrated publications and its soundly militant director, David Brower. The *Natural Area Council* (145 E. 52 Street, New York, N.Y. 10022), linked with the name of Richard H. Pough, plays a critical role. Numerous state organizations are ever more active. Massachusetts, for example, has two organizations, the *Massachusetts Audubon Society,* and the *Trustees for Public Reservations.* However, state governments are much slower to enter these fields. Michigan, Wisconsin, and Illinois are leaders, and Indiana is the most recent state to pass favorable legislation. On the other hand, other states are meeting resistances, sometimes from political unsophistication on the part of conservationists or from petty political jealousies. For example, Connecticut legislation for a state system of nature preserves was favorably reported in the 1967 Connecticut General Assembly, but was killed at the last moment when the governor lent an ear to the protesting Director of the State Park and Forest Commission, whose empire would be thereby diminished. The "Summary Report, First Conference on State Natural Area Systems" (Milton, 1964) provides other information on this general subject.

In addition to specific citizen and government organizations, other types of organizations, especially those at the city level, must be considered. They are, especially, museums, city parks, botanical gardens, zoological gardens, and nature centers.

Museums of natural history have changed markedly in the last half-century. People living now can remember when they were little more than "cabinets" containing rows of·individual "stuffed" animals on endless shelves, totally devoid of evidence of their differing environments. As museum techniques improved, and as ecological awareness developed, the so-called "habitat groups" emerged as brilliant replicas of entire landscapes, so cunningly contrived and lighted that background paintings and foreground materials merged imperceptibly. Except for consciousness of the "window frame," the viewer could feel that he was a part of the very landscape itself. Today there is a growing tendency for museum administrators to lose themselves in admiration of gadgetry, gimmickry, and technologic redundancy. Buttons to press, levers to throw, panel boards, taped talks, questions sent by radio to a control tower, closed-circuit television—these developments are threatening to turn museums from inspirational experiences in a variety of natural landscapes to a noisy automated midway, where the viewer is bombarded by sights, sounds, and smells far beyond his ability to absorb.

The museum problem is unquestionably critical. As reported in the

A.I.B.S. *Newsletter* for July 1967, "Last month President Johnson re-quested S. Dillon Ripley, Chairman of the Federal Council on the Arts and Humanities, to make a thorough study of the nation's 5,000 museums, and recommend ways to support and strengthen them." In a letter to Mr. Ripley, the President noted that American museums have shown a will-ingness to promote the "increase and diffusion of knowledge among men" and "certainly they should have the wherewithal to do that great work effectively."

City parks are also evolving, even to the point of extinction. Gone is the day when places like the Bois de Boulogne (Paris) and Hyde Park (Lon-don), and the Central Park of Frederick Law Olmsted were sites for carriage driving, for promenading on a Sunday afternoon, and for clan-destine meetings at night which, even if immoral, were at least relatively safe. City parks are deteriorating. As one official observed, the type of people who originally used the parks no longer enjoy them. They are places for the poor, the avant garde, and the criminal. Only a change in national life can bring back the role of parks in urban society. The sad tale of Prospect Park in Brooklyn is told by Shomon (1967). Vandalism by the citizenry is bad enough, but what might be called "official van-dalism" can be even worse. Bulldozers, additional roads, intensive recreational facilities, the encroachments of museum buildings, schools, swimming pools, and restaurants gradually but inevitably take their toll and permanently destroy the very nature of the park.

Possibly the most unbelievable example of official park vandalism, and the grossest example of ecological illiteracy in urban government is occurring in the Bronx. The New York City Sanitation Commissioner has made persistent efforts to use one of the last tidal marshes of Pelham Bay Park for what would be one of the largest garbage dumps in the country. At a time when the ecologic importance of estuarine areas in the total human ecosystem is being widely recognized (Anon., 1967b; Lauff, 1967; Niering, 1966), when states are passing laws to protect the remaining wetlands, when a bill is being currently presented to the Fed-eral Congress (HR-25) to preserve these areas, it is simply inconceivable that the Sanitation Commissioner of the largest city in the world should, with the blessing of the Park Commissioner, be allowed to destroy sites of such high practical and scientific value for research education and recreation. What became known as the Battle of Tallapoosa Creek broadened to include state agencies when an armada manned by civilian sailors moved upstream, thus pronouncing the tidal marshes "navigable waterways." Through action of the Department of Conservation of the State and its Water Resources Commission, a partial victory was won in

November 1967, and an even greater victory in May 1968 in a decision that was a definite slap at New York city officials. Chief credit for the victory should not go to state officials, nor to scientists, nor to academe, but to those informed and spirited citizens who set an example for citizens in other cities to follow.

Another classic example of park destruction is being perpetrated in Meriden, Connecticut, where the Connecticut Highway Department is exerting its right of eminent domain by running a new highway through three major city parks. Here too a group of public spirited citizens have waged a notable battle. They lost, but more through the apathy of the masses of Meriden than for any lack of vigor on their own part. But these masses are improperly educated and the fault lies in the schools.

Botanical gardens represent another urban institution of significance in this discussion. Two of the world's outstanding gardens are the New York Botanical Garden and the Brooklyn Botanic Garden. Botanical gardens go back several centuries (Avery, 1957) when they were either gardens of medicinal plants (physic gardens), or gardens laid out to show the taxonomic relationships of plants. The medical interest has been essentially lost. The interest of scientists in taxonomy, systematics, and flora has continued strongly, and taxonomic research and herbaria constitute the dominant scientific activity of such gardens. In their relationships to the citizens the botanical gardens have stressed landscaping, horticulture, and gardening. The outdoor display gardens, and the indoor conservatories, largely for tropical plants, have brought within the orbit of these institutions the woman's world of the garden clubs. These groups can be an extremely powerful force in American society. Would that ecologists would woo them as successfully as have the extremists among the organic gardeners on the one hand, and the pesticide manufacturers on the other. Perhaps the fault is with the ecologists, who prefer to talk only to each other.

In consideration of botanical gardens and of presentation of the concept of an urban outdoor natural area museum, mention must be made of the Hemlock Forest of the New York Botanical Garden, an area that could be priceless to the citizens of New York City. It is the rocky, hilly area on the west bank of the Bronx River that once bore a magnificent hemlock forest. Recently, a 40 million dollar development program was announced for the New York Garden. If only a very small percentage of that sum could be devoted to a natural area museum at that hemlock forest, New York City would have an ecological research and educational venture second to none.

Zoological gardens today are approaching the idea of a natural area museum, but their growing pains are severe. A zoo is slightly different from a natural history museum. In the museum, habitat groups involve once-living animals in a recreation of their natural homes. The old-style zoo involved living animals confined in iron-barred cages or in restricted habitats.

There is now a glimmer of hope for the animals of our zoos. Field *et al.* (1967) have discussed "The Obsolete Zoo" and have recommended large "animal parks" approaching the concept of a natural area. The New York Zoological Garden is here taking the lead in this field (Miller, 1967), with a timber wolf exhibit in a large area in which the animals are allowed to live a relatively natural life, even if they are not on exhibition to the public for every moment.

Nature centers are a relatively new development among educational institutions which are playing increasingly important roles, both as adjuncts to the schools and for the general citizen. Several specific organizations are involved, chief of which is the Nature Centers Division of the National Audubon Society. Although their work is very commendable, it needs scientific upgrading in many directions. The emphasis has been on "things to do" and on special facets of nature, rather than on an interpretation and understanding of nature-as-a-whole. For example, in an article by Shoman and Holmes (1964–1965), of Nature Centers Division, a two-page colored spread of the layout of a "model school outdoor conservation area" identifies forty-five types of land use and land management, from bee trees to soil pits to parking areas. But unbelievably, nowhere in all this anatomical dissection of nature is there a single Natural Area, where nature can do as *she* pleases. It is like trying to understand an automobile by looking only at the parts on the assembly line, but never riding in one on a country lane.

Later in 1965, in the article on "Nature Centers" in the *Audubon Encyclopedia* (National Audubon Society, 1965), there is a quite different layout. It is true that there are forty identified items, but also the statement that "A community nature center should have a *natural area* that is not developed except for simple foot-trails. This area should comprise one-third to one-half of the nature center land." It is to be hoped that this superior philosophy is thoroughly penetrating the Nature Centers Division and the groups which it influences.

Research on natural areas is one of the last investigative fields to be developed. Those who wish guidelines of what to do in scientific research should consult Leopold's original statement (1941), and to Fosberg's (1964) bulletin for nature conservancy areas. Several sources describe what has been done in a specific area. For example, Wilimovsky and

Wolfe's volume (1966) on Cape Thompson is the result of a money-is-no-limit documentation of an Alaskan area that was to have been the site of a peaceful application of atomic energy; it did not materialize. Editor Graham Netting's series of research papers is a collection of studies on the Powdermill Reserve of the Carnegie Museum in western Pennsylvania. The subject of research on natural areas was investigated extensively by the A.A.A.S. (1963), although, like most committee reports, the contributors leave much to be desired.

Conservation organizations have been slow to develop research programs on lands under their administration, perhaps because, by psychology and temperament, the average conservationist is a "preserver" rather than a scientist. The effectual and efficient research program of the National Audubon Society is now budgeted at $64,000 for the biennial period. Although this research is directed toward population studies of such species as the eagle, the whooping crane, the condor, and the flamingo, the Society has lent considerable encouragement to such broad ecosystem problems as those involving persistent insecticides. Nevertheless, no surveys or reconnaissances of the vegetation types of their lands—a type of study which is basic to all other biologic studies—have been made.

Unfortunately, the research situation with the Nature Conservancy organization is woefully inadequate. Although this organization was originally formed by scientists, and although scientists have always been prominent on its board and a few of them have exerted considerable effort to the end that administration of research might result in reasonable standards, these efforts are negated by other scientists and by laymen. At present, Nature Conservancy scientists are allowed only to advise on completed research manuscripts, projects which may have been planned and executed in a scientifically inferior and unsuitable manner.

Education on natural areas is best represented in the literature by a series of Educational Releases (No. 71, 1967) on a great variety of topics. An outstanding "active" education program is offered by the Arizona-Sonora Museum as reported by Carr (1957).

The university record for use of natural areas in biology education is spotty. There are some—University of Michigan, University of Wisconsin, Antioch College, Connecticut College (New London), for example—which have done admirably. But there are others, even big-name universities, which have either ignored their natural areas or, as in one case, have contrived to divest themselves of the land by "friendly condemnation" when they could not otherwise sell the land openly. There is a list, "Official administrative recognition of natural area programs by colleges and universities," in "Symposium: The Role of the Biologist in Preservation of the Biotic Environment." This is a collection of ten articles that appeared in *Bio-Science* **18**(5), 383–424, May 1968.

Cultural recreation in a natural area is a field far removed from the organized picnicking, camping and swimming facilities that are also a part of contemporary society.

The first requisite for use of a natural area by an inquiring citizenry is an adequate trail system. This subject has recently gained national and federal recognition through bills before Congress and a publication by the U.S. Department of the Interior (1966). In this publication there is a section entitled "Metropolitan Area Trails." It is within this scope that *trails through urban natural areas can probably become the most important single factor, per person per mile,* in solving the ecological crisis of the times – if they are supported by adequate guidance and literature.

The ecological crisis of the times requires daring, imagination, and innovative action to put man back into harmony with his total environment. Two thousand years ago, the Judeo-Christian religion separated man from nature and led him to believe that nature was made *for* man, and was to be exploited and conquered *by* man. This was a reasonable working hypothesis, not dangerous so long as nature really remained the master. The accepted philosophy of economic advisers – the fables of an ever-expanding economy, more production for more consumption, more food for more people – are dreams spun in fancy for the personal profit of those who are living now, and are not based on the hard realities of the ecosystem web. Now that man has the ability to conquer and destroy nature, he has come to a parting of the ways. He will destroy nature, including himself, or he will realize that he is but a part of nature, part of a man-plus-environment "system" within a philosophic context, a way of life, that may yet develop into a religious reformation. The urban outdoor natural area museum could be a major element in the solution of the ecological problems of the times.

REFERENCES

American Association for the Advancement of Science (1963). Report of the A.A.A.S. Council Study Committee on Natural Areas as research facilities. A.A.A.S., Washington, D.C.

Anon. (1967a). Cities. Light in the frightening corners. *Time* Magazine **90**(4), 10–12. July 28.

Anon. (1967b). Estuaries – wasteland or rich resource? 12 pp. Conservation Foundation Letter.

Avery, G. S., Jr. (1957). Botanic gardens – what role today? An "operation bootstraps" opportunity for botanists. *Am. J. Botany* **44,** 268–271.

Carr, W. H. (1957). Tunnel in the desert. An underground venture in education. 34 pp. Arizona-Sonora Museum, Tucson, Arizona.

Ewald, W. H., Jr. (ed.) (1967). "Environment for Man: The Next Fifty Years." Indiana Univ. Press, Bloomington.

Field, J. A., Mather, J. A., and Mather, Robert (1967). The obsolete zoo vs. future animal parks. *Landscape Architecture* **57,** 111–112, 119.

Fosberg, F. R. (1964). Basic reference for research on natural areas. *Nature Conservation Inf. Bull.* **35.** Mimeogr.

Lauff, Geo. H. (ed.) (1967). "Estuaries." A.A.A.S., Washington, D.C.

Leopold, Aldo (1941). Wilderness as a land laboratory. *Living Wilderness.* July.

Miller, J. L. (1967). A natural habitat for wolves. *Defenders of Wildlife News* **42,** 57–59, 75. January-February-March.

Milne, L. J., and Milne, Margery (1960). "The Balance of Nature." Knopf, New York.

Milton, John (1964). (First) Conference on State Natural Area Systems, Nov. 13, 14, 1964, Madison, Wisconsin, Summary Rept. Conservation Foundation (30 E. 40 St., N.Y. 10016), New York. Mimeogr.

Mumford, Lewis (1968). "The Urban Prospect." Harcourt, New York.

National Audubon Society (1965). Nature centers. *In* "Audubon Nature Encyclopedia." Vol. 7.

Netting, M. G. (ed.) (1957–date). Educational releases of Powdermill Reserve, a research station of Carnegie Museum, Pittsburgh.

Netting, M. G. (ed.) (1958–date). Research reports of Powdermill Nature Reserve, a research station of Carnegie Museum, Pittsburgh.

Niering, W. A. (1966). "The Life of the Marsh." A volume of "Our Living World of Nature." McGraw-Hill, New York.

Shomon, J. J. (1967). Will a park die in Brooklyn? *Audubon Mag.* **69,** 80–81.

Shomon, J. J., and Holmes, R. F. (1964–1965). A conservation area to enrich your school. *(N.Y. State) Conservationist* **19,** 22–27, 34.

U. S. Dept. Interior, Bur. Outdoor Recreation (1966). Trails for America. Report of the Nationwide Trail Study. U.S. Dept. Interior, Washington, D.C.

Wilimovsky, N. J., and Wolfe, J. N. (eds.) (1966). "Environment of the Cape Thompson Region, Alaska." U. S. Atomic Energy Commission, Washington, D.C.

Woods, F. W. (1964). One acre, one million, or none? An examination of the native-area conservation problem. *BioScience* **14**(1), 17–19.

Man and His Environment

Tom Stonier

The most ubiquitous species on earth is *man*. No other species has been able to proliferate in habitats as diverse as the steaming rain forests of the Amazon, the rugged slopes of the Himalayas, the frozen tundras of the Arctic, or the sandy deserts of the Sahara. This phenomenol success in exploiting the earth's habitats derives not only from man's remarkable ability to adapt himself to the environment, but even more from his ability to adapt the environment to himself. He covers himself with fur or cloth, tames animals, builds shelters, converts forests into farms, irrigates the desert, and does a thousand ingenious things to manipulate the environment to his advantage.

Nowhere is man's ability to dominate his natural environment more dramatically illustrated than in his cities. A city constitutes a synthetic environment, a man-made ecosystem. Its maintenance makes many demands on the natural environment and, as it grows, the demands increase.

The growth of a city involves not only an increase in the number of people within its gates, or an increase in the number living in the surrounding suburbs, but also an increase in per capita energy requirements. A hundred years ago there were no trucks or buses in the streets, or airplanes flying overhead, and the per capita horsepower available for transportation was a fraction of what it is today. Similarly, in terms of maintaining a more comfortable microclimate, today's citizens are warmer in their homes in winter, cooler in summer, and the houses are brightly lighted all year around. The last two advantages, of course, represent the presence of another source of energy not available a hundred years ago: electricity.

With cheap electricity at his disposal, man has filled his life with an ever-increasing number of energy-consuming devices, from television sets to dishwashers, and the ever-increasing horsepower placed at his disposal in his automobile is well known, as is the increasing number of cars. In America, the "two-car family" is no longer a rarity.

Even a relatively innocuous act such as drinking frozen orange juice for breakfast entails a sizable consumption of energy, for industrial energy is required to process the juice, put it into a can, transport it from California to New York in refrigerated freight cars, transport and store it in the frozen state locally, and dispose of the can after use. Thus the planet is confronted not only with a "population explosion" but also with an "energy explosion."

This increase in energy consumption has placed new stresses on the environment. The examples cited above, in fact, contribute most significantly to one of the chief problems confronting the relationship between New York City and its environment — air pollution. Furthermore, as long as the major source of industrial energy continues to be the oxidation of fossil fuels, air pollution problems will continue to increase. In fact, in a recent interim report to Mayor John V. Lindsay, a special Task Force on Air Pollution stated that "the conclusion is inescapable that most of the large cities in the United States would slide beyond the danger line in air pollution within seven to ten years. Putting it in its bluntest form, New York City could be considered uninhabitable within a decade."

Why have things been allowed to slide so precariously close to this danger point? In retrospect, it is clear that it took time to recognize the problem and, once the problem was recognized, it took time to transmit the seriousness of the situation to the community at large, including its political leaders.

Air pollution can be considered a perfect example of a much broader problem, namely, man's increasing stress on his natural environment. Like other components of our environment, fresh air is a renewable resource. This has led to our blind faith that air is, in fact, in infinite supply. Only now has man come to realize that fresh air is a limited resource, like timber, like coal, like fresh water, and so on.

As the problem of air pollution becomes more acute, the city must either obtain more resource (air) or utilize what it has more efficiently by reducing the pollutants in the atmosphere. Reduction of pollutants could be achieved by either of two techniques: removal of the pollutants from the air, or prevention of pollution in the first place. At the moment, almost all attention is being focused on prevention, and rightly so. However, more research should be directed toward the removal of pollutants already in the air. It is not inconceivable, for example, that growing large quantities of certain types of plants might contribute significantly to the reduction of certain atmospheric pollutants absorbed by such plants. Furthermore, in addition to esthetic advantages, covering buildings with ivy and roof gardens also reduces the heat absorption by such buildings in the summer, thus lowering their requirements for air conditioning. This, in turn, would reduce the demand for electricity and would represent a more efficient utilization of the environment.

Air pollution, as an aspect of stress put on the environment by man, illustrates another principle: it is not technologically impossible to reduce air pollution to acceptable levels, but it is expensive. And, for this reason, the decision to solve the air pollution problem becomes a social and economic problem and, in turn, ultimately a political problem. As Egler has pointed out many times in the past, environmental problems are 90% social and political problems, only 10% ecological.

Existing technology could solve New York City's air pollution problem today. However, this technology varies from the politically questionable, such as supplying the city's electrical needs primarily from hydroelectric power in Labrador (Canada) to the economically unacceptable, such as using electric automobiles. Other nontechnological solutions — banning all automobiles from Manhattan — are equally unacceptable. Yet there is much that could be done if the public were sufficiently aroused, and the political leaders sufficiently motivated. Hydroelectric power from Labrador would be economically feasible in spite of Canada's time limitation (no power after 1975), if the U.S. Government were to subsidize the project (at a cost far smaller than its subsidy of atomic energy). Pressure could be put on automobile manufacturers to speed up research on electric cars, while certain classes of vehicles, such as buses, could be electrified again (trolley buses); and a dynamic and imaginative public transportation system could dramatically cut the number of private automobiles in use in the city. The problem is to persuade the public (and hence their political representatives) to enact appropriate legislation, subsidize private enterprise, or merely foot the bills themselves, e.g., by increasing rents to pay for improved apartment house incinerators.

Because man will continue to increase his destructive pressure on the environment, he must evolve means for accelerating the flow of information at all levels of society so as to reduce the lag between the time a problem is first perceived by experts and the time a solution is put into effect by society. In addition, it is necessary to increase understanding of the relationship between man and his environment, so that potential problems can be recognized before they assume tragic dimensions. This is particularly true in view of the increasing numbers of esoteric chemicals that man is dumping into the environment, and in view of the extension of his engineering capability to the point of damming up whole seas or changing the weather.

Toward this end it is necessary to adopt the following program:

1. Funds for research and training of investigators concerned with ecological problems must be increased. A great body of data and insight must be developed before the environment can be understood sufficiently well to manipulate it with impunity.

2. Scientists must make greater efforts to communicate with the rest of society. These efforts should include citizen education via public lectures, articles in the press and popular magazines, radio and television interviews, and so on. The impetus must come from the scientist himself; he must not wait until someone discovers him in his ivory tower. Communication also includes making oneself available for consultation to political leaders and government officials.

3. Primary, secondary, and college curricula must be revised. What do students learn about air-pollution? About conservation? At no point are the vast majority of our college students made to concern themselves with the environment in which they live today, and of which they are going to expect more tomorrow. A mere handful may be exposed to a brief introduction to ecology in some freshman biology course.

There is need for a curriculum in which *every* college student takes one course in science which deals with significant contemporary problems, including the unresolved problems of the urban environment such as air pollution and microclimate, the impact of an expanding population with increasing per capita energy requirements on the biosphere, the impact of automation and other technology on society, the effect of the new military technology on such well-established social institutions as the nation-state and war, and similar problems which relate the student to the future of man's changing environment, both physical and social.

Such a "Science and Society" course should be interdisciplinary and should involve not only the natural sciences, but also the behavioral, social, political, and economic sciences. For example, one course might examine how urban economics brings about a massive concentration of brick and concrete, to the exclusion of plants, in certain parts of the city; how such a concentration of building material affects the microclimate, contributing in turn to the discomfort of the inhabitants in these areas, and how these undesirable climatological effects of building concentrations have contributed to the summer riots in the black ghettos of American urban areas. The chain of events could be explored further: The hot, rising air currents in the center of the city produce a convection pattern resulting in a canopy over the city which prevents the polluted air from being blown away. Further complications are introduced by the massive use of air conditioning, which contributes to the heat generated by a city and also increases air pollution by virtue of the increased energy demands on electric generating facilities. Thus the poor, lacking air conditioning, are made more uncomfortable still, their irritability being enhanced by physical factors such as excess heat and noxious gases in their environment, and by sociological factors such as the contrast between their sweltering mode of life and that of the privileged cool.

It would be interesting to ask students how to break this chain of undesirable effects. Would any of them come up with an ecological solution, such as introducing green belts, roof gardens, and covering walls with ivy? Would they have the sophistication to understand not only the beneficial effects on air pollution, noise abatement, and microclimate, as well as on the psyche, but also the economic, political and social obstacles that would have to be overcome to implement the desire for such a solution?

There are other equally complex chains which have great pertinence to the students of today. Such studies are almost second nature to ecologists studying food chains, for example. The problem is that it is so much more difficult to teach such a problem-oriented course than the standard subject-oriented course. It requires interdisciplinary cooperation, and teachers with a competence far greater than most of them possess at the moment.

Yet the rapid pace of scientific and technological advance requires a corresponding change in education. And the place to start is in educating the young scientists. They must be taught that a scientist can no longer cloister himself in his laboratory, or hide in the classroom behind impersonal "facts." He must be taught to participate actively in the society of which he is a member. He must become personally involved in the problems of his generation without giving up the tradition of objectivity. He must learn how to communicate his worries and his uncertainties to the public, to the political leaders, and to his students. A scientist's aloofness from problems that have a large social, economic, or political component is a luxury that contemporary society can no longer afford. The successful and intelligent exploitation of the *finite* resources of the terrestrial environment demand an alert and sophisticated scientific community, an enlightened political leadership, and an educated citizenry. Anything less will court disaster.

Air Pollution and Plant Response

Robert H. Daines

Man's dependence on the vast supplies of energy from the sun that was stored millions of years ago in plant tissue has resulted in some of our most challenging air pollution problems. The release of stored energy by complete combustion results in the return of carbon dioxide and water vapor to the atmosphere. In addition, the sulfur present in the fuels is converted into sulfur oxides, while other elements are released as gases (fluorides) or particulates. The release of stored energy by the combustion of fossil fuels (coal, oil, gas) is usually less than complete, and the hydrocarbons that escape are often partly oxidized by the combustion process. Such effluents contain traces of ethylene, acetylene, and propylene that may constitute a problem of air pollution to sensitive plant species. The unsaturated hydrocarbons constitute a group of compounds that readily take part in chemical reaction in the ambient air. In addition to these primary pollutants that have their genesis in the fuel itself, nitrogen oxide is formed by a reaction between atmospheric nitrogen and oxygen in the high temperatures attained in the combustion process. Although nitrogen dioxide (NO_2) may under some conditions serve as a phytotoxic air pollutant, the chief role of the nitrogen oxides is twofold. First, they absorb energy from the short rays of the sun (absorber) and transfer this energy to other molecules, thereby increasing their reactivity. Second, they participate directly in reactions that occur in the sunlight and result in the production of new compounds, among them such phytotoxicants as ozone, peroxyacetyl nitrate (PAN) and its analogs. Although such air pollutants as sulfur dioxide (SO_2), fluorides, hydrocarbons, and nitrogen oxides are produced in large quantities from combustion, they also result from many chemical operations. The ever-increasing demand for power by an affluent society, together with the pollution controls used by industry to reduce pollution from industrial operations, emphasizes the growing importance of fuel consumption as a source of air pollutants.

Primary Products of Combustion

SULFUR DIOXIDE

Historically, SO_2 has been associated with specific industrial operations, and severe damage to a broad spectrum of vegetation has occurred in a rather limited area around these operations. In recent years, in some metropolitan areas, marginal and intercostal necrosis of leaves of very sensitive plants, such as tulips, violets, and some apple varieties, has been observed in the spring of the year. The source of the SO_2 involved in this plant response is believed to be the combustion of oil and coal used in heat and power generation. In excess of 2300 tons of SO_2 is emitted daily into New Jersey's air space from combustion alone.

Katz and Pasternak (1938) found that, when the stomata are open, vegetation may be affected by SO_2 when ground levels of the gas exceed 0.3 to 0.5 ppm for 8 hr. Temperatures favorable for growth, adequate water supply, high relative humidity, and high light intensity are conducive to the opening of stomata. Plants which close their stomata at night become much more tolerant to SO_2 during that period. These investigators also found that conifers are more susceptible to SO_2 during the spring and early summer months, when the needles are elongating, than during the rest of the year. Brennan *et al.* (1964) report that the presence of moisture on leaves during a SO_2 exposure intensifies the injury. When SO_2 is absorbed by the leaf cells, it unites with water to form phytotoxic sulfurous acid, which may be oxidized to sulfuric acid and converted into less toxic sulfate salts. The toxicity of SO_2 is, therefore, a function of the rate at which it is absorbed. A given amount of gas, when absorbed rapidly, produces a higher concentration of the more injurious toxicants in the cells and, hence, more injury than the same amount of gas absorbed at a slower rate. Prolonged exposures to sublethal concentrations of SO_2 may result in chronic or sulfate toxicity (Thomas, 1961) expressed by the development of chlorotic, to brownish red, to white areas, the tissue adjoining the veins remaining green. Studies indicate that plants exposed to SO_2 concentrations which do not produce visible symptoms are not injured by the gas (Hill *et al.*, 1933; Katz and Pasternak, 1938). O'Gara found (Thomas and Hill, 1958) that the usual concentration × time applies to SO_2 fumigations of plants. He suggested that the exposure in time (T) and the concentration (C, ppm) that would produce incipient injury on alfalfa leaves grown under conditions that make for maximum sensitivity of the plant to this gas are

$$T(C - 0.33) = 0.92$$

Thomas and Hill (1958) generalized this equation as follows:

$$T(C - 0.24) = 0.94 = \text{incipient injury}$$
$$T(C - 1.4) = 2.1 = 50\% \text{ leaf destruction}$$
$$T(C - 2.6) = 3.2 = 100\% \text{ leaf destruction}$$

Laboratory and field studies have shown that SO_2 may be oxidized to sulfur trioxide (SO_3), which readily unites with water vapor to form sulfuric acid. On hydration this sulfuric acid may form small, airborne droplets (sulfuric acid mist) which vary in size with the relative humidity. Studies have shown that humidity, sunlight, catalytic particulate matter, hydrocarbons, and oxides of nitrogen increase the speed of conversion of sulfur dioxide into the trioxide. Up to 1% or more per hour of the SO_2 present may be oxidized to the trioxide under most favorable conditions. It is not clear whether the sulfuric acid thus formed has affected plants in nature; however, Middleton *et al.* (1950a,b, 1958) have reported spots on the upper surface of foliage in the Los Angeles area after foggy periods. Thomas *et al.* (1952) produced upper surface foliage spotting from sulfuric acid mist under conditions that provide moist leaf surfaces.

FLUORIDES

Research has indicated that hydrogen fluoride is an extremely phytotoxic gas; certain species of gladiolus plants, for example, have been injured by concentrations as low as a fraction of a part per billion (ppb). In addition to gladiolus, day lilies, Ponderosa pine, Chinese apricots, and blueberries are among the most sensitive plants to fluoride fumigations. In a New Jersey experiment, gladiolus were injured by a 21-day fumigation of HF at 1 ppb, and moist peach foliage was burned by a 3-hr fumigation at 50 ppb. A 3-hr fumigation of 40 ppb of HF produced on corn leaves a mottled chlorosis consisting of small green and faded-green areas interspersed irregularly over the leaf; and it persisted throughout the life of the leaf. Prolonged exposure of more elevated concentrations resulted in the occurrence of light-colored leaves with yellow coloration and necrotic tissue along the margins. Apparently fluoride at this low level damaged the chlorophyll of the corn leaf before killing the cells.

No explanation for the injury pattern of fluorides is presently available except possibly for gladiolus. The tip and marginal location of fluoride injury in gladiolus leaves appears to be dependent on the translocation of fluorine to these particular areas. When a fluoride solution is applied to the base of a leaf, terminal and marginal injury soon results. Chemical analysis of parts of the leaves reveals that much of the fluoride becomes concentrated in the leaf tips and margins, which is where the injury subsequently appears.

Plants vary in their capacity to absorb fluoride and in their tolerance for this gas. Usually the plants that accumulate fluoride most readily are the most tolerant of it. For example, where corn and tomatoes were fumigated together, pronounced injury occurred on the corn foliage, but no injury developed on the tomato leaves. A composite analysis of foliage showed that corn absorbed 70 to 76 ppm of the fluoride by weight of dry-leaf tissue, but the tomato leaf accumulated nearly 200 ppm (Leone *et al.*, 1956). Plants are most susceptible to injury when the leaves are moist or during those seasons of the year and under those cultural and nutritional treatments that provide the most rapid growth (Daines *et al.*, 1952). Light washing of freshly fumigated tomato leaves or allowing fumigated plants to stand for 1 week in ambient air (Daines *et al.*, 1952; Leone *et al.*, 1956) has resulted in the removal of a large percentage (about 50%) of the fluoride occurring in or on the leaf.

All instances of plant damage resulting from airborne fluorides known to the writer have resulted from fluorides escaping from industrial process operations or from the burning of fluoride-containing waste.

Studies in New Jersey have shown that plants may absorb soluble fluoride from the soil, especially under acid conditions. This fluoride tends to accumulate in the roots, but some is translocated into the leaves. Chemical analysis of leaves and roots makes it possible to determine the sources of the pollutant (air or soil) involved in plant toxicity. Airborne fluorides result in high foliage and low root accumulations, whereas the gradient is reversed (Prince *et al.*, 1948; Daines *et al.*, 1952) for the fluoride that enters the plant via the roots.

CHLORINE

Chlorine damage to vegetation has been experienced in New Jersey on only a few occasions. Injury has been observed from the release of this gas by industrial operations and its accidental leakage from storage facilities or transfer equipment. The burning of fuels does not create a problem of chlorine air pollution since this element is absent or, at most, present in negligible amounts in fossil fuels. Perhaps because injury to vegetation occurs so infrequently from this pollutant, very little is found in the literature concerning it. The typical symptoms of chlorine toxicity

include bleaching and necrosis. The fully expanded leaves of the dicotyledonous plants and the elongating needles of pine (Brennan *et al.*,
1965, 1966) are the most sensitive. The injury pattern for most species of
dicots tends to be intercostal rather than marginal, while the injury to pine
needles is normally terminal. In experiments conducted in New Jersey,
Brennan *et al.* (1965, 1966) found that alfalfa, tobacco, and radish foilage
were injured by a 4-hr exposure of 0.10 ppm of chlorine. Benedict and
Breen (1955), using concentrations of 0.5 to 2.5 ppm for 4 hr, included
the foliage of the common mustard, chickweed, and sunflower in the
sensitive group. Zimmerman (1955), using concentrations of chlorine
ranging from 0.46 to 4.67 ppm, reported injury to 16 of the 19 species of
plants fumigated.

ETHYLENE

For many years manufactured illuminating gas, which contains about
3% ethylene, took its toll of greenhouse, ornamental, and shade plants
located near gas line leaks. With the change to natural gas this source of
vegetation damage has been largely eliminated; however, ethylene in the
ambient air coming from certain chemical industries and combustion,
chiefly auto exhaust, has taken its place.

As early as 1901 Neijubow disclosed that ethylene at concentrations as
low as 1 ppm in air caused the garden pea epicotyl to elongate horizontally instead of perpendicularly. This negative geotropic response
was later confirmed by Crocker and Knight (1908; Knight and Crocker,
1913), who also reported that exposures to concentrations of ethylene as
low as 0.4 ppm caused garden peas to develop a declination from the
vertical, a swelling of the declined portion, and a reduction in growth. This
they called the triple response. These workers further reported that 1
ppm ethylene or 250 ppm of acetylene prevented the growth of young
carnation buds, and 0.5 ppm of ethylene caused open flowers to close.
This flower closing, called "sleepiness," from an exposure to ethylene is
an irreversible response.

Perhaps the most costly plant damage resulting from ethylene is that
exhibited in many metropolitan areas by greenhouse-grown orchids. The
symptoms expressed by these plants are dry sepal injury, failure of buds
to open, sleepiness, and the occurrence of yellow leaves. The most
sensitive structures in the cattleya orchid are the opening flower buds,
which develop sepal injury when exposed to concentrations as low as 2
ppb of ethylene (Davidson, 1949). Older flowers are more tolerant to this
olefin; they require about 40 to 50 ppb to produce sepal response and, if
exposed to 10 to 15 ppb of this pollutant, an opening flower may close.

Phalenopsis (moth) orchid buds are prevented from opening by exposures of 10 to 15 ppb of ethylene (Davidson, 1966). Some investigators are of the opinion that ethylene injury to the orchid flower results from the speeding up of the life process, which brings on symptoms of decline. This opinion receives support in the findings of Smith and Parker (1966), who reported that cut carnation blooms showed a reduced vase life when exposed to 0.05 ppm of ethylene, and this effect was overcome by mixing 2.2% carbon dioxide with the ethylene-air mixture. They further report that the total life of the flowers was reduced below that in ethylene-free air only when the carbon dioxide was less than 0.35%.

Ethylene was first identified as affecting plant life in large areas in the field in 1957 when (Heck *et al.,* 1961) it affected cotton and other plants in the vicinity of a polyethylene plant located on the gulf coast of Texas.

Products of Reactions in the Atmosphere

Of the phytotoxicants produced as reaction products in the ambient air, ethylene, ozone, and PAN (peroxyacetyl nitrate) and its analogs have been demonstrated clearly to be involved in plant injury, and ozone olefin reaction products and NO_2 have been implicated as probable toxicants responsible for plant damage under some conditions. In addition, the investigations of Stephens *et al.* (1961) and Hindawi *et al.* (1965) indicate the possibility of the existence of other toxicants as well.

Ozone

During the late fall of 1958 a New Jersey farmer who experienced damage to his spinach crop requested that various members of the New Jersey Agricultural Experiment Station staff inspect his field to diagnose the cause of the injury and recommend corrective measures. At the time of the first inspection, chlorosis and leaf spotting were conspicuous. These symptoms were variously diagnosed as being due to nutritional deficiences, hardpan, root rot, and air pollution. Inspection of spinach fields throughout New Jersey and adjoining states revealed that chlorosis and leaf spotting were widespread.

During the 1959 growing season, injury to spinach and certain other plants was frequently observed. The most prevalent type of foliage injury (ozone) first appeared as dark, oily-appearing areas on the upper leaf surface. On close inspection these dark areas appeared to be water-soaked; on further development, milk-white necrotic spots and upper surface glazed areas resulted. The injury occurred regularly on the older leaves of young plants and the middle-aged leaves of old plants, and spots developed over all portions of the leaf surface. The area of the leaf exhibiting injury became more terminal, however, on the younger responding leaves. Observations suggested that the older true leaves of plants in the 6- to 10- or 12-leaf stage and the cotyledons on young plants were most susceptible. The new leaves produced by rapidly growing plants soon obscured these injury symptoms.

For many years, ozone has been known to be toxic to vegetation (Homan, 1937), but not until 1958, when Richards *et al.* described a stipple to the upper surface of grape leaves in California vineyards attributable to ozone, was ozone toxicity known to occur in nature. The next year Heggestad and Middleton (1959) described a light-colored flecking of the upper surface of tobacco leaves in the eastern part of the United States as due to ozone toxicity. This type of injury, called "weather fleck," has been observed over much of the eastern seaboard, extending as far north as Toronto, Canada, and, before the substitution of a more resistant variety, was charged with annually reducing the value of the Connecticut cigar wrapper tobacco crop at well over 1 million dollars. Early in 1960 Daines *et al.* reported ozone as a cause of damage to over a dozen plant species in New Jersey. This took ozone out of the class of minor pollutants and identified it as a major air pollutant affecting agriculture. Since these three reports were published, the list of plants occasionally injured in nature by this pollutant has been lengthened considerably to include forest trees, ornamentals, vegetables, fruit crops, and certain weed plants as well.

Ozone toxicity symptoms appear as flecks, stipple, streaks, spots, tip burn, and premature yellowing and shedding of the foliage. An upper-surface injury (fleck) first observed on tobacco has since been observed in New Jersey on the following plants (Daines 1963): tobacco, potato, swiss chard, spinach, cucumber, turnip, mustard, carrot, radish, onion, parsley, watermelon, squash, tomato, cantaloupe, sunflower, sweet pea, escarole, chicory, endive, and chickweed. A dark, upper-surface stipple first observed on grapes also occurs on white potatoes. In the field, cereal crops have frequently exhibited necrotic spots and streaks that can be attributed to ozone. These streaks appear in the well-aerated tissue between the veins. In addition, the list of plants that typically develop milk-white spots of varying size as a result of ozone toxicity includes spinach, alfalfa, clover, radish, turnip, tomato, and cucumber. Tip burn to white pine needles has also been shown to be ozone-induced (Berry and Ripperton, 1963), while such injury to onions has been produced experimentally and observed in Wisconsin and New Jersey fields. The premature yellowing and dropping of foilage as a result of ozone injury has been reported for tobacco (Menser and Street, 1962), grapes (Ledbetter *et al.*, 1959), and citrus crops (Richards and Taylor, 1961). Menser and Grosso reported (1966) that tobacco plants grown in a greenhouse receiving charcoal-filtered air did not develop ozone fleck or premature senescence.

Although ozone may produce leaf spots visible on both upper and lower surfaces of mature leaves, they occasionally are visible only on the upper surface. This happens because the palisade cells (occurring next to the upper epidermis) are the first to be injured (Ledbetter *et al.*, 1959). The variation in symptom response characteristic of plant species (upper-surface response fleck and stipple versus large spots showing on both surfaces) probably reflect a varying ratio of sensitivity existing between the palisade cells and the loosely arranged mesophyll cells below. Since a number of plants do not have palisade cells, injury to such leaves is usually about equal on upper and lower surfaces. Engle *et al.* (1965) attribute onion tip necrosis to the destruction of vascular bundles in local necrotic (fleck) areas.

Engle and Gableman (1966), in investigating resistance exhibited by an onion seedling, found that resistance is controlled by a dominant genetic system, possibly a single gene pair, which regulates the sensitivity of the membranes of the guard cells to ozone. These investigators report that the guard cells of resistant varieties leak water on exposure to this gas. This reduces turgidity and the stomata close, thereby protecting the underlying cells against injury. Under similar exposures to ozone, the stomata of susceptible varieties remain open, thus allowing ozone to enter the stomatal chamber and the intercellular spaces of the leaf.

Research (Bobrov, 1952; Dugger *et al.*, 1962a; MacDowall, 1965) has indicated that, while open stomata are important in the occurrence of plant injury, they are not the sole factor that governs plant response. The variation in the response to ozone of leaves of different ages has been noted by many. Dugger *et al.* (1962b) showed that the occurrence of visible injury on pinto beans varies with the soluble carbohydrates present. These investigators reported that, at low and high concentrations of soluble sugar in the leaves, susceptibility to ozone was reduced, and that maximum response occurred at intermediate levels of soluble sugar (2 to 4 mg/g fresh weight). From a study of carbohydrate fractions from lemon leaves, Dugger *et al.* (1966) reported a reduction in total carbohydrates with a considerable increase in the amount of reducing sugars present in the leaves receiving a prolonged ozone treatment as compared with check foliage. In addition to the increase in soluble sugar, leaf tissue exposed to ozone shows a considerable increase in permeability to exogenous sugars. These investigators also found that ozone-treated tissue decarboxylated glucose at a higher rate than did the control. By labeling the various carbon atoms in glucose, it was found that ozone did not induce changes in catabolic pathways, but did significantly increase the rate of glucose utilization. These discoveries led Dugger *et al.* (1966) to suggest that the increased decarboxylation stimulated by sublethal levels of ozone over an extended period caused a premature starvation and abscission of citrus leaves.

Seidman *et al.* (1965) reported that plants grown in vermiculite were both more vigorous and more sensitive to irradiated auto exhaust than plants grown in clay soil. These observations may be explained in part by data obtained in this laboratory (Matthee and Daines, 1968) which revealed that root aeration markedly affects stomatal activity.

"Certain varieties of tobacco" (Bel W3) "are the most sensitive indicators known of the presence of air-polluting ozone, usually displaying symptoms in the field when concentrations exceed 0.05 ppm" (Menser and Heggerstad, 1966).

However, these researchers have shown that ozone-like symptoms develop after exposures to mixtures of ozone and sulfur dioxide at subthreshold concentrations. In their experiments such symptoms occurred after 2-hr exposures to 0.037 ppm of ozone and 0.24 ppm of sulfur dioxide.

When Hindawi *et al.* (1965) exposed tobacco (Bel C), pinto bean, and petunia (Celestial Rose) to irradiated automobile exhaust, they observed, in addition to ozone and PAN injury, what they considered to be evidence of two additional phytotoxicants. Although both of these additional phytotoxicants produced what appeared to be ozone injury on the upper-leaf surface of all three test plants, there was a difference in the age of leaves which the phytotoxicants affected. Ozone is known to affect mature leaves first, and Hindawi *et al.* reported the occurrence of such injury even on the expanding leaves, which they interpreted as indicative of the existence of additional phytotoxic pollutants in irradiated auto exhaust. Although this leaf-age response may be significant, further study seems to be indicated. Varying the ozone concentrations alters the number of leaves responding on a plant, as does the modification of the nutritional status. For example, on one such exposure to a naturally occurring, polluted atmosphere in New Jersey, tobacco plant on high, medium, and low nitrogen nutrition exhibited upper-surface flecking as follows: high nitrogen (plants generally showed such injury on the 3rd to the 6th youngest leaf), medium nitrogen (from the 4th to the 6th youngest); low nitrogen (on the 5th and 6th youngest leaves only). Likewise the age of the plant may influence symptom expression. Whereas the symptom of ozone toxicity on leaves of young spinach plants is generally spotting and bleaching of the upper surface, on old plants it is often a flecking of this same surface. The younger responding tobacco leaves usually show flecking, while the older leaves may show flecking and area burn. When necrotic spots occur, they become terminal in the younger affected leaves, and intercostal as well on the older leaves.

Underleaf Injury

Injury occurring predominantly to the lower leaf surface of sensitive plants, first observed by Middleton *et al.* (1950a,b), has characterized most of the damage reported from California. Such plant injury also occurs in the Northeast, as well as in many of the world's metropolitan areas. Although PAN and its analogs (PPN, PBN) are believed to be largely responsible for injury to vegetation in California (Darley *et al.*, 1963), injury attributed to ozone predominates in the Northeast.

Investigations of petunia and Pinto bean symptom expression to several reaction products by Taylor *et al.* (1960) and Stephens *et al.* (1961) demonstrated their possible role in the production of leaf injury symptoms of this type. Data from these investigations given in Table 1 indicate that more than one of the phytotoxicants studied are required to produce all symptoms resulting from exposure to ambient air in the Los Angeles area.

TABLE 1
TYPE AND DEGREE OF INJURY ON PLANT LEAVES

	Petunia			Pinto Bean			
	Bronzing and silvering of immature leaves	Banding of expanding leaves	Tissue collapse of mature leaves	Bronzing and glazing		Tissue collapse	
Injury caused by				7-day-old leaves	14-day-old leaves	7-day-old leaves	14-day-old leaves
Ambient air	XXX	XXX	O	XXX	XX	X	XXX
Ozone (above 0.3 ppm)	O	O	XXX	O	X	X	XXX
Ozone-hexene	O	O	O	O	XXX	O	O
Irradiated NO_2[a] + 1-hexene	XXX	XXX	O	XXX	O	O	O

[a] According to Stephens *et al.* (1961), irradiated auto exhaust, irradiated ozone-olefin (1-pentene, 1-hexene, and 3-heptene), irradiated aldehydes, or PAN produced the same symptoms as given for irradiated NO_2 + 1-hexene.

PAN

PAN (peroxyacetyl nitrate) and its analogs (PPN-peroxypropionyl nitrate, PBN-peroxybutryl nitrate) are highly phytotoxic, producing foilage symptoms similar to those observed in the Los Angeles area since the late 1940s. The symptoms called "silver leaf" and "leaf banding" affect many plant species, not only in California but also throughout the northeastern United States and other areas where urbanization occurs. In California, leaf injury of this type occurs frequently to sensitive plants (Nobel and Wright, 1958). In the Northeast, however, such injury to plants listed as being PAN-sensitive in California occurs much less frequently, perhaps 1 to 3 times a year at most.

PAN readily attacks the spongy parenchyma cells just above the lower epidermis, but under more severe conditions it destroys palisade cells as well (Bobrov, 1952, 1955). The youngest fully expanded leaves are the most susceptible to PAN injury. The oxidant produces a glazing of the lower epidermis (Middleton *et al.,* 1950a,b), which may exhibit a sunken appearance, perhaps due to the collapse of cells adjoining the epidermis, or it may produce extensive necrotic areas on both leaf surfaces. These areas may vary from light buff in spinach to gray in cultivated dandelion and chicory and a brownish coloration in the herb *burraccia.*

Some varieties of petunia (white) are especially sensitive to a phytotoxicant that produces under-leaf surface injury; greenhouse-grown chrysanthemums may occasionally exhibit this type of injury. Other plants in the East showing injury symptoms resembling those produced by PAN are swiss chard, table beets, romaine and iceberg lettuce, spinach, curley endive, white potatoes, tomatoes, and annual bluegrass. In addition to destroying the market value of the affected leaves of the salad crops, increased costs for hand labor in sorting out damaged leaves from the produce in preparation for market are considerable.

In an investigation in which the relationship of leaf structure and sensitivity to air pollution damage in Los Angeles County was considered, Bobrov (1952, 1955) found a correlation between stomatal distribution and activity, the volume of the intercellular air space, and the age of the cells with cellular sensitivity. She reported that the areas of the leaf (*Poa annua* and oat) that had just obtained maximum enlargement were most sensitive to smog damage, while the very young and the older (senescent) tissue were least responsive. Bobrov showed that the most sensitive leaf areas possess well-developed intercellular spaces and responsive stomata, while the very young tissue is composed of compactly arranged cells and nonfunctional stomata. The senescent tissue is protected from injury by virtue of the extent of suberization, which acts as a barrier to damage. Bobrov reported that, although the structure and development of the leaf helps to explain the distribution and extent of damage to sensitive leaves, the explanation for the susceptibility of plants to damage cannot be found in the leaf structure alone, as great variation exists in the sensitivity of different plant species.

In studies of the effect of light on susceptibility to injury from PAN, Dugger and Taylor (1961), Dugger *et al.* (1962a), and Taylor *et al.* (1961) report that injury to plants from PAN is prevented by a dark period. They report that, even though the stomata are open, fumigation in the dark does not produce tissue necrosis. They also state that PAN fumigation during the early hours of morning light does not elicit plant response, nor do fumigations that are followed immediately by a dark period. Pronounced tissue destruction, however, may follow PAN fumigations in midmorning and much of the afternoon. These responses led the group of investigators (Dugger *et al.,* 1963) to suggest that PAN interacts with some plant constituent produced in the light to cause injury. "PAN has been reported to inhibit O_2 evolution, TPN reduction and non-cyclic photophosphorylation in chloroplast preparations. These observations suggest that the photochemical reaction is at the photosynthetic level." In using light of varying wavelengths, Dugger *et al.* (1963) found that the wavelengths at which the fumigated plants are the most responsive (420 and 480 mμ) would suggest that the carotenoid pigments are involved.

From continuing investigations (Dugger *et al.,* 1966) it was found that bean plants grown under high light intensity and then immediately placed in the dark and exposed to 1 ppm of PAN for 15 min were damaged by the fumigation. When plants were grown under medium or low light intensity and then exposed immediately to PAN in the dark, no injury developed. However, when such plants were exposed to 660 mμ light during the exposure to PAN, typical PAN injury occurred. These investigators further report that plants grown under low or moderate light intensity and exposed to a mixture of 660 and 700 mμ light during the exposure to PAN were not damaged. Furthermore, it was found that 700 mμ light partly overcame the susceptibility of plants to PAN that had been grown under high light intensity immediately preceding the exposure to this oxidant. Dugger *et al.* then make the following interesting observation concerning the mechanism of photosynthesis: "The Radiant Energy of 700 mμ light causes the production of a strong reductant and a weak oxidant (System 1); whereas 600 mμ light drives the reactions in both systems 1 and 2, and reactions occurring in system 2 produce a strong oxidant and a weak reductant." They then suggest the possibility that the ratio of the products of these two systems control the degree of response to PAN.

Dugger *et al.* (1966) further report that experiments using ^{14}C-labeled PAN revealed that, immediately after fumigation, bean plants contained the same amounts of PAN whether they had been grown under a normal light regime or had been held in the dark for 24 hr just before the fumigation. However, if these plants are held in the light for 2½ hr after the fumigation, the nonsusceptible plants that received the 24-hr dark treatment before the fumigation showed considerably less labeled ^{14}C than did the susceptible light-treated plants. These researchers further state that ^{14}C is found in the chloroplasts of the treated plants.

Studies designed to find the biochemical basis for the phytotoxicity oxidants (Freebairn, 1957; Mudd, 1963) provided evidence that enzyme inactivation resulted from reactions involving PAN and sulfhydryl groups. In this connection, Dugger *et al.* (1966) report that the −SH content of young primary leaves of Black Valentine bean plants was considerably higher than in less susceptible leaves of 14- to 17-day-old plants. They also record that the −SH content is higher in plants grown under a normal photoperiod than in those held in the dark for 24 hr. However, when plants held for 24 hr in the dark are placed in the light, the −SH content as well as susceptibility to PAN is restored in 3 hr.

Ozonated Hydrocarbons

Many investigators have fumigated plants with the reaction products of ozone-olefin mixtures. These products, which possibly contain aldehydes and a zwitterion, produce injury to the lower leaf surface that resembles injury resulting from an exposure to ambient Los Angeles air (Darley *et al.*, 1963; Taylor *et al.*, 1957; Middleton, 1956). Such products typically produce under-leaf surface injury, close stomata, increase respiration, and adversely affect growth. Reduced growth of tomato seedlings (Koritz and Went, 1953), Red Kidney and Bountiful beans (Todd and Garber, 1958), and Lisbon lemon (Taylor, 1958) without visible leaf injury from exposures to synthetic smog has been reported. This was reflected in reduced linear growth, leaf area, fresh and dry weights, and fruit production. Early leaf fall has also been noted on some plants. Todd and Garber reported that ozone used without the hydrocarbon elicited no growth response. Taylor reported the suppression of blossom initiation in petunias, blossom abortion in tomatoes, and water use by lemon cuttings and by exposures to synthetic smog. As a corollary to this, improved plant growth in greenhouses supplied with charcoal-filtered air has been reported by Menser and Grosso (1966) and others.

In 1953 Koritz and Went (1953) reported that plant response to ozonated 1-*N*-hexene is affected by light. They maintained that fumigations conducted during dark periods were not effective in producing plant response. They further stated that, even though the stomata were open, fumigations in the early morning hours (8:00–8:30 A.M.) elicited only minor responses as judged by tissue weights. Much greater response occurred, however, from fumigations occurring in midmorning. These investigators stated that glucose solutions reduced the amount of injury somewhat.

An investigation by Wedding and Erickson (1955) revealed that a 3-hr fumigation using ozone and 1-*N*-hexene resulted in an increased cellular permeability of bean leaf tissue and potato discs.

The reaction products of such ozonated compounds as 2-pentene, 1-pentene, 3-pentene, and 1-hexene are highly phytotoxic; however, the effective life of the reactive phytotoxicant of some of these compounds is very short, ½ hr or less (Darley *et al.*, 1959; Middleton, 1963). This fact led Dugger *et al.* (1962a) to doubt the importance of this group as phytotoxicant in nature.

In 1961 Stephens *et al.* used irradiated and nonirradiated ozone-olefin mixtures (see Table 1) in fumigations of petunia (sp. not given) and pinto bean plants. The pronounced differences between plant responses to the irradiated and nonirradiated mixtures suggested the formation of new phytotoxicants by irradiation. In the same investigations, these workers obtained essentially the same plant responses from the following irradiated pollutants: auto exhaust, NO_2 + olefins, certain ozone and olefin mixtures, and aldehydes (see Table 1). The symptoms, like those produced by PAN, consisted in the bronzing and banding of petunia leaves and bronzing of the leaves of 8-day-old pinto bean plants. Unless the air used in these studies contained enough NO_2 to account for the production of PAN under the conditions of the experiments, the products of these reactions would result in the generation of unlike products. Hence it appears that PAN-like plant injury may result from more than one type of pollutant.

NITROGEN DIOXIDE (NO_2)

It is now generally believed that NO is generated from the reaction of nitrogen and oxygen under the influence of high temperatures and is converted into NO_2 in the presence of sunshine and hydrocarbons in the free air (Wayne, 1962). Air analysis in New Jersey has shown that, while hourly concentrations of NO_2 vary from 0.00 to 0.4 ppm, an average daytime concentration during the plant-growing months is about 0.02 to

0.03 ppm. The analysis also reveals that periods when NO_2 concentrations are high are of relatively short duration.

While nitrogen dioxide has been known to play an important part in photochemical reactions, its role as a plant toxicant *per se* has been questioned. In controlled fumigations, Benedict and Breen (1955) found that 20 ppm of NO_2 were required to produce visible markings to the foliage of the most sensitive weeds tested. However, Taylor and Eaton (1966) report that continuous exposure to concentrations of NO_2 ranging from 0.3 to 0.5 ppm caused a gradual change in appearance of pinto bean plants. The symptoms produced were a downward cupping and a darker green leaf color than that exhibited by untreated plants. The plants exposed to the NO_2 fumigations exhibited growth suppression after 1 week to 10 days.

Although these experiments reported by Taylor and Eaton indicate that NO_2 may injure some plants at prolonged exposures to rather low levels of NO_2, the writer is unfamiliar with such injury symptoms in the Northeast.

REFERENCES

Benedict, H. M., and Breen, W. H. (1955). The use of weeds as a means of evaluating vegetation damage caused by pollution. *Proc. 3rd Natl. Air Pollution Symp.,* pp. 177–190.

Berry, C. R., and Ripperton, L. A. (1963). Ozone—a possible cause of white pine emergence tipburn. *Phytopathology* **53**, 552–557.

Bobrov, Ruth Ann (1952). The effect of smog on the anatomy of oat leaves. *Phytopathology* **42**, 558–563.

Bobrov, Ruth Ann (1955). The leaf structure of Poe annua with observations on its smog sensitivity in Los Angeles County. *Am. J. Botany* **42**, 467–474.

Brennan, E., Leone, Ida A., and Daines, R. H. (1964). Investigations of SO_2 effects on rubber trees as a means of forestalling injury to Malayan plantations from refinery emmissions. *J. APCS* **14**, 229–233.

Brennan, E., Leone, Ida A., and Daines, R. H. (1965). Chlorine as a phytotoxic air pollutant. *Intern. J. Air Pollution* **9**, 791–797.

Brennan, E., Leone, Ida A., and Daines, R. H. (1966). Response of pine trees to chlorine in the atmosphere. *Forest Sci.* **12**(4), 386–390.

Crocker, W., and Knight, L. I. (1908). Effect of illuminating gas and ethylene upon flowering carnations. *Botan. Gaz.* **46**, 259–276.

Daines, R. H. (1963). Effects of air pollution on crops and livestock, pp. 179–182. *Natl. Conf. Air Pollution Proc.* U.S. Dept. Health, Education and Welfare, Public Health Service.

Daines, R. H., Leone, Ida A., and Brennan, Eileen (1952). The effects of fluorine on plants as determined by soil nutrition and fumigation studies. "Air Pollution Proceedings of U.S. Technical Conference Air Pollution." Chapter 9, 97–105. McGraw-Hill, New York.

Daines, R. H., Leone, Ida A., and Brennan, Eileen (1960). Air pollution as it affects agriculture in New Jersey. *N. J. Agr. Expt. Sta. Bull.* **794.**

Darley, E. G., Duggar, W. M., Mudd, J. B., Ordin, L., Taylor, O. C., and Stephens, E. R. (1963). Plant damage by pollution derived from automobiles. *Arch. Envir. Health* **6**(6), 761–770.

Darley, Ellis, Stephens, E. R., Middleton, J. T., and Hanst, P. L. (1959). Oxidant plant damage from ozone-olefin reactions. *Intern. J. Air Water Pollution* **1**, 55–126.

Davidson, O. W. (1966). Personal communication.

Davidson, O. W. (1949). Effects of ethylene on orchid flowers. *Proc. Am. Soc. Hort. Sci.* 53: 440–446.

Dugger, W. M., Jr., Koukol, Jane, and Palmer, R. L. (1966). Physiological and biochemical effects of atmospheric oxidants on plants. *J. of APCA.* **16**, 467–471.

Dugger, W. M., Jr., and Taylor, O. C. (1961). Interaction of light and smog components in plants. *Plant Physiol. Suppl.* **36**, 44.

Dugger, W. M., Jr., Taylor, O. C., Cardiff, Eugene, and Thompson, Ray (1962a). Stomatal action of plants as related to damage from photochemical oxidants. *Plant Physiol.* **37**, 487–491.

Dugger, W. M., Jr., Taylor, O. C., Cardiff, Eugene, and Thompson, Ray (1962b). Relationship between carbohydrates content and susceptibility to Pinto Bean plants to Ozone damage. *Proc. Am. Soc. Hort. Science* **81**, 304–315.

Dugger, W. J., Jr., Taylor, O. C., Klein, W. H., and Shropshire, W., Jr. (1963). Action spectrum of peroxyacetyl nitrate damage to Pinto bean plants. *Nature* **198**, 75–76.

Engle, R. L., and Gableman, W. H. (1966). Inheritance and mechanism for resistance to ozone damage in onions, *Allium cepa* L. *Proc. Am. Soc. Hort. Sci.* **89**, 423–430.

Engle, R. L., Gableman, W. H., and Romanowski, R. R., Jr. (1965). Tipburn and ozone incited response in onion, *Allium cepa* L. *Proc. Am. Soc. Hort. Sci.* **86**, 468–474.

Freedbairn, H. T. (1957). Reversal of inhibitory effects of ozone on ozygen uptake of mitochondria. *Science* **126**, 303–304.

Heck, W. W., Pires, W. B., and Hall, W. C. (1961). The effect of a low ethylene concentration on the growth of cotton. *54th Ann. Meeting APCA,* June 11–15, New York.

Heggestad, H. F., and Middleton, J. T. (1959). Ozone in high concentrations as cause of tobacco leaf injury. *Science* **129**, 208–210.

Hill, G. R., Jr., and Thomas, M. D. (1933). Influence of leaf distruction by SO_2 and by clipping on yield of alfalfa. *Plant Physiol.* **8**, 223–245.

Hindawi, I. J., Dunning, J. A., and Brandt, C. S. (1965). Morphological and microscopical changes in tobacco, bean, and petunia leaves exposed to irradiated automobile exhaust. *Phytopathology* **55**, 23–30.

Homan, G. (1937). Effects of ionized air and ozone on plants. *Plant Physiol.* **12**, 957–978.

Katz, M., and Pasternak, D. C. (1938). "Effects of Sulfur Dioxide on Vegetation, Chapter 14, pp. 369–392. Natl. Res. Council Canada, Ottawa.

Knight, L. I., and Crocker, W. (1913). Toxicity of smoke. *Botan. Gaz.* **55**, 337–371.

Koritz, H. G., and Went, F. W. (1953). The physiological action of smog on plants. 1. Initial growth and transpiration studies. *Plant Physiol.* **28**, 50–62.

Ledbetter, M. C., Zimmerman, P. W., and Hitchcock, H. E. (1959). The histophatological effects of ozone on plant foliage. *Contrb. Boyce Thompson Inst. Plant Res.* **20**, 275–282.

Leone, Ida A., Brennan, E., and Daines, R. H. (1956). Atmospheric fluoride – its uptake and distribution in tomato and corn plants. *Plant Physiol.* **31**, 329–333.

MacDowall, F. D. H. (1965). Predisposition ot tobacco to ozone damage. *Can. J. Plant Sci.* **45**, 1–112.

Matthee, N., and Daines, R. H. (1968). Effects of soil types and substrate aeration on stomatal activity, water diffusion pressure defect, water congestion, and bacterial infection of peach and pepper foliage. *Phytopathology* **58**, 1298–1301.

Menser, H. A., and Heggerstad, H. E. (1966). Ozone and sulfur dioxide synergism: injury to tobacco plants. *Science* **153**, 424–425.

Menser, J. A., Jr., and Grosso, J. J. (1966). Carbon filter prevents ozone fleck and premature senescence of tobacco leaves. *Phytopathology* **56**, 466–467.

Menser, H. A., and Street, O. E. (1962). Effects of air pollution, nitrogen levels, supplemental irrigation, and plant spacing on weather fleck and leaf loss of Maryland tobacco. *Tobacco Sci.* **6**, 165–169.

Middleton, J. T., Jr. (1956). Response of plants to air pollution. *J. APCA* **6**(1).

Middleton, J. T. (1963). Air conservation and the protection of our national resources, pp. 166–172. *Natl. Conf. Air Pollution Proc.*, U.S. Department of Health, Education and Welfare

Middleton, J. T., Darley, E. F., and Brewer, R. F. (1958). Damage to vegetation from polluted atmosphere. *J. A.P.C.A.* **8**, 7–15.

Middleton, J. T., Kendrick, J. B., Jr., and Schwalm, H. W. (1950a). Smog in the South Coastal Area. *Calif. Agr.* **4**(11), 7–10.

Middleton, J. T., Kendrick, J. B., Jr., and Schwalm, H. W. (1950b). Injury to herbaceous plants by smog or air pollution. *P.D.R.* **34**, 245–252.

Mudd, J. B. (1963). Enzyme inactivation by peroxyacetyl nitrate. *Arch. Biochem. Biophys.* **102**, 59–65.

Neijubow, D. (1901). Ueber die horizontal nutation der stengel von pisum sativum und einiger audaren pflagzen. *Botan. Zentr. Beih.* **10**, 128–193.

Nobel, W. M., and Wright, L. A. (1958). Air pollution with relation to agronomic crops. *Agron. Crops* **50**, 551–553.

Prince, A. L., Bear, F. E., Brennan, E. G., Leone, Ida A., and Daines, R. H. (1948). Fluorine: its toxicity to plants and its control in soils. *Soil Sci.* **67**, 269–277.

Richards, B. L., Middleton, J. T., and Heritt, W. B. (1958). Air pollution with relation to agronomic crops; V. Oxidant stipple of grapes. *Agron. J.* **50**, 559–561.

Richards, B. L., and Taylor, O. C. (1961). Status and redirection of research on the atmospheric pollutants toxic to field grown crops in southern California. *J. A.P.C.A.* **10**, 1–4.

Seidman, T., Hindawi, I. J., and Heck, W. W. (1965). Environmental conditions affecting the use of plants as indicators of air pollution. *J. A.P.C.A.* **15**, 168–170.

Smith, W. H., and Parker, J. C. (1966). Prevention of ethylene injury to carnation by low concentrations of carbon dioxide. *Nature* **211**, 100–101.

Stephens, E. R., Darley, E. F., Taylor, O. C., and Scott, W. E. (1961). Photochemical reactions products in air pollution. *Intern. J. Air Water Pollution* **4**, 79–100.

Taylor, O. C. (1958). Plant growth suppressed by exposure to air-borne oxidants (smog). *Agron. J.* **50**, 556–558.

Taylor, O. C., Cardiff, E. A., Mersereau, J. D., and Middleton, J. T. (1957). Smog reduces seedling growth. *Calif. Agri.* **11**(3), 9–12.

Taylor, O. C., Dugger, W. M., Jr., Cardiff, E. A., and Darley, E. F. (1961). Interaction of light and atmosphere photochemical (smog) within plants. *Nature* **192**, 814–816.

Taylor, O. C., and Eaton, F. M. (1966). Suppression of plant growth by nitrogen dioxide. *Plant Physiol.* **41**, 132–135.

Taylor, O. C., Stephens, E. R., Darley, E. F., and Cardiff, E. A. (1960). Effect of air-borne oxidant on leaves of Pinto bean and petunia. *Proc. Am. Soc. Hort. Sci.* **75**, 435–444.

Thomas, M. D., Hendricks, R. H., and Hill, G. R. (1952). Some impurities in the air and their effects on plants, pp. 41–47. "Air Pollution, Proceedings U.S. Technical Conference on Air Pollution. McGraw-Hill, New York.

Thomas, M. D., and Hill, G. R., Jr. (1958). Air Pollution with relation to agronomic crops: 1. general status of research on the effects of air pollution on plants. *Agron. J.* **50,** 544–550.

Thomas, M. D. (1961). Effects on plants, in air pollution. *WHO Momograph* **46,** 233–278.

Todd, G. S., and Garber, M. J. (1958). Some effects of air pollutants on the growth and productivity of plants. *Botan. Gaz.* pp. 75–80.

Wayne, L. G. (1962). The chemistry of urban atmospheres. Technical Progress Report Vol. III, Air Pollution Control District, County of Los Angeles.

Wedding, R. T., and Erickson, L. C. (1955). Changes in permeability of plant cells to $P^{32}O_4$ and water as a result of exposure to ozonated hexene (smog). *Am. J. Botany* **42,** 570–575.

Zimmerman, P. W. (1955). Chemicals involved in air pollution and their effects upon vegetation. *Contrib. Boyce Thompson Inst. Plant Res., Prof. Paper* **2,** 124–245.

INDEX